COMPREHENSIVE RENEWABLE ENERGY

COMPREHENSIVE RENEWABLE ENERGY

EDITOR-IN-CHIEF
Ali Sayigh
Chairman of WREC, Director General of WREN, and Chairman of IEI, Brighton, UK

VOLUME 7
GEOTHERMAL ENERGY

VOLUME EDITOR
Thorsteinn I. Sigfusson
Innovation Center of Iceland and University of Iceland, Reykjavik, Iceland

ELSEVIER

AMSTERDAM BOSTON HEIDELBERG LONDON NEW YORK OXFORD
PARIS SAN DIEGO SAN FRANCISCO SINGAPORE SYDNEY TOKYO

Elsevier
Radarweg 29, PO Box 211, 1000 AE Amsterdam, The Netherlands
The Boulevard, Langford Lane, Kidlington, Oxford OX5 1GB, UK
225 Wyman Street, Waltham, MA 02451, USA

Copyright © 2012 Elsevier Ltd. All rights reserved.

4.04   Hydrogen Safety Engineering: The State-of-the-Art and Future Progress
Copyright © 2012 V Molkov

5.16   Renewable Fuels: An Automotive Perspective
Copyright © 2012 Lotus Cars Limited

The following articles are US Government works in the public domain and not subject to copyright:
1.19   Cadmium Telluride Photovoltaic Thin Film: CdTe
1.37   Solar Power Satellites
4.02   Current Perspective on Hydrogen and Fuel Cells
5.02   Historical Perspectives on Biofuels

No part of this publication may be reproduced, stored in a retrieval system or transmitted in any form or by any means electronic, mechanical, photocopying, recording or otherwise without the prior written permission of the publisher

Permissions may be sought directly from Elsevier's Science & Technology Rights Department in Oxford, UK: phone (+44) (0) 1865 843830; fax (+44) (0) 1865 853333; email: permissions@elsevier.com. Alternatively you can submit your request online by visiting the Elsevier web site at http://elsevier.com/locate/permissions, and selecting *Obtaining permission to use Elsevier material*

Notice
No responsibility is assumed by the publisher for any injury and/or damage to persons or property as a matter of products liability, negligence or otherwise, or from any use or operation of any methods, products, instructions or ideas contained in the material herein. Because of rapid advances in the medical sciences, in particular, independent verfication of diagnoses and drug dosages should be made.

British Library Cataloguing in Publication Data
A catalogue record for this book is available from the British Library

The Library of Congress Control Number: 2012934547

ISBN: 978-0-08-087872-0

For information on all Elsevier publications
visit our website at books.elsevier.com

Printed and bound in Italy

11 12 13 14 10 9 8 7 6 5 4 3 2 1

Working together to grow
libraries in developing countries

www.elsevier.com | www.bookaid.org | www.sabre.org

ELSEVIER   BOOK AID International   Sabre Foundation

Editorial: Gemma Mattingley, Joanne Williams
Production: Edward Taylor, Maggie Johnson

EDITOR-IN-CHIEF

Professor Ali Sayigh, BSc, DIC, PhD, CEng, a British citizen, graduated from Imperial College London and the University of London in 1966. He is a fellow of the Institute of Energy, a fellow of the Institution of Electrical Engineers, and is a chartered engineer.

From 1966 to 1985, Prof. Sayigh taught in the College of Engineering at the University of Baghdad and at King Saud University, Saudi Arabia, as a full-time professor, and also at Kuwait University as a part-time professor. From 1981 to 1985, he was Head of the Energy Department at the Kuwait Institute for Scientific Research (KISR) and expert in renewable energy at the Arab Organization of Petroleum Exporting Countries (AOPEC), Kuwait.

He started working in solar energy in September 1969. In 1984, he established links with Pergamon Press and became Editor-in-Chief of his first international journal, *Solar & Wind Technology*. Since 1990 he has been Editor-in-Chief of *Comprehensive Renewable Energy* incorporating *Solar & Wind Technology*, published by Elsevier Science Ltd., Oxford, UK. He is the editor of several international journals published in Morocco, Iran, Bangladesh, and Nigeria.

He has been a member of the International Society for Equitation Science (ISES) since 1973, founder and chairman of the ARAB Section of ISES since 1979, chairman of the UK Solar Energy Society for 3 years, and consultant to many national and international organizations, among them, the British Council, the Islamic Educational, Scientific and Cultural Organization (ISESCO), the United Nations Educational, Scientific and Cultural Organization (UNESCO), the United Nations Development Programme (UNDP), the Economic and Social Commission for Western Asia (ESCWA), and the United Nations Industrial Development Organization (UNIDO).

Since 1977 Prof. Sayigh has founded and directed several renewable energy conferences and workshops in the International Centre for Theoretical Physics (ICTP) – Trieste, Italy, Canada, Colombia, Algeria, Kuwait, Bahrain, Malaysia, Zambia, Malawi, India, the West Indies, Tunisia, Indonesia, Libya, Taiwan, UAE, Oman, the Czech Republic, Germany, Australia, Poland, the Netherlands, Thailand, Korea, Iran, Syria, Saudi Arabia, Singapore, China, the United States, and the United Kingdom.

In 1990 he established the World Renewable Energy Congress (WREC) and, in 1992, the World Renewable Energy Network (WREN), which hold their Congresses every 2 years, attracting more than 100 countries each time. In 2000, he and others in UAE, Sharjah, founded the Arab Science and Technology Foundation (ASTF) and regional conferences have been held in Sweden, Malaysia, Korea, Indonesia, Australia, UAE, and Libya, to name but a few. Prof. Sayigh has been running an annual international seminar on all aspects of renewable energy since 1990 in the United Kingdom and abroad. In total, 85 seminars have been held.

Prof. Sayigh supervised and graduated more than 34 PhD students and 64 MSc students at Reading University and the University of Hertfordshire when he was a professor from 1986 to 2004.

He has edited, contributed, and written more than 32 books and published more than 500 papers in various international journals and conferences.

In 2000–09, he initiated and worked closely with Sovereign Publication Company to produce the most popular magazine at annual bases called *Renewable Energy*, which was distributed freely to more than 6000 readers around the world. Presently, he is the editor-in-chief of *Comprehensive Renewable Energy*, coordinating 154 top scientists', engineers', and researchers' contributions in eight volumes published by Elsevier Publishing Company, Oxford, UK.

VOLUME EDITORS

Dr. Wilfried G. J. H. M. van Sark graduated from Utrecht University, the Netherlands, with an MSc in experimental physics in 1985, and with an MSc thesis on measurement and analysis of I–V characteristics of c-Si cells. He received his PhD from Nijmegen University, the Netherlands; the topic of his PhD thesis was III–V solar cell development, modeling, and processing. He then spent 7 years as a postdoc/senior researcher at Utrecht University and specialized in a-Si:H cell deposition and analysis. He is an expert in plasma chemical vapor deposition, both radio frequency and very high frequency. After an assistant professor position at Nijmegen University, where he worked on III–V solar cells, he returned to Utrecht University, with a focus on (single-molecule) confocal fluorescence microscopy of nanocrystals. In 2002, he moved to his present position as assistant professor at the research group Science, Technology and Society of the Copernicus Institute at Utrecht University, the Netherlands, where he performed and coordinated research on next-generation photovoltaic devices incorporating nanocrystals; for example, luminescent solar concentrators, as well as photovoltaic performance, life cycle analysis, socioeconomics, and policy development. He is member of the editorial board of Elsevier's scientific journal *Renewable Energy*, and member of various organizing committees of the European Union, the Institute of Electrical and Electronics Engineers (IEEE), and the SPIE PV conferences. He is author or coauthor of over 200 peer-reviewed journal and conference paper publications and book chapters. He has (co-)edited three books, including the present one.

Professor John K. Kaldellis holds a mechanical engineering degree from the National Technical University of Athens (NTUA) and a business administration diploma from the University of Piraeus. He obtained his PhD from NTUA (Fluid Sector) sponsored by Snecma–Dassault, France, and Bodossakis Foundation, Greece. He is currently the head of the Mechanical Engineering Department and since 1991 the director of the Soft Energy Applications and Environmental Protection Laboratory of the Technological Education Institute (TEI) of Piraeus. Prof. Kaldellis is also the scientific director (for TEI of Piraeus) of the MSc in Energy program organized by Heriot-Watt University and TEI of Piraeus. His scientific expertise is in the fields of energy and the environment. His research interests include feasibility analysis of energy sector applications; technological progress in wind, hydro, and solar energy markets; hybrid energy systems; energy storage issues; social attitudes toward renewable energy applications; and environmental technology–atmospheric pollution. He has participated in numerous research projects, funded by the European Union, European/Greek Industries, and the Greek State. Prof. Kaldellis has published six books concerning renewable energy applications and environmental protection. He is also the author of more than 100 scientific/research papers in international peer-reviewed journals and more than 300 papers for international scientific conferences. During the last decade, he was also a member of the Scientific Committee of the Hellenic Society of Mechanical–Electrical Engineers as well as a member of the organizing and scientific committee of several national and international conferences. He is currently a member of the editorial board of the *Renewable Energy International* journal and reviewer in more than 40 international journals in the energy and environment sector. He is the editor of the book *Stand-Alone and Hybrid Wind Energy Systems: Technology, Energy Storage and Applications* that has recently been published.

Dr. Soteris A. Kalogirou is a senior lecturer at the Department of Mechanical Engineering and Materials Science and Engineering at the Cyprus University of Technology, Limassol, Cyprus. He received his Higher Technical Institute (HTI) degree in mechanical engineering in 1982, his MPhil in mechanical engineering from the Polytechnic of Wales in 1991, and his PhD in mechanical engineering from the University of Glamorgan in 1995. In June 2011, he received the title of DSc from the University of Glamorgan.

For more than 25 years, he has been actively involved in research in the area of solar energy and particularly in flat-plate and concentrating collectors, solar water heating, solar steam generating systems, desalination, and absorption cooling. Additionally, since 1995, he has been involved in pioneering research dealing with the use of artificial intelligence methods, such as artificial neural networks, genetic algorithms, and fuzzy logic, for the modeling and performance prediction of energy and solar energy systems.

He has 29 books and book contributions and published 225 papers, 97 in international scientific journals and 128 in refereed conference proceedings. To date he has received more than 2550 citations on this work. He is Executive Editor of *Energy*, Associate Editor of *Renewable Energy*, and Editorial Board Member of another 11 journals. He is the editor of the book *Artificial Intelligence in Energy and Renewable Energy Systems*, published by Nova Science Inc.; coeditor of the book *Soft Computing in Green and Renewable Energy Systems*, published by Springer; and author of the book *Solar Energy Engineering: Processes and Systems*, published by Academic Press of Elsevier.

He has been a member of the World Renewable Energy Network (WREN) since 1992 and is a member of the Chartered Institution of Building Services Engineers (CIBSE), the American Society of Heating Refrigeration and Air-Conditioning Engineers (ASHRAE), the Institute of Refrigeration (IoR), and the International Solar Energy Society (ISES).

Dr. Andrew Cruden, a British citizen, was born in 1968. He obtained his BEng, MSc, and PhD in electrical engineering from the University of Strathclyde and CEng, MIEE Dr. Cruden is a past member of BSI GEL/105 Committee on Fuel Cells and Committee member of the IET Scotland Power Section. He is Director of the Scottish Hydrogen and Fuel Cell Association (SHFCA; www.shfca.org.uk) and Director of Argyll, Lomond and the Islands Energy Agency (www.alienergy.org.uk).

Dr. Cruden has been active in the field of hydrogen and fuel cells since 1995, when he acted as a consultant for Zevco Ltd., providing assistance with power electronic interfaces for early fuel cell systems. Later in 1998, he helped found the Scottish Fuel Cell Consortium (SFCC), supported by the Scottish Enterprise Energy Team, which ultimately developed a battery/fuel cell hybrid electric vehicle based on an AC Cobra kit car. The experience and contacts from the SFCC eventually gave rise to the formation of the Scottish Hydrogen and Fuel Cell Association (SHFCA), a trade body for the industry to promote and commercialize Scottish expertise in this field. Dr. Cruden was the founding chairman of the SHFCA.

Dr. Cruden is currently investigating alkaline electrolyzers in terms of improving their part load efficiency and lifetime when powered by variable renewable power sources, for example, wind turbines, as part of a £5 million EPSRC Supergen project on the 'Delivery of Sustainable Hydrogen' (EP/G01244X/1). He is also working with a colleague within Electronic and Electrical Engineering (EEE) at Strathclyde, studying the concept of vehicle-to-grid energy storage, as a mechanism not only to allow controlled load leveling on the power system, but also to potentially 'firm' up renewable energy generation. This work is supported by two research grants, an international E.On Research Initiative 2007 award and an ESPRC grant (EP/F062133/1).

Dr. Cruden is a senior lecturer within the Department of Electronic and Electrical Engineering at the University of Strathclyde. His current fields of research are modeling fuel cell and electrolyzer systems, fuel cell combined heat and power (CHP) systems, power electronic devices for interfacing both vehicular and stationary fuel cell systems, condition monitoring systems for renewable energy sources (i.e., wind turbines as part of EPSRC Supergen on Wind Energy Technologies, EP/D034566/1), and energy management systems for hybrid electric vehicles.

His areas of expertise include hydrogen-powered fuel cells and electrolyzers, energy storage for electric vehicles, and renewable energy generation.

Professor Dermot J. Roddy, BSc, PhD, CEng, FIET, joined Newcastle University as Science City Professor of Energy in 2008 after a period of some 20 years in the energy industry and petrochemical sectors. He is also Director of the Sir Joseph Swan Centre for Energy Research, which integrates energy research across Newcastle University and links with a powerful external industrial base in the energy sector. Outside of the university he is Chairman of Northeast Biofuels, Finance Director of the UK Hydrogen Association, and Vice-President of the Northern England Electricity Supply Companies Association. Prior to coming to Newcastle University, he was Chief Executive of Renew Tees Valley Ltd. – a company which he set up in 2003 to create a viable and vibrant economy in the Tees Valley based on renewable energy and recycling – where he was instrumental in a wide range of major renewable energy and low-carbon projects relating to biomass, biofuels, hydrogen, carbon capture and storage, wind, and advanced waste processing technologies. From 1998 to 2002, he ran the crude oil refinery on Teesside as a site director for a $5 billion turnover facility before moving to the Netherlands to work on Petroplus' international growth plans. Roddy's experience in the petrochemical industry began in 1985, involving a variety of UK and international roles in operations, engineering, and technology with ICI and others. Prior to that he developed leading-edge technology at Queen's University, Belfast, for optimization and control in aerospace applications.

André G. H. Lejeune was born on 2 August 1942 in Belgium. He was graduated in 1967 as a civil engineer, in 1972 as doctor in applied sciences (PhD), and in 1973 as master in oceanography in the University of Liège in Belgium. He was appointed full-time professor in the same university in 1976, and was visitor professor at the UNESCO–IHE Institute for Water Education in the Netherlands and Ecole Polytechnique Fédérale de Lausanne (EPFL) in Switzerland. Within the framework of his activities of professor, director of the Hydraulic Constructions and Hydraulic Research Laboratory, and expert, he took part in studies of dams and hydraulic structures and went on site in more than 90 countries of the world. In particular, he was for the last 6 years the chairman of the Technical Committee on Hydraulics for Dams in ICOLD (International Commission of Large Dams). He is a member of the Belgian Royal Academy of Sciences. He made his PhD thesis in hydraulic numerical modelization. This thesis received the Lorenz G. Straub Award in Minneapolis, USA (H. Einstein Jr. was a member of the Jury), and was used in particular by Chinese colleagues in the Three Gorges Project. Due to his practice and experience, he has a very complete knowledge of the hydraulic phenomena modelizations through both numerical and physical means.

With his wife, he has 3 children and 11 grandchildren. He likes books, tennis, and diving.

Thorsteinn I. Sigfusson is an internationally recognised physicist, educated in Copenhagen, Denmark, and Cambridge, UK. He is Director-General of the Innovation Center, Iceland and Professor of physics at the University of Iceland. He has been a visiting professor at Columbia University, New York, and he is currently the lead scientist in a prize-winning energy technology project performed at Tomsk Polytechnic University in Tomsk, Russia.

He has been a key figure in the introduction of new ideas and opportunities in the further greening of Icelandic society through the energy industry, and instrumental in the challenge of saving imported hydrocarbons by focusing on hydrogen from renewable energy.

He has started over a dozen start-up companies from research in Iceland and chaired various international societies in alternative energy. Among his achievements in geothermal energy is the construction of the world's largest solid-state thermoelectric generator powered with geothermal steam in southern Iceland. At the Innovation Center, Iceland, efforts are made to develop materials to withstand erosion in geothermal environments.

AbuBakr S. Bahaj is Professor of Sustainable Energy at the University of Southampton. After completing his PhD, he was employed by the University, progressing from a researcher to a personnel chair of Sustainable Energy. Over the past 20 years, Prof. Bahaj has established the energy theme within the University and directed his Sustainable Energy Research Group (SERG, www.energy.soton.ac.uk), which is now considered to be one of the United Kingdoms's leading university-based research groups in renewable energy and energy in buildings. He initiated and managed research in ocean energy conversion (resources, technologies, and impacts), photovoltaics, energy in buildings, and impacts of climate change on the built environment in the University. This work has resulted in over 230 articles published in academic refereed journals and conference series of international standing (see www.energy.soton.ac.uk).

Prof. Bahaj is the head of the Energy and Climate Change Division (ECCD) within the highly rated Faculty of Engineering and the Environment – Civil Engineering and the Environment – (www.civil.soton.ac.uk/research/divisions/divlist.asp?ResearchGroupID=1) (second in the United Kingdom, Research Assessment Exercise in 2008, with 80% of research judged to be either 'World Leading' or 'Internationally Excellent'). The aims of the Division and SERG are to promote and execute fundamental and applied research and preindustrial development in the areas of energy resources, technologies, energy efficiency, and the impact of climate change.

Prof. Bahaj is an experienced research team director and has many internationally focused research projects including collaborative projects in China, the European Union, the Middle East, and Africa. He also coordinated (2006–10) the United Kingdom's Engineering and Physical Sciences Research Council (EPSRC), Ecoregion Research Networks that aim to develop research themes and projects to study eco-city development encompassing resource assessment, technology pathways for the production and conservation of energy, planning, and social and economic studies required in establishing eco-regions in China and elsewhere (http://www.eco-networks.org). He is a founding member of the Sino-UK Low Carbon City Development Cooperation (LCCD) which aims to promote and undertake research into pathways for low-carbon development in Chinese cities. His work also encompasses an ongoing multimillion pound program in Africa, 'Energy for Development' for promoting and implementing village electrification systems, addressing villager's needs, and establishing coherent approaches to the commercial sustainability of the projects. This program is funded by the Research Councils and the UK Department for International Development (DFID; www.energyfordevelopment.net).

Prof. Bahaj is the editor-in-chief of the *International Journal of Sustainable Energy* and associate Editor of the *Renewable & Sustainable Energy Review*. He was on the editorial boards of the journals *Sustainable Cities and Society* and *Renewable Energy* (2005–11), and the United Kingdom's Institute of Civil Engineering journal *Energy* (2006–09). He was a member of the Tyndall Centre for Climate Change Research Supervisory Board (2005–10), and from 2001 to 2007 he was a member of the UK Government Department of Business, Enterprise and Regulatory Reform (now Department for Business Innovations and Skills, BIS), Technology Programmes Panels on Water (including ocean energy) and Solar Energy, now being administered by the Technology Strategy Board (TSB). Prof. Bahaj was the chair of the Technical Committees of the World Renewable Energy Congress – held in Glasgow (July 2008) and in Abu Dhabi (September 2010). He was a member of the Technical Committee of the 27th International Conference on Offshore Mechanics and Arctic Engineering (OMAE, 2008), a member of the management and technical committees of the European Wave and Tidal Energy Conferences (EWTEC, Porto, Portugal, September 2007; and Uppsala, Sweden, September 2009). He is also a member of the British Standards Institution (BSI) Committee GEL/82 on PV Energy Systems. Recently, at the invitation of the International Energy Agency, he has completed the 2008 status report on tidal stream energy conversion and in September 2009 was elected to chair the next EWTEC conference in the series – EWTEC2011 which was held in Southampton, 5–9 September 2011, and attended by around 500 participants.

To address training in the areas of energy and climate change Prof. Bahaj has coordinated and developed a set of MSc programs under the banner 'Energy and Sustainability' that address Energy Resources and Climate Change and Energy, Environment and Buildings.

CONTRIBUTORS FOR ALL VOLUMES

P Agnolucci
Imperial College London, London, UK

EO Ahlgren
Chalmers University of Technology, Gothenburg, Sweden

D Aklil
Pure Energy Center, Unst, Shetland Isles, UK

D-C Alarcón Padilla
Centro de Investigaciones Energéticas Medioambientales y Tecnológicas (CIEMAT), Plataforma Solar de Almeria, Almeria, Spain

K Alexander
University of Canterbury, Christchurch, New Zealand

S Alexopoulos
Aachen University of Applied Sciences, Jülich, Germany

A Altieri
UNICA – Brazilian Sugarcane Industry Association, São Paulo, Brazil

A Anthrakidis
Aachen University of Applied Sciences, Jülich, Germany

E Antolín
Universidad Politécnica de Madrid, Madrid, Spain

P Archambeau
University of Liège, Liège, Belgium

H Ármannsson
Iceland GeoSurvey (ISOR), Reykjavík, Iceland

MF Askew
Wolverhampton, UK

A Athienitis
Concordia University, Montreal, QC, Canada

G Axelsson
University of Iceland, Reykjavik, Iceland

V Badescu
Polytechnic University of Bucharest, Bucharest, Romania

AS Bahaj
The University of Southampton, Southampton, UK

P Banda
Instituto de Sistema Fotovoltaicos de Concentración (ISFOC), Puertollano, Spain

VG Belessiotis
'DEMOKRITOS' National Center for Scientific Research, Athens, Greece

P Berry
ADAS High Mowthorpe, Malton, UK

F Bidault
Imperial College London, London, UK

D Biro
Fraunhofer Institute for Solar Energy Systems, Freiburg, Germany

G Boschloo
Uppsala University, Uppsala, Sweden

C Boura
Aachen University of Applied Sciences, Jülich, Germany

E Bozorgzadeh
Iran Water and Power Resources Development Company (IWPCO), Tehran, Iran

CE Brewer
Iowa State University, Ames, IA, USA

M Börjesson
Chalmers University of Technology, Gothenburg, Sweden

RC Brown
Iowa State University, Ames, IA, USA

F Bueno
University of Burgos, Burgos, Spain

K Burke
NASA Glenn Research Center, Cleveland, OH, USA

LF Cabeza
GREA Innovació Concurrent, Universitat de Lleida, Lleida, Spain

L Candanedo
Dublin Institute of Technology, Dublin, Ireland

YG Caouris
University of Patras, Patras, Greece

UB Cappel
Uppsala University, Uppsala, Sweden

JA Carta
Universidad de Las Palmas de Gran Canaria, Las Palmas de Gran Canaria, Spain

P Chen
Dalian Institute of Chemical Physics, Dalian, China

DG Christakis
Wind Energy Laboratory, Technological Educational Institute of Crete, Crete, Greece

DA Chwieduk
Warsaw University of Technology, Warsaw, Poland

J Clark
University of York, York, UK

G Conibeer
University of New South Wales, Sydney, NSW, Australia

AJ Cruden
University of Strathclyde, Glasgow, UK

MC da Silva

B Davidsdottir
University of Iceland, Reykjavík, Iceland

O de la Rubia
Instituto de Sistema Fotovoltaicos de Concentración (ISFOC), Puertollano, Spain

E Despotou
Formerly of the European Photovoltaic Industry Association, Brussels, Belgium

BJ Dewals
University of Liège, Liège, Belgium

AL Dicks
The University of Queensland, Brisbane, QLD, Australia

R DiPippo
University of Massachusetts Dartmouth, Dartmouth, MA, USA

E Dunlop
European Commission DG Joint Research Centre, Ispra, Italy

NM Duteanu
Newcastle University, Newcastle upon Tyne, UK; University 'POLITEHNICA' Timisoara, Timisoara, Romania

LM Eaton
Oak Ridge National Laboratory, Oak Ridge, TN, USA

H-J Egelhaaf
Konarka Technologies GmbH, Nürnberg, Germany

T Ehara
Mizuho Information & Research Institute, Tokyo, Japan

B Erable
Newcastle University, Newcastle upon Tyne, UK; CNRS-Université de Toulouse, Toulouse, France

S Erpicum
University of Liège, Liège, Belgium

G Evans
NNFCC, Biocentre, Innovation Way, Heslington, York, UK

AFO Falcão
Instituto Superior Técnico, Technical University of Lisbon, Lisbon, Portugal

G Faninger
University of Klagenfurt, Klagenfurt, Austria; Vienna University of Technology, Vienna, Austria

GA Florides
Cyprus University of Technology, Limassol, Cyprus

ÓG Flóvenz
Iceland GeoSurvey (ISOR), Reykjavík, Iceland

RN Frese
VU University Amsterdam, Amsterdam, The Netherlands

Þ Friðriksson
Iceland GeoSurvey (ISOR), Reykjavík, Iceland

VM Fthenakis
Columbia University, New York, NY, USA; Brookhaven National Laboratory, Upton, NY, USA

M Fuamba
École Polytechnique de Montréal, Montreal, QC, Canada

A Fuller
University of Canterbury, Christchurch, New Zealand

LMC Gato
Instituto Superior Técnico, Technical University of Lisbon, Lisbon, Portugal

R Gazey
Pure Energy Center, Unst, Shetland Isles, UK

TA Gessert
National Renewable Energy Laboratory (NREL), Golden, CO, USA

MM Ghangrekar
*Newcastle University, Newcastle upon Tyne, UK;
Indian Institute of Technology, Kharagpur, India*

M Giannouli
University of Patras, Patras, Greece

EA Gibson
University of Nottingham, Nottingham UK

A Gil
Hydropower Generation Division of Iberdrola, Salamanca, Spain

SW Glunz
Fraunhofer Institute for Solar Energy Systems, Freiburg, Germany

JC Goldschmidt
Fraunhofer Institute for Solar Energy Systems ISE, Freiburg, Germany

R Gottschalg
Loughborough University, Leicestershire, UK

MA Green
The University of New South Wales, Sydney, NSW, Australia

J Göttsche
Aachen University of Applied Sciences, Jülich, Germany

J Guo
China Institute of Water Resources and Hydropower Research (IWHR), Beijing, China

A Hagfeldt
Uppsala University, Uppsala, Sweden

B Hagin
Ingénieur-Conseil, Lutry, Switzerland

K Hall
Technology Transition Corporation, Ltd., Tyne and Wear, UK

O Hamandjoda
University of Yaounde, Yaounde, Republic of Cameroon

AP Harvey
Newcastle University, Newcastle upon Tyne, UK

JA Hauch
Konarka Technologies GmbH, Nürnberg, Germany

D Heinemann
University of Oldenburg, Oldenburg, Germany

V Heller
Imperial College London, London, UK

GP Hersir
Iceland GeoSurvey (ISOR), Reykjavík, Iceland

T Heyer
Technical University of Dresden, Dresden, Germany

P Hilger
Aachen University of Applied Sciences, Jülich, Germany

B Hillring
Swedish University of Agricultural Sciences, Skinnskatteberg, Sweden

T Hino
CTI Engineering International Co., Ltd., Chu-o-Ku, Japan

LC Hirst
Imperial College London, London, UK

B Hoffschmidt
Aachen University of Applied Sciences, Jülich, Germany

H Horlacher
Technical University of Dresden, Dresden, Germany

N Hughes
Imperial College London, London, UK

SL Hui
Bechtel Civil Company, San Francisco, CA, USA

D Husmann
University of Wisconsin–Madison, Madison, WI, USA

JTS Irvine
University of St Andrews, St Andrews, UK

D Jacobs
Freie Universität Berlin, Berlin, Germany

Y Jestin
Advanced Photonics and Photovoltaics Group, Bruno Kessler Foundation, Trento, Italy

A Jäger-Waldau
Institution for Energy Transport, Ispra, Italy

S Jianxia
Design and Research Institute, Yangzhou City, Jiangsu Province, China

E Johnson
Pure Energy Center, Unst, Shetland Isles, UK

HF Kaan
TNO Energy, Comfort and Indoor Quality, Delft, The Netherlands

JK Kaldellis
Technological Education Institute of Piraeus, Athens, Greece

SA Kalogirou
Cyprus University of Technology, Limassol, Cyprus

HD Kambezidis
Institute of Environmental Research and Sustainable Development, Athens, Greece

M Kapsali
Technological Education Institute of Piraeus, Athens, Greece

M Karimirad
Norwegian University of Science and Technology, Trondheim, Norway

T Karlessi
National and Kapodistrian University of Athens, Athens, Greece

SN Karlsdóttir
Innovation Center Iceland, Iceland

D Al Katsaprakakis
Wind Energy Laboratory, Technological Educational Institute of Crete, Crete, Greece

O Kaufhold
Aachen University of Applied Sciences, Jülich, Germany

CA Kaufmann
Helmholtz Zentrum für Materialien und Energie GmbH, Berlin, Germany

KA Kavadias
Technological Education Institute of Piraeus, Athens, Greece

LL Kazmerski
National Renewable Energy Laboratory, Golden, CO, USA

A Kazmi
University of York, York, UK

K Kendall
University of Birmingham, Birmingham, UK

J Kenfack
University of Yaounde, Yaounde, Republic of Cameroon

R Kenny
European Commission DG Joint Research Centre, Ispra, Italy

HC Kim
Brookhaven National Laboratory, Upton, NY, USA

L Kloo
KTH—Royal Institute of Technology, Stockholm, Sweden

G Knothe
USDA Agricultural Research Service, Peoria, IL, USA

FR Kogler
Konarka Technologies GmbH, Nürnberg, Germany

D Kolokotsa
Technical University of Crete, Crete, Greece

K Komoto
Mizuho Information & Research Institute, Tokyo, Japan

E Kondili
Technological Education Institute of Piraeus, Athens, Greece

H Kristjánsdóttir
University of Iceland, Reykjavík, Iceland

LA Lamont
Petroleum Institute, Abu Dhabi, UAE

GA Landis
NASA Glenn Research Center, Cleveland, OH, USA

JGM Lee
Newcastle University, Newcastle upon Tyne, UK

G Leftheriotis
University of Patras, Patras, Greece

A Lejeune
University of Liège, Liège, Belgium

T Leo
FuelCell Energy Inc., Danbury, CT, USA

E Lester
The University of Nottingham, Nottingham, UK

E Lorenz
University of Oldenburg, Oldenburg, Germany

JW Lund
Geo-Heat Center, Oregon Institute of Technology, Klamath Falls, OR, USA

A Luque
Universidad Politécnica de Madrid, Madrid, Spain

BP Machado
Intertechne, Curitiba, PR, Brazil

EBL Mackay
GL Garrad Hassan, Bristol, UK

T-F Mahdi
École Polytechnique de Montréal, Montreal, QC, Canada

GG Maidment
London South Bank University, London, UK

A Malmgren
BioC Ltd, Cirencester, UK

C Manson-Whitton
Progressive Energy Ltd., Stonehouse, UK

Á Margeirsson
Magma Energy Iceland, Reykjanesbaer, Iceland

A Martí
Universidad Politécnica de Madrid, Madrid, Spain

M Martinez
Instituto de Sistema Fotovoltaicos de Concentración (ISFOC), Puertollano, Spain

S Mathew
University of Brunei Darussalam, Gadong, Brunei Darussalam

PH Middleton
University of Agder, Grimstad, Norway

R Mikalsen
Newcastle University, Newcastle upon Tyne, UK

D Milborrow
Lewes, East Sussex, UK

H Müllejans
European Commission DG Joint Research Centre, Ispra, Italy

V Molkov
University of Ulster, Newtownabbey, Northern Ireland, UK

M Moner-Girona
Joint Research Centre, European Commission, Institute for Energy and Transport, Ispra, Italy

PE Morthorst
Technical University of Denmark, Roskilde, Denmark

N Mortimer
North Energy Associates Ltd, Sheffield, UK

E Mullins
Teagasc, Oak Park Crops Research Centre, Carlow, Republic of Ireland

P Mulvihill
Pioneer Generation Ltd., Alexandra, New Zealand

DR Myers
National Renewable Energy Laboratory, USA

D Nash
University of Strathclyde, Glasgow, UK

GF Nemet
University of Wisconsin–Madison, Madison, WI, USA

H Nfaoui
Mohammed V University, Rabat, Morocco

T Nikolakakis
Columbia University, New York, NY, USA

X Niu
Changjiang Institute of Survey, Planning, Design and Research, Wuhan, China

B Norton
Dublin Institute of Technology, Dublin, Ireland

A Nuamah
The University of Nottingham, Nottingham, UK; RWE npower, Swindon, UK

B O'Connor
Aachen University of Applied Sciences, Jülich, Germany

O Olsson
Swedish University of Agricultural Sciences, Skinnskatteberg, Sweden

V Ortisi
Pure Energy Center, Unst, Shetland Isles, UK

H Ossenbrink
European Commission DG Joint Research Centre, Ispra, Italy

AG Paliatsos
Technological Education Institute of Piraeus, Athens, Greece

A Pandit
VU University Amsterdam, Amsterdam, The Netherlands

E Papanicolaou
'DEMOKRITOS' National Center for Scientific Research, Athens, Greece

A Paurine
London South Bank University, London, UK

N Pearsall
Northumbria University, Newcastle, UK

RJ Pearson
Lotus Engineering, Norwich, UK

RD Perlack
Oak Ridge National Laboratory, Oak Ridge, TN, USA

H Pettersson
Swerea IVF AB, Mölndal, Sweden

GS Philip
KCAET, Malapuram, Kerala, India

S Pillai
The University of New South Wales, Sydney, NSW, Australia

M Pirotton
University of Liège, Liège, Belgium

BG Pollet
University of Birmingham, Birmingham, UK

D Porter
Association of Electricity Producers, London, UK

A Pouliezos
Technical University of Crete, Hania, Greece

R Preu
Fraunhofer Institute for Solar Energy Systems, Freiburg, Germany

CM Ramos

C Rau
Aachen University of Applied Sciences, Jülich, Germany

AA Refaat
Cairo University, Giza, Egypt

TH Reijenga
BEARiD Architecten, Rotterdam, The Netherlands

AHME Reinders
Delft University of Technology, Delft, The Netherlands;
University of Twente, Enschede, The Netherlands

G Riley
RWE npower, Swindon, UK

DJ Roddy
Newcastle University, Newcastle upon Tyne, UK

S Rolland
Alliance for Rural Electrification, Brussels, Belgium

A Roskilly
Newcastle University, Newcastle upon Tyne, UK

F Rubio
Instituto de Sistema Fotovoltaicos de Concentración (ISFOC), Puertollano, Spain

F Rulot
University of Liège, Liège, Belgium

L Rybach
GEOWATT AG, Zurich, Switzerland

M Santamouris
National and Kapodistrian University of Athens, Athens, Greece

J Sattler
Aachen University of Applied Sciences, Jülich, Germany

M Sauerborn
Aachen University of Applied Sciences, Jülich, Germany

TW Schmidt
The University of Sydney, Sydney, NSW, Australia

N Schofield
University of Manchester, Manchester, UK

REI Schropp
Utrecht University, Utrecht, The Netherlands

K Scott
Newcastle University, Newcastle upon Tyne, UK

SP Sen
NHPC Ltd., New Delhi, India

TI Sigfusson
Innovation Center, Reykjavik, Iceland

L Sims
Konarka Technologies GmbH, Nürnberg, Germany;
Universität Augsburg, Augsburg, Germany

C Smith
NNFCC, Biocentre, Innovation Way, Heslington, York, UK

K Sæmundsson
Iceland GeoSurvey (ISOR), Reykjavík, Iceland

BK Sovacool
Vermont Law School, South Royalton, VT, USA

J Spink
Teagasc, Oak Park Crops Research Centre, Carlow, Republic of Ireland

JN Sørensen
Technical University of Denmark, Lyngby, Denmark

T Stallard
The University of Manchester, Manchester, UK

GS Stavrakakis
Technical University of Crete, Chania, Greece

R Steim
Konarka Technologies GmbH, Nürnberg, Germany

BJ Stokes
CNJV LLC, Washington, DC, USA

L Sun
KTH—Royal Institute of Technology, Stockholm, Sweden;
Dalian University of Technology (DUT), Dalian, China

L Suo
Science and Technology Committee of the Ministry of Water Resources, Beijing, China

DT Swift-Hook
Kingston University, London, UK;
World Renewable Energy Network, Brighton, UK

A Synnefa
National and Kapodistrian University of Athens, Athens, Greece

S Szabo
Joint Research Centre, European Commission, Institute for Energy and Transport, Ispra, Italy

MJY Tayebjee
The University of Sydney, Sydney, NSW, Australia

A Tesfai
University of St Andrews, St Andrews, UK

P Thornley
The University of Manchester, Manchester, UK

Y Tripanagnostopoulos
University of Patras, Patras, Greece

L Tsakalakos
General Electric – Global Research Center, New York, NY, USA

JWG Turner
Lotus Engineering, Norwich, UK

E Tzen
Centre for Renewable Energy Sources and Saving (CRES), Pikermi, Attica, Greece

T Unold
Helmholtz Zentrum für Materialien und Energie GmbH, Berlin, Germany

J van der Heide
imec vzw, Leuven, Belgium

P van der Vleuten
Free Energy Consulting, Eindhoven, The Netherlands

F Van Hulle
XP Wind Consultancy, Leuven, Belgium

GC van Kooten
University of Victoria, Victoria, BC, Canada

WGJHM van Sark
Utrecht University, Utrecht, The Netherlands

I Waller
FiveBarGate Consultants Ltd, Cleveland, UK

I Walsh
Opus International Consultants Ltd., New Zealand

Y Wang
Newcastle University, Newcastle upon Tyne, UK

T Wizelius
Gotland University, Visby, Sweden; Lund University, Lund, Sweden

LL Wright
University of Tennessee, Knoxville, TN, USA

H Xie
Changjiang Institute of Survey, Planning, Design and Research, Wuhan, China

M Yamaguchi
Toyota Technological Institute, Tempaku, Nagoya, Japan

P Yianoulis
University of Patras, Patras, Greece

EH Yu
Newcastle University, Newcastle upon Tyne, UK

H Yu
Newcastle University, Newcastle upon Tyne, UK

DP Zafirakis
Technological Education Institute of Piraeus, Athens, Greece

G Zaragoza
Centro de Investigaciones Energéticas Medioambientales y Tecnológicas (CIEMAT), Plataforma Solar de Almeria, Almeria, Spain

M Zeman
Delft University of Technology, Delft, The Netherlands

PREFACE

Comprehensive Renewable Energy is the only multivolume reference work of its type at a time when renewable energy sources are increasingly in demand and realistically sustainable, clean, and helping to combat climate change and global warming. Renewable energy investment has exceeded US$10 billion per year during the past 5 years. The World Renewable Energy Network (WREN) predicts that this figure is set to increase to US$20 billion per year by 2015.

As Editor-in-Chief, I have assembled an impressive world-class team of 154 volume editors and contributing authors for the eight volumes. They represent policy makers, researchers, industrialists, financiers, and heads of organizations from more than 80 countries to produce this definitive complete work in renewable energy covering the past, explaining the present, and giving the ideas and prospects of development for the future. There are more than 1000 references from books, journals, and the Internet within the eight volumes. *Comprehensive Renewable Energy* is full of color charts, illustrations, and photographs of real projects and research results from around the world. Each chapter has been painstakingly reviewed and checked for consistent high quality. The result is an authoritative overview that ties the literature together and provides the user with reliable background information and a citation resource.

The field of renewable energy research and development is represented by many journals that are directly and indirectly concerned with the field. But no reference work encompasses the entire field and unites the different areas of research through in-depth foundational reviews. *Comprehensive Renewable Energy* fills this vacuum, and is the definitive work for this subject area. It will help users apply context to diverse journal literature, aiding them in identifying areas for further research and development.

Research into renewable energy is spread across a number of different disciplines and subject areas. These areas do not always share a unique identifying factor or subject themselves to clear and concise definitions. This work unites the different areas of research and allows users, regardless of their background, to navigate through the most essential concepts with ease, saving them time and vastly improving their understanding so that they can move forward, whether in their research, development, manufacturing, or purchase of renewable energy.

The first volume is devoted to Photovoltaic Technology and is edited by Mr. Wilfried G. J. H. M. van Sark from the Netherlands. It consists of 38 chapters, written by 41 authors from Europe, the United States, Japan, China, India, Africa, and the Middle East. The topics covered range from the smallest applications to MW projects. A brief introduction and history is followed by chapters on finance and economics, solar resources, up- and downconversion, crystalline photovoltaic (PV) cells, luminescent concentrators, thin-film and multiple-junction plastic solar cells, dye-sensitized solar cells, bio-inspired converters, application of micro- and nanotechnology, building integrated photovoltaics (BIPV) application in architecture, and very large-scale PV systems. Without doubt, this is an impressive tour of an immense field.

Volume 2 is devoted to Wind Energy and is edited by Professor John K. Kaldellis from Greece. It consists of 22 chapters written by 22 authors, again from various parts of the world, covering all aspects of wind energy from small wind mills to very large wind farms. The volume includes chapters on the history of wind power, the potential of wind power, wind turbine development, aerodynamic analysis, mechanical and electrical loads, control systems, noise and testing, onshore and offshore wind systems, policy, industry, and special wind power applications.

Volume 3 is devoted to Solar Thermal Applications and the editor is Professor Soteris A. Kalogirou from Cyprus. It consists of 19 chapters written by 17 authors. All aspects of solar thermal energy and its applications are covered. The volume begins with solar energy as a source of heat and goes on to describe the history of thermal applications, low-temperature and high-temperature storage systems, selective coating, glazing, modeling and simulation, hot water systems, space heating and cooling, water desalination, industrial and agricultural applications, concentration power, heat pumps, and passive solar architecture. The authors have looked at the Sun from the thermal energy aspect and put together a very informative and up-to-date volume from which every interested person, no matter what their level of knowledge, can benefit.

Volume 4 is on Fuel Cells and Hydrogen Technology and is edited by Dr. Andrew Cruden from the United Kingdom. It consists of 14 chapters covering the following topics: introduction and perspectives on hydrogen and fuel cells; theory and application of alkaline fuel cells; application of proton exchange membrane (PEM) fuel cells; molten carbonate fuel cells; solid oxide fuel cells; microbial and biological fuel cells; storage of compressed gas and hydrogen; the economy and policy of hydrogen technology; hydrogen safety engineering and future progress; the use of hydrogen for transport; and hydrogen and fuel cell power electronics. The 14 chapters were written by 16 authors. All aspects of practice, innovative technology, and future guidelines for researchers and industry have been addressed in this definitive volume.

Volume 5 deals with the huge field of Biomass and Biofuels and is edited by Professor Dermot J. Roddy from the United Kingdom. This work consists of 21 chapters written by 23 authors, again covering all aspects of biomass and biofuels, including their past, present, and future. The volume explains the history and prospective future of biofuels; bioethanol development in Brazil; power generation from biomass; biomass co-firing stations; biomass world market; a critical assessment of biomass – combined heat and power (CHP) energy systems; the ethics of biofuel production – issues, constraints, and limitations; greenhouse gases life cycle analysis; six different solutions from gasification and pyrolysis; new processes in biomass-to-liquid technology; new processes in biofuel production; biofuels from waste materials; novel feedstocks and woody biomass; feedstocks with the potential of yield improvement; renewable fuels – an automotive prospective; and novel use of biofuels in a range of engine configurations. Under Expanding the Envelope, there are chapters on biochar, extracting additional value from biomass, and biomass to chemicals. Finally, the chapter on bioenergy policy development concludes the volume.

Volume 6 is concerned with Hydro Power and is edited by Professor André G. H. Lejeune from Belgium. This is the oldest of all the renewable energy applications and has progressed over the ages from pico-hydro of a few hundred watts to large- and mega-scale dams generating more than 3000 MW with innovative civil engineering capability. This volume consists of 18 chapters prepared by 21 authors. It contains introduction – benefits and constraints of hydropower, recent developments and achievements in hydraulic research in China, and the management of hydropower and its impacts through construction and operation. The volume then assesses nine hydropower schemes around the world: the Three Gorges Project in China; large hydropower plants of Brazil; hydropower in Iran – vision and strategy; the recent trend in developing hydropower in India; the evolution of hydropower in Spain; hydropower in Japan; hydropower in Canada; an overview of institutional structure reform of the Cameroon power sector and assessment; and hydropower reliability in Switzerland. Other important issues are covered: pumped storage power plants; simplified generic axial-flow microhydro turbines; the development of a small hydroelectric scheme at Horseshoe Bend, Teviot River, New Zealand; concrete durability in dam design structure; and long-term sediment management for sustainable hydropower.

Volume 7 deals with Geothermal Energy. The editor of this volume is Professor Thorsteinn I. Sigfusson from Iceland. The volume consists of 10 chapters, which are written by 15 different authors. It covers the following areas: introduction and the physics of geothermal resources and management during utilization; geothermal shallow systems – heat pumps; geothermal exploration techniques; corrosion, scaling, and material selection in geothermal power production; direct heat utilization of geothermal energy; geothermal power plants; geochemical aspects of geothermal utilization; geothermal cost and investment factors; and the role of sustainable geothermal development.

Volume 8 is devoted to Generating Electricity from the Oceans, edited by Professor AbuBakr S. Bahaj from the United Kingdom. It consists of six chapters written by five authors. The volume covers the historical aspects of wave energy conversion, resource assessment for wave energy, development of wave devices from initial conception to commercial demonstration, air turbines, and the economics of ocean energy.

One chapter is totally devoted to Renewable Energy Policy and Incentives. It is included in the first volume only. The author of this chapter is Mr. David Porter, Chief Executive of the Association of Electricity Producers in the United Kingdom, an author who has had vast experience of dealing with electricity generation in the United Kingdom over many years. He has advised the British Government on how to meet supply and demand of electricity and coordinate with all electricity producers regarding their sources and supply. The chapter outlines the types of mechanisms used to promote renewable energy and their use, the impact on their deployment, ensuring investor certainty, the potential for harmonizing support schemes, and the conclusion.

In short, my advice to anyone who wants to acquire comprehensive knowledge concerning renewable energy, no matter which subject or application, is that they should acquire this invaluable resource for their home, research center and laboratory, company, or library.

Professor Ali Sayigh BSc, DIC, PhD, FIE, FIEE, CEng
Chairman of WREC (World Renewable Energy Congress)
Director General of WREN (World Renewable Energy Network)
Chairman of IEI (The Institution of Engineers (India))
Editor-in-Chief of *Renewable Energy*
Editor-in-Chief of *Renewable Energy Magazine*

CONTENTS

Editor-in-Chief	v
Volume Editors	vii
Contributors for All Volumes	xi
Preface	xix

Volume 1 Photovoltaic Solar Energy

Renewable Energy

1.01	Renewable Energy Policy and Incentives *D Porter*	1

Photovoltaic Solar Energy

1.02	Introduction to Photovoltaic Technology *WGJHM van Sark*	5
1.03	Solar Photovoltaics Technology: No Longer an Outlier *LL Kazmerski*	13
1.04	History of Photovoltaics *LA Lamont*	31

Economics and Environment

1.05	Historical and Future Cost Dynamics of Photovoltaic Technology *GF Nemet and D Husmann*	47
1.06	Feed-In Tariffs and Other Support Mechanisms for Solar PV Promotion *D Jacobs and BK Sovacool*	73
1.07	Finance Mechanisms and Incentives for Photovoltaic Technologies in Developing Countries *M Moner-Girona, S Szabo, and S Rolland*	111
1.08	Environmental Impacts of Photovoltaic Life Cycles *VM Fthenakis and HC Kim*	143
1.09	Overview of the Global PV Industry *A Jäger-Waldau*	161
1.10	Vision for Photovoltaics in the Future *E Despotou*	179

| 1.11 | Storage Options for Photovoltaics
VM Fthenakis and T Nikolakakis | 199 |

Resource and Potential

| 1.12 | Solar Radiation Resource Assessment for Renewable Energy Conversion
DR Myers | 213 |
| 1.13 | Prediction of Solar Irradiance and Photovoltaic Power
E Lorenz and D Heinemann | 239 |

Basics

| 1.14 | Principles of Solar Energy Conversion
LC Hirst | 293 |
| 1.15 | Thermodynamics of Photovoltaics
V Badescu | 315 |

Technology

1.16	Crystalline Silicon Solar Cells: State-of-the-Art and Future Developments SW Glunz, R Preu, and D Biro	353
1.17	Thin-Film Silicon PV Technology M Zeman and REI Schropp	389
1.18	Chalcopyrite Thin-Film Materials and Solar Cells T Unold and CA Kaufmann	399
1.19	Cadmium Telluride Photovoltaic Thin Film: CdTe TA Gessert	423
1.20	Plastic Solar Cells L Sims, H-J Egelhaaf, JA Hauch, FR Kogler, and R Steim	439
1.21	Mesoporous Dye-Sensitized Solar Cells A Hagfeldt, UB Cappel, G Boschloo, L Sun, L Kloo, H Pettersson, and EA Gibson	481
1.22	Multiple Junction Solar Cells M Yamaguchi	497
1.23	Application of Micro- and Nanotechnology in Photovoltaics L Tsakalakos	515
1.24	Upconversion TW Schmidt and MJY Tayebjee	533
1.25	Downconversion MJY Tayebjee, TW Schmidt, and G Conibeer	549
1.26	Down-Shifting of the Incident Light for Photovoltaic Applications Y Jestin	563
1.27	Luminescent Solar Concentrators JC Goldschmidt	587
1.28	Thermophotovoltaics J van der Heide	603
1.29	Intermediate Band Solar Cells E Antolín, A Martí, and A Luque	619
1.30	Plasmonics for Photovoltaics S Pillai and MA Green	641
1.31	Artificial Leaves: Towards Bio-Inspired Solar Energy Converters A Pandit and RN Frese	657

Applications

1.32	Design and Components of Photovoltaic Systems *WGJHM van Sark*	679
1.33	BIPV in Architecture and Urban Planning *TH Reijenga and HF Kaan*	697
1.34	Product-Integrated Photovoltaics *AHME Reinders and WGJHM van Sark*	709
1.35	Very Large-Scale Photovoltaic Systems *T Ehara, K Komoto, and P van der Vleuten*	733
1.36	Concentration Photovoltaics *M Martinez, O de la Rubia, F Rubio, and P Banda*	745
1.37	Solar Power Satellites *GA Landis*	767
1.38	Performance Monitoring *N Pearsall and R Gottschalg*	775
1.39	Standards in Photovoltaic Technology *H Ossenbrink, H Müllejans, R Kenny, and E Dunlop*	787

Volume 2 Wind Energy

2.01	Wind Energy – Introduction *JK Kaldellis*	1
2.02	Wind Energy Contribution in the Planet Energy Balance and Future Prospects *JK Kaldellis and M Kapsali*	11
2.03	History of Wind Power *DT Swift-Hook*	41
2.04	Wind Energy Potential *H Nfaoui*	73
2.05	Wind Turbines: Evolution, Basic Principles, and Classifications *S Mathew and GS Philip*	93
2.06	Energy Yield of Contemporary Wind Turbines *DP Zafirakis, AG Paliatsos, and JK Kaldellis*	113
2.07	Wind Parks Design, Including Representative Case Studies *D Al Katsaprakakis and DG Christakis*	169
2.08	Aerodynamic Analysis of Wind Turbines *JN Sørensen*	225
2.09	Mechanical-Dynamic Loads *M Karimirad*	243
2.10	Electrical Parts of Wind Turbines *GS Stavrakakis*	269
2.11	Wind Turbine Control Systems and Power Electronics *A Pouliezos*	329
2.12	Testing, Standardization, Certification in Wind Energy *F Van Hulle*	371
2.13	Design and Implementation of a Wind Power Project *T Wizelius*	391
2.14	Offshore Wind Power Basics *M Kapsali and JK Kaldellis*	431

2.15	Wind Energy Economics D Milborrow	469
2.16	Environmental-Social Benefits/Impacts of Wind Power E Kondili and JK Kaldellis	503
2.17	Wind Energy Policy GC van Kooten	541
2.18	Wind Power Integration JA Carta	569
2.19	Stand-Alone, Hybrid Systems KA Kavadias	623
2.20	Wind Power Industry and Markets PE Morthorst	657
2.21	Trends, Prospects, and R&D Directions in Wind Turbine Technology JK Kaldellis and DP Zafirakis	671
2.22	Special Wind Power Applications E Kondili	725

Volume 3 Solar Thermal Systems: Components and Applications

Solar Thermal Systems

3.01	Solar Thermal Systems: Components and Applications – Introduction SA Kalogirou	1
3.02	Solar Resource HD Kambezidis	27
3.03	History of Solar Energy VG Belessiotis and E Papanicolaou	85

Components

3.04	Low Temperature Stationary Collectors YG Caouris	103
3.05	Low Concentration Ratio Solar Collectors SA Kalogirou	149
3.06	High Concentration Solar Collectors B Hoffschmidt, S Alexopoulos, J Göttsche, M Sauerborn, and O Kaufhold	165
3.07	Thermal Energy Storage LF Cabeza	211
3.08	Photovoltaic/Thermal Solar Collectors Y Tripanagnostopoulos	255
3.09	Solar Selective Coatings P Yianoulis, M Giannouli, and SA Kalogirou	301
3.10	Glazings and Coatings G Leftheriotis and P Yianoulis	313
3.11	Modeling and Simulation of Passive and Active Solar Thermal Systems A Athienitis, SA Kalogirou, and L Candanedo	357

Applications

3.12	Solar Hot Water Heating Systems *G Faninger*	419
3.13	Solar Space Heating and Cooling Systems *SA Kalogirou and GA Florides*	449
3.14	Solar Cooling and Refrigeration Systems *GG Maidment and A Paurine*	481
3.15	Solar-Assisted Heat Pumps *DA Chwieduk*	495
3.16	Solar Desalination *E Tzen, G Zaragoza, and D-C Alarcón Padilla*	529
3.17	Industrial and Agricultural Applications of Solar Heat *B Norton*	567
3.18	Concentrating Solar Power *B Hoffschmidt, S Alexopoulos, C Rau, J Sattler, A Anthrakidis, C Boura, B O'Connor, and P Hilger*	595
3.19	Passive Solar Architecture *D Kolokotsa, M Santamouris, A Synnefa, and T Karlessi*	637

Volume 4 Fuel Cells and Hydrogen Technology

4.01	Fuel Cells and Hydrogen Technology – Introduction *AJ Cruden*	1
4.02	Current Perspective on Hydrogen and Fuel Cells *K Burke*	13
4.03	Hydrogen Economics and Policy *N Hughes and P Agnolucci*	45
4.04	Hydrogen Safety Engineering: The State-of-the-Art and Future Progress *V Molkov*	77
4.05	Hydrogen Storage: Compressed Gas *D Nash, D Aklil, E Johnson, R Gazey, and V Ortisi*	111
4.06	Hydrogen Storage: Liquid and Chemical *P Chen*	137
4.07	Alkaline Fuel Cells: Theory and Application *F Bidault and PH Middleton*	159
4.08	PEM Fuel Cells: Applications *AL Dicks*	183
4.09	Molten Carbonate Fuel Cells: Theory and Application *T Leo*	227
4.10	Solid Oxide Fuel Cells: Theory and Materials *A Tesfai and JTS Irvine*	241
4.11	Biological and Microbial Fuel Cells *K Scott, EH Yu, MM Ghangrekar, B Erable, and NM Duteanu*	257
4.12	Hydrogen and Fuel Cells in Transport *K Kendall and BG Pollet*	281
4.13	H_2 and Fuel Cells as Controlled Renewables: FC Power Electronics *N Schofield*	295
4.14	Future Perspective on Hydrogen and Fuel Cells *K Hall*	331

Volume 5   Biomass and Biofuel Production

Biomass and Biofuels

5.01	Biomass and Biofuels – Introduction *DJ Roddy*	1
5.02	Historical Perspectives on Biofuels *G Knothe*	11

Case Studies

5.03	Bioethanol Development in Brazil *A Altieri*	15
5.04	Biomass Power Generation *A Malmgren and G Riley*	27
5.05	Biomass Co-Firing *A Nuamah, A Malmgren, G Riley, and E Lester*	55

Issues, Constraints & Limitations

5.06	A Global Bioenergy Market *O Olsson and B Hillring*	75
5.07	Biomass CHP Energy Systems: A Critical Assessment *M Börjesson and EO Ahlgren*	87
5.08	Ethics of Biofuel Production *I Waller*	99
5.09	Life Cycle Analysis Perspective on Greenhouse Gas Savings *N Mortimer*	109

Technology Solutions – New Processes

5.10	Biomass Gasification and Pyrolysis *DJ Roddy and C Manson-Whitton*	133
5.11	Biomass to Liquids Technology *G Evans and C Smith*	155
5.12	Intensification of Biofuel Production *AP Harvey and JGM Lee*	205
5.13	Biofuels from Waste Materials *AA Refaat*	217

Technology Solutions – Novel Feedstocks

5.14	Woody Biomass *LL Wright, LM Eaton, RD Perlack, and BJ Stokes*	263
5.15	Potential for Yield Improvement *J Spink, E Mullins, and P Berry*	293

Technology Solutions – Novel End Uses

5.16	Renewable Fuels: An Automotive Perspective *RJ Pearson and JWG Turner*	305
5.17	Use of Biofuels in a Range of Engine Configurations *A Roskilly, Y Wang, R Mikalsen, and H Yu*	343

Expanding the Envelope

5.18 Biochar 357
CE Brewer and RC Brown

5.19 Extracting Additional Value from Biomass 385
MF Askew

5.20 Biomass to Chemicals 395
A Kazmi and J Clark

5.21 Bioenergy Policy Development 411
P Thornley

Volume 6 Hydro Power

Hydro Power

6.01 Hydro Power – Introduction 1
A Lejeune

Constraints of Hydropower Development

6.02 Hydro Power: A Multi Benefit Solution for Renewable Energy 15
A Lejeune and SL Hui

6.03 Management of Hydropower Impacts through Construction and Operation 49
H Horlacher, T Heyer, CM Ramos, and MC da Silva

Hydropower Schemes Around the World

6.04 Large Hydropower Plants of Brazil 93
BP Machado

6.05 Overview of Institutional Structure Reform of the Cameroon Power Sector and Assessments 129
J Kenfack and O Hamandjoda

6.06 Recent Hydropower Solutions in Canada 153
M Fuamba and TF Mahdi

6.07 The Three Gorges Project in China 179
L Suo, X Niu, and H Xie

6.08 The Recent Trend in Development of Hydro Plants in India 227
SP Sen

6.09 Hydropower Development in Iran: Vision and Strategy 253
E Bozorgzadeh

6.10 Hydropower Development in Japan 265
T Hino

6.11 Evolution of Hydropower in Spain 309
A Gil and F Bueno

6.12 Hydropower in Switzerland 343
B Hagin

Design Concepts

6.13 Long-Term Sediment Management for Sustainable Hydropower 355
F Rulot, BJ Dewals, S Erpicum, P Archambeau, and M Pirotton

6.14 Durability Design of Concrete Hydropower Structures 377
S Jianxia

6.15 Pumped Storage Hydropower Developments 405
T Hino and A Lejeune

6.16	Simplified Generic Axial-Flow Microhydro Turbines *A Fuller and K Alexander*	435
6.17	Development of a Small Hydroelectric Scheme at Horseshoe Bend, Teviot River, Central Otago, New Zealand *P Mulvihill and I Walsh*	467
6.18	Recent Achievements in Hydraulic Research in China *J Guo*	485

Volume 7 Geothermal Energy

7.01	Geothermal Energy – Introduction *TI Sigfusson*	1
7.02	The Physics of Geothermal Energy *G Axelsson*	3
7.03	Geothermal Energy Exploration Techniques *ÓG Flóvenz, GP Hersir, K Sæmundsson, H Ármannsson, and Þ Friðriksson*	51
7.04	Geochemical Aspects of Geothermal Utilization *H Ármannsson*	95
7.05	Direct Heat Utilization of Geothermal Energy *JW Lund*	169
7.06	Shallow Systems: Geothermal Heat Pumps *L Rybach*	187
7.07	Geothermal Power Plants *R DiPippo*	207
7.08	Corrosion, Scaling, and Material Selection in Geothermal Power Production *SN Karlsdóttir*	239
7.09	Geothermal Cost and Investment Factors *H Kristjánsdóttir and Á Margeirsson*	259
7.10	Sustainable Energy Development: The Role of Geothermal Power *B Davidsdottir*	271

Volume 8 Ocean Energy

8.01	Generating Electrical Power from Ocean Resources *AS Bahaj*	1
8.02	Historical Aspects of Wave Energy Conversion *AFO Falcão*	7
8.03	Resource Assessment for Wave Energy *EBL Mackay*	11
8.04	Development of Wave Devices from Initial Conception to Commercial Demonstration *V Heller*	79
8.05	Air Turbines *AFO Falcão and LMC Gato*	111
8.06	Economics of Ocean Energy *T Stallard*	151
Index		171

7.01 Geothermal Energy – Introduction

TI Sigfusson, Innovation Center, Reykjavik, Iceland

© 2012 Elsevier Ltd. All rights reserved.

This volume is dedicated to geothermal energy, one of the most fundamental energy sources that characterizes the environment and influences the lifestyle of humans. The volume is the product of a team of experts from a number of corners of the world. It should reflect the increased awareness and status of the subject as a viable alternative to the use of hydrocarbons, which, in turn, will help mitigate climate change.

Enormous amounts of heat are stored within planet Earth. This heat originates from the original formation of the planet and from radioactive decay of minerals, most likely partly accreted from space as well as solar energy absorbed at the surface. Built on the Greek language roots for the words 'earth' and 'heat' – *geo* and *thermos*, respectively – this energy is commonly called *geothermal energy*. The Earth's internal heat naturally flows to the surface by conduction and is subsequently replenished by radioactive decay of minerals. There is a net surface loss of this energy at a rate of about 14 TW.

The energy flow out of the Earth's crust gives rise to temperature gradients, which are highest near plate boundaries. Combined with fluids naturally occurring inside the crust, these gradients form the conductive mechanism that drives the geothermal energy source. Fluid flows in the form of magmatic conduits and hydrothermal circulation characterize the overall energy stream of the geothermal scenario.

In daily use, most geothermal energy is converted into electricity, with over 10 TW online in about 25 countries. Some of it is used directly for district heating, in spas, or in various industrial processes. The first use of this energy source can be traced back to Paleolithic times – the earliest being reported in the Qin Dynasty in China in the third century BC. Some twenty-two centuries later, in Lardarello in Italy at the beginning of the nineteenth century, the industrial application of geothermal energy began.

Although geothermal energy is very reliable and in most cases environmentally friendly, it has historically been limited to the tectonic plate boundaries. In scientific analysis, geothermal energy is generally counted as sustainable, primarily because any projected heat extraction is small compared to the Earth's heat content. This, on the other hand, has to be monitored closely in some local situations where an accelerated pace of harnessing could result in overexploitation.

Unlike most other sustainable energy sources, which originate from the Sun or the Moon, the roots of geothermal energy are derived from heat generated from nuclear processes within the Earth. Theoretically, the Earth's geothermal resources are more than adequate for supplying the energy needs of modern society, although only a very small fraction may be profitably exploited given present state-of-the-art technology.

Recent findings point to increasing potential of geothermal energy exploitation as a viable method for mitigating global warming, because only a relatively small proportion of greenhouse gases are emitted per energy unit during conversion.

This volume of *Comprehensive Renewable Energy* is devoted to geothermal energy. It will help reflect recent technological advances that have dramatically expanded the range and size of viable resources. It should be able to function as a general reference for anyone wanting to study the connectivity of the subject, which requires knowledge of physics, thermodynamics, chemistry, and geology as well as material engineering. Together, these span the world of geothermal exploitation. Energy cannot be created – geothermal energy utilization is about energy conversion. It is about converting the heat energy of the Earth to useful sources of energy in many forms, from heat to electric current. Endless engineering possibilities exist to convert this energy further for other possible applications and innovations.

The approach of the volume is very much like the approach of anyone wanting to make a geothermal system work. We study the hot rock close to the surface, for which we need sufficient permeability or porosity of the rock as well as sufficient quantity – and quality – of water or steam, which are the natural energy-carrying substances for energy transfer from the Earth. Alternatively, we can choose to inject water from external reservoirs or even use a third energy-carrying substance and create binary systems. All these aspects form the subject of the narrative ahead of us.

The volume starts with a thorough investigation into the physical and chemical nature of the resource. The first chapter describes physical and chemical methodologies in order to create and present a thorough picture of the origins of geothermal energy. The reader will then be able to assess geothermal energy resources, their distribution around the planet, and ways to assess and utilize them. Considerable effort is put into reservoir physics, exploitation techniques, and extraction methods, along with subsequent materials degradation and wear. This brings us to the important aspect of materials and engineering solutions for optimizing efficiency and longevity of any infrastructure associated with the harnessing of geothermal energy.

Power plants are studied, as well as common use of geothermal energy for other purposes. The most straightforward use of geothermal steam is to connect it directly to a flash turbine. When the primary geothermal fluid has a low temperature, the so-called binary power generating system can be used. This is often based on the Rankine cycle, with geothermal fluid as the heating source and a low-boiling-point medium as working fluid. When adopting the low-boiling-point medium as the working fluid, the system can generate electric power from a low-temperature source.

The economics of geothermal energy utilization are also analyzed to give a comprehensive overview of the subject. It is here that some of the best qualities of the geothermal resource come clearly into view. Utilization can include space heating, encompassing district heating systems; greenhouse and covered ground heating; aquaculture pond and raceway heating; agricultural drying; a multitude of industrial applications; and finally bathing, swimming pools, and spa heating. In arctic areas, snow melting is carried out by geothermal means. The possibility of space cooling exists where geothermal resources are present in warm climates, such as in the tropics. This last point is a good example of how thermal physics can be utilized in order to make geothermal energy conversion so wide ranging and colorful.

Last but not least, this volume contains important considerations about geothermal energy as an investment opportunity. A chapter dealing with this subject analyzes the driving forces behind international investment in geothermal electricity projects. It addresses the important factor of a generally higher investment risk (e.g., in the exploration phase) than in the traditional energy sector, which in turn means that relatively few investors are attracted. On the other hand, returns can be better, as the authors point out. Although it covers the subject from a different angle, this chapter fits into the overall content of this volume.

When looking toward the future, it seems obvious that geothermal energy holds many promises in terms of humanity's increased technological skills as well as increased awareness of the need for greater use of renewable energy sources. One of the ways explored intensively at present is deep drilling, which is a way to get closer to the warmer part of the ground – closer to the magma chambers, in some cases. Recent studies in the United States point toward a possible 10-fold increase in the proportion of geothermal energy in the energy portfolio of the country by the middle of the century. This would mean that geothermal energy could account for 10% of the total energy use. If this proves feasible, geothermal energy would become one of the most important energy sources in the world.

It is in this spirit that this volume is written at the onset of a century that will celebrate renewable energy. As volume editor, I want to thank the authors for their contributions and express my sincere hope that the contents will help shed light on the subject and reveal the interconnectivity of the various disciplines affected by the heat of the Earth.

7.02 The Physics of Geothermal Energy

G Axelsson, University of Iceland, Reykjavik, Iceland

© 2012 Elsevier Ltd. All rights reserved.

7.02.1	Introduction	3
7.02.2	Geothermal Systems	4
7.02.3	Geothermal System Properties and Processes	8
7.02.4	Pressure Diffusion and Fluid Flow	10
7.02.5	Heat Transfer	12
7.02.5.1	Porous Layer Model	14
7.02.5.2	Horizontal Fracture Model	14
7.02.5.3	Porous Model with Cold Recharge	15
7.02.6	Two-Phase Regions or Systems	15
7.02.7	Geothermal Wells	18
7.02.8	Utilization Response of Geothermal Systems	22
7.02.9	Monitoring	24
7.02.10	Modelling of Geothermal Systems – Overview	29
7.02.11	Static Modeling (Volumetric Assessment)	30
7.02.12	Dynamic Modeling	31
7.02.12.1	Lumped Parameter Modeling	31
7.02.12.2	Detailed Numerical Modeling	35
7.02.13	Geothermal Resource Management	36
7.02.14	Reinjection	39
7.02.15	Renewability of Geothermal Resources	43
7.02.16	Sustainable Geothermal Utilization	43
7.02.17	Conclusions	47
References		47

7.02.1 Introduction

Geothermal energy stems from the Earth's outward heat flux, which originates from the internal heat of the Earth left over from its creation as well as from the decay of radioactive isotopes in the Earth's continental crust (providing about half of the continental heat flux). Geothermal systems are regions in the Earth's crust where this flux and the associated energy storage are abnormally great. In the majority of cases, the energy transport medium is water and such systems are, therefore, called hydrothermal systems. Geothermal springs have been used for bathing, washing, and cooking for thousands of years in a number of countries worldwide [1]. China and Japan are good examples and ruins of baths from the days of the Roman Empire can be found from England in the north to Syria in the south. Yet commercial utilization of geothermal resources for energy production only started in the early 1900s. Electricity production was initiated in Larderello, Italy, in 1904 and operation of the largest geothermal district heating system in the world in Reykjavik, Iceland, started in 1930. At about the same time, extensive greenhouse heating with geothermal energy started in Hungary. Since this time, utilization of geothermal resources has increased steadily.

The understanding of the nature of hydrothermal systems did not really start advancing until their large-scale utilization began during the twentieth century. Some studies and development of ideas had of course been ongoing during the preceding centuries, but various misconceptions were prevailing [1]. In Iceland, where highly variable geothermal resources are abundant and easily accessible, geothermal research started during the eighteenth century [2]. A breakthrough in understanding, however, did not occur until the middle of the nineteenth century when the German scientist Robert Bunsen deducted on the basis of chemical studies that rainwater was the source of all geothermal fluids, not juvenile water from magma. This breakthrough was forgotten, or beyond Bunsen's contemporaries, and did not resurface to be confirmed until well into the twentieth century.

In addition to the hydrothermal systems – sometimes called conventional geothermal resources – ground-coupled heat pumps (GHPs) utilizing thermal energy stored in the top layers of the Earth's crust and the utilization of thermal energy in poorly permeable, deep, and hot volumes of the Earth's crust through the development or creation of so-called enhanced, or engineered, geothermal systems (EGS systems, previously called hot dry rock (HDR) systems), is also classified as geothermal utilization. The GHPs involve the operation of either horizontal or vertical heat exchanger pipes or groundwater boreholes. In the case of the heat exchanger pipes, the energy source is, in fact, to a large extent, solar radiation, and not strictly geothermal energy. The energy content of groundwater originates mainly from the Earth's outward heat flux, however. The EGS concept is based on the fact that an enormous amount of energy is stored within drillable depths in the Earth's crust, outside the hydrothermal systems (see later). It has been estimated roughly that about 35–140 GW of electricity can be produced from conventional geothermal resources and that through EGS technology about an order of magnitude more power can be generated from this energy in the Earth's crust [3].

This chapter deals with the physics of geothermal resources and of geothermal utilization. This is done by briefly reviewing the basics of geothermal reservoir physics, including the physics of fluid flow and energy transport in underground systems. The factors that control the potential and utilization response of geothermal systems will also be reviewed along with the modeling methods used to estimate their potential and response. The main ingredients of successful management of geothermal resources during their long-term utilization will also be discussed, including comprehensive monitoring and reinjection. Finally, the possibility of geothermal resources contributing to sustainable development will be discussed. The focus of the chapter is on hydrothermal systems because knowledge on these and utilization experience is quite well advanced, compared to EGS technology, which is in its infancy. Most of the basic aspects discussed in the chapter also apply to EGS systems, as well as to GHP utilization.

Geothermal reservoir physics, most often referred to as geothermal reservoir engineering, emerged as a separate scientific discipline in the 1970s [4]. However, before that some isolated studies of the physics of geothermal systems had been conducted. The studies of Einarsson [5] and Bödvarsson [6] in Iceland, Wooding [7] in New Zealand, and White [8] in the United States can be mentioned as examples. Geothermal reservoir engineering, as well as geothermal technology in general, draws heavily from the theory of groundwater flow and petroleum reservoir engineering, the former having emerged in the 1930s. However, geothermal reservoirs are in general considerably more complex than groundwater systems or petroleum reservoirs.

Definite differences between geothermal systems and their groundwater and petroleum counterparts necessitate that different approaches be employed. This includes the fact that heat transport as well as mass transport is important in geothermal systems in contrast to most groundwater and petroleum cases, where only mass flow needs to be considered. Heat extraction, rather than simple fluid extraction, is also at the core of geothermal utilization. In addition, two-phase conditions often prevail in high-temperature geothermal systems (see later). Geothermal reservoirs are, furthermore, embedded in fractured rocks in most cases, while groundwater and petroleum reservoirs are usually found in porous sedimentary rocks. In addition, geothermal reservoirs are most often of great vertical extent in contrast to groundwater and petroleum reservoirs, which have limited vertical extent, but may be quite extensive horizontally. Finally, many geothermal systems are uncapped and the hot fluid may be directly connected to cooler surrounding systems.

Geothermal reservoir physics is the scientific discipline that deals with mass and energy transfer in geothermal systems. It attempts to understand and quantify flow of fluid and heat through the reservoir rocks and through wellbores. This flow is in fact the unifying feature of all geothermal reservoir analysis. Geothermal reservoir physics deals with both the fluid and energy flow in the natural state of a geothermal system and the changes in this flow caused by exploitation. The purpose of geothermal reservoir engineering is, in fact, twofold: to obtain information on the nature reservoir properties and physical conditions in a geothermal system and to use this information to predict the response of reservoirs and wells to exploitation, that is, estimate the power potential of a geothermal resource, as well as aid in the different aspect of its management.

Comprehensive and efficient resource management is an essential part of successful geothermal utilization. Such management relies on proper understanding of the geothermal system involved, which depends on extensive data and information. The most important data on a geothermal system's nature and properties are obtained through careful monitoring of its response to long-term production. This includes physical monitoring of mass and heat transport as well as monitoring changes in reservoir pressure and energy content, and chemical monitoring and indirect monitoring of reservoir changes and conditions.

There is reason to claim that geothermal resources can be utilized in a sustainable manner, that is, that certain production scenarios can be maintained for a very long time (100–300 years). This is based on decades of experience of utilizing several geothermal systems, which have shown that if production is maintained below a certain limit it reaches a kind of balance that may be maintained for a long time. Examples are also available where production has been so extensive that equilibrium was not attained. Such overexploitation mostly occurs because of poor understanding, due to inadequate monitoring, and when many users utilize the same resource without common management. The sustainable production potential of a geothermal system is controlled either by energy content or by pressure decline due to limited recharge. In the latter case, reinjection of some or all of the extracted fluid can increase the sustainable potential of a system considerably. Geothermal resources can be utilized in a sustainable manner through different utilization scenarios, as will be discussed later. Finally, it should be mentioned that even though geothermal energy can be considered a clean and renewable source of energy, its development has both environmental and social impacts that appropriately demand attention in the overall resource management.

7.02.2 Geothermal Systems

Geothermal resources are distributed throughout the planet. Even though most geothermal systems and the greatest concentration of geothermal energy are associated with the Earth's plate boundaries, geothermal energy may be found in most countries. It is highly concentrated in volcanic regions, but may also be found as warm groundwater in sedimentary formations worldwide. In many cases, geothermal energy is found in populated, or easily accessible, areas. Moreover, geothermal activity is also found at great depths on the ocean floor, in mountainous regions, and under glaciers and ice caps. Numerous geothermal systems probably still remain to be discovered because many systems have no surface activity. Nevertheless, some of these are slowly being discovered. The following definitions are used here.

- *Geothermal field* is a geographical definition, usually indicating an area of geothermal activity at the earth's surface. In cases without surface activity, this term may be used to indicate the area at the surface corresponding to the geothermal reservoir below.

Table 1 Classifications of geothermal systems on the basis of temperature, enthalpy, and physical state [9, 10]

Low-temperature (LT) systems with a reservoir temperature at 1 km depth below 150 °C; often characterized by hot or boiling springs. Medium-temperature (MT) systems	Low-enthalpy geothermal systems with a reservoir fluid enthalpy less than 800 kJ kg^{-1}, corresponding to temperatures less than about 190 °C	Liquid-dominated geothermal reservoirs with the water temperature at, or below, the boiling point at the prevailing pressure and the water phase controls the pressure in the reservoir. Some steam may be present.
High-temperature (HT) systems with reservoir temperature at 1 km depth above 200 °C; characterized by fumaroles, steam vents, mud pools, and highly altered ground	High-enthalpy geothermal systems with reservoir fluid enthalpy greater than 800 kJ kg^{-1}	Two-phase geothermal reservoirs where steam and water coexist and the temperature and pressure follow the boiling point curve. Vapour-dominated geothermal where temperature is at, or above, the boiling point at the prevailing pressure and the steam phase controls the pressure in the reservoir. Some liquid water may be present.

- *Geothermal system* refers to all parts of the hydrological system involved, including the recharge zone, all subsurface parts, and the outflow of the system.
- *Geothermal reservoir* indicates the hot and permeable part of a geothermal system that may be directly exploited. For spontaneous discharge to be possible, geothermal reservoirs must also be pressurized.

Geothermal systems and reservoirs are classified on the basis of different aspects, such as reservoir temperature or enthalpy, physical state, and their nature and geological setting. **Table 1** summarizes classifications based on the first three aspects.

It should be pointed out that hardly any geothermal systems in Iceland fall in between 150 and 200 °C reservoir temperature, that is, in the MT range; also, a common classification is not to be found in the geothermal literature, even though one based on enthalpy is often used. Different parts of geothermal systems may be in different physical states and geothermal reservoirs may also evolve from one state to another. As an example, a liquid-dominated reservoir may evolve into a two-phase reservoir when pressure declines in the system as a result of production. Steam caps may also evolve in geothermal systems as a result of lowered pressure. Low-temperature systems are always liquid-dominated, but high-temperature systems can be liquid-dominated, two-phase, or vapor-dominated.

Geothermal systems may also be classified based on their nature and geological setting (see **Figure 1**):

A. *Volcanic systems* are in one way or another associated with volcanic activity. The heat sources for such systems are hot intrusions or magma. They are most often situated inside, or close to, volcanic complexes such as calderas and/or spreading centers. Permeable fractures and fault zones mostly control the flow of water in volcanic systems.
B. In *convective systems* the heat source is the hot crust at depth in tectonically active areas, with above average heat flow. Here the geothermal water has circulated to considerable depth (> 1 km), through mostly vertical fractures, to extract the heat from the rocks.
C. *Sedimentary systems* are found in many of the major sedimentary basins of the world. These systems owe their existence to the occurrence of permeable sedimentary layers at great depths (> 1 km) and above average geothermal gradients (> 30 °C km^{-1}). These systems are conductive in nature rather than convective, even though fractures and faults play a role in some cases. Some convective systems (B) may, however, be embedded in sedimentary rocks.
D. *Geopressured systems* are sedimentary systems analogous to geopressured oil and gas reservoirs where fluid caught in stratigraphic traps may have pressures close to lithostatic values. Such systems are generally fairly deep; hence, they are categorized as geothermal.
E. *HDR systems or EGS* consist of volumes of rock that have been heated to useful temperatures by volcanism or abnormally high heat flow, but have low permeability or are virtually impermeable. Therefore, they cannot be exploited in a conventional way. However, experiments have been conducted in a number of locations to use hydrofracturing to try to create artificial reservoirs in such systems, or to enhance already existent fracture networks. Such systems will mostly be used through production/reinjection doublets.
F. *Shallow resources* refer to the thermal energy stored near the surface of the Earth's crust. Recent developments in the application of ground source heat pumps have opened up a new dimension in utilizing these resources.

Numerous volcanic geothermal systems (A) are found, for example, in the Pacific Ring of Fire, in countries such as New Zealand, the Philippines, and Japan, and in Central America. Geothermal systems of the convective type (B) exist outside the volcanic zone in Iceland, in the Southwestern United States and in southeast China, to name a few countries. Sedimentary geothermal systems (C) are, for example, found in France, Central Eastern Europe, and throughout China. Typical examples of geopressured systems (D) are found in the northern Gulf of Mexico Basin in the United States, both offshore and onshore. The Fenton Hill project in New Mexico in the United States and the Soultz project in Northeast France are well-known HDR and EGS projects (E), while shallow resources (F) can be found all over the globe.

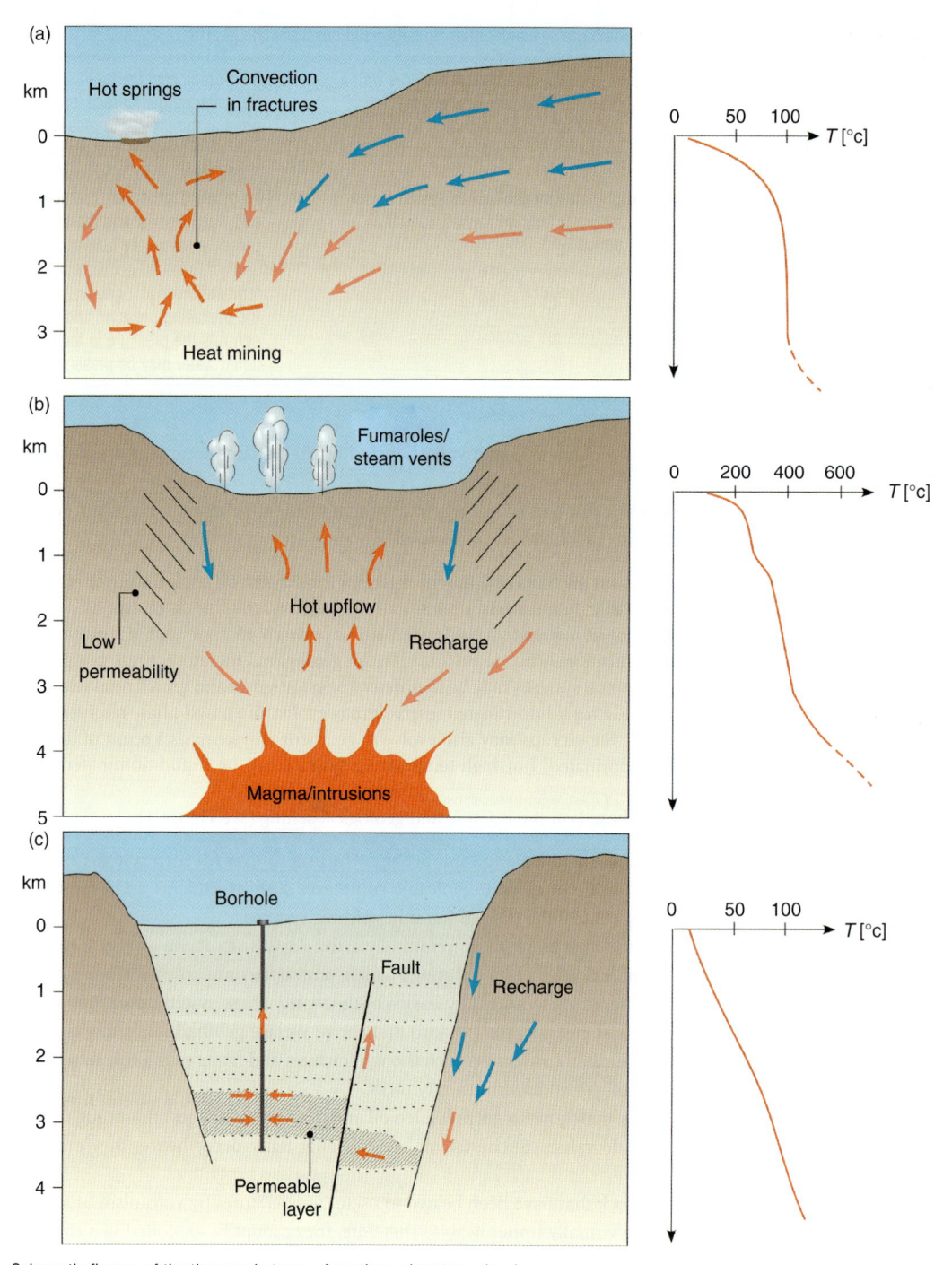

Figure 1 Schematic figures of the three main types of geothermal systems (a–c).

Saemundsson et al. [11] discuss the classification and geological setting of geothermal systems in more detail. They present a further subdivision principally based on tectonic setting, volcanic association, and geological formations. Volcanic geothermal systems (A) are, for example, subdivided into systems associated with (1) rift zone volcanism (diverging plate boundaries), (2) hot-spot volcanism, and (3) subduction zone volcanism (converging plate boundaries). The heat-source mechanism of the volcanic high-temperature activity has been studied indirectly and discussed extensively by various researchers [6, 12–16], but the mechanism has obviously not been directly observable. The mechanism envisioned does not assume a direct contact between the circulating water and the magma or hot intrusive rocks, but rather a relatively thin insulating layer between them. Heat is assumed to be transported through the layer by heat conduction. As the outer parts of the layer cool down, it cracks because of thermal contraction allowing the circulating water to penetrate further downward. Through a downward migration like this, that is, that of a relatively thin conductive layer, the extremely high heat output of volcanic geothermal systems is ensured. A similar process is envisioned for convective low-temperature geothermal systems (B), at least for the more powerful ones, such as many systems in Iceland.

The heat source for the low-temperature activity in Iceland is believed to be the abnormally hot local crust, but faults and fractures, which are kept open by the continuously ongoing tectonic activity, also play an essential role by providing the channels for the water circulating through the systems and mining the heat. The geothermal gradient in Iceland varies from about 50 C km^{-1} to about 150 C km^{-1} outside the volcanic zone. The nature of the low-temperature activity has been discussed by several authors during the last century [5, 12, 16–19]. A highly simplified conceptual model may be described as follows: Precipitation, mostly falling in the highlands, percolates down into the bedrock to a depth of a few kilometers (1–3) where it takes up heat from the hot rock and ascends subsequently toward the surface because of reduced density. Some of the systems may simply be deep-rooted groundwater systems, of great horizontal extent, but most of the systems are believed to be more localized convection systems, wherein heat is transported from depth to shallower formations [12, 18]. The former may constitute practically steady-state phenomena, whereas the latter must in essence be transient.

Temperature profiles from deep wells in geothermal systems in Iceland clearly demonstrate the convective nature of the systems [18, 20]. In addition, they demonstrate how heat has been transported from depth to shallower levels, cooling down the deeper half of the systems and heating up the upper half. **Figure 2** presents a few such examples from low-temperature systems in southwestern Iceland.

A steady-state process cannot account for the high natural heat output of the largest low-temperature systems in Iceland, which may be of the order of 200 MW$_t$. Therefore, Bödvarsson [12, 20] proposed a model for the heat-source mechanism of the activity, which can explain the high heat output. This model appears to be consistent with the data now available on most of the major low-temperature systems [18]. According to his model, presented in **Figure 3**, the recharge to a low-temperature system is shallow groundwater flow from the highlands to the lowlands. Inside a geothermal area, the water sinks through an open fracture, or along a dike, to a depth of a few kilometers where it takes up heat and ascends. In the model, the fracture is closed at depth, but opens up and continuously migrates downward during the heat mining process by cooling and contraction of the adjacent rock.

Theoretical calculations based on Bödvarsson's model [22] indicate that the existence and heat output of such low-temperature systems are controlled by the temperature and stress conditions in the crust. In particular, the local stress field, which controls whether open fractures are available for the heat mining process and how fast these fractures can migrate downward. Given the

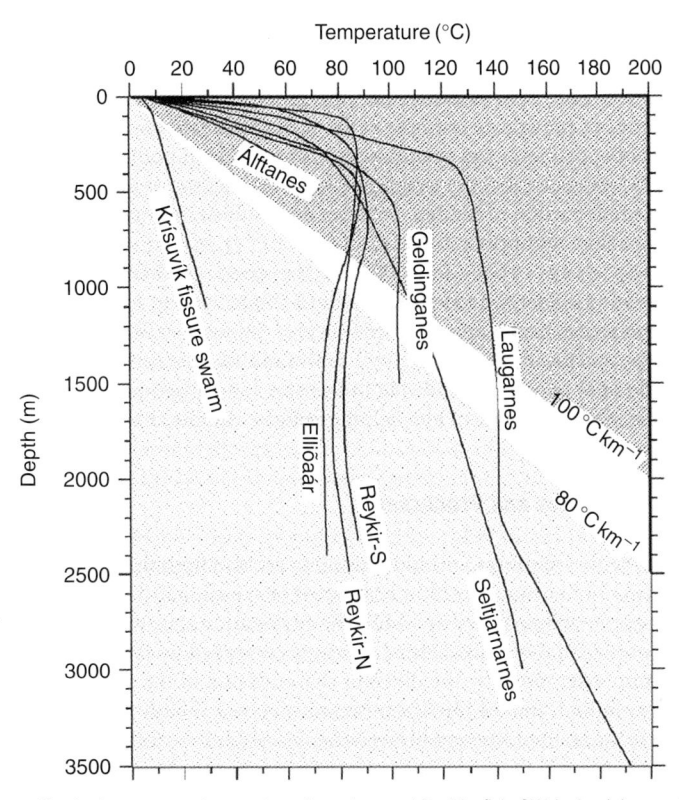

Figure 2 Formation temperature profiles for low-temperature systems in and around Reykjavík in SW-Iceland demonstrating the convective nature of the systems, through which heat has been transported from depth up to shallower levels. From Björnsson G, Thordarson S, and Steingrímsson B (2000) Temperature distribution and conceptual reservoir model for geothermal fields in and around the city of Reykjavík, Iceland. *Proceedings of the 25th Workshop on Geothermal Reservoir Engineering*, Stanford, 7pp. Stanford University, CA, January [21]. Lighter shading denotes temperatures lower than to be expected from the regional gradient and darker shading the opposite.

of the reservoir properties. It is important to keep in mind that the resulting values are model-dependent, that is, different models give different estimates. It is also very important to keep in mind that the longer the tests, the more information is obtained on the system in question. Therefore, the most important data on a geothermal reservoir are obtained through careful monitoring during long-term exploitation (see further).

Predictions on reservoir response to possible future utilization scenarios, which play a major role in geothermal reservoir management, are calculated by reservoir models. Various modeling approaches are currently in use by geothermal reservoir specialists, and geothermal modeling is discussed below. In a few words, modeling involves a model being developed that *simulates* some, or most, of the data available on the geothermal system involved. The model will provide information on the conditions in and the properties of the actual geothermal system. Yet again this information is not unique, but model-dependent. Consequently, the model is used to predict the future changes in the reservoir involved, estimate its production potential, and address various management-related issues.

7.02.4 Pressure Diffusion and Fluid Flow

When dealing with flow of fluids through pipes and other surface channels, as well as macroscopic channels in the Earth's crust, the equations of fluid mechanics apply. When dealing with the flow of fluid through porous media in the crust, as well as fractured media when the scale of the fracture passages is small in comparison with the scale of the whole flow system, the pressure diffusion equation and Darcy's law are used to describe the process involved. The rock and fluid properties, which control the process, are as follows:

Permeability (k) of the reservoir rock describes the flow resistance of the flow paths in the rock (fractures and pores). It is the reservoir property that most greatly influences the reservoir response to production. Permeability has the SI unit of m^2, but the unit Darcy (named after Henry Darcy; D) is more commonly used, with 1 Darcy corresponding to about $10^{-12}\,m^2$. The flow is also controlled by the viscosity of the fluid involved, which primarily depends on temperature. The reservoir fluid flow may in most cases be described by Darcy's law:

$$\vec{q} = -\frac{k}{v}(\nabla p - \vec{z}g\rho) \qquad [1]$$

$$\text{with} \quad \vec{q} = \rho \vec{v} \qquad [2]$$

$$\text{and for} \quad v_i = u_i \varphi \quad \text{for } i = x, y, z \qquad [3]$$

Darcy's law is presented here in its most general vector form with $\vec{q}$ the fluid mass flux vector $(kg\,(s\,m^2)^{-1})$, k the rock permeability (m^2), v the kinematic viscosity of the fluid $(m\,s^{-2})$, p is the fluid pressure (Pa), ∇p its gradient vector $(Pa\,m^{-1})$, $\vec{z}$ the unit vector in the z-direction, g the acceleration of gravity $(m\,s^{-2})$, and ρ the fluid density. In addition, $\vec{v}$ is the fluid volume flux vector $(m^3\,(s\,m^2)^{-1})$ equivalent to an average velocity vector $(m\,s^{-1})$, in fact often called Darcy velocity. The average velocity v is related to the actual fluid particle velocity u by eqn [3] where φ is the porosity of the rock (–) or the ratio between the volume of the open pores and fractures of the rock and its total volume. To be completely correct, this should be the effective porosity, that is, porosity based on volume of interconnected pores and fractures through which fluid can flow. Thus isolated pores are not included.

Permeability values of rocks in underground hydrological systems, and in nature in general, are extremely variable (see **Table 2**) varying by several orders of magnitude. Other rock and fluid properties are only slightly variable, even porosity.

Storage describes the ability of a reservoir to store fluid or release it in response to an increase or lowering of pressure. *Storativity* (s) gives the mass of fluid that is stored (released) by a unit volume of a reservoir as a result of a unit pressure increase (decrease). Consequently,

$$\nabla m = s\nabla p \quad \text{or} \quad \frac{dm}{dt} = s\frac{dp}{dt} \qquad [4]$$

with Δm the change in mass (kg) stored corresponding to the change in pressure Δp (Pa), or the time rate of change of both (dm/dt and dp/dt), and s the storativity $(kg\,(m^3\,Pa)^{-1})$. Even though storativity is a function of reservoir *porosity*, different kinds of reservoirs have different storage mechanisms (for more details, see, for example, Reference 4):

Table 2 Representative permeability values for different geological materials.

Example	k (m²)	k (mD)
Medium gravel	3×10^{-10}	300 000
Sand	10^{-11}	10 000
Sandstone	3×10^{-12}	3000
Basalt	10^{-14}	10
Clay	2×10^{-16}	0.2
Geothermal systems – overall averages	10^{-15}–10^{-13}	1–100

(a) The storativity of confined liquid-dominated reservoirs (i.e., not connected to shallower hydrological systems) is controlled by water and rock *compressibility* and is given by

$$s = \rho_w(\varphi c_w + (1-\varphi)c_r) \quad [5]$$

with ρ_w the water density (kg m^{-3}), φ the rock porosity, and c_w and c_r the water and rock matrix compressibility (1/Pa), respectively.

(b) The storativity of unconfined (free-surface) liquid-dominated reservoirs is controlled by *free-surface lowering*, in the long term, and is given by

$$s = \phi/gH \quad [6]$$

where g is the acceleration of gravity (m s^{-2}) and H the reservoir thickness (m).

(c) The storativity of dry steam reservoirs (rare in reality) is controlled by the *compressibility of dry steam*, which is much greater than the compressibility of liquid water, and is given by

$$s = \rho_s \varphi/p \quad [7]$$

with ρ_s the steam density (kg m^{-3}) and p the absolute reservoir pressure (Pa). In fact, ρ_s/p is approximately constant (see Reference 4).

(d) The storativity of two-phase reservoirs depends only weakly on porosity, but is controlled by the *phase change* resulting from the pressure change. When pressure increases, some steam condenses allowing the rock to store more fluid. In addition, the heat released during the process heats up the rock surrounding the pores and fractures of the rock. An approximate equation for two-phase storativity is as follows:

$$s = \rho_t \frac{\langle \rho \beta \rangle T}{L^2} \left(\frac{\rho_w - \rho_s}{\rho_w \rho_s} \right)^2 \quad [8]$$

with the average density of the liquid/steam mixture defined by

$$\frac{1}{\rho_t} = \frac{X}{\rho_s} + \frac{(1-X)}{\rho_w} \quad [9]$$

In addition, $\langle \rho \beta \rangle$ is the volumetric heat capacity of the 'wet' rock (J (m^3 °C)$^{-1}$), T the reservoir temperature (°C), L the latent heat of fusion of water (J kg^{-1}) at reservoir conditions, ρ_w and ρ_s the liquid water and steam densities, respectively (kg m^{-3}), and X the steam mass fraction (kg kg^{-1}). Note that two-phase storativity does not depend on compressibility at all.

It should be noted that storativity varies by several orders of magnitude between different kinds of reservoirs, compressibility–storativity (a) being the smallest and two-phase storativity (b) being the greatest. **Table 3** presents representative values for the four different storage mechanisms, which demonstrate this.

The pressure diffusion equation discussed in the following shows what role each of the key parameters, permeability and storativity, play in overall pressure variations and fluid flow. In general, it can be stated that permeability controls how great pressure changes are and that storativity controls how fast pressure changes occur and spread.

It should be kept in mind that permeability and porosity of geothermal reservoirs is associated with both the rock matrix of the system and the fissures and fractures intersecting it. Overall permeability in geothermal systems is usually dominated by fracture permeability, with the fracture permeability commonly being of the order of 1 mD (milli-Darcy) to 1 D, while matrix permeability is much lower or 1 µD (micro-Darcy) to 1 mD. Yet fracture porosity is usually of the order of 0.1–1%, while matrix porosity may be of the order of 5–30% (highest in sedimentary systems). Therefore, fissures and fractures control the flow in most geothermal systems, while matrix porosity controls their storage capacity.

Table 3 Representative storativities for geothermal systems with different storage mechanisms. A 1000 m thick reservoir with 10% porosity and at 250 °C is assumed

Reservoir type	Storage mechanism	Storativity, s (kg Pa^{-1} m^{-3})
Confined liquid-dominated	Compressibility	1.2×10^{-7}
Unconfined liquid-dominated	Free-surface mobility	1.0×10^{-5}
Dry steam	Steam compressibility	5.1×10^{-7}
Two-phase wells, $X = 0.3$	Two-phase	6.4×10^{-5}
Two-phase wells, $X = 0.7$	Two-phase	2.1×10^{-5}

The relationship between fracture properties, in particular fracture width, can be roughly demonstrated by combining the equation for one-dimensional fluid flow between parallel plates in fluid mechanics with Darcy's law. Assuming several fractures of constant width b, with a fixed spacing h, one obtains the relationship:

$$k = \frac{b^3}{12h} \qquad [10]$$

which both demonstrates how sensitive permeability is to fracture properties and also partly explains the great variability in permeability in nature.

The differential equation, which is used in geothermal reservoir physics to evaluate the mass transfer in models of geothermal reservoirs as well as estimate reservoir pressure changes, is the so-called *pressure diffusion equation*. It is derived by combining the conservation of mass and Darcy's law for the mass flow, which in fact replaces the force balance equation in fluid mechanics. This results in

$$s\frac{\partial p}{\partial t} = \nabla \cdot \left(\frac{k}{v}\nabla p\right) - f(x, y, z, t) \qquad [11]$$

with f a mass source density $(kg\,(s\,m^3)^{-1})$, which can simulate mass extraction from wells as well as injection into reinjection wells. Other parameters are the same as above. By defining the geometry of a problem, and prescribing boundary and initial conditions, a mathematical problem has been fully defined (i.e., a model). Theoretically, a solution to the problem will exist, which can be used to calculate pressure changes and flow in the model.

It should be mentioned that in more complex situations, permeability can be anisotropic and needs to be represented by a tensor in eqn [11]. In homogeneous and isotropic conditions, a property termed hydraulic diffusivity is defined as follows:

$$a_p = \frac{k}{sv} \qquad [12]$$

The pressure diffusion equation is in fact a parabolic differential equation of exactly the same mathematical form as the heat diffusion equation (see further). Therefore, the same mathematical methods may be used to solve these equations (see, e.g., Reference 29). Pressure diffusion is, however, an extremely fast process compared to heat conduction. Strictly speaking, Darcy's law and consequently the pressure diffusion equation apply only to porous media such as sedimentary rocks. Yet in most cases fractured reservoirs behave hydraulically as equivalent porous media. This is due to how fast a process pressure diffusion is and pressure changes diffuse very rapidly throughout a reservoir. The fractured nature is only relevant on a much smaller spatial and temporal scale. The fractured nature of most geothermal reservoirs cannot be neglected when dealing with heat transfer, however (see further).

Various solutions to the pressure diffusion equation, for corresponding models, provide the basis for the different tools of geothermal reservoir physics or engineering. This includes models used to interpret well test data such as the well-known Theis model (see further). Many such models actually originate from groundwater hydrology or petroleum reservoir engineering where Darcy's law and the pressure diffusion equation are also applicable.

7.02.5 Heat Transfer

In addition to mass transfer and pressure changes, thermal energy (heat) transfer and changes in energy content play a key role in the physics of geothermal resources. These processes are of course interconnected, as will become evident below. When dealing with heat transfer in porous and permeable materials such as the rocks of the Earth's crust, we need to take into account the interaction of moving fluids with the solid material of the rock matrix and the heat transfer by conduction in the material. Here the solid materials are the porous rocks of the Earth's crust, either sedimentary-type rocks with mainly intergranular permeability or igneous and metamorphic rocks with mainly fracture permeability. The following are the heat transport processes involved:

i. Heat conduction wherein molecules transmit their kinetic energy to other molecules by colliding with them, both in the solid rock and in the fluids filling the pores, fissures, and fractures of the rock.
ii. Forced advection, that is, fluid movement driven by pressure gradients that can be of natural origin or caused by the extraction (or injection) of fluids (such as cold or hot water extraction from (injection into) wells), described by the pressure diffusion equation.
iii. Free convection through the permeable rocks, that is, fluid movement driven by buoyancy forces.

Heat conduction is described by the well-known Fourier's law, which in the general case of three-dimensional flow in inhomogeneous and anisotropic media is written as

$$\vec{Q} = -K\nabla T \qquad [13]$$

with $\vec{Q}$ the heat flux density $(J\,(s\,m^2)^{-1})$, K the thermal conductivity of the material $(J\,(s\,°C\,m)^{-1})$, and ∇T the temperature gradient vector. In the most general case, K is a tensor that is a function of space (x,y,z). We should keep in mind that this equation holds strictly only for 'small' gradients just like all other comparable equations of physics (Darcy's law, Ohm's law, etc.), but in natural underground systems these are normally relatively 'small'.

Just as in the case of pressure diffusion, the *heat diffusion equation* or *heat conduction equation*, which describes heat transfer by heat conduction in the material involved (fluid or solid), is derived by combining the principle of conservation of energy with Fourier's law, resulting in

$$\rho\beta\frac{\partial T}{\partial t} = \nabla\cdot(K\nabla T) + M\rho \qquad [14]$$

Here ρ and β are the density and heat capacity (J (kg °C)$^{-1}$) of the material, respectively, and M an impressed heat source (heat sink if negative) density (J (s kg)$^{-1}$). Through appropriate initial and boundary conditions, a particular problem is fully defined. If the material is isotropic and homogeneous, this equation may be simplified:

$$\frac{1}{a_T}\frac{\partial T}{\partial t} = \nabla^2 T + \frac{M\rho}{K} \qquad [15]$$

$$\text{with } a_T = \frac{K}{\rho\beta} \qquad [16]$$

$$\text{and } \nabla^2 = \frac{\partial^2}{\partial x^2} + \frac{\partial^2}{\partial y^2} + \frac{\partial^2}{\partial z^2} \qquad [17]$$

Here a_T is the thermal diffusivity of the material (m^2 s^{-1}) and ∇^2 is the Laplacian operator.

This equation and the pressure diffusion equation are of exactly the same mathematical form, as already mentioned. The extremely different rates of these processes can be compared through the ratio between the respective diffusivities:

$$\frac{a_P}{a_T} = \frac{k\rho\beta}{svK} \qquad [18]$$

This ratio is of course quite variable because of the great variability in permeability (k) and storativity (s), but an order of magnitude estimate shows that the ratio is approximately in the range of 10^4–10^7. The extremely different rates of these processes indicate that in many modeling situations, mass transfer and heat transfer can be simulated separately.

Heat advection through permeable media involves heat transport by the fluid percolating through pores and fractures, heat conduction through the rock matrix, and heat transfer between the fluid and the matrix. The following differential equation, *the heat transport equation*, describes this process in single-phase situations (see Section 7.02.6 on two-phase systems):

$$\langle\rho\beta\rangle\frac{\partial T}{\partial t} = -\beta_w\rho_w\vec{v}\cdot\nabla T + \nabla\cdot(K\nabla T) \qquad [19]$$

$$\text{with } \vec{q} = \rho_w\vec{v} \qquad [20]$$

$$\text{and } \langle\rho\beta\rangle = \rho_w\beta_w\varphi + \rho_r\beta_r(1-\varphi) \qquad [21]$$

with $\vec{q}$ the mass flux vector, given by Darcy's law (eqn [1]) and $\langle\rho\beta\rangle$ is the volumetric heat capacity of the 'wet' rock (J (m^3 °C)$^{-1}$). In addition, β_w is the heat capacity of the fluid (J (kg °C)$^{-1}$), ρ_w the heat capacity of the fluid (J (kg °C)$^{-1}$), and $\vec{v}$ the Darcy velocity vector (average flow rate per unit area, m s^{-1}). The equation may be solved for a given model, including appropriate boundary and initial conditions, by solving the pressure diffusion equation (eqn [11]) and by applying Darcy's law (eqn [1]).

Forced advection, or forced convection, is the dominant heat transfer mechanism in geothermal systems during utilization. During their natural state, free convection is the dominant heat transfer process, however. During free convection, buoyancy forces, caused by density differences, drive the flow instead of impressed pressure gradients. The equations describing this process are the pressure diffusion equation (eqn [11]), the heat transport equation (eqn [19]), Darcy's law (eqn [1]), and the appropriate equation of state for the fluid (i.e., equations describing how density depends on temperature and pressure). The buoyancy effect can be incorporated into Darcy's law through the vertical component of the Darcy velocity:

$$v_z = -\frac{k}{v}\left(\frac{dp}{dz} + \alpha_V g\Delta T\right) \qquad [22]$$

with α_V the volumetric thermal expansivity of the fluid (1/°C) and ΔT the temperature variation relative to a chosen reference temperature. Just as in the classical convection model of a layer of fluid heated from below, a comparable model of a layer of fluid-saturated permeable material can be set up. An approximate solution to that problem reveals that when the Rayleigh number defined by eqn [23] below is above a certain critical Rayleigh number, free convection is possible:

$$Ra = \frac{\rho_w\beta_w\alpha_V g\Delta THk}{vK} > 4\pi^2 \qquad [23]$$

Most symbols in the equation have already been defined except that H stands for the thickness of the layer (m) and ∇T the temperature difference between the bottom and the top of the layer (°C). This simple equation can be used to estimate roughly the minimum permeability, under given physical conditions and dimensions, required for free convection to be possible. Thus it can be used to estimate roughly the conditions required for natural hydrothermal systems to develop. Another outcome of the analysis

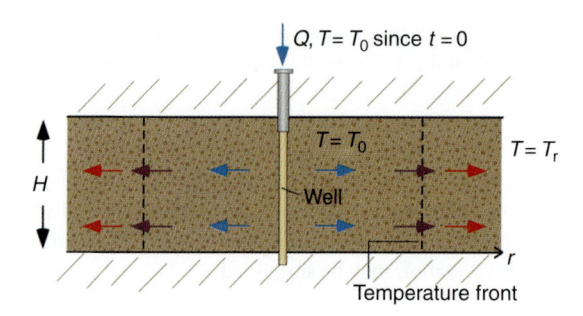

Figure 5 A schematic model used to estimate the rate of heat transfer (cold-front propagation) in a porous layer of constant thickness with a centrally located injection well.

associated with the model is that at the critical Rayleigh number, the wavelength associated with the convection, corresponding to the distance between convection cells, equals twice the thickness of the layer, that is, $\lambda = 2b$.

Theoretical solutions for two simple heat transfer models, solved using the equations above, will be presented below. One of the models involves a hot layer of porous, liquid-saturated material with a well drilled centrally through the layer (**Figure 5**) and the other a thin, horizontal fracture in impermeable rock, also with a central well (**Figure 6**). Approximate solutions for the responses of the models to cold water injection will be presented, both based on Reference [30], which demonstrate the drastic differences between heat transfer in porous and fractured rocks in geothermal systems.

7.02.5.1 Porous Layer Model

This model involves an infinite, homogeneous, isotropic, fluid-saturated, hot (at temperature T_r), horizontal layer of porous material with porosity and thickness H. At time $t = 0$, injection of cold (at temperature T_0, cold relative to the initially hot layer) water at a rate Q (kg s^{-1}) is initiated at the location $r = 0$ (location of the injection well).

By assuming that heat transport by conduction is negligible compared to the advective heat transport, one can show that a cold front travels radially away from the reinjection well (two-dimensional flow). On the inside of the front, the temperature is T_0, while on the outside of the front, the temperature is undisturbed at T_r. The distance to the cold front is then given by [30]

$$r_{\text{cold-front}} = \sqrt{\frac{\beta_w Q t}{\pi H \langle \rho \beta \rangle}} \qquad [24]$$

7.02.5.2 Horizontal Fracture Model

This second model involves an infinite, horizontal fracture in an otherwise impermeable, hot ($T = T_r$) rock. At time $t = 0$, injection of cold ($T = T_0$) water at a rate Q (kg s^{-1}) is initiated at the location $r = 0$ (location of the injection well).

Here heat conduction is the dominant process and solving the heat conduction equation ([14]) results in the following solution for the temperature in the model [30]:

$$T(r, y, t) = T_0 + (T_r - T_0)\, erf\left(\frac{\zeta \pi r^2 + y}{2\sqrt{a_T t}}\right) \qquad [25]$$

with erf the error function $\zeta = 2K/\rho_w Q$ and y the vertical distance away from the fracture. A sharp cold front does not arise in this situation because of horizontal heat conduction (neglected in the porous model). But the distance from the injection well, the temperature disturbance has traveled can be estimated by defining the distance where the temperature has dropped to $T_0 + 0.5(T_r - T_0)$ or by

$$r_{1/2} = \sqrt{\frac{\beta_w Q \sqrt{a_T t}}{2 \pi K}} \qquad [26]$$

The ratio between the two distances is given by the following equation. It is also plotted in **Figure 7** as a function of time, for a few different porous reservoir thicknesses and representative values for other parameters:

$$\frac{r_{1/2}}{r_{\text{cold-front}}} = \frac{[H\langle \rho \beta \rangle]^{1/2}}{[4\rho_r \beta_r K t]^{1/4}} \qquad [27]$$

The figure demonstrates clearly the differences between heat transfer in geothermal systems dominated by porous rocks and fractured geothermal systems, and how much faster temperature disturbances travel in fracture systems. This is, in particular, relevant in reinjection planning (see below).

The above results apply to highly simplified models, but they demonstrate clearly the main aspects of the issue. Various authors have studied heat transport in porous or fractured hydrological systems, such as geothermal systems, on the basis of more complex

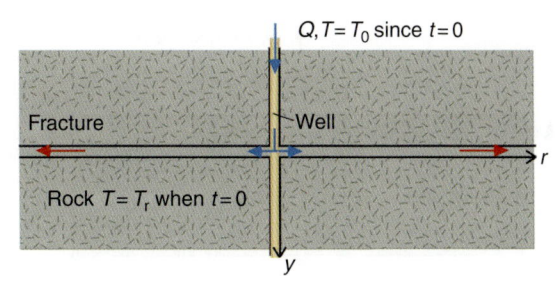

Figure 6 A schematic model used to estimate the rate of heat transfer (cold-front propagation) in a thin, horizontal fracture in impermeable rock with a centrally located injection well.

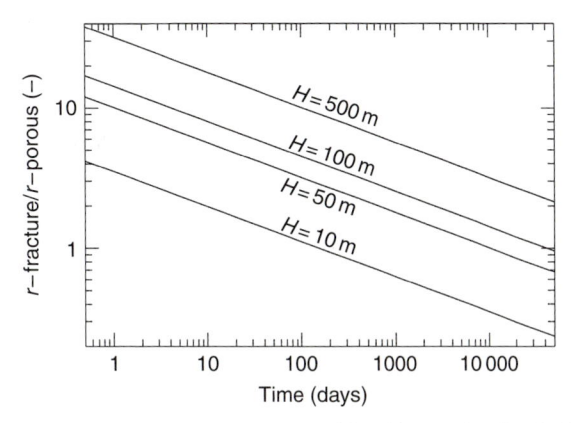

Figure 7 A comparison between heat transfer rates in porous (layer of thickness H) and fractured media (single fracture) presented as the ratio between cold-front distances during reinjection.

models. This is increasingly being done through the application of complex numerical models, but older analytical work is still highly relevant, such as that of Gringarten and Sauty [31] and Pruess and Bödvarsson [32].

7.02.5.3 Porous Model with Cold Recharge

A variant of the porous layer with cold injection above is a comparable model with a hot ($T = T_r$) central region with a radius R, simulating a geothermal system, surrounded by colder ($T = T_0$) fluid saturated porous rocks. At time $t = 0$, production of the hot fluid at a rate Q (kg s^{-1}) is initiated at the location $r = 0$ (centrally located production well).

By again assuming that heat transport by conduction is negligible compared to the advective heat transport, one can show that the boundary between the hot and cold regions travels radially toward the center (two-dimensional flow). On the inside of the front, the temperature is T_r, while on the outside of the front, the temperature is T_0. The distance to the boundary is then given by [30]

$$r_{\text{cold-inflow}} = \sqrt{R^2 - \frac{\beta_w Q t}{\pi H \langle \rho \beta \rangle}} \qquad [28]$$

The time it takes for the boundary to reach the center, that is, the time of so-called cold-front breakthrough, is then given by

$$t = \frac{\pi H \langle \rho \beta \rangle R^2}{\beta_w Q} \qquad [29]$$

This model, and the two equations above, can be used to make simple estimations of the longevity particular types of geothermal systems (e.g., systems with open boundaries and limited hot recharge) during production, when the size of the hot core of the systems is approximately known. The model neglects effects, which may be important in real situations, such as effects of fractures, dispersion causing flow velocity variations, and horizontal heat conduction.

7.02.6 Two-Phase Regions or Systems

Two-phase conditions, where liquid water and steam coexist in the voids of the reservoir rocks, often occur in geothermal systems. Quite often two-phase regions develop in geothermal systems because of the pressure drop caused by production. This can range

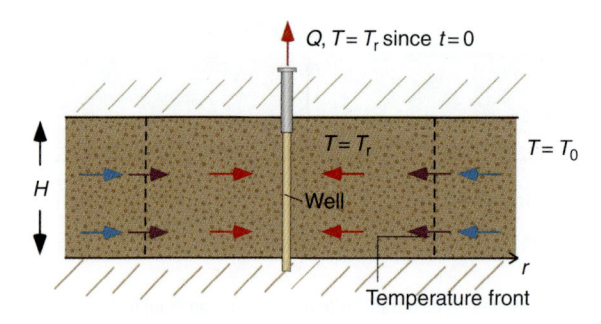

Figure 8 A schematic model used to evaluate heat transfer in a porous layer of constant thickness with a hot central region, as well as a centrally located production well, surrounded by colder fluid. When production starts from the center of the model, the colder outer boundary propagates radially toward the center.

from small regions around the feed zones of production wells to extensive steam caps at shallow levels in such systems. Two-phase conditions are not as common in geothermal systems in the natural state, but can develop in certain parts of volcanic high-temperature systems. In addition, some steam can exist in liquid-dominated systems near the boiling point and some water in steam-dominated systems near the saturation point, as discussed in section Geothermal Systems. The physics of two-phase conditions is among the more complex aspects of geothermal reservoir physics, which will not be discussed in detail here. Some of the elementary aspects will be presented below, however. Two-phase storativity has been discussed in section Pressure Diffusion and Fluid Flow.

In two-phase systems, pressure and temperature are related through the boiling point curve of water. Because of this correlation, temperature and pressure are not sufficient to determine the physical state of a reservoir. To fully specify the physical state, information on the energy content of the fluid (water and steam mixture) or the steam/water ratio is needed. It is customary to use enthalpy of the two-phase mixture, h_t (J kg^{-1}), as a measure of the energy content, and the steam/water ratio is specified as either the mass fraction of steam, X, or the volumetric steam saturation, S. Both the mass fraction and saturation range between 0 and 1, with X or $S = 0$ indicating pure liquid water and with X or $S = 1$ indicating pure steam. The following equations relate enthalpy and steam fraction:

$$h_t = Xh_s + (1-X)h_w \quad [30]$$

$$X = \frac{h_t - h_w}{h_s - h_w} \quad [31]$$

with h_w and h_s the enthalpies of the water and steam phases, respectively. Note that the density of the two-phase mixture is given by eqn [9] above. The properties of the two phases, such as density, enthalpy, and viscosity, can be found through conventional steam tables, as functions of either temperature or pressure. **Figure 9** presents the temperature and pressure variations with depth in a geothermal system, which is at boiling conditions throughout. It should be mentioned that dissolved chemicals do affect the water and steam properties as well as the boiling point. This is particularly significant in systems containing brine with salinity comparable to or greater than that of sea-water.

The mass and energy content of a unit volume of a two-phase geothermal system (rock + fluid) are given by the following equations, respectively:

$$m_{total} = \varphi(S\rho_s + (1-S)\rho_w) + (1-\varphi)\rho_r \quad [32]$$

$$h_{total} = \varphi(S\rho_s h_s + (1-S)\rho_w h_w) + (1-\varphi)\beta_r \rho_r T_{res} \quad [33]$$

with T_{res} the average reservoir rock temperature. Note that it is customary to use steam saturation in static calculations, as in this case, but the mass fraction in flow calculations (see below).

During two-phase flow, the two phases have different mobility, which is addressed through the introduction of relative permeabilities (see also References 27 and 33). This methodology is partly inherited from the petroleum industry, but is further complicated in the case of geothermal systems by the interaction between the phases [34]. In spite of considerable research over the past few decades, relative permeability in two-phase geothermal systems is not fully understood and relative permeability curves for geothermal reservoir rocks have not been accurately defined. **Figure 10** shows examples of two kinds of relative permeability curves. First, it shows the so-called Corey curves, which are believed to apply to sedimentary systems. They demonstrate clearly the fact that both water and steam are immobile at relatively low saturation. The figure also shows the so-called X-curves, which have been proposed as approximations for volcanic rocks in geothermal systems.

By using the concept of relative permeability, the following equation can be used to define the mass flow in two-phase geothermal systems, here presented for the simple case of one-dimensional horizontal flow:

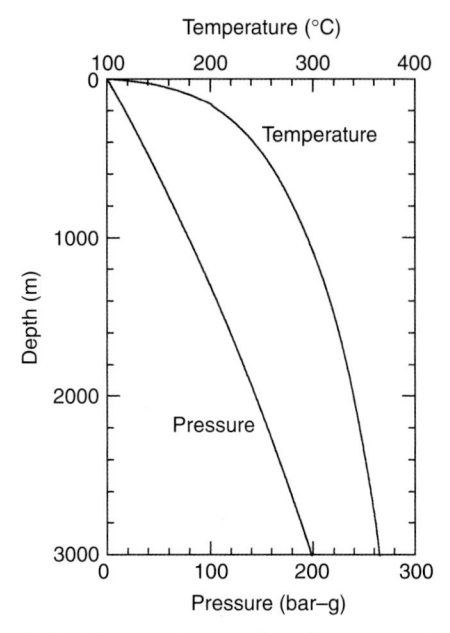

Figure 9 Temperature and pressure variations with depth in a two-phase geothermal system containing pure water.

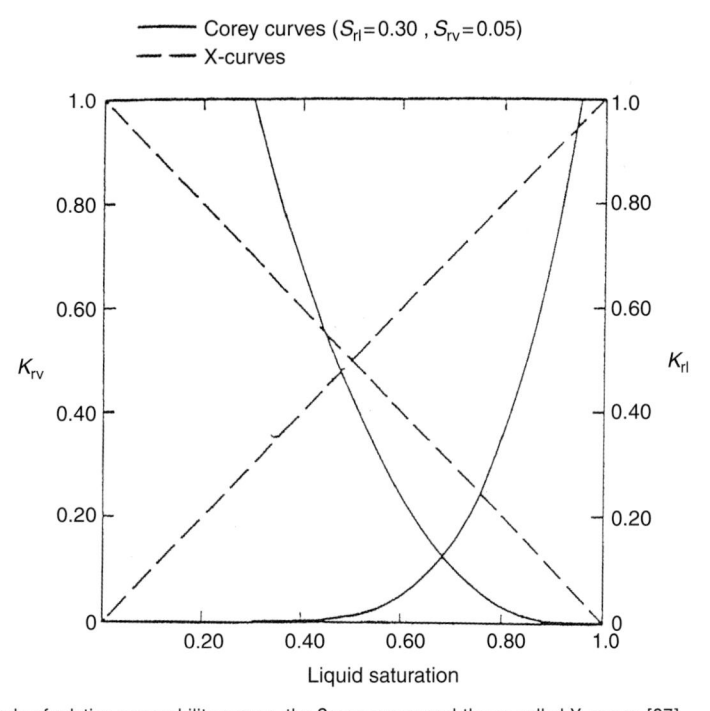

Figure 10 Examples of two kinds of relative permeability curves, the Corey curves and the so-called X-curves [27].

$$q_{\text{total}} = q_w + q_s = -k\left(\frac{k_{rw}}{v_w}\right)\frac{dp}{dx} - k\left(\frac{k_{rs}}{v_s}\right)\frac{dp}{dx} \quad [34]$$

Here q_w and q_s are the water and steam mass flow rates, k_{rw} and k_{rs} the water and steam relative permeabilities, and v_w and v_s the kinematic viscosities of water and steam, respectively. Note that $0 \leq k_{rw}$ and $k_{rs} \leq 1$. By defining the kinematic viscosity of the water/steam mixture as follows:

$$\frac{1}{v_t} = \frac{k_{rw}}{v_w} + \frac{k_{rs}}{v_s} \quad [35]$$

the equation for the total mass flow (eqn [32]) can be rewritten as

$$q_{\text{total}} = -\left(\frac{k}{v_t}\right)\frac{dp}{dx} \qquad [36]$$

Thus the pressure diffusion equation for two-phase flow can be written as

$$s_t \frac{\partial p}{\partial t} = \frac{k}{v_t}\nabla^2 p - f(x,y,z) \qquad [37]$$

with s_t the two-phase storativity (eqn [8]). Equation [37] is based on the assumption that v_t is approximately constant. It is of the same form as the pressure diffusion equation for liquid-phase flow through the introduction of the two-phase viscosity. This enables the application of many of the same interpretation methods for two-phase systems, as for liquid-dominated systems, for example, well test interpretation methods.

Finally, the following equation applies to the total energy flow:

$$q_{\text{total}} h_t = q_w h_w + q_s h_s \qquad [38]$$

It can be combined with eqn [34] to derive the following equation for the ratio between the relative permeabilities of water and steam:

$$\frac{k_{rw}}{k_{rs}} = \left(\frac{v_w}{v_s}\right)\frac{1-X}{X} \qquad [39]$$

Often the X-curve approximation (**Figure 10**) is used for geothermal systems in volcanic rocks, as mentioned above. In that case $k_{rw} + k_{rs} \approx 1$, which together with eqns [34] and [38] can be used to get a somewhat better handle on the relative permeabilities in different situations.

Two particular aspects of two-phase geothermal systems are worth mentioning. First of all, the fact that heat extraction from two-phase systems can be more efficient than conventional (without reinjection) heat extraction through fluid production from liquid-dominated geothermal systems [33]. In the convectional liquid-dominated case, no heat is extracted from the reservoir rocks, only the heat contained in the fluid produced. In two-phase situations, the mass extraction causes a pressure drop that in turn causes the temperature of the two-phase mixture to drop (along the boiling-point curve). This causes thermal energy to flow from the reservoir rock to the fluid in pores and fractures of the reservoir rock, which is in effect heat extraction from the rock. This energy causes some of the liquid water to boil and the steam fraction and fluid enthalpy to increase. Finally, this higher enthalpy fluid flows to the production wells and to the surface.

Second, heat transfer in two-phase systems can be extremely powerful compared to heat transfer by regular convection/advection in single-phase systems, regardless of whether they are liquid- or steam-dominated. This applies in particular to the so-called heat pipe process [27]. It involves vertical flow of the two phases in opposite directions. At depth within the system involved, liquid water is boiled off through heat flow from below. The steam consequently rises, and near the top of the heat pipe system, the steam condenses and sinks down again. As the steam condenses, it releases the latent heat of condensation that constitutes the heat transferred to the top of the system.

7.02.7 Geothermal Wells

Wells or boreholes are vital components in both geothermal research and utilization, since they provide essential access for both energy extraction and information collection. The basic aspects of the production characteristics of geothermal wells will be reviewed below along with the main research conducted through the wells and other relevant issues. For more details, the reader is referred to References 4, 26, 27, and 35. The design, drilling, and construction of geothermal wells are, furthermore, discussed in a separate chapter.

Typically, the upper parts of a geothermal well are closed off by a series of casings in order to stabilize the well, close off nongeothermal hydrological systems, and for security reasons. The deeper parts of the well are either fully open or cased with a so-called liner, which is open in selected intervals. The well is connected to the geothermal reservoir through feed zones of the open section or intervals. The feed zones are either particular open fractures or permeable aquifer layers. In volcanic rocks, the feed zones are often fractures or permeable layers such as interbeds (layers in between different rock formations), while in sedimentary systems, the feed zones are most commonly associated with a series of thin aquifer layers or thicker permeable formations. Yet fractures can also play a role in sedimentary systems. In some instances, a well is connected to a reservoir through a single feed zone, while in other cases, several feed zones may exist in the open section. Geothermal wells range in depth from a few meters to several kilometers while ranging in diameter from a few centimeters to several tens of centimeters.

Geothermal wells can be classified as:

a. liquid-phase low-temperature wells, which produce liquid water at wellhead (pressure may be higher than atmospheric, however);
b. two-phase high-temperature wells where the flow from the feed zone(s) is to some extent, or fully, two-phase and the wells produce either a two-phase mixture or a dry steam; or
c. dry steam high-temperature wells where the flow from the feed zone(s) to the wellhead is steam-dominated.

In the liquid-phase and dry steam wells, the inflow is single-phase liquid water or steam, respectively, while two-phase wells can be furthermore classified as either liquid or two-phase inflow wells. In multifeed zone, two-phase wells, one feed zone can even be single phase, while another one is two phase.

The energy productivity of geothermal wells is usually presented through a relationship between the mass flow rate or production and the corresponding pressure change, in either downhole or wellhead pressure. This relationship is often termed production characteristics or well deliverability. In general, the productivity of geothermal wells is a complex function of:

i. wellbore parameters such as diameter, friction factors, and feed zone depth;
ii. feed zone temperature and enthalpy;
iii. feed zone pressure, which depends directly on reservoir pressure;
iv. wellhead pressure or depth to water level during production; and temperature conditions around the well.

Most of these parameters can be assumed approximately constant except for the reservoir pressure (iii), which varies with time and the overall mass extraction from the reservoir in question. The feed zone temperature and enthalpy may also vary with time in some cases, albeit usually more slowly than reservoir pressure.

For liquid-phase low-temperature wells, a simplified relationship can usually be put forward relating mass flow rate (q) and well pressure (p):

$$p = p_0 - b(t)q - Cq^2 \qquad [40]$$

The pressure can be measured as either downhole pressure, depth to water level if pumping from the well is required, or wellhead pressure if flow from the well is artesian. The term p_0 represents the initial well pressure before production starts, $b(t)q$ transient changes in well pressure reflecting transient changes in reservoir pressure, and Cq^2 turbulent and frictional pressure changes in the feed zones next to the well, where flow velocities are at a maximum, and in the well itself. The term $b(t)$ depends on the properties of the reservoir in question, such as permeability and storativity, as well as interference (due to production and/or reinjection) from other wells drilled into the geothermal reservoir.

Figure 11 shows examples of productivity, or deliverability, curves for three liquid-phase low-temperature geothermal wells with vastly variable production characteristics. The examples are based on real Icelandic low-temperature examples.

In addition to this dependence between mass flow and pressure, temperature conditions (items (ii) and (v) above) control energy output of geothermal wells. Some cooling of the produced liquid takes place, in particular, as the liquid flows up the well because the surrounding rock is usually colder than the liquid. This cooling depends, furthermore, on the flow rate; the higher the flow rate the smaller the cooling is. The following equation can be used to estimate the temperature conditions in a flowing liquid-phase well, based on a solution presented by Carslaw and Jaeger [29]:

$$\text{for } q\beta_w \frac{dT}{dz} = \frac{4K\pi(T-T_r)}{\left\{ \ln\left(\frac{4Kt}{\rho_r \beta_r r_w^2}\right) - 1.154 \right\}} \text{ for } t \gg r_w^2/a_T \qquad [41]$$

Here T is the temperature at depth z in the well, T_r the undisturbed reservoir temperature outside the well, and r_w the radius of the well at depth z. Other parameters have been defined above. The left-hand side of the equation denotes the energy loss per unit length of well, while the right-hand side denotes the heat transported away from the well, in the reservoir rock, by heat conduction.

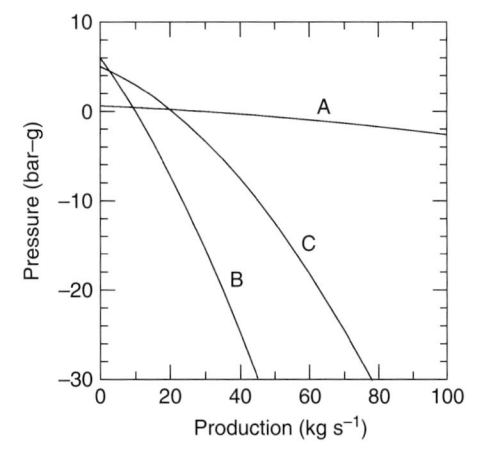

Figure 11 Examples of productivity curves for liquid-phase low-temperature geothermal wells with varying characteristics. Based on real Icelandic examples [10].

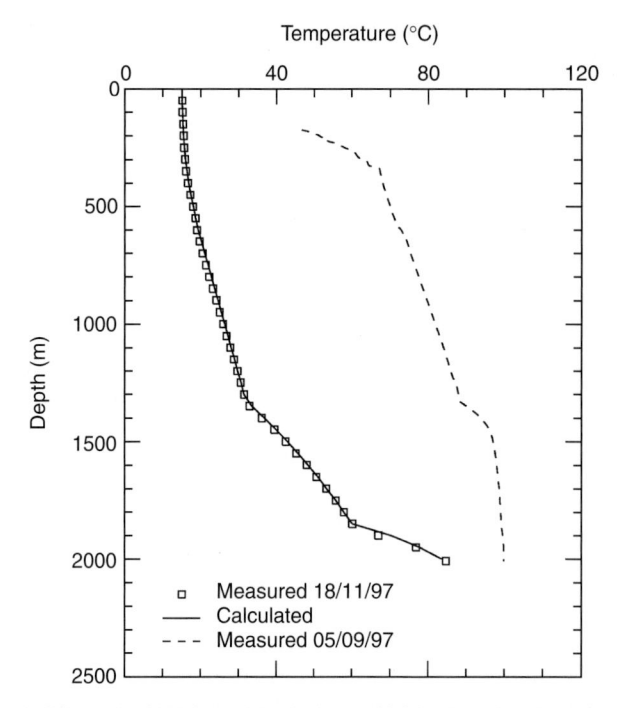

Figure 12 A temperature log measured 18 November 1997 during injection into well LJ-8 at Laugaland in north central Iceland along with a temperature profile simulated by eqn [41]. From Axelsson G, Sverrisdóttir G, Flóvenz ÓG, et al. (1998) Thermal energy extraction, by reinjection from a low-temperature geothermal system in N-Iceland. *Proceedings of the 4th International HDR Forum*, 10pp. Strasbourg, France, September [36]. Also shown is an older temperature log representing the undisturbed temperature conditions around the well.

This equation can be used to simulate measured temperature conditions in flowing wells, during both production and injection. **Figure 12** shows an example of this.

For two-phase high-temperature wells, a simple relationship as given by eqn [40] cannot be set up. In such cases, researchers need to resort to so-called wellbore simulators, that is, computer software that numerically solves the relevant physical equations to simulate flow, pressure, and energy conditions in the wells in question. These include mass conservation, pressure changes due to acceleration, friction and gravitation as well as energy conservation (eqn [41] can be used for this purpose). The HOLA wellbore simulator is a good example of such software [37].

In the case of two-phase wells, the flow through a feed zone into a well can be specified by the following equation:

$$q = \frac{PI}{v_t}(p_{res} - p_{well}) \qquad [42]$$

where PI (m^2) is the so-called productivity index of the feed zone, which in principle should only depend on the permeability of the feed zone and the geometrical parameters of the well; v_t is the kinematic viscosity of the two-phase mixture defined by eqn [31] above; p_{res} is the reservoir pressure outside the feed zone; and p_{well} is the pressure in the well at the feed zone. In this way, the productivity index is independent of phase conditions and steam fraction. It is also common to define a productivity index simply as the ratio between a change in mass flow rate and a corresponding change in well pressure based on short-term testing (thus with units (kg s^{-1}) Pa^{-1}). Similarly, an injectivity index is defined based on injection test data. The difference between these two definitions needs to be kept in mind to avoid confusion.

Figure 13 shows examples of productivity curves for several two-phase high-temperature geothermal wells in Iceland with vastly variable production characteristics. A clear distinction can be seen between wells with single-phase feed zone inflow, which show typical bell-shaped curves like liquid-phase wells (**Figure 11**), and wells with two-phase inflow, which show little variation in output with changes in wellhead pressure. The possible reasons for the characteristics of the latter wells have been discussed by Stefánsson and Steingrímsson [38] as well as by Bödvarsson and Witherspoon [27].

Measuring the well discharge of single-phase wells is relatively straightforward, while measuring the discharge (both mass and energy flow) is much more involved. Some of the different methods available are, for example, discussed by Grant et al. [4]. Measuring two-phase flow involves measuring two out of the four key parameters: liquid flow, steam flow, total flow, or enthalpy of the flow. Once any two have been determined, the third one can be estimated based on equations in section Two-Phase Regions or Systems. Often the so-called Russel James method is used, an empirical method based on measuring the critical lip pressure at lip of a pipe discharging the two-phase mixture, which relates total flow and flowing enthalpy [4, 39]. The following are the main methods used to estimate the output of two-phase wells:

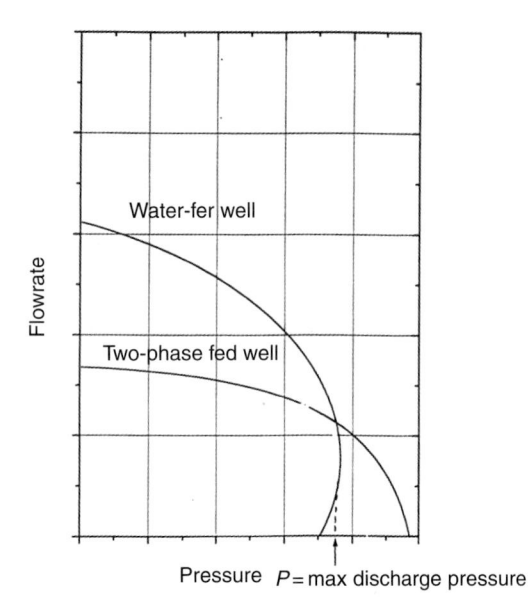

Figure 13 Examples of productivity curves for Icelandic two-phase high-temperature geothermal wells with varying characteristics.

(1) Liquid and steam phases are separated and each phase is measured separately. Probably, it is the most accurate method but requires the most complex instrumentation.
(2) Applies to wells with liquid inflow and known feed zone temperature. Liquid flow is measured after separation and enthalpy of flow is estimated on basis of feed zone temperature.
(3) Also applies to wells with liquid inflow and known feed zone temperature. Total flow is estimated by Russel James method and enthalpy of flow on the basis of feed-zone temperature.
(4) A combination of using the Russel James method on the total flow and consequently measuring the liquid flow rate after separation.
(5) Using two different chemical tracers to measure the flow rate of each of the phases in a pipeline. This method is increasingly being used with success and does not require disruption of power production.

Geothermal wells provide the principal access points of geothermal reservoirs, whether it is for research purposes or as points for monitoring (see further). Steingrímsson and Gudmundsson [40] review the main investigations commonly done through geothermal wells, both during and after drilling. The main investigations are the following:

A. Lithological logging to estimate physical properties of the reservoir rocks and to aid in the analysis of the geological structures intersected by a well.
B. Temperature and pressure logging during drilling to locate feed zones, analyze well conditions, and to obtain initial estimates of reservoir temperature and pressure conditions.
C. Short-term well testing, with associated pressure change monitoring, through controlled, often step-wise, fluid injection or production, to estimate injectivity/productivity index and principal reservoir properties such as permeability.
D. Temperature and pressure logging during warming-up period of well to estimate reservoir temperature and pressure around a well.
E. Production testing to estimate production capacity of well with temperature logging and pressure change monitoring; spontaneous discharge of high-temperature wells and pumping from low-temperature wells; pressure interference monitoring in nearby wells if possible with pressure-transient analysis to estimate principal reservoir parameters.

Finally, it should be mentioned that geothermal wells are often stimulated following drilling, to recover permeability reduced by the drilling operation itself, to enhance lower than expected near-well permeability, or to open up connections to permeable structures not directly intersected by the well in question. Axelsson and Thórhallsson [41] review the main methods of geothermal well stimulation with emphasis on methods applied successfully in Iceland. The methods most commonly used involve applying high-pressure water injection, sometimes through open-hole packers, or intermittent cold water injection with the purpose of thermal shocking. Stimulation operations commonly last a few days, while in some instances stimulation operations have been conducted for some months. The stimulation operations often result in well productivity being improved by a factor of 2–3.

7.02.8 Utilization Response of Geothermal Systems

The energy production potential of geothermal systems, in particular hydrothermal systems, is predominantly determined by pressure decline due to production. This is because there are technical limits to how great a pressure decline in a well is allowable, because of, for example, pump depth. The production potential is also determined by the available energy content of the system, that is, by the temperature or enthalpy of the extracted mass. The pressure decline is determined by the rate of production, on one the hand, and the nature and characteristics of the geothermal system, on the other hand. Natural geothermal reservoirs can be classified as either *open* or *closed*, with drastically different long-term behavior, depending on their boundary conditions (see also **Figure 14**):

A. Pressure declines continuously with time at constant production, in systems that are closed, or with small recharge. In such systems, the production potential is limited by lack of water rather than lack of thermal energy. Such systems are ideal for reinjection, which provides man-made recharge. Examples are many sedimentary geothermal systems, systems in areas with limited tectonic activity, and systems that have been sealed off from surrounding hydrological systems by chemical precipitation.
B. Pressure stabilizes in open systems because recharge eventually equilibrates with the mass extraction. The recharge may be both hot deep recharge and colder shallow recharge. The latter will eventually cause the reservoir temperature to decline and production wells to cool down. In such systems, the production potential is limited by the reservoir energy content (temperature and size) as the energy stored in the reservoir rocks will heat up the colder recharge as long as it is available/accessible.

The situation is somewhat different for EGS systems and sedimentary systems utilized through production–reinjection *doublets* (well pairs) and heat exchangers with 100% reinjection. Then the production potential is predominantly controlled by the energy content of the systems involved. But permeability, and therefore, pressure decline, is also of controlling significance in such situations. This is because it controls the pressure response of the wells and how much flow can be achieved and maintained, for example, through the doublets involved (it is customary in the EGS business to talk about intra-well impedance based on the electrical analogy). In sedimentary systems, the permeability is natural, but in EGS systems, the permeability is to a large degree created, or at least enhanced.

Water or steam extraction from a geothermal reservoir causes, in all cases, some decline in reservoir pressure, as already discussed. The only exception is when production from a reservoir is less than its natural recharge and discharge. Consequently, the pressure decline manifests itself in further changes, which for natural geothermal systems may be summarized in a somewhat simplified manner as follows:

A. Direct changes caused by *lowered reservoir pressure*, such as changes in surface activity, decreasing well discharge, lowered water level in wells, increased boiling in high-enthalpy reservoirs, and changes in noncondensable gas concentration.
B. Indirect changes caused by *increased recharge* to the reservoir, such as changes in chemical composition of the reservoir fluid, changes in scaling/corrosion potential, changes in reservoir temperature conditions (observed through temperature profiles of wells), and changes in temperature/enthalpy of reservoir fluid.
C. *Surface subsidence*, which may result in damage to surface installations.

Table 4 presents examples of the effect of long-term, large-scale production in several geothermal systems, both in Iceland and other parts of the world. These are both high- and low-enthalpy systems, of quite contrasting nature. Some exhibit a drastic pressure

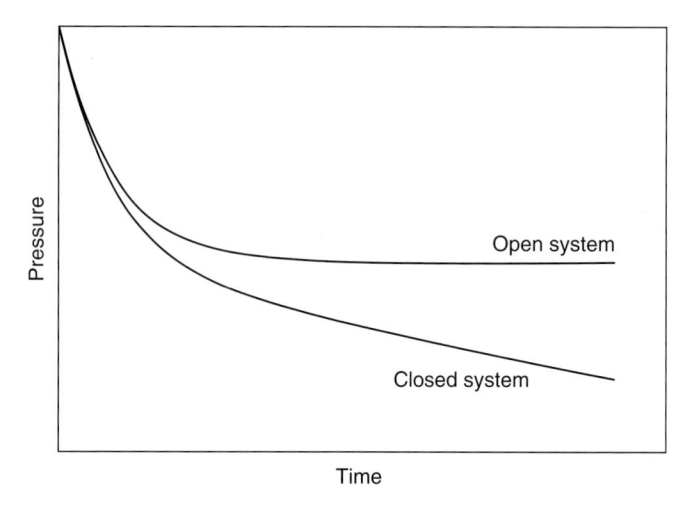

Figure 14 Schematic comparison of pressure decline in open (with recharge) or closed (with limited or no recharge) geothermal systems at a constant rate of production.

Table 4 Information on the effect of large-scale production on selected geothermal systems, for example, in Iceland, China (Urban Area), the Philippines (Palinpinion-1), and El Salvador (Ahuachapan). Note that the data are approximate, but representative, values based on information from 2000 to 2006

System (location)	Production initiated	Number of production wells	Average production ($kg\,s^{-1}$)	Reservoir temperature (°C)	Draw down	Temperature decline (°C)
Svartsengi (SW-Iceland)	1976	10	380	240	275 m	0
Laugarnes (SW-Iceland)	1930	10	160	127	110 m	0
Reykir (SW-Iceland)	1944	34	850	70–97	100 m	0–13[a]
Nesjavellir (SW-Iceland)	1975	11	390	280–340	7 bar	0
Hamar (N-Iceland)	1970	2	30	64	30 m	0
Laugaland (N-Iceland)	1976	3	40	95	370 m	0
Krafla (N-Iceland)	1978	21	300	210–340	10–15 bar	0
Urridavatn (E-Iceland)	1980	3	25	75	40 m	2–15[b]
Gata (S-Iceland)	1980	2	17	100	250 m	1–2
Urban Area (China)	late 1970s	90–100	~100	~40–90	45 m	0
Xi'an (China)[c]	1994	~80	~240	~40–105	150 m	0
Palinpinion-1 (the Philipinnes)	1983	23	710	240	55 bar	-
Ahuachapan (El Salvador)	1976	~16	~700	240–260	14 bar	-

[a] Only 3 of the 34 production wells have experienced some cooling.
[b] Two older production wells, not used after 1983, experienced up to 15 °C cooling.
[c] Inaccurate data.

drawdown for limited production, while others experience very limited drawdown for substantial mass extraction. The table also shows examples of reservoir cooling due to long-term production. **Figures 15–18** show the production and response histories of four of the fields in the table, as examples.

It should be mentioned that reinjection affects the production response of geothermal systems, primarily by providing pressure support and thus reducing pressure decline. This is discussed in detail later.

The simple model shown in **Figure 19** has been used to simulate geothermal systems of the open type ((B) above), that is, systems where the pressure decline due to production has induced a recharge of colder water from outside the reservoir, in particular low-temperature systems in Iceland. It is presented here to demonstrate the characteristics of such systems. The model consists of a fixed volume production reservoir overlain by an infinite groundwater system. A fixed inflow of geothermal water into the production reservoir has a temperature and chemical content, distinctively different from that of the groundwater above. Production of water from the system induces a downflow of groundwater, through some fractures extending to the surface, and

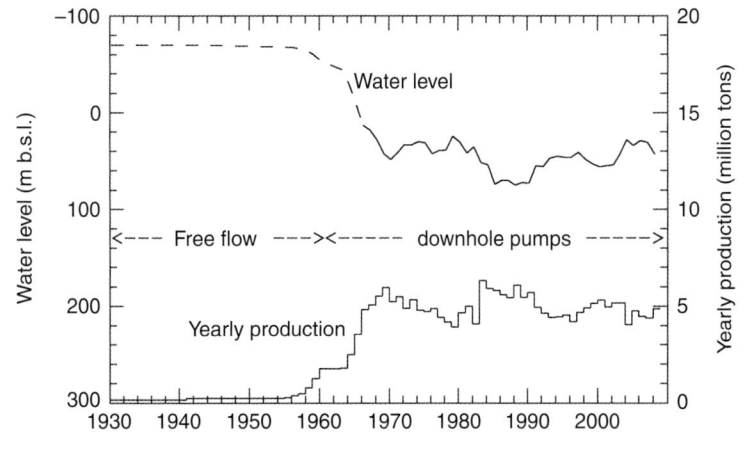

Figure 15 History of production and water-level response of the Laugarnes geothermal field in SW-Iceland from 1930.

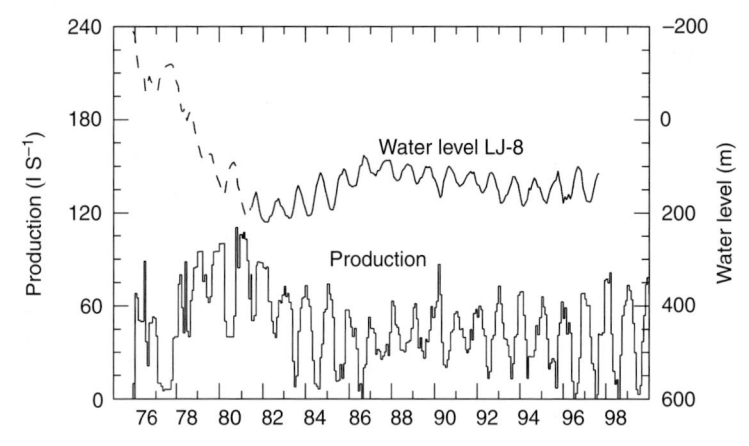

Figure 16 Production and water-level response history of the Laugaland geothermal field in N-Iceland.

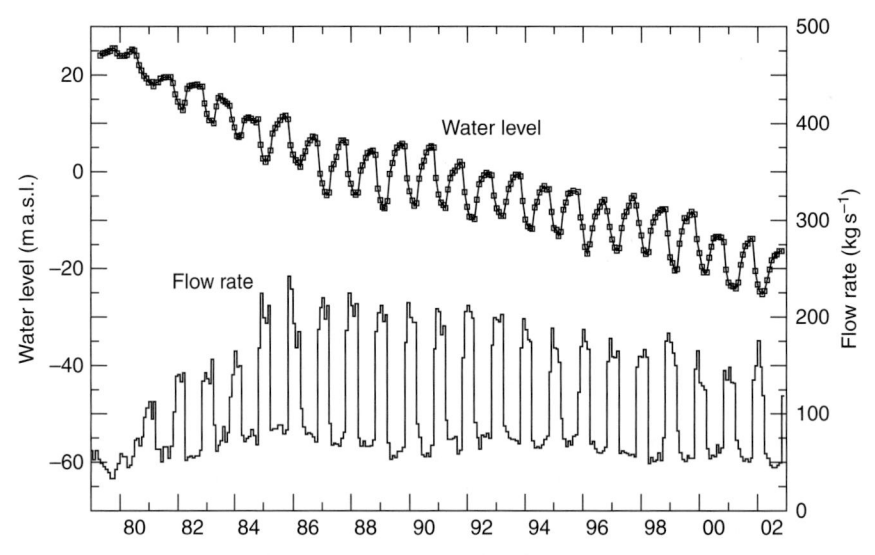

Figure 17 Production and water-level response history of the Urban Area in Beijing, China, since the late 1970s [42].

into the production reservoir. This causes the chemical content and temperature of the water produced to decline. The equations describing the response of this model are presented by Björnsson *et al.* [44].

Figure 20 shows the response of this model to prolonged production, as relative changes in pressure chemical content and temperature. It demonstrates clearly the very different timescales of the different changes, pressure changes being very fast, whereas thermal changes are extremely slow, due to the thermal inertia of the rock formation involved. The figure also shows that colder downflow may usually be detected as changes in the chemical content of the hot water produced, before its temperature starts to decline. This also shows in a simple manner why chemical monitoring is an essential part of geothermal reservoir management (see further).

Björnsson *et al.* [44] present the results of the application of this model to the Thelamork low-temperature system in Central N-Iceland, where chemical changes during a 9-month production test clearly indicated colder water inflow into the system. Axelsson and Gunnlaugsson [10] present the results of another comparable study for the Botn low-temperature system, also in Central N-Iceland, which has been utilized since 1981. Considerable chemical changes and cooling have been observed in the Botn field through its utilization history and the purpose of the modeling study was to evaluate the relationship between the rates of production and cooling, for future management of the field.

7.02.9 Monitoring

Management of a geothermal reservoir relies on adequate information on the geothermal system in question [45]. Data yielding this knowledge through appropriate interpretation is continuously gathered throughout the exploration and exploitation history of a

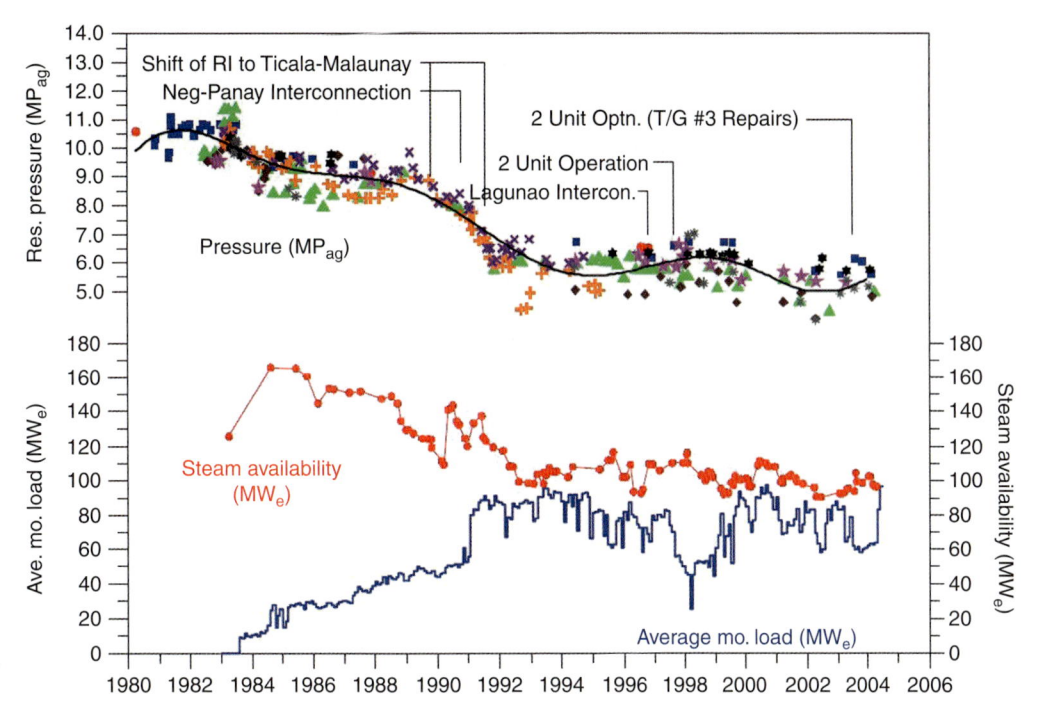

Figure 18 The production and pressure response history of the Palinpinion-1 geothermal field in the Philippines [43].

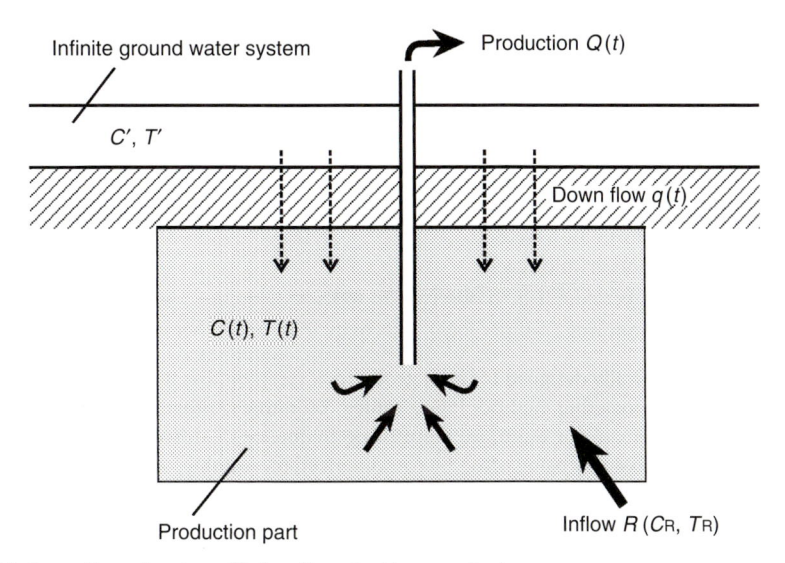

Figure 19 A simple model of a geothermal system with downflow of colder groundwater.

geothermal reservoir. The initial data come from surface exploration, that is, geological, chemical, and geophysical data. Additional information is provided by exploratory drilling, in particular through logging and well testing. The most important data on a geothermal system's nature and properties, however, are obtained through monitoring of its response to long-term production. These data form the basis for geothermal reservoir modeling, one of the key tools of geothermal resource management, which will be discussed in the following sections. The modeling is based on the basic theory of reservoir processes presented above.

Careful monitoring of a geothermal reservoir during exploitation is, therefore, an indispensable part of any successful management program. If the understanding of a geothermal system is adequate, monitoring will enable changes in the reservoir to be seen in advance. Timely warning is thus obtained from undesirable changes such as decreasing generating capacity due to declining reservoir pressure or steam flow, insufficient injection capacity, or possible operational problems such as scaling in wells and surface equipment or corrosion. The importance of a proper monitoring program for any geothermal reservoir being utilized can thus never be overemphasized.

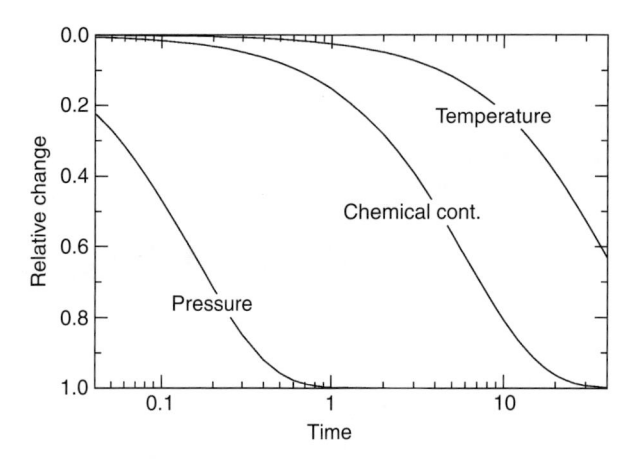

Figure 20 Pressure, chemical, and thermal response of the model in **Figure 19** (logarithmic timescale).

Monitoring the physical changes in a geothermal reservoir during exploitation is, in principle, simple and only involves measuring the (1) mass and heat transport, (2) pressure, and (3) energy content (temperature in most situations). This is complicated in practice, however [10]. Measurements must be made at high temperatures and pressures, and reservoir access for measurements is generally limited to a few boreholes, and these parameters cannot be measured directly throughout the remaining reservoir volume.

The parameters that need to be monitored to quantify a reservoir's response to production may, of course, differ somewhat, as well as methods and monitoring frequency, from one geothermal system to another [10, 46]. Monitoring may also be either direct or indirect, depending on the observation technique adopted. Below is a list of directly observable basic aspects that should be included in conventional geothermal monitoring programs.

(1) Mass discharge histories of production wells (pumping for low-temperature wells)
(2) Temperature or enthalpy (if two-phase) of fluid produced
(3) Water level or wellhead pressure (reflecting reservoir pressure) of production wells
(4) Chemical content of water (and steam) produced
(5) Injection rate histories of injection wells
(6) Temperature of injected water
(7) Wellhead pressure (water level) for injection wells
(8) Reservoir pressure (water level) in observation wells.
(9) Reservoir temperature through temperature logs in observation wells.
(10) Well status through diameter monitoring (calliper logs), injectivity tests, and other methods.

Monitoring programs have to be specifically designed for each geothermal reservoir, because of their individual characteristics and the distinct differences inherent in the metering methodology adopted. Monitoring programs may also have to be revised as time progresses, and more experience is gained, for example, monitoring frequency of different parameters. The practical limits to manual monitoring frequency are increasingly being offset by computerized monitoring, which actually presents no upper limit to monitoring frequency, except for that set by the available memory space in the computer system used. Data transmission through phone networks is also increasingly being used. **Figures 21–24** show examples of different kinds of direct monitoring data.

Indirect monitoring involves monitoring the changes occurring at depth in geothermal systems through various surface observations and measurements. Such indirect monitoring methods are mainly used in high-temperature fields, but also have a potential for contributing significantly to the understanding of low-temperature systems. These methods are mostly geophysical measurements carried out at the surface; airborne and even satellite measurements have also been attempted. All these methods have in common that a careful baseline survey must be carried out before the start of utilization and repeated at regular intervals.

Some of the indirect monitoring methods are well established by now, while others are still in the experimental stage or have met limited success. A review of the geothermal literature reveals that the following methods have been used [10]:

a. Topographic measurements
b. Microgravity surveys
c. Electrical resistivity surveys
d. Ground temperature and heat flow measurements
e. Micro-seismic monitoring
f. Water-level monitoring in groundwater systems
g. Self-potential surveys.

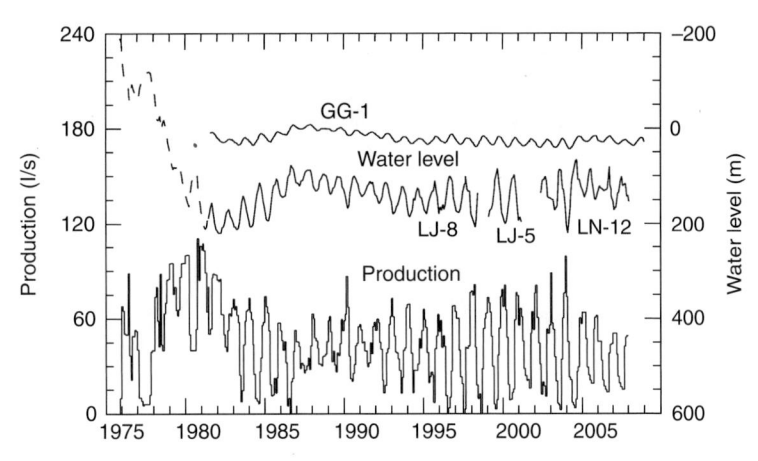

Figure 21 Production and water-level history of the Laugaland low-temperature geothermal system in the south of Akureyri in N-Iceland from 1976 to 2007 [47]. The broken line indicates estimated water level. Wells LJ-5, LJ-8, and LN-12 are inside the field, while well GG-1 is 2 km from the center of the field.

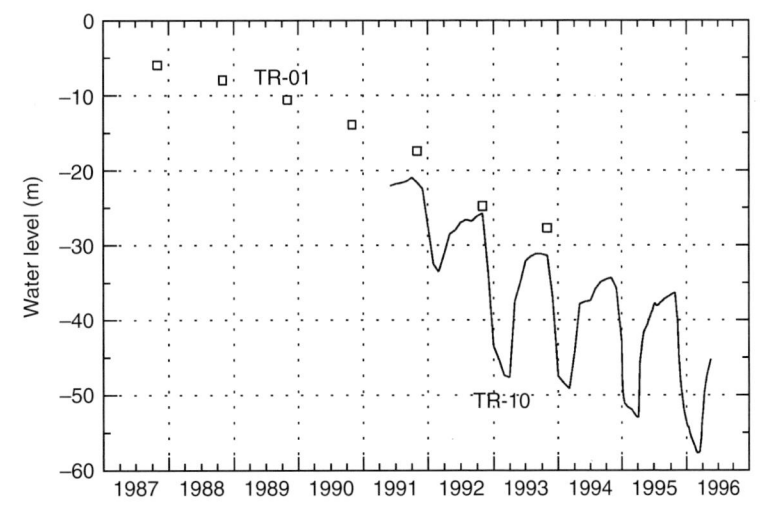

Figure 22 The water-level history of the Tanggu geothermal system in Tianjin, China, during 1987–96 [48]. It demonstrates the distinct difference between intermittent (yearly) monitoring and continuous monitoring. From Axelsson G (2003) Essence of geothermal resource management. Lectures on the sustainable use and operating policy for geothermal reservoirs. IGC2003 short course. *United Nations University Geothermal Training Programme, Report 2003-1*, pp. 129–152. Reykjavík, Iceland, September [49].

The reasons why these monitoring methods are seldom used in low-temperature fields are the fact that physical changes in low-temperature systems are generally not as great as in high-temperature systems as well as relatively high costs. A few of the methods are rather widely used in high-temperature fields, such as (a), (b), and (e).

Topographic measurements are carried out to enable detection of ground elevation changes, mostly subsidence. This may occur in all geothermal systems during exploitation because of compaction of the reservoir rocks, following fluid withdrawal. Reinjection may also cause topographic changes (uplift). Recently, satellite radar interferometry (INSAR) has been increasingly used for surface deformation studies. Such studies for the Krafla volcanic and geothermal system in N-Iceland provide a good example [51].

Microgravity monitoring has been used successfully in a number of geothermal fields. Changes in gravity can provide information on the net mass balance of a geothermal reservoir during exploitation, that is, the difference between the mass withdrawal from a field and the recharge to the reservoir. The mass-balance effects of enlarging steam zones may also be seen through gravity monitoring. In addition, the mass-balance effects of reinjection may be detected by gravity monitoring. Methods for analyzing gravity changes in geothermal fields are presented by Allis and Hunt [52]. **Figure 25** presents an example of the results of gravity and subsidence monitoring in the Svartsengi high-temperature geothermal field in SW Iceland. Nishijima *et al.* [53, 54] also provide good examples from Japanese high-temperature fields of the application of repeated microgravity monitoring for reservoir monitoring.

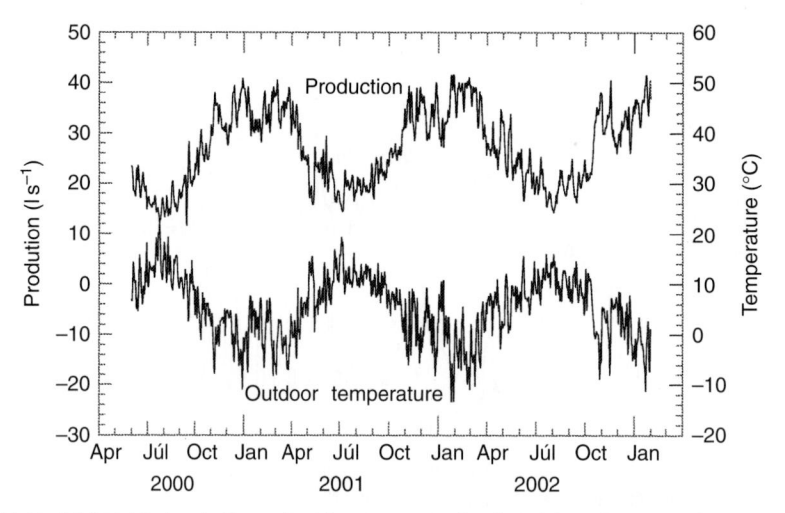

Figure 23 An example of highly detailed data (production and outdoor temperature) collected through computerized monitoring at the Urridavatn low-temperature geothermal system near Egilsstadir, E-Iceland [50]. Note that all variations in outdoor temperature are reflected in variations in production. From Axelsson G (2003) Essence of geothermal resource management. Lectures on the sustainable use and operating policy for geothermal reservoirs. IGC2003 short course. *United Nations University Geothermal Training Programme, Report 2003-1*, pp. 129–152. Reykjavík, Iceland, September.

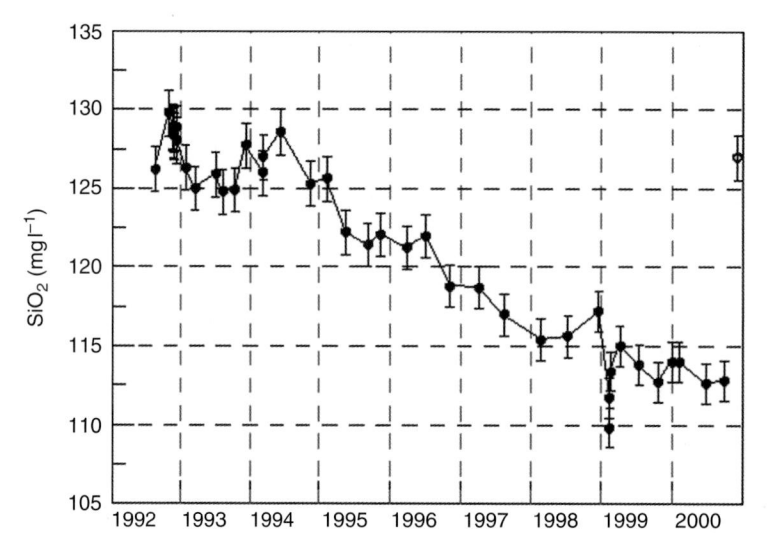

Figure 24 Changes in silica content of water produced from the Thelamork low-temperature geothermal system in Central N-Iceland during 1992–2000 [44]. The data are interpreted as reflecting inflow of colder water (with lower silica content) into the geothermal system. From Axelsson G (2003) Essence of geothermal resource management. Lectures on the sustainable use and operating policy for geothermal reservoirs. IGC2003 short course. *United Nations University Geothermal Training Programme, Report 2003-1*, pp. 129–152. Reykjavík, Iceland, September.

Repeated *electrical resistivity surveys* have not been conducted in many geothermal fields, but might help delineate cold, freshwater inflow into geothermal reservoirs, induced by production. Such surveys may also be helpful in locating reservoir volumes affected by reinjection.

Surface activity and heat flow may either decrease or increase during production from a geothermal field. Monitoring of these changes is, however, more often associated with monitoring of the environmental effects of geothermal exploitation. These may be monitored through repeated (1) ground temperature measurements, (2) airborne infrared measurements, and (3) observations of thermal features (hot springs, fumaroles, mud pools, etc.).

The purpose of *monitoring seismic activity* may be twofold: first, to monitor changes in seismic activity in an already active area – this may be considered environmental rather than reservoir monitoring; second, to delineate the regions in a geothermal reservoir affected by exploitation or reinjection, because in some cases the pressure and thermal changes associated with geothermal exploitation and reinjection may be sufficient to generate some microseismic activity.

Water level changes in shallow ground water systems above geothermal reservoirs are monitored in some geothermal fields. *Self-potential monitoring* has been proposed as a tool to study the changes in geothermal reservoirs due to mass extraction and reinjection.

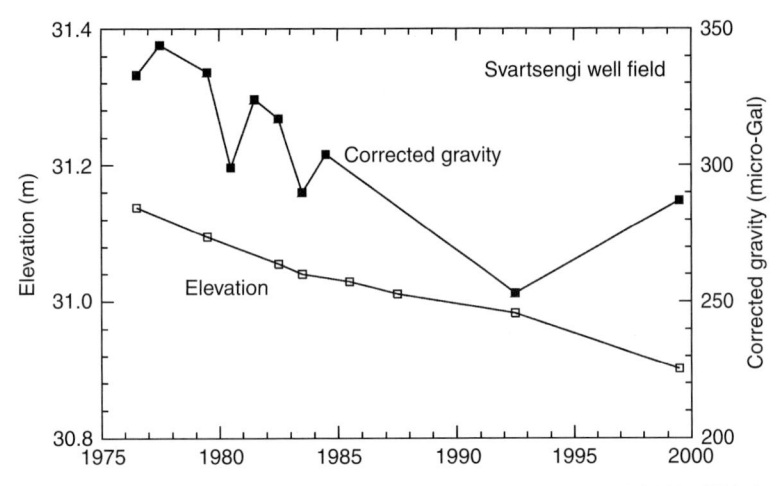

Figure 25 Results of gravity and subsidence monitoring in the Svartsengi high-temperature geothermal field in SW-Iceland. These data were used to infer that about 70% of the mass extracted from the reservoir had been restored through natural recharge [55].

Finally, it may be pointed out that a combination of indirect monitoring with numerical reservoir simulation should enhance the reliability of such models, as wells as aiding in the correct understanding of the nature of the geothermal system involved.

7.02.10 Modelling of Geothermal Systems – Overview

Various methods have been used over the past several decades to assess geothermal resources during both exploration and exploitation phases of development. These range from methods used to estimate resource temperature and size to complex numerical modeling aimed at predicting the production response of systems and estimating their production potential. Being able to assess a given resource during different stages of its development, as accurately as possible, is essential for its successful development. The main methods used are as follows:

a. Deep temperature estimates (based on chemical content of surface manifestations)
b. Surface thermal flux
c. Volumetric methods (adapted from mineral exploration and oil industry)
d. Decline curve analysis (adapted from oil/gas industry)
e. Simple mathematical modeling (often analytical)
f. Lumped parameter modeling
g. Detailed numerical modeling of natural state and/or exploitation state (often called distributed parameter models).

The first two methods are not modeling methods *per se*, but are the methods that can be used for resource assessment prior to extensive geophysical surveying and drilling. The remaining methods in the list can all be considered modeling methods, which play an essential role in geothermal resource development and management. These range from basic volumetric resource assessment (c) and simple analytical modeling (e) of the results of a short well test to detailed numerical modeling (g) of a complex geothermal system, simulating an intricate pattern of changes resulting from long-term production. In the early days of geothermal reservoir studies, decline curve analysis (d) proved to be an efficient method to predict the future output of individual high-temperature wells [27], but today other modeling methods are usually applied. Decline curve analysis is particularly applicable to wells in dry steam reservoirs.

The purpose of geothermal modeling is first to obtain information on the conditions in a geothermal system as well as on the nature and properties of the system. This leads to proper understanding of its nature and successful development of the resource. Second, the purpose of modeling is to predict the response of the reservoir to future production and estimate the production potential of the system as well as to estimate the outcome of different management actions.

The diverse information, which is the foundation for all reservoir modeling, needs to be continuously gathered throughout the exploration and exploitation history of a geothermal reservoir. Information on reservoir properties is obtained by disturbing the state of the reservoir (fluid flow, pressure) and by observing the resulting response, and is done through well and reservoir testing and data collection. Different methods of testing geothermal reservoirs are available, but it should be emphasized that the data collected do not provide the reservoir properties directly. Instead, the data are interpreted or analyzed, on the basis of appropriate models yielding estimates of reservoir properties. It is important to keep in mind that the resulting values are model-dependent, that is, different models give different estimates. It is also very important to keep in mind that the longer and more extensive the tests are, the more information is obtained on the system in question. Therefore, the most important data on a geothermal reservoir is obtained through careful monitoring during long-term exploitation (see above), which can be looked upon as prolonged and extensive reservoir testing.

The modeling methods may be classified as either *static modeling methods* or *dynamic modeling methods*, with the volumetric method (c) being the main static method. Both involve development of some kind of a mathematical model that *simulates* some, or most, of the data available on the system involved. The volumetric method, discussed below, is based on estimating the total heat stored in a volume of rock and how much of that can be efficiently recovered. The dynamic modeling methods ((d–g) in the list above) are based on modeling the dynamic conditions and behavior (production response) of geothermal systems. These will also be discussed below, with the lumped parameter method (f) taken as an example.

7.02.11 Static Modeling (Volumetric Assessment)

The volumetric method is the main static modeling method, as already stated. It is often used for first-stage assessment, when data are limited, and was more commonly used in the past [56, 57], but is still the main assessment method in some countries, for example, for Chinese low-temperature resources. It is increasingly being used, however, through application of the Monte Carlo method [58]. This method enables the incorporation of overall uncertainty in the results. The main drawback of the volumetric method is the fact that the dynamic response of a reservoir to production is not considered, such as the pressure response and the effect of fluid recharge. Reservoirs with the same heat content may have different permeabilities and recharge and, hence, very different production potentials.

It is based on estimating the total heat stored in a volume of rock (referred to some base temperature), thermal energy in both rock matrix and water/steam in pores. In the volumetric method, the likely surface area and thickness of a resource are estimated from geophysical and geological data. Resistivity surveying data are most important in this respect. Consequently, likely temperature conditions are assumed on the basis of chemical studies and well temperature data, if available. Based on these estimates of reservoir porosity and thermal properties of water and rock involved, the total energy content is estimated by the following set of equations:

$$E_{\text{total}} = E_{\text{r}} + E_{\text{w}} \quad [43]$$

$$\text{with } E_{\text{r}} = V(1-\varphi)\rho_{\text{r}}\beta_{\text{r}}(T-T_{\text{ref}}) \quad [44]$$

$$\text{and } E_{\text{w}} = V\varphi\rho_{\text{w}}\beta_{\text{w}}(T-T_{\text{ref}}) \quad [45]$$

$$\text{or } E_{\text{w}} = V\varphi\rho_{\text{r}}(h-h_{\text{ref}}) \quad [46]$$

In the above equation, E_{r} stands for the energy content of the reservoir rocks, E_{w} for the energy content of the reservoir fluid, and V for the reservoir volume, or the volume of a part of a system being assessed. In addition, T is the reservoir temperature, which can be assumed to be approximately constant, to be variable between different reservoir parts, or to be a certain fraction of the boiling point curve at prevailing pressure conditions. The reference temperature, T_{ref}, is the base temperature of the energy production process involved (space heating, electricity generation, etc.). During two-phase reservoir conditions, eqn [46] can be used, with h the fluid enthalpy. Other parameters have already been defined.

Subsequently, surface accessibility is incorporated in the estimation through the parameter A, which describes what proportion of the reservoir volume can be accessed through drilling from the surface. Finally, a recovery factor (R) is incorporated, a factor that indicates how much of accessible energy may be technically recovered. The recovery factor is the parameter in the volumetric method, which is most difficult to estimate. The results of the volumetric assessment are also highly dependent on the factor. It depends on the nature of the system (permeability, porosity, significance of fractures, and recharge) as well as on the mode of production, that is, whether reinjection is applied. It is also to some extent dependent on time. Williams [59] provides a good review on the estimation of the recovery factor. It may be mentioned that it is often assumed to be in the range of 0.05–0.25. The recoverable energy, above an assumed reference temperature, is given by

$$E_{\text{recoverable}} = A \cdot R \cdot E_{\text{total}} \quad [47]$$

For electrical generation, the resource potential is assessed using an appropriate conversion efficiency, η, for the recoverable energy above a reference temperature applicable to the production process used (conventional steam turbine, binary fluid generation, etc.). Thus,

$$E_{\text{e}} = \eta \cdot E_{\text{recoverable}} \quad [48]$$

$$P_{\text{e}} = \frac{E_{\text{e}}}{\Delta t} \quad [49]$$

with E_{e} the total electrical energy that can be produced according to the assessment and P_{e} the electrical power potential when the electricity is generated over a time period of length Δt.

The volumetric method can be applied to individual geothermal reservoirs, whole geothermal systems, or on a regional scale, that is, for a whole country. For individual systems, the Monte Carlo method is often applied. It involves assigning probability

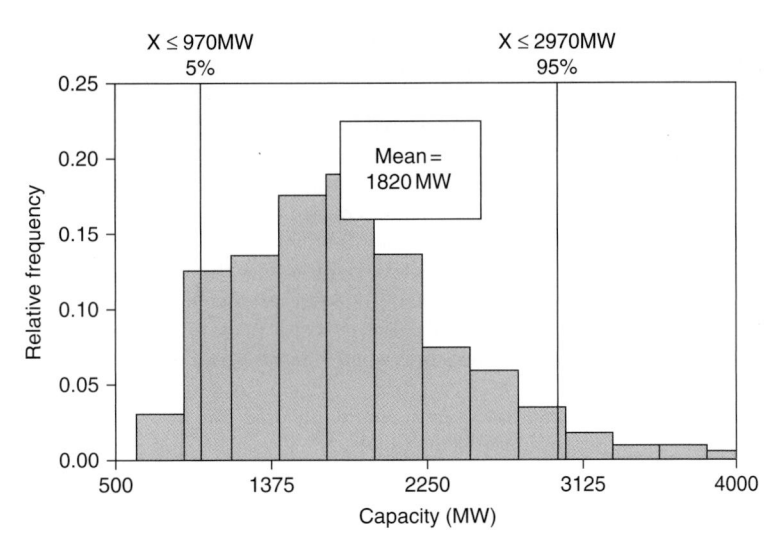

Figure 26 An example of the results of a volumetric resource assessment for the greater Hengill geothermal region in SW-Iceland. The Monte Carlo method was applied in the assessment [58].

distributions to the different parameters of the equations above and estimating the system potential with probability. An example of the results of such an assessment is presented in **Figure 26**.

7.02.12 Dynamic Modeling

The main dynamic modeling methods applied to geothermal systems are simple analytical modeling methods (*l*), lumped parameter methods (*m*), and detailed numerical modeling (*n*). If properly developed and calibrated by actual data, the models provide information on conditions in, and on the properties of, the actual geothermal system in question. Consequently, the models are used to predict future changes in the reservoir involved and to estimate its production potential. Dynamic reservoir models are also helpful in estimating the outcome of different management actions. Numerous examples are available on the successful role of modeling in geothermal resource management [10, 60].

The initial step in model development should be the development of a good conceptual model [28, 61]. This is a qualitative or descriptive model incorporating all the essential features of a geothermal system revealed by analysis of all available data, as described previously in this chapter. The next step is the development of a quantitative natural state model, which should simulate the physical state of a geothermal system prior to production. Finally, an exploitation model is developed to simulate changes in the physical state of a system during long-term production and to calculate predictions as well as for other management purposes.

In simple models, such as simple analytical models and lumped parameter models, the real structure and spatially variable properties of a geothermal system are greatly simplified so that analytical mathematical equations, describing the response of the model to hot water production, may be derived. These models, in fact, often only simulate one aspect of a geothermal system's response. Detailed and complex numerical models, on the other hand, can accurately simulate most aspects of a geothermal system's structure, conditions, and response to production. Simple modeling takes relatively little time and only requires limited data on a geothermal system and its response, whereas numerical modeling takes a long time and requires powerful computers as well as comprehensive and detailed data on the system in question. The complexity of a model should be determined by the purpose of a study, the data available, and its relative cost. In fact, simple modeling, such as lumped parameter modeling, is often a cost-effective and time-saving alternative. It may be applied in situations when available data are limited and when funds are restricted or as parts of more comprehensive studies, such as to validate results of numerical modeling studies.

Simple modeling, on the other hand, has been used extensively to study and manage the low-temperature geothermal systems utilized in Iceland, in particular to model their long-term response to production [10]. Lumped parameter modeling of water level and pressure change data has been the principal tool for this purpose [62]. Lumped models can simulate such data very accurately, even very long data sets (several decades). Lumped parameter modeling will be discussed in more detail below to illustrate the general methodology of geothermal system modeling.

7.02.12.1 Lumped Parameter Modeling

Axelsson [63] presents an efficient method of lumped parameter modeling of pressure response data from geothermal systems and other underground hydrological systems. The method tackles the simulation as an inverse problem and can simulate such data very accurately, if the data quality is sufficient. It automatically fits the analytical response functions of the lumped models to observed data by using a nonlinear iterative least-squares technique for estimating the model parameters. Today, lumped models have been developed by this method for more than 20 low-temperature and 3 high-temperature geothermal systems in Iceland, as well as geothermal systems in China, Turkey, Eastern Europe, Central America, and the Philippines [62]. It may be mentioned that the method presented by Axelsson [63] has been employed and revised by, for example, Sarak *et al.* [64] and Onur *et al.* [65].

The theoretical basis of this automatic method of lumped parameter modeling is presented by Axelsson [22, 63], and in fact Bödvarsson [66] discussed the usefulness of lumped methods of interpreting geophysical exploration data. The computer code LUMPFIT has been used since 1986 in the lumped modeling studies carried out in Iceland [67].

A general lumped model is shown in **Figure 27**. It consists of a few tanks and flow resistors. The tanks simulate the storage capacity of different parts of a geothermal system, and the water level or pressure in the tanks simulates the water level or pressure in corresponding parts of the system. A tank has a storage coefficient (capacitance) when it responds to a load of liquid mass m with a pressure increase $p = m/\kappa$. The resistors (conductors) simulate the flow resistance in the reservoir, controlled by the permeability of its rocks. The mass conductance (inverse of resistance) of a resistor is when it transfers $q = \sigma \nabla p$ units of liquid mass, per unit time, at the impressed pressure differential ∇p.

Figure 28 shows the type of lumped parameter model most commonly used. The first tank of the model in the figure can be looked upon as simulating the innermost (production) part of the geothermal reservoir, and the second and third tanks simulate the outer parts of the system. The third tank is connected by a resistor to a constant pressure source, which supplies recharge to the geothermal system. The model in **Figure 28** is, therefore, open. Without the connection to the constant pressure source, the model would be closed. An open model may be considered optimistic, since equilibrium between production and recharge is eventually reached during long-term production, causing the water-level drawdown to stabilize. In contrast, a closed model may be considered pessimistic, since no recharge is allowed for such a model and the water level declines steadily with time during long-term production. In addition, the model presented in **Figure 28** is composed of three tanks; in many instances, models with only two tanks have been used.

Axelsson [63] presents the system of basic equations describing the behavior of a general lumped parameter model in matrix form as well as a general solution for the pressure response to variable production. The mass flow from tank k to tank i is given by

$$q_{ik} = \sigma_{ik}(p_k - p_i) \qquad [50]$$

with σ_{ik} the mass flow conductance of the resistor connecting the tanks and p_k and p_i the pressures in tanks k and i, respectively. The mass balance for tank i when connected to N other tanks is given by

$$\kappa_i \frac{dp_i}{dt} = \sum_{k=1}^{N} q_{ik} - \sigma_i(p_i - p_0) + f_i \qquad [51]$$

Figure 27 A general lumped parameter model used to simulate water-level or pressure changes in geothermal systems. From Axelsson G (1989) Simulation of pressure response data from geothermal reservoirs by lumped parameter models. *Proceedings of the 14th Workshop on Geothermal Reservoir Engineering*, pp. 257–263. Stanford University, USA.

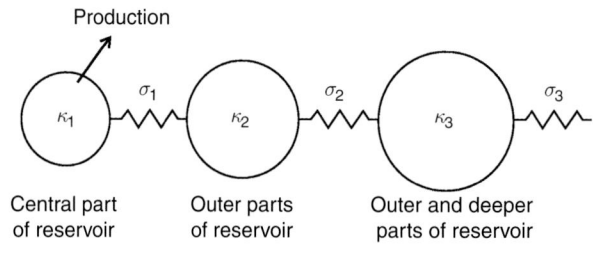

Figure 28 A three-tank lumped ladder commonly used to simulate geothermal systems. From Axelsson G, Björnsson G, and Quijano J (2005) Reliability of lumped parameter modelling of pressure changes in geothermal reservoirs. *Proceedings of the World Geothermal Congress 2005*, 8pp. Antalya, Turkey, April.

with σ_i the mass flow conductance of the resistor connecting tank i to an external constant pressure source with pressure p_0 and f_i the rate of mass injection (negative if extraction) into the tank. The variable f_i therefore simulates the effect of mass injection or extraction through wells. The initial model pressure is also generally assumed to equal p_0. The above completely defines the problem and Axelsson [63] describes how pressure solutions for general lumped parameter models are obtained.

When the source term f_i varies with time, the solution is found through the following convolution integral:

$$p(t) = p_0 + \int_0^t h(t-\tau) f(\tau) d\tau \qquad [52]$$

where $h(t)$ is the impulse response of the tank in question, and corresponding model, that is, the theoretical response to an instantaneous injection of 1 kg of liquid mass (a delta-function injection). The impulse response is given by [63]

$$h(t) = \sum_{j=1}^{N} m_j e^{-m_{j+N} t} \qquad [53]$$

The parameters m_j and m_{j+N} are related to eigenvector components and eigenvalues of the problem and are functions of the σ's and κ's of the lumped model in question.

In the simple case of a one-tank open model (i.e., a single tank connected to an outside pressure source through a single resistor), the pressure change in the model due to a constant mass extraction Q, as a function of time, is given by

$$p(t) = p_0 - \frac{Q}{\sigma_1}\left(1 - e^{\frac{\sigma_1}{\kappa_1} t}\right) \qquad [54]$$

Similarly, the pressure change in the first tank of a closed two-tank model (i.e., a model composed of two tanks connected by a single resistor) due to a constant mass extraction from the same tank, is given by

$$p(t) = p_0 - \frac{Q}{\kappa_1 + \kappa_2}\left(\frac{\kappa_2}{\kappa_1}\left(1 - e^{-\lambda t}\right) + t\right) \qquad [55]$$

with

$$\lambda = \frac{\sigma_1(\kappa_1 + \kappa_2)}{\kappa_1 \kappa_2} \qquad [56]$$

In the more general lumped parameter model of **Figure 28**, hot water is assumed to be pumped out of the first tank, which causes the pressure and water level in the model to decline. This in turn simulates the decline of pressure and water level in the real geothermal system. When using this method of lumped parameter modeling, the data fitted (simulated) are the pressure or water-level data for an observation well inside the well field, while the input for the model is the production history of the geothermal field in question.

Figures 29–31 present examples of long pressure response histories of three geothermal systems distributed throughout the world. These are the histories of the Ytri-Tjarnir low-temperature system in N-Iceland; the Urban low-temperature sedimentary system in Beijing, China; and the Ahuachapan high-temperature volcanic system in El Salvador. These examples are all discussed in more detail by Axelsson *et al.* [62], but the figures show that in all of the cases, the lumped parameter models developed simulate the pressure changes quite accurately.

Because of how simple the lumped parameter models are, their reliability is sometimes questioned. Experience has shown that they are quite reliable, however, and examples involving repeated simulations demonstrate this clearly [62]. This applies, in particular, to simulations based on long data sets, which is in agreement with the general fact that the most important data on a geothermal reservoir are obtained through careful monitoring during long-term exploitation. Lumped parameter modeling is less reliable when based on shorter data sets, which is valid for all such reservoir engineering predictions.

Future pressure changes in geothermal systems are expected to lie somewhere between the predictions of open and closed versions of lumped parameter models, which represent extreme kinds of boundary conditions. The differences between these predictions simply reveal the inherent uncertainty in all such predictions. Real examples demonstrate that the shorter the data period a simulation is based on, the more uncertain the predictions are [62]. They also demonstrate that the uncertainty in the predictions increases with increasing length of the prediction period. **Figure 32** presents an example of such predictions for the Hamar low-temperature geothermal system in N-Iceland, in fact for an unusually long prediction period (see Section 7.02.16). Normally such predictions are only calculated for a few decades, or ideally for a prediction period of a length comparable to the data simulation period.

Finally, it should be reiterated that even though lumped parameter models have been set up for high-temperature systems, they are strictly developed for isothermal, single-phase conditions. In addition, simulating internal changes in reservoir conditions and properties is beyond the capacity of lumped parameter models. Furthermore, the method of lumped parameter modeling discussed

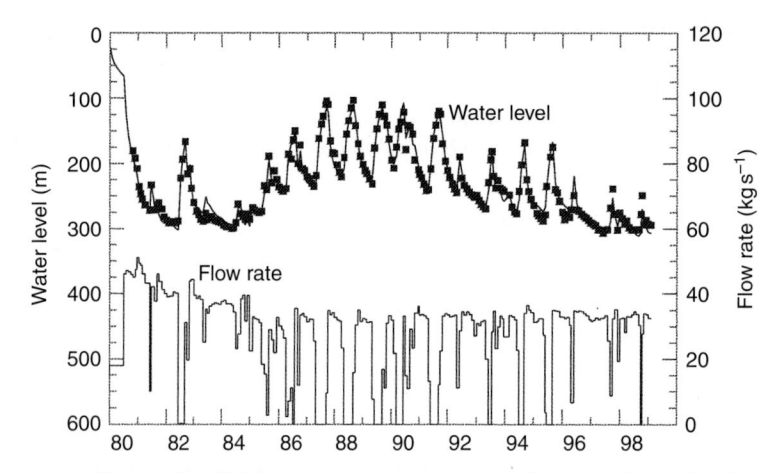

Figure 29 Production and water-level history of the Ytri-Tjarnir low-temperature geothermal system in Central N-Iceland during 1980–99. The water-level history has been simulated by a lumped parameter model. Squares indicate observed data and line indicates simulated data. From Axelsson G, Björnsson G, and Quijano J (2005) Reliability of lumped parameter modelling of pressure changes in geothermal reservoirs. *Proceedings of the World Geothermal Congress 2005*, 8pp. Antalya, Turkey, April.

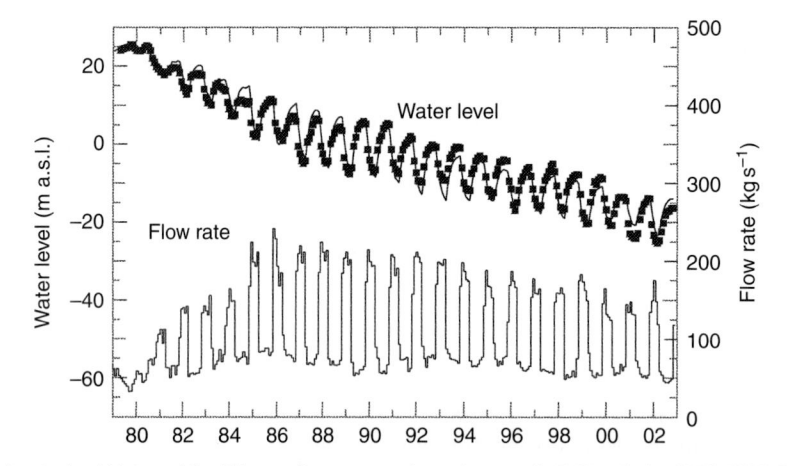

Figure 30 Production and water-level history of the Urban sedimentary geothermal system in Beijing during 1979–2002. The water level history has been simulated by a lumped parameter model. Squares indicate observed data and line indicates simulated data. From Axelsson G, Björnsson G, and Quijano J (2005) Reliability of lumped parameter modelling of pressure changes in geothermal reservoirs. *Proceedings of the World Geothermal Congress 2005*, 8pp. Antalya, Turkey, April.

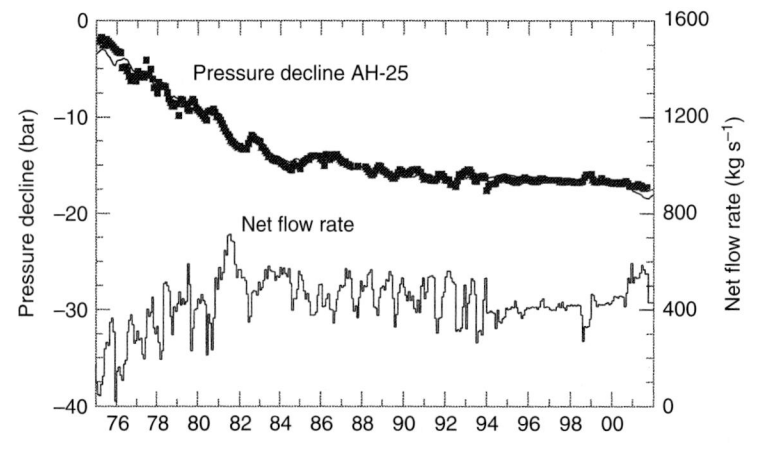

Figure 31 Production and pressure decline history of the Ahuachapan high-temperature geothermal field in El Salvador during 1975–2001. The pressure history has been simulated by a lumped parameter model based on the net production (mass extraction − infield reinjection). Squares indicate observed data and line indicates simulated data. From Axelsson G, Björnsson G, and Quijano J (2005) Reliability of lumped parameter modelling of pressure changes in geothermal reservoirs. *Proceedings of the World Geothermal Congress 2005*, 8pp. Antalya, Turkey, April.

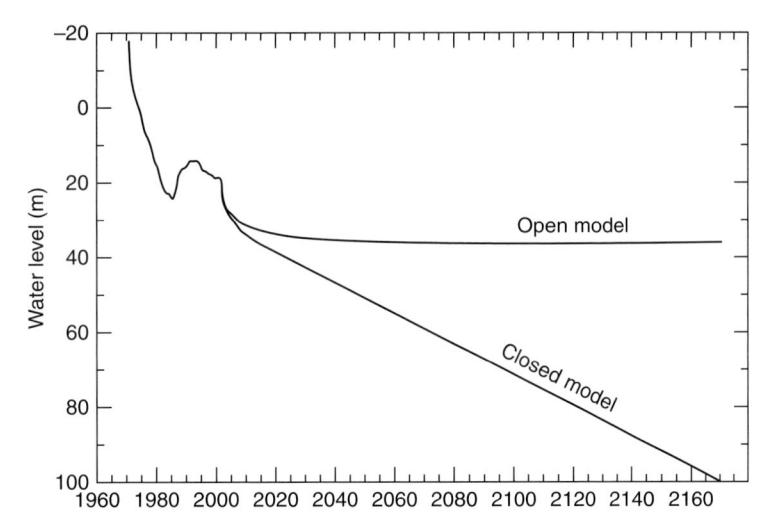

Figure 32 Predicted water-level changes in the Hamar geothermal system for a 200-year production history calculated by a lumped parameter model based on data up to 2001. Predictions by an open (optimistic) and a closed (pessimistic) version of the model, for a 40 kg s^{-1} constant production, are presented. From Axelsson G, Björnsson G, and Quijano J (2005) Reliability of lumped parameter modelling of pressure changes in geothermal reservoirs. *Proceedings of the World Geothermal Congress 2005*, 8pp. Antalya, Turkey, April.

here is neither directly applicable to EGS systems or doublet operations. Other types of simple models are more applicable for such situations.

7.02.12.2 Detailed Numerical Modeling

Detailed numerical reservoir modeling has become the most powerful tool of geothermal reservoir physics parallel with the rapid development of high-capacity modern-day computers and is increasingly being used to simulate geothermal systems in different parts of the world. This method will not be discussed here in detail. Instead the reader is referred to an early work by the pioneers in this field [68], a later comprehensive review by O'Sullivan *et al.* [60], and the detailed lectures of Pruess [28]. The numerical modeling method is extremely powerful when based on comprehensive and detailed data. Without good data, however, detailed numerical modeling can only be considered speculative, at best. In addition, numerical modeling is time-consuming and costly and without the necessary data, the extensive investment needed is not justified.

The details and different aspects of detailed numerical reservoir modeling are described by Pruess [28]. The principal steps of the method involve dividing the whole volume of the reservoir/system into numerous subvolumes (grid blocks), often a few hundred to several thousand blocks. Each block (or in fact families of blocks) is assigned hydrological and thermal properties. Sinks and sources are then assigned to selected blocks to simulate natural inflow and outflow as well as production wells and injection wells. In addition, appropriate boundary conditions are specified. The above is mostly based on a comprehensive conceptual model of the geothermal system and to some extent on well test data. Finite difference methods, or finite element methods, are subsequently used to solve relevant equations for conservation and flow of mass and heat.

The most elaborate part of the modeling process then involves varying the model properties listed above until the model adequately simulates all relevant data. Such models are required to simulate available data on pressure and temperature conditions as well as main flow patterns in the system in question during the natural state. They also need to simulate observed changes in pressure and temperature conditions during production as well as variations in well output (mass flow and enthalpy). During the early days of numerical modeling, when computers were far less powerful than today, separate natural state models and production models were often developed [61]. Today, these are most often combined in one overall model. It should be mentioned that computer code developments have been underway for some time aimed at incorporating chemical data into the modeling process. Attempts have also been made to incorporate other data, such as surface deformation data, gravity data, and resistivity data, into the modeling process. In principle, all such additional data should aid in the modeling process, help constrain the models, and make them more reliable.

Computer codes, like the well-known TOUGH2 code, are used for the calculations [28]. The items below are varied throughout the modeling process until a satisfactory data fit is obtained:

- Permeability distribution
- Porosity distribution
- Boundary conditions (nature/permeability of outer regions of model)
- Productivity indices for wells (the relation between flow and pressure drop from reservoir into a well)

- Mass recharge to the system
- Energy recharge to the system.

Björnsson *et al.* [69] and O'Sullivan *et al.* [70] provide information on two large-scale reservoir modeling projects. These are the Hengill geothermal region in southwest Iceland and Wairakei geothermal system on the North Island of New Zealand. **Figure 33** shows the computational grid of the most recent numerical reservoir model for Wairakei as an example of such a model.

7.02.13 Geothermal Resource Management

The key to successful geothermal development is efficient and comprehensive interdisciplinary geothermal research, during both the exploration and exploitation phases, as well as proper resource management during utilization. Geothermal exploitation involves energy extraction from highly complex underground systems, and geothermal resource management implies controlling this energy extraction, including how to maximize the resulting benefits without overexploiting the resource.

Comprehensive and efficient management is an essential part of any successful geothermal resource utilization endeavor. Such management can be highly complicated, however, as the energy production potential of geothermal systems is highly variable. The generating capacity of many geothermal systems is, furthermore, not properly defined and they often respond unexpectedly to long-term energy extraction. This is because the internal structure, nature, and properties of these complex underground systems are not fully understood and can only be observed indirectly. Successful management relies on proper understanding of the geothermal system involved, which in turn relies on adequate information on the system being available.

An important element of geothermal resource management involves controlling energy extraction from a geothermal system in order to avoid overexploitation of the underlying resource. When geothermal systems are overexploited, production from the

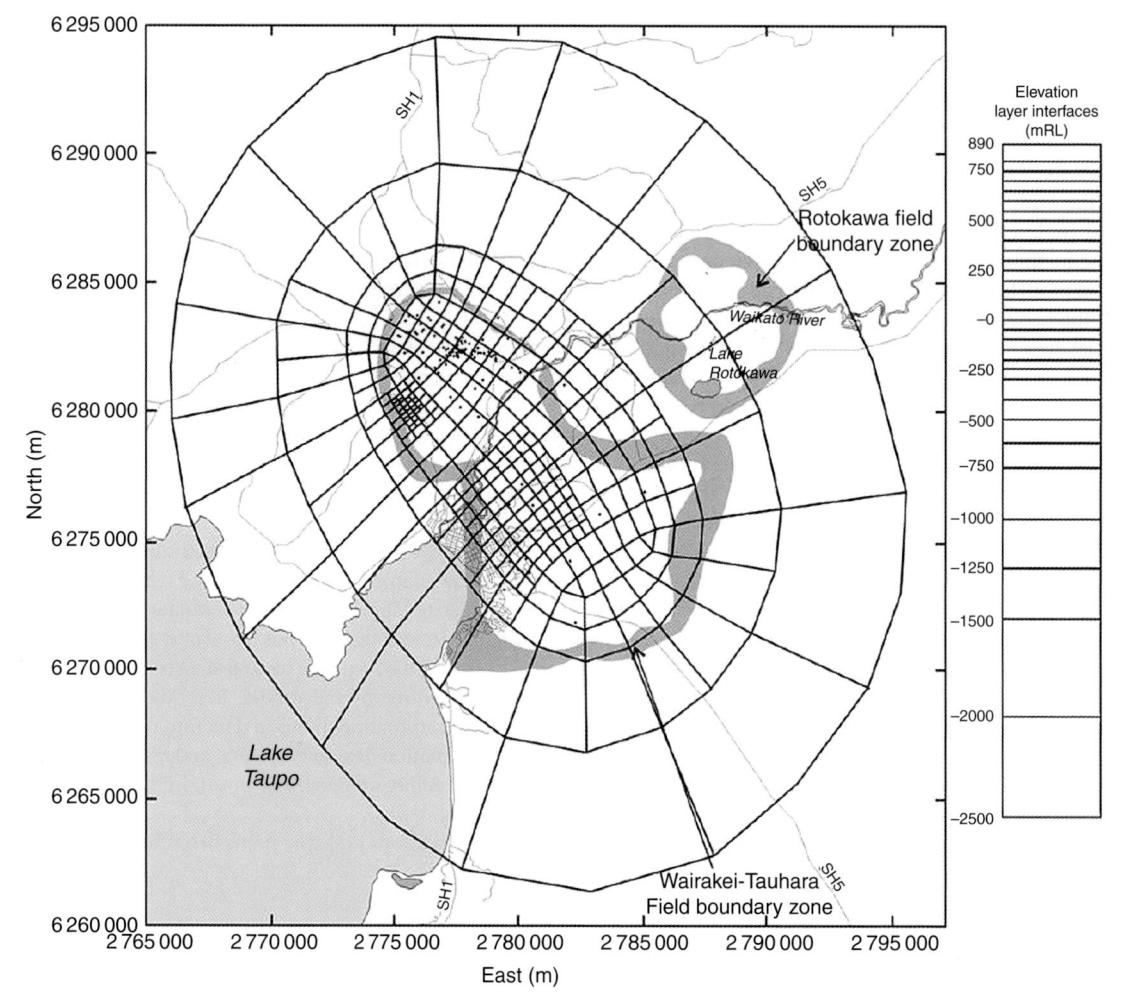

Figure 33 A sketch of the computational grid of the most recent numerical reservoir model for the Wairakei geothermal system in New Zealand [70].

systems has to be reduced, often drastically. Overexploitation mostly occurs for two reasons: first, because of inadequate monitoring and data collection – understanding of systems is thus poor and reliable modeling is also not possible; therefore, the systems respond unexpectedly to long-term production – and second, cases where the same resource/system is utilized by many users, without implementing common management or control (see more below).

Management of a geothermal resource involves deciding between different courses of action in the exploitation of the resource [4, 10, 45, 49]. Most often management decisions are made to improve the operating conditions of a geothermal reservoir. In some cases, unfavorable conditions may have evolved in a reservoir, while in others improvements in production technology may justify changes in production strategy. The operators of a geothermal resource must have some idea of the possible results of the different courses of action available, to be able to make these decisions. This is why careful monitoring is an essential ingredient of any management program.

Geothermal resource management may have different objectives [45]. These may include

(1) minimizing operation costs,
(2) maximizing energy extraction from a given resource,
(3) ensuring the security of continuous energy delivery,
(4) counteracting reservoir changes such as lowered pressure and/or increased boiling,
(5) minimizing environmental effects,
(6) avoiding operational difficulties like scaling and corrosion, and adhering to the energy policy of the respective country.

Real management objectives are quite often a mixture of two or more of such objectives, as listed above.

One of the more difficult aspects of reservoir management is to determine the most appropriate time span for a given option. There are cases, for example, where depleting a given reservoir in a few years' time is most advantageous from a purely financial point of view. This is usually unacceptable from a political or sociological point of view, where a reliable supply of energy for a long time is considered more valuable (see section Sustainable Geothermal Utilization).

Some of the management options, which are commonly applied in geothermal resource management, are [45]:

a. modification of production strategy (increased/reduced production),
b. drilling of additional wells such as in-fill or make-up wells,
c. hanges in well-completion programs (casings, etc.),
d. lowering of downhole pumps,
e. search for new production areas or drilling targets, and
f. search for new geothermal systems.

A multitude of challenges and issues face those responsible for the management of geothermal resources. A few of these are listed below, some interlinked in one way or another:

1. Lack of monitoring results in insufficient knowledge on the geothermal reservoir in question. Thus unexpected and detrimental changes may occur, such as reservoir cooling or drastic pressure drop. Lack of monitoring is one of the factors, which can cause overexploitation (item (3) below).
2. Overexploitation mostly occurs because of lack of monitoring (item (1)) and/or when many users utilize the same resource without common management (item (5)).
3. Common monitoring is important in situations when many production/reinjection wells have been drilled in the same geothermal area; it can be computerized as well as centralized (using a local phone system or other communication network).
4. Management of geothermal systems with large surface areas, and many users, needs special attention. This is because each user cannot operate as if he is utilizing his own isolated geothermal system. Therefore, some kind of common management (item (5)) is essential, in particular to prevent overexploitation (item (2)). Common monitoring (item (3)) may aid common management significantly.
5. Common management is essential when more than one user utilizes a single geothermal resource.
6. Reinjection has become an essential part of sustainable and energy-efficient geothermal utilization. It is used to counteract pressure drawdown (i.e., provide additional recharge), to dispose of wastewater, to counteract surface subsidence, and to maintain valuable surface activity [71].
7. A variety of operational aspects and problems require a multitude of technical solutions, both to general operational aspects and problems and to more site-specific ones. These aspects may be classified as (1) related to hardware such as wells and pipeline, (2) related to chemical content (corrosion and scaling), and (3) related to reservoir conditions.

The best known example of overexploitation due to lack of common management is the Geysers field in California [72, 73]. Another more recent example is the Xi'an field in China [74]. A good example of the opposite, that is, common management with centralized monitoring is the Paris Basin [71, 75]. Utilization of the geothermal resources in Tianjin, China, is also increasing along these lines [76].

Even though geothermal energy can be considered a clean and renewable source of energy, its development has both environmental and social impacts, which is receiving ever increasing attention. These are not the main focus of this chapter, but will be reviewed briefly here. For further information, the reader is referred to, for example, References 77 and 78.

The main environmental issues associated with geothermal developments are (based on Reference 77):

- Surface disturbances such as due to drilling, road construction, pipelines, and power plants as well as general untidiness. Here the local scenery also needs attention and often protection. In some instances, landslides are liable to occur, if care is not exercised.
- Physical effects of fluid withdrawal and reinjection such as changes in surface manifestations, that is, fading of hot springs and geysers or increased steam discharge from fumaroles, land subsidence, lowering of groundwater tables, and induced seismicity.
- Noise such as that associated with drilling, discharging of wells, and power plant operation.
- Thermal effects of excess energy contained in wastewater and steam discharge.
- Chemical pollution in the water phase, particularly from arsenic (As) and mercury (Hg), and through the discharge of geothermal gases such as carbon dioxide (CO_2) and hydrogen sulphide (H_2S).
- Impact on local biology, that is, fauna and flora.
- Protection of natural features that are of scientific or historical interest as well as being tourist attractions.

Various solutions to these issues have been proposed, tested, and implemented, with reinjection being one of the most widely beneficial. Bromley et al. [78] discuss practical environmental enhancement strategies that may include improved discharges from surface thermal features through targeted injection or extraction, creation of enhanced thermal habitats, and treatment or injection of toxic chemicals and gases.

Social acceptance, in particular by local communities, is an important prerequisite for a successful implementation of geothermal projects. This applies, especially, to projects aimed at electrical generation because of their size and overall impact. Direct geothermal applications have not encountered significant social constraints, or opposition, because of their obvious social benefits, a case in point being Iceland where almost 90% of the space heating market utilizes geothermal energy. Social acceptance of direct geothermal development should not be neglected, however. According to Cataldi [79], the three main conditions for gaining social acceptance are minimization of environmental impact, prevention of adverse effects on people's health, and creation of tangible benefits for the local population. Milos and Nisyros in Greece, Mt. Amiata in Italy, Ohaaki in New Zealand, and Puna (Hawaii) in the United States are examples where opposition by local populations, concerned with the possible impacts of project activities on environment, economy, tourism, and cultural or religious traditions, has hindered geothermal power developments [79]. In situations where local knowledge on the nature of geothermal resources is available and cooperation with local communities is maintained, such opposition has been largely avoided.

Social issues of geothermal developments have been decisively addressed in the Philippines during the last decade or two [80]. The following have been the main issues:

a. Lack of consultation
b. Physical and economic dislocation of settlements
c. Lack of benefits
d. Encroachment of ancestral domain
e. Privatization of the people's forest heritage.

The measures that have been developed to successfully address these concerns include

(a) awareness and acceptance campaigns,
(b) opening up communication,
(c) translating commitments into action,
(d) third-party multistakeholder monitoring,
(e) installation of environmental guarantee fund,
(f) resettlement,
(g) provision of benefits,
(h) protection of prior and ancestral rights, and
(i) protection of heritage and advocacy for appropriate public policies.

The relationship between the existence and development of conventional geothermal systems, in tectonically active regions, and seismic activity is well known. On the one hand, seismic activity is simply a signature of the tectonic movements needed to create and maintain the flow paths of geothermal systems. On the other hand, geothermal development and utilization, that is, drilling, production, and injection, can cause changes in the natural seismic activity. Majer et al. [81] review present knowledge on seismicity induced in EGS and conclude that induced seismicity does not pose any threat to the development of geothermal resources. In fact, induced seismicity provides a direct benefit because it can be used as a monitoring tool and the effects of induced seismicity have been dealt with in a successful manner. They point out that open communication between geothermal developer and local inhabitants must be ensured. It is, perhaps, important not to view induced seismicity as 'earthquakes' but rather focus on the resulting surface movement (acceleration and frequency). By proper management, it should be possible to maintain these parameters within limits set by local building regulations, as is successfully done in both the mining and petroleum industry.

7.02.14 Reinjection

Geothermal reinjection involves returning some, or even all, of the water produced from a geothermal reservoir back into the geothermal system, after energy has been extracted from the water. In some instances, water of a different origin is even injected into geothermal reservoirs. Reinjection started out as a method of wastewater disposal in a few geothermal operations, but it has slowly become more and more widespread in later years. By now, reinjection is considered an important part of comprehensive geothermal resource management as well as an essential part of sustainable and environmentally friendly geothermal utilization. Reinjection provides an additional recharge to geothermal reservoirs and as such counteracts pressure drawdown due to production and extracts more of the thermal energy from reservoir rocks than conventional utilization. Reinjection will, therefore, in most cases, increase the production capacity of geothermal reservoirs, which counteracts the inevitable increase in investment and operation costs associated with reinjection. It is likely to be an economical way of increasing the energy production potential of geothermal systems in most cases. Without reinjection, the mass extraction, and hence energy production, would only be a part of what it is now in many geothermal fields. Reinjection is also a key part of all EGS operations.

Stefánsson [82] describes the status of geothermal reinjection more than a decade ago, which at that time was a rather immature technology. Since then, considerable advances have been made in the associated technology and much has been learned through reinjection testing and research. Axelsson [71] reviews the status and discusses the importance of geothermal reinjection a decade later.

Reinjection is believed to have started as soon as in the late 1960s, in both high-temperature and low-temperature fields. Some smaller scale reinjection experiments may, however, have been conducted before that. The first known instance of reinjection into a high-temperature geothermal system is in the Ahuachapan field in El Salvador, starting in 1969 [82]). This was during the initial testing period of the field, some years before operation of the field for power production started. Reinjection in Ahuachapan was later discontinued, only to be restarted more than two decades later. Low-temperature reinjection also started in the Paris Basin in 1969 and has continued ever since (see further).

During the 1970s, the number of reinjection operations started picking up and reinjection experience started growing. Two well-known examples are The Geysers in California where reinjection started in 1970 and Larderello in Italy where it started in 1974. In both cases, the purpose was the disposal of steam condensate, but the operators of both fields soon realized that this improved the reservoir performance [71, 82]. Emphasis on reinjection at The Geysers, which substitutes limited natural recharge to some degree, has been increasing ever since. In addition to the condensate, surface water and recently sewage water, piped long distances, is injected [83, 84]. This appears to have slowed down the decline in electricity production at The Geysers considerably [84]. At Larderello, reinjection is now an integral part of the field operation and has caused a significant increase in steam production as well as some reservoir pressure recovery [82, 85].

Even though the focus in the geothermal literature has been on high-temperature operations, reinjection in low-temperature operations has become the rule rather than the exception in many countries. In many European countries, regulations require, for example, that all return water be reinjected. Yet in countries like Iceland and China, among the world leaders in direct geothermal utilization, only a small part of the water produced is reinjected [71]. The reasons for limited low-temperature reinjection in Iceland are the fact that most low-temperature water in Iceland is relatively low in chemical content, which does not pose an environmental threat, as well as the fact that the recharge to the systems is in most cases substantial due to their tectonic setting. Technical as well as management-related obstacles have prevented reinjection from becoming the rule in China up to now [71].

The increasing role of reinjection during the last decade or so is reflected in the number of geothermal fields where reinjection is an integral part of the field operation, as reported by different authors. Stefánsson [82] reports 20 fields in 8 countries, Axelsson and Gunnlaugsson [10] 29 fields in 15 countries, and Axelsson [49] at least 50 fields in 20 countries, that is, a 150% increase. Some of this apparent increase may be the result of better information, however. A recent, reliable number has not been compiled, but the number of fields is likely to be more than 60 today.

The purpose of employing reinjection in the management of geothermal resources may be one or more of the following:

1. Disposal of wastewater (separated water and steam condensate) from power plants and return water from direct applications for environmental reasons. Such waters often contain chemicals harmful to the environment as well as cause thermal pollution. Environmental issues are discussed briefly above.
2. Additional recharge to supplement the natural recharge to geothermal systems, which is often limited.
3. Pressure support to counteract, or reduce, pressure decline due to mass extraction.
4. To enhance thermal extraction from reservoir rocks along flow paths from injection wells.
5. To offset surface subsidence caused by production-induced pressure decline. Subsidence has been substantial and detrimental in a number of geothermal operations.
6. Targeted reinjection to enhance, or revitalize, surface thermal features such as hot springs and fumaroles [78].

Several of these items are, of course, interlinked. Supplemental recharge (item (2)), for example, results in pressure support (item (3)) and enhanced thermal extraction (item (4)). It also counteracts surface subsidence (item (5)). The actual purpose of reinjection in the management of geothermal resources is in most situations a combination of several of the above items.

Reinjection clearly provides supplemental recharge and theoretical studies, as well as operational experience, have shown that injection may be used as an efficient tool to counteract pressure drawdown due to production, that is, for pressure support. Since the production capacity of geothermal systems is controlled by their pressure response (see above), reinjection will increase their production capacity. This applies, in particular, to systems with closed, or semiclosed, boundary conditions and thus limited recharge. **Figures 34** and **35** show examples of the results of modeling calculations for two low-temperature geothermal systems, based on actual monitoring data, which clearly demonstrate this beneficial effect. One is the Urban system in Beijing, China, and the other the Hofstadir system in W-Iceland.

Through supplemental recharge, reinjection extracts more of the thermal energy in place in geothermal reservoirs. Most of this energy is stored in the reservoir rocks, and only a minor part in the reservoir fluid (10–20%). Therefore only a fraction of the energy may be utilized by conventional exploitation. Reinjection is thus a method of geothermal energy production, which can greatly improve the efficiency, and increase the longevity, of geothermal utilization.

Injection wells, or injection zones intended for the location of several injection wells, are sited in different locations depending on their intended function. In addition, reinjection wells are designed and drilled so as to intersect feed zones, or aquifers, at a certain depth interval. The following options are possible:

a. Inside the main production reservoir, that is, in-between production wells; often production/reinjection doublets.
b. Peripheral to the main production reservoir, that is, on its outskirts but still in direct hydrological connection.
c. Above the main reservoir, that is, at shallower levels.
d. Below the main reservoir, that is, at deeper levels.
e. Outside the main production field, either in the production depth range or at shallower or deeper levels. In this case, direct hydrological connection to the production reservoir may not exist.

Which option is used depends on the main purpose of the reinjection. If it is pressure support, option (a) is the most appropriate even though options (b–d) can be used. If the main purpose is environmental protection, option (e) is often used. In that case, not much pressure support is to be expected. Therefore, options (b) through (d) are often used as kind of compromises.

Various examples are available on the successful application of reinjection in geothermal resource management, some of which are discussed by Stefánsson [82] and Axelsson [71]. The best example of successful long-term reinjection in a low-temperature geothermal field is the reinjection applied in the Paris Basin in France [10, 75, 86]. Another example of a successful reinjection operation is the Miravalles high-temperature geothermal field in Costa Rica. Almost all (the separated water corresponding to 85%) of the immense mass extraction has been reinjected back into the geothermal reservoir right from the beginning of utilization [87] as shown in **Figure 36**. Reinjection has long been employed in the geothermal fields utilized for power production in the Philippines, mainly because of environmental reasons, but it has also been adopted to improve reservoir performance [82]. Reinjection is also successfully applied in low-temperature projects in Germany, such as the Landau project and the Neustadt-Glewe project [88]. Axelsson [71] discusses a few other low-temperature reinjection examples. Axelsson [71] also lists examples of various theoretical reinjection modeling studies presented in the literature.

Some operational dangers and obstacles are associated with reinjection with the main problems being the following:

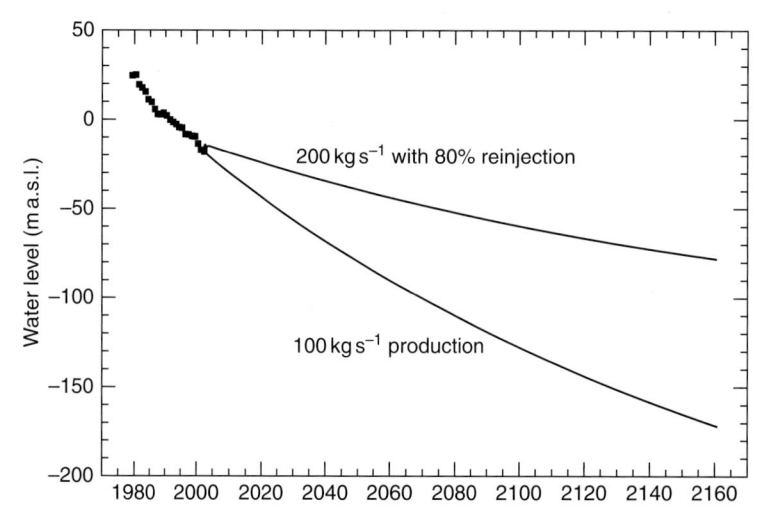

Figure 34 Predicted water-level changes (pressure changes) in the Urban geothermal system under Beijing city in China until 2160 for production scenarios with and without reinjection [23].

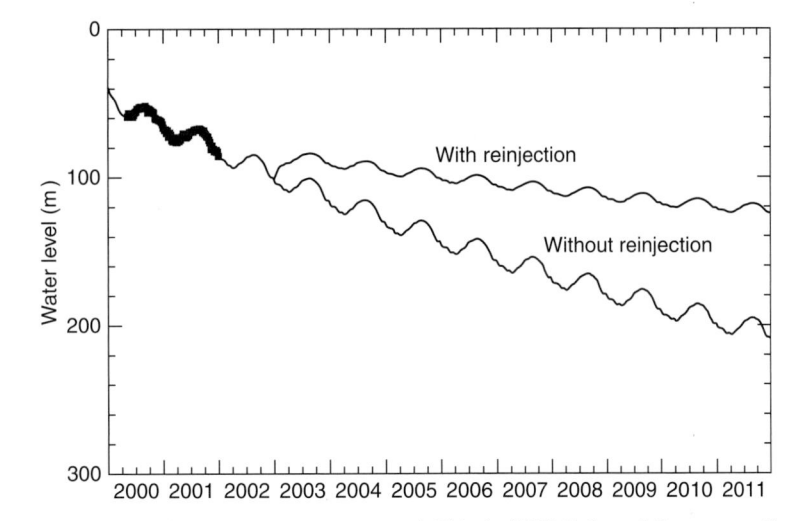

Figure 35 Water-level predictions for the Hofstadir low-temperature system in W-Iceland [62]. Both predictions assume the same production, while one assumes full reinjection and the other no reinjection.

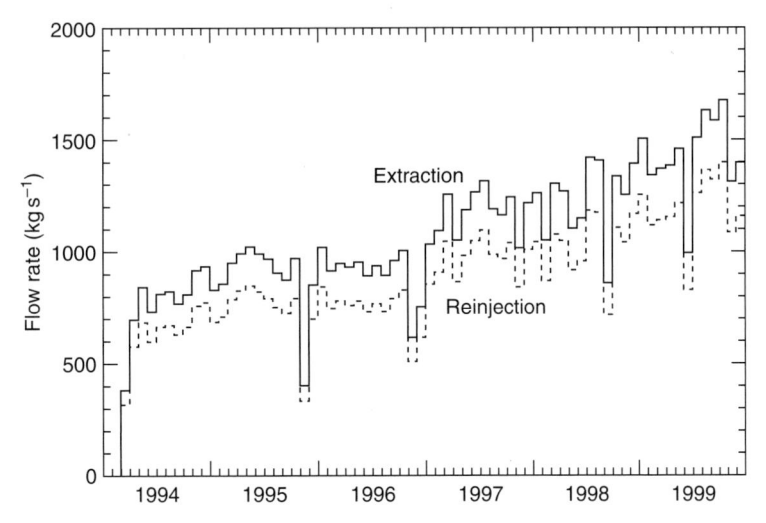

Figure 36 Extraction and reinjection history of the Miravalles high-temperature field in Costa Rica during 1994–99 [87].

A. Cooling of production wells, or cold-front breakthrough, often because of 'short-circuiting' along direct flow paths such as open fractures.
B. Silica scaling in surface pipelines and injection wells in high-temperature geothermal fields. After flashing in a separator/power plant, the separated fluid becomes supersaturated in SiO_2 and silica will precipitate from the fluid.
C. Other types of scaling and corrosion in both low-temperature and high-temperature operations. This includes, for example, carbonate scaling in low-temperature systems.
D. Rapid clogging of aquifers next to injection wells in sandstone reservoirs by fine sand and precipitation material.

The possible cooling of production wells has discouraged the use of injection in some geothermal operations although actual thermal breakthroughs, caused by cold water injection, have been observed in relatively few geothermal fields. In cases where the spacing between injection and production wells is small, and direct flow paths between the two wells exist, the fear of thermal breakthrough has been justified, however. Stefánsson [82] reports that actual cooling, attributable to injection, has only been observed in a few high-temperature fields worldwide. The temperature decline of well PN-26 in Palinpinon in the Philippines, reviewed by Malate and O'Sullivan [89], is a good example. The thermal breakthrough occurred about 18 months after reinjection started. Subsequently, the temperature declined rapidly, dropping by about 50 °C in 4 years (**Figure 37**). Such examples are exceptions rather than the rule, however. Experience in the Paris Basin, lasting three to four decades, has, for example, indicated that no significant cooling has yet taken place in any production wells [86].

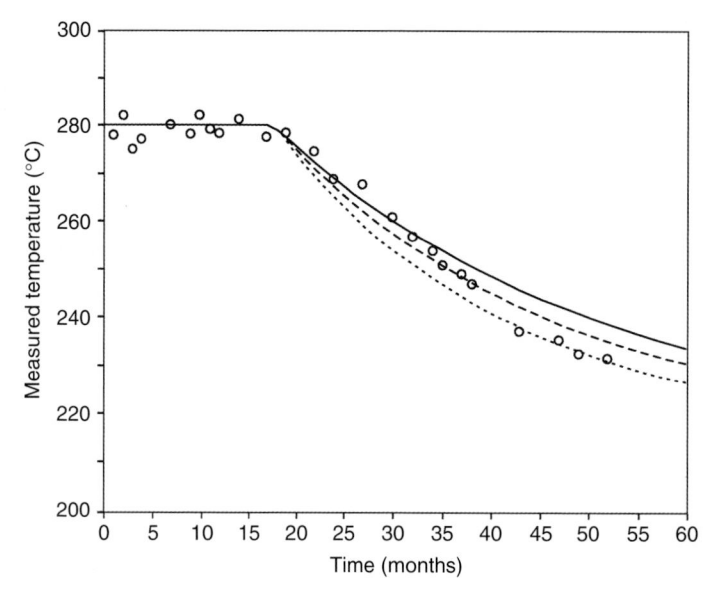

Figure 37 Measured and simulated temperature decline in well PN-26 in the Palinpinon field, the Philippines. From Malate RCM and O'Sullivan MJ (1991) Modelling of chemical and thermal changes in well PN-26 Palinpinon geothermal field, Philippines. *Geothermics* 20: 291–318.

Silica scaling in high-temperature operations occurs because the geothermal fluid involved is in equilibrium with the rocks at reservoir conditions. After flashing in a separator or a power plant, the separated fluid becomes supersaturated in SiO_2 and silica will precipitate from the fluid. This is a complex process partly controlled by temperature, pH of the fluid, and the concentration of SiO_2. The problem of silica scaling may be avoided, in most cases, by proper system design. One design involves applying 'hot' injection where the separated water is injected directly from a separator, at a temperature of 160–200 °C, that is, above the saturation temperature for silica scaling. Other designs use 'cold' injection where the return water temperature is below the saturation temperature for silica scaling, because of cooling to 15–100 °C. This calls for preventive measures such as deposition of silica in ponds/lagoons or by special treatment such as with scaling inhibitors. Dilution of the silica by steam condensate is also used. Stefánsson [82] discusses this issue in more detail with particular reference to the experience in Japan, New Zealand, and the Philippines. Carbonate precipitation is usually curtailed by operating the production/reinjection system at sufficiently high pressures or by utilizing scale inhibitors (usually injected into production wells at depth). Corrosion can also be controlled by inhibitors.

According to Stefánsson [82], reinjection into sandstone reservoirs had been attempted at several locations at the time of his study, but with limited success. During these experiments, or operations, the injectivity of the injection wells involved decreases very rapidly, even in hours or days, rendering further reinjection impossible. This is most likely because the aquifers next to the injection wells become blocked by fine sand and precipitation particles from the reinjection fluids. Some attempts at solving this problem have involved flow reversal, that is, by installing downhole pumps in reinjection wells, which are used to produce from the wells for periods of a few hours, once their injectivity has dropped after a period of reinjection [10, 48].

Another solution to the sandstone injection problem was developed in Thisted, Denmark, and has, for example, been adopted in the Neustadt-Glewe sandstone geothermal reservoir in N-Germany [88, 90]. The Thisted system has been in operation since 1984. This solution involves a sophisticated closed loop system wherein the reinjection water is kept completely oxygen free as well as passed through very fine filters (down to 1 μm). Oxygen is believed to facilitate chemical reactions creating precipitation material. The solution also involves not allowing injection after plant construction work, and other breaks in operation, until the water is checked clean and oxygen free. In addition, pressures are kept up by nitrogen during operation and when the operation is stopped. This solution to the sandstone injection problem, which has to be adapted to the specific reservoir conditions at each location, is believed to be the most dependable and lasting method available today [91, 92].

The danger of cooling due to reinjection can be minimized by placing injection wells far away from production wells, while the main benefit from reinjection (pressure support) is maximized by locating injection wells close to production wells. A proper balance between these two contradicting requirements must be found. Therefore, careful testing and research are essential parts of planning injection. Tracer testing is probably the most important tool for this purpose [93]. Tracer tests are used extensively in surface and groundwater hydrology as well as pollution and nuclear waste storage studies. Tracer tests involve injecting a chemical tracer into a hydrological system and monitoring its recovery, through time, at various observation points. The results are, consequently, used to study flow paths and quantify fluid flow. Tracer tests are, furthermore, applied in petroleum reservoir engineering. The methods employed in geothermal applications have mostly been adopted from these fields.

The main purpose in employing tracer tests in geothermal studies, and resource management, is to predict possible cooling of production wells due to long-term reinjection of colder fluid through studying connections between injection and production wells.

Their power lies in the fact that the thermal breakthrough time is usually some orders of magnitude (2–3) greater than the tracer breakthrough time, bestowing tracer tests with predictive powers.

The theoretical basis of tracer interpretation models is the theory of solute transport in porous and permeable media, which incorporates transport by advection, mechanical dispersion, and molecular diffusion. Axelsson et al. [93, 94] present a method of tracer test interpretation, which is conveniently based on the assumption of specific flow channels connecting injection and production wells.

7.02.15 Renewability of Geothermal Resources

Geothermal resources are normally classified as renewable energy sources, because they are maintained by a continuous energy current. This is in accordance with the definition that the energy extracted from a renewable energy source is always replaced in a natural way by an additional amount of energy with the replacement taking place on a timescale comparable to that of the extraction timescale [95]. Such a classification may be an oversimplification because geothermal resources are in essence of a double nature, that is, a combination of an energy current (through heat convection and conduction) and stored energy [96]. The renewability of these two aspects is quite different as the energy current is steady (fully renewable), while the stored energy is renewed relatively slowly, in particular the part renewed by heat conduction. During production, the renewable component (the energy current) is greater than the recharge to the systems in the natural state, however, because production induces in most cases an additional inflow of mass and energy into the systems [95].

The renewability of the different types of geothermal systems, discussed in section Geothermal Systems above, is quite diverse. This is because the relative importance of the energy current compared with the stored energy is highly variable for the different types. In 'volcanic systems', the energy current is usually quite powerful, comprising both magmatic and hot fluid inflow. In *convective systems of the open type*, that is, with strong recharge, the energy current (hot fluid inflow) is also highly significant. But the inflow can originate either as hot inflow from depth or as shallower inflow, colder in origin. In shallow inflow situation, the inflow is heated up by heat extraction from hot rocks at the outskirts of the system in question. The renewability of such systems is then supported by the usually enormous energy content of the hot rocks of the systems. Axelsson et al. [47] present examples of several very long production histories of such low-temperature systems in Iceland, many of which appear to demonstrate a high degree of renewability. In *convective systems of the closed type*, that is, with limited or no recharge, the renewability is more questionable. The energy extracted from the reservoir rocks through reinjection in such situations is only slowly renewed through heat conduction, but again the energy content of the systems is usually enormous. They can, therefore, be considered slowly renewable in nature.

Sedimentary systems, which are mostly utilized through doublet operations, are comparable to the closed convective systems as the energy current is usually relatively insignificant compared to the stored energy. Their renewability is, therefore, mainly supported by heat conduction and hence relatively slow. The same applies to EGS or HDR systems. Both these types can thus also be considered slowly renewable. In most such cases, the stored energy component is extremely large because of the large extent and volume of the systems.

Sustainable geothermal utilization is discussed in the following section. It depends to a large extent on the nature of the geothermal resource in question and hence its renewability. If energy production from a geothermal system is within some kind of sustainable limits (see below), one may expect that the stored energy is depleted relatively slowly and that the energy in the reservoir is renewed at a rate comparable to the extraction rate.

7.02.16 Sustainable Geothermal Utilization

The term *sustainable development* became fashionable after the publication of the Brundtland report in 1987 [97]. There, sustainable development is defined as "development that meets the needs of the present without compromising the ability of future generations to meet their own needs." This definition is inherently rather vague and it has often been understood somewhat differently.

At the core of the issue of sustainable development is the utilization of the various natural resources available to us today, including the world's energy resources. Sustainable geothermal utilization has been discussed to some degree in the literature in recent years. A general and logical definition has been missing, however, and the term has been used at will. In addition, the terms renewable and sustainable are often confused. The former should refer to the nature of a resource, while the latter should refer to how it is used. As examples of recent discussions of the issue, the papers by Wright [98], Stefánsson [95], Rybach et al. [99], Cataldi [100], Sanyal [101], Stefánsson and Axelsson [102], Ungemach et al. [86], and O'Sullivan and Mannington [103] may be mentioned. Furthermore, Axelsson et al. [96] discuss sustainable geothermal utilization for 100–300 years and present the results of a few relevant modeling studies. Bromley et al. [78] discuss sustainable utilization strategies and associated environmental issues. Finally, Rybach and Mongillo [104] present a good review of recent sustainability research.

Experience from utilization of numerous geothermal systems over the past few decades has shown that it is possible to produce geothermal energy in such a manner that a geothermal system, which previously was in an undisturbed natural state, reaches a new equilibrium after massive production starts, which may be maintained for a long time. Pressure decline in geothermal systems, due to production, can cause the recharge to the systems to increase approximately in proportion to the rate at which mass is extracted.

Axelsson and Stefánsson [105] and Axelsson et al. [96] discuss a few such examples. One of the best examples is the Laugarnes geothermal systems in Reykjavík, Iceland, where a semiequilibrium has been maintained over the past four decades, indicating that the inflow, or recharge, to the systems is now about 10-fold what it was before production started. Another good example is the Matsukawa geothermal system in Japan [106], which has also been utilized for about four decades for an approximately steady electricity generation. In other cases, geothermal production has been excessive and it has not been possible to maintain it in the long term. The utilization of the Geysers area in California is a good example of excessive production [72, 96]. Axelsson [107] discusses a few other examples of excessive production.

It seems natural to classify sustainable geothermal utilization as energy production that somehow can be maintained for a very long time. Based on this understanding and case histories, such as the ones above, Axelsson et al. [108] proposed the following definition for the term 'sustainable production of geothermal energy from an individual geothermal system':

> For each geothermal system, and for each mode of production, there exists a certain level of maximum energy production, E_0, below which it will be possible to maintain constant energy production from the system for a very long time (100–300 years). If the production rate is greater than E_0 it cannot be maintained for this length of time. Geothermal energy production below, or equal to E_0, is termed *sustainable production*, while production greater than E_0 is termed *excessive production*.

This definition neither considers load factors, utilization efficiency, economical aspects, environmental issues, nor technological advances. The value of E_0 depends on the mode of production and may be expected to increase with time through technological advances (e.g., deeper drilling). The value of E_0 is not known *a priori*, but it may be estimated, through modeling, on the basis of exploration and production data as they become available (see below).

The definition is based on a much longer timescale than the customary economical time frame for geothermal power plants (often of the order of 30 years), which is often used as the time frame when the production potential of geothermal systems is being assessed. In contrast, a geological timescale (> 10 000 years) was considered unrealistic in view of the timescale of human endeavors. Therefore, a time frame within the bounds of these different timescales was chosen [108].

If energy production from a geothermal system is within the sustainable limit defined above, one may assume that the stored energy is depleted relatively slowly and that the energy in the reservoir is renewed at approximately the same rate as it is extracted at. To maintain a semi-steady state for a long time thus requires the renewable part of the underlying resource to be relatively powerful. Yet it is likely that the 'volume of influence' of the geothermal energy extraction is very large and that the renewability is to some degree supported by energy extraction from the outer and deeper parts of the geothermal system in question.

Axelsson et al. [109] discuss briefly sustainability aspects of ground-coupled, or geothermal, heat pumps (GHPs) and EGS systems. The GHPs operate through either horizontal or vertical heat exchanger pipes or groundwater boreholes [110]. Their sustainability depends on the particular technique applied, but in all such systems it is to some extent supported by the heat supply from the atmosphere (solar radiation). In combined heating/cooling systems, it is also supported by heat storage in summer and in groundwater systems by the energy carried by the groundwater flow. Rybach and Eugster [111] discuss the theoretical and experimental basis of the sustainable utilization of borehole heat exchanger GPHs, which is the most common type today, with particular emphasis on work done in Switzerland.

The sustainability of EGS systems depends on the accessible thermal energy and, in particular, on the surface area of the fracture network opened or created in such systems. Under favorable natural conditions, like at Soultz-sous-Forêts in France, convective/advective energy resupply can add to this [112]. Sanyal and Butler [113] discuss production longevity from EGS resources and various operational strategies that may help sustain EGS operations.

Modeling studies, which are performed on the basis of available data on the structure and production response of geothermal systems, or simulation studies, are the most powerful tools to estimate the sustainable potential of the systems [114]. They can also be used to assess what will be the most appropriate mode of utilization in the future and to evaluate the effect of different utilization methods, such as reinjection, as well as assess the possible interference between nearby systems during long-term utilization. It is possible to use either complex numerical models or simpler models such as lumped parameter models for such modeling studies [96]. The former models can be much more accurate and they can simulate both the main features in the structure and nature of geothermal systems and their response to production. Yet lumped parameter models are very powerful for simulating pressure changes, which are in fact the changes that are the main controlling factor for the short- and long-term responses of conventional geothermal systems (hydrothermal) systems. The basis of reliable modeling studies is accurate and extensive data, including data on the geological structure of a system, their physical state, and not least their response to production. The last-mentioned information is most important when the sustainable potential of a geothermal system is being assessed, and if the assessment is to be reliable, the response data must extend over a few years at least, or even a few decades, as the model predictions must extend far into the future.

The sustainable potential of geothermal systems, which have still not been harnessed, can only be assessed very roughly. This is because in such situations the response data mentioned above are not available. It is, however, possible to base a rough assessment on available ideas on the size of a geothermal system and temperature conditions as well as knowledge on comparable systems.

Axelsson et al. [96] present the results of modeling studies for three geothermal systems that were performed to assess the sustainable production potential of the systems or provide answers to questions related to the issue. These are the Hamar geothermal system in N-Iceland, the Urban geothermal system below the city of Beijing in China, and the Nesjavellir geothermal system in the Hengill region in SW-Iceland, all of which are listed in Table 2 of Axelsson [74]. The results for Hamar (see Figure 8 in Reference 74 and **Figure** 38 below) indicate that the sustainable production potential of the Hamar reservoir is controlled by the

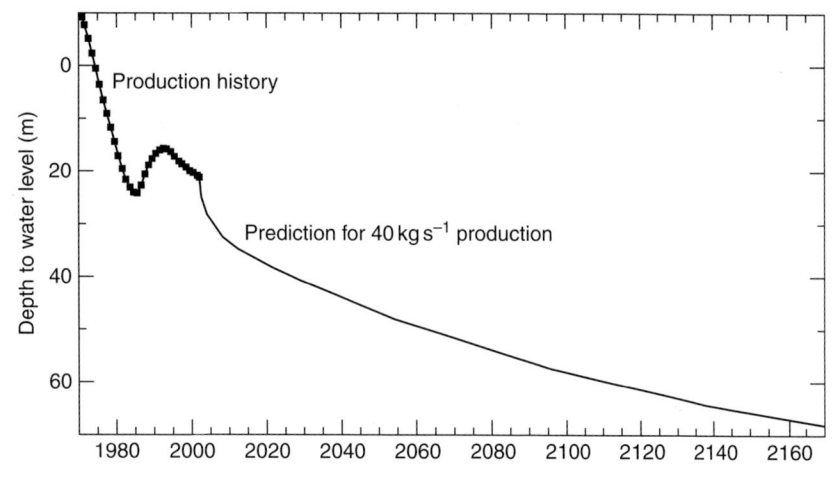

Figure 38 Long-term water-level prediction for the Hamar low-temperature geothermal system in N-Iceland, as it was calculated by a lumped parameter model. Prediction calculated for a constant rate of production up to 2170 for a sustainability study for the system [96].

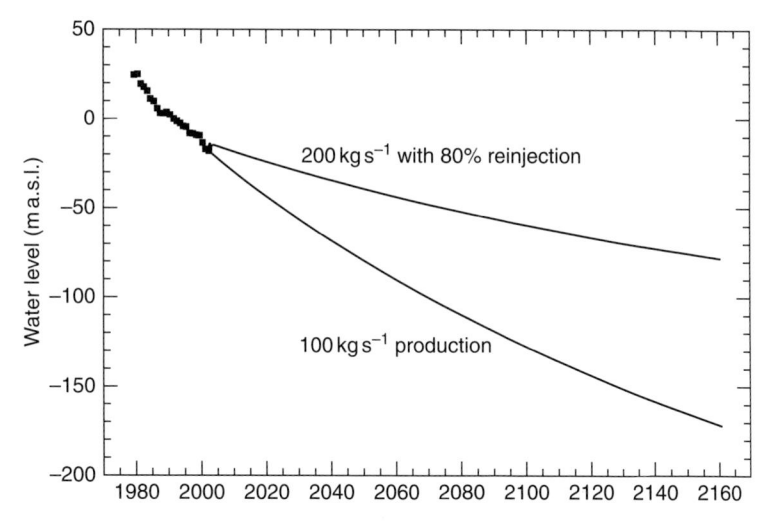

Figure 39 Predicted water-level changes (pressure changes) in the Urban low-temperature sedimentary geothermal system under Beijing city in China until 2160 for production scenarios with and without reinjection [96].

energy content of the small system rather than pressure decline. Results for the Urban system (see Figure 5 in Reference 74 and **Figure 39** below) indicate that the sustainable potential of the system is limited by lack of fluid recharge rather than lack of thermal energy. Because of this, the Urban system requires full reinjection for sustainable utilization.

Finally, the modeling results for the Nesjavellir high-temperature system [96] demonstrate that the present rate of utilization of the system (400 MW$_{th}$ and 120 MW$_e$) can clearly not be sustained for the next 100–300 years. The model calculations indicate, however, that the effects of the present intense production should mostly be reversible, and that the reservoir pressure should recover at approximately the same timescale as the period of intense production (**Figure 40**). This result, which is also believed to apply to other comparable geothermal systems, is relevant for the possible modes of sustainable utilization that are reviewed below. Axelsson *et al.* [109] also present some results of ongoing sustainability modeling for the Wairakei system in New Zealand and the Ahuachapan system in El Salvador.

Geothermal resources can be utilized through various different modes of operation, all of which may adhere to the sustainability definition presented above. In addition to utilization modes in which production is always below the sustainable limit, much more aggressive utilization modes can be envisioned (with maximum utilization not sustainable in the long term), either initially or intermittently. Modeling studies have demonstrated that following a period of excessive production geothermal systems are able to recover approximately back to their preproduction state, that is, the effects of intense production are mostly reversible [96]. Such production modes are more in-line with the utilization of many high-temperature geothermal systems today. They are harnessed in great steps, which are unlikely to be sustainable along the lines of the definition above, but are economically feasible due to their size.

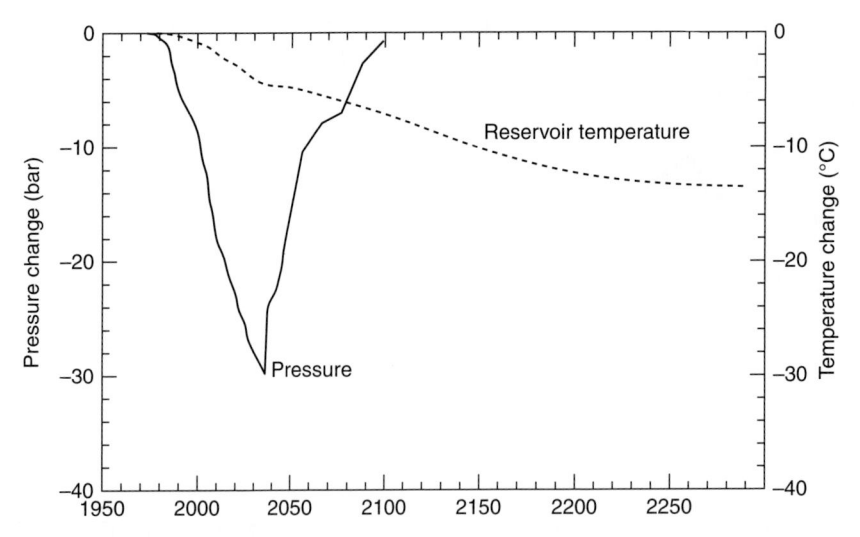

Figure 40 Calculated changes in reservoir pressure and temperature in the Nesjavellir high-temperature geothermal system in SW-Iceland during a 30-year period of intense production followed by 250 years of recovery (production stopped in 2036).

The main methods/modes of sustainable geothermal utilization that may be envisioned are the following (see **Figure 41**):

1. Constant production (aside from variations due to temporary demand such as annual variations) for 100–300 years. This is hardly a realistic option because the sustainable production capacity of geothermal systems is unknown beforehand. Therefore, a kind of test period is required initially until the sustainable potential has been assessed.
2. Production increased in a few steps until the sustainable potential has been assessed and the sustainable limit attained (see, e.g., Reference 102).
3. Excessive production (not sustainable) for a few decades (perhaps about 30 years) with total breaks in-between, perhaps a little longer than the production periods (about 50 years), wherein a geothermal system is able to recover almost fully.
4. Excessive production for 30–50 years followed by steady, but significantly reduced production for the next 150–270 years. The production following the excessive period would thus be considerably less than the sustainable potential at constant production (mode (1)).

It should be pointed out that the sustainable development of energy resource utilization must eventually be viewed in a broader context than for single geothermal systems independent of other systems. The following must be kept in mind:

i. During long-term utilization, some interference, even considerable, may be expected between adjacent geothermal fields being used, even over considerable distances (tens of kilometers). This possible interference must be kept in mind.

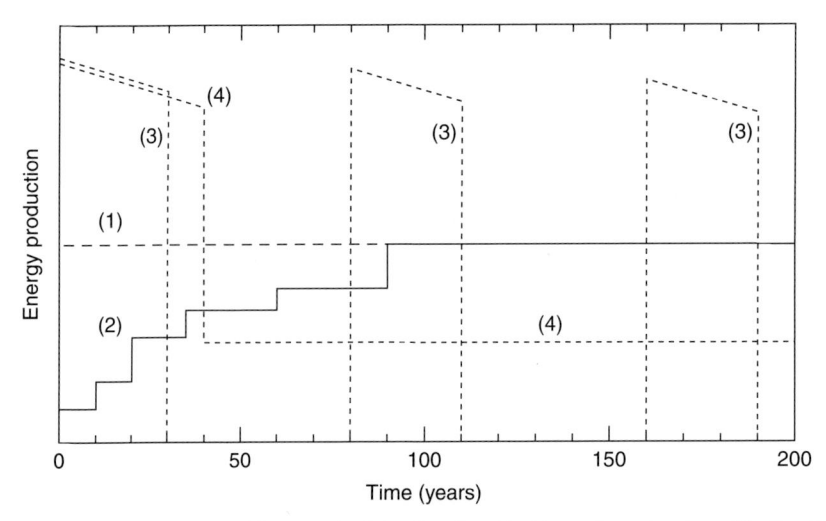

Figure 41 A schematic figure showing examples of different methods/modes of sustainable geothermal system utilization. The numbers refer to the production methods/modes discussed in the chapter.

ii. If single geothermal systems are being utilized in an intense/excessive manner during a certain period, other geothermal systems may need to be available in the same general region, which could then be utilized, while the former systems are being rested. Thus the overall geothermal resource utilization in the region may be managed as sustainable, even though single geothermal systems are not.
iii. If geothermal development in a region is, on the other hand, in a stepwise manner, the development may be required to be ongoing in several geothermal fields at the same time, because the steps in each field are likely to be so small.

Work on sustainability issues is continuing in different parts of the world, in particular work aimed at understanding the nature of the geothermal systems and their long-term response to utilization. Some ongoing work under the auspices of the Geothermal Implementing Agreement of the International Energy Agency focuses on several relevant research issues identified [115]. In Iceland, work is in progress intended to find ways to introduce sustainability logically into the legislation and regulatory framework of the country, including a study of the possibility of developing a geothermal sustainability protocol to assess the progress toward sustainable geothermal development [116].

7.02.17 Conclusions

In this chapter, the physics and nature of geothermal resources as well as the essence of successful geothermal resource management and utilization were reviewed. The different types of geothermal systems have been classified based on their nature and setting, the key properties and processes reviewed, and the basic equations describing these processes and the responses of geothermal systems to production presented.

Even though energy content (mainly depending on temperature and size) controls the energy production potential of a geothermal system, the pressure decline caused by hot water production is really the determining factor in this regard for natural (conventional) hydrothermal systems. This has been revealed by numerous geothermal production case histories. The pressure response is controlled by the nature and properties of a geothermal system, which can be classified as being of approximately two main types: closed systems where pressure declines continuously with time, at constant production, because of small or no recharge – in such systems, the production potential is limited by lack of water rather than lack of thermal energy – and open systems where recharge eventually equilibrates with the mass extraction. The colder shallow part of the recharge will eventually cause the reservoir temperature to decline and production wells to cool down. In such systems, the production potential is limited by the reservoir energy content. The situation is somewhat different for EGS systems and sedimentary systems utilized through production–reinjection doublets (well pairs) and heat exchangers with 100% reinjection. Then the production potential is predominantly controlled by the energy content of the systems involved. But permeability, and therefore, pressure decline, is also of controlling significance in such situations.

The nature of the geothermal system must, therefore, be kept in mind when planning exploitation and during management. This requires full-scale geothermal research continuing from the initial stages of exploration throughout the long-term utilization phase. Modeling plays a key role in understanding the nature of geothermal systems and is the most powerful tool for predicting their response to future production. The nature of a system also determines how beneficial reinjection can be.

Comprehensive management is essential for successful long-term geothermal exploitation, both for direct applications and for electrical production, in particular to prevent overexploitation and general operational problems. This requires extensive, continuous, and careful monitoring of various physical and chemical parameters. Such monitoring data provide the basis for geothermal reservoir modeling, which are used to estimate the production potential of geothermal reservoirs as well as for other reservoir management purposes. In addition, indirect monitoring, such as surface elevation measurements, microgravity observations, and microseismic monitoring, can help in understanding as well as in quantifying reservoir changes caused by production.

It is argued that geothermal resources can be utilized in a sustainable manner based on a definition that sustainable utilization involves utilization according to a scenario that can be operated/maintained for 100–300 years. The sustainable potential of a geothermal resource is controlled either by the pressure decline caused by production or by the energy content of the system in question, depending on the nature of the resource. Case histories of numerous geothermal systems worldwide, which have been utilized for several decades, provide the most important data on which to found system-specific sustainability studies and research aimed at understanding the renewability of geothermal resources. Such studies should involve appropriate modeling and long-term future predictions. They will be of great value to the geothermal industry where sustainability and renewability are receiving ever increasing attention. Various sustainable utilization scenarios can be envisioned, such as through constant production below a sustainable limit, stepwise increase in production, intermittent excessive production with breaks, or reduced production after a shorter period of excessive production.

References

[1] Cataldi R, Hodgson SF, and Lund JW (1999) *Stories from a Heated Earth*, 569pp. Geothermal Resources Council; International Geothermal Association.
[2] Björnsson A (2005) Development of thought on the nature of geothermal fields in Iceland from medieval times to the present. *Proceedings of the World Geothermal Congress 2005*, 11pp. Antalya, Turkey, April.

[3] Fridleifsson IB, Bertani R, Huenges E, *et al.* (2008) The possible role and contribution of geothermal energy to the mitigation of climate change. In: Hohmeyer O and Trittin T (eds.) *Proceedings of the IPCC Scoping Meeting on Renewable Energy Sources*, pp. 59–80. Luebeck, Germany, 20–25 January.
[4] Grant MA, Donaldson IG, and Bixley PF (1982) *Geothermal Reservoir Engineering*, 369pp. New York: Academic Press.
[5] Einarsson T (1942) Über das Wesen der Heissen Quellen Islands [The nature of the hot springs in Iceland, in German]. *Society Sciences of Islandica* 42: 91pp.
[6] Bödvarsson G (1951) Report on the Hengill thermal area. *Journal of Engineering Association in Iceland* 36: 1–69.
[7] Wooding RA (1957) Steady state free convection of liquid in a saturated permeable medium. *Journal of Fluid Mechanics* 2: 273–285.
[8] White DE (1957) Thermal waters of volcanic origin. *Geological Society of America Bulletin* 68: 1637–1658.
[9] Bödvarsson G (1964) Physical characteristics of natural heat sources in Iceland. *Proceedings of the UN Conference on New Sources of Energy, Vol. 2: Geothermal Energy*, pp. 82–89. Rome, Italy, August 1961.New York: United Nations.
[10] Axelsson G and Gunnlaugsson E (convenors) (2000) Long-term monitoring of high- and low-enthalpy fields under exploitation. *International Geothermal Association, World Geothermal Congress 2000 Short Course*, 226pp. Kokonoe, Kyushu District, Japan, May.
[11] Saemundsson K, Axelsson G, and Steingrímsson B (2009) Geothermal systems in global perspective. *Proceedings of a Short Course on Surface Exploration for Geothermal Resources*, 16pp. San Salvador, El Salvador, October.
[12] Bödvarsson G (1982) Glaciation and geothermal processes in Iceland. *Jökull* 32: 21–28.
[13] Lister CRB (1974) On the penetration of water into hot rock. *Geophysical Journal of the Royal Astronomical Society* 44: 508–521.
[14] Lister CRB (1976) Qualitative theory on the deep end of geothermal systems. *Proceedings of the 2nd UN Symposium on the Development and Use of Geothermal Resources*, pp. 456–463. San Francisco, CA, USA, 1975.
[15] Björnsson H, Björnsson S, and Sigurgeirsson Th (1982) Penetration of water into hot rock boundaries of magma in Grimsvötn. *Nature* 295: 580–581.
[16] Arnórsson S, Axelsson G, and Saemundsson K (2008) Geothermal systems in Iceland. *Jökull* 58: 269–302.
[17] Árnason B (1976) Groundwater Systems in Iceland Traced by Deuterium. *Society Sciences of Islandica* 42: 236pp.
[18] Björnsson A, Axelsson G, and Flóvenz ÓG (1990) The nature of hot spring systems in Iceland (in Icelandic with an English abstract). *Náttúrufraedingurinn* 60: 15–38.
[19] Arnórsson S (1995) Geothermal systems in Iceland: Structure and conceptual models. II. Low-temperature areas. *Geothermics* 24(5/6): 603–629.
[20] Bödvarsson G (1983) Temperature/flow statistics and thermomechanics of low-temperature geothermal systems in Iceland. *Journal of Volcanology and Geothermal Research* 19: 255–280.
[21] Björnsson G, Thordarson S, and Steingrímsson B (2000) Temperature distribution and conceptual reservoir model for geothermal fields in and around the city of Reykjavík, Iceland. *Proceedings of the 25th Workshop on Geothermal Reservoir Engineering*, Stanford, 7pp. Stanford University, CA, January.
[22] Axelsson G (1985) Hydrology and Thermomechanics of Liquid-Dominated Hydrothermal Systems in Iceland, 291pp. PhD Thesis, Oregon State University, Corvallis, OR.
[23] Axelsson G, Björnsson G, Egilson Th, *et al.* (2005) Nature and properties of recently discovered hidden low-temperature geothermal reservoirs in Iceland. *Proceedings of the World Geothermal Congress 2005*, 10pp. Antalya, Turkey, April.
[24] Stefánsson V (2005) World geothermal assessment. *Proceedings of the World Geothermal Congress 2005*, 5pp. Antalya, Turkey, April.
[25] IEA-GIA (2008).
[26] Kjaran SP and Elíasson J (1983) Geothermal reservoir engineering lecture notes. *United Nations University Geothermal Training Programme, Report 1983-2*, 250pp. Reykjavík, Iceland.
[27] Bödvarsson GS and Witherspoon P (1989) Geothermal reservoir engineering. Part I. *Geothermal Science and Technology* 2: 1–68.
[28] Pruess K (2002) Mathematical modelling of fluid flow and heat transfer in geothermal systems. An introduction in five lectures. *United Nations University Geothermal Training Programme, Report 2002-3*, 84pp. Reykjavík, Iceland.
[29] Carslaw HW and Jaeger JC (1959) *Conduction of Heat in Solids*, 2nd edn., 403pp. Oxford: Clarendon Press.
[30] Bödvarsson G (1972) Thermal problems in the siting of reinjection wells. *Geothermics* 1: 63–66.
[31] Gringarten AC and Sauty JP (1975) A theoretical study of heat extraction from aquifers with uniform regional flow. *Journal of Geophysical Research* 80: 4956–4962.
[32] Pruess K and Bödvarsson GS (1984) Thermal effects of reinjection in geothermal reservoirs with vertical fractures. *Journal of Petroleum Technology* 36: 1567–1578.
[33] Grant *et al.* (1981).
[34] Elíasson J, Kjaran SP, and Gunnarsson G (1980) Two phase flow in porous media and the concept of relative permeability. *Proceedings of the 6th Workshop on Geothermal Reservoir Engineering*, pp. 288–296. Stanford University, USA.
[35] Stefánsson V and Steingrímsson B (1980) Geothermal Logging I – An introduction to techniques and interpretation. *National Energy Authority of Iceland (Orkustofnun), Report OS-89917/JHD-09*, 117pp.
[36] Axelsson G, Sverrisdóttir G, Flóvenz ÓG, *et al.* (1998) Thermal energy extraction, by reinjection from a low-temperature geothermal system in N-Iceland. *Proceedings of the 4th International HDR Forum*, 10pp. Strasbourg, France, September.
[37] Björnsson G and Bödvarsson GS (1987) A multi-feedzone wellbore simulator. *GRC Transactions* 11: 503–507.
[38] Stefánsson V and Steingrímsson B (1980) Production characteristics of wells tapping two-phase reservoir at Krafla and Námafjall. *Proceedings of the 6th Workshop on Geothermal Reservoir Engineering*, pp. 49–59. Stanford University, CA, January.
[39] James R (1970) Factors controlling borehole performance. *Geothermics* 2: 1502–1515.
[40] Steingrímsson B and Gudmundsson Á (2006) Geothermal borehole investigations during and after drilling. *Proceedings of a Workshop for Decision Makers on Geothermal projects in Central America*, 10pp. San Salvador, El Salvador, November–December.
[41] Axelsson G and Thórhallsson S (2009) Review of well stimulation operations in Iceland. *GRC Transactions* 33: 11pp.
[42] Liu J, Pan X, Yang Y, *et al.* (2002) Potential assessment of the Urban geothermal field, Beijing, China. *Proceedings of the International Symposium on Geothermal and the 2008 Olympics in Beijing*, pp. 211–217. Beijing, PR China, October.
[43] Aqui AR, Aragones JS, and Amistoso AE (2005) Optimization of Palinpinon-1 production field based on exergy analysis – The Southern Negros geothermal field, Philippines. *Proceedings of the World Geothermal Congress 2005*, 7pp. Antalya, Turkey, April.
[44] Björnsson G, Axelsson G, and Flovenz ÓG (1994) Feasibility study for the Thelamork low-temperature system in N-Iceland. *Proceedings of the 19th Workshop on Geothermal Reservoir Engineering*, pp. 5–13. Stanford University, USA.
[45] Stefánsson V, Axelsson G, Sigurdsson Ó, and Kjaran SP (1995) Geothermal reservoir management in Iceland. *Proceedings of the World Geothermal Congress 1995*, pp. 1763–1768. Florence, Italy, May.
[46] Kristmannsdóttir H, Ármannsson H, Axelsson G, *et al.* (1995) Monitoring of Icelandic geothermal fields during production. *Proceedings of the World Geothermal Congress 1995*, pp. 1813–1818. Florence, Italy, May.
[47] Axelsson G, Jónasson Th, Ólafsson M, and Ragnarsson Á. (2010) Successful utilization of low-temperature geothermal resources in Iceland for district heating for 80 years. *Proceedings of the World Geothermal Congress 2010*, 10pp. Bali, Indonesia, April.
[48] Axelsson G and Dong Z (1998) The Tanggu geothermal reservoir (Tianjin, China). *Geothermics* 27: 271–294.
[49] Axelsson G (2003) Essence of geothermal resource management. Lectures on the sustainable use and operating policy for geothermal reservoirs. IGC2003 short course. *United Nations University Geothermal Training Programme, Report 2003-1*, pp. 129–152. Reykjavík, Iceland, September.
[50] Axelsson G (1991) Reservoir engineering studies of small low-temperature hydrothermal systems in Iceland. *Proceedings of the 16th Workshop on Geothermal Reservoir Engineering*, pp. 143–149. Stanford University, USA, January.
[51] Sturkell E, Sigmundsson F, Geirsson H, *et al.* (2008) Multiple volcano deformation sources in a post-rifting period: 1989–2005 behaviour of Krafla Iceland constrained by levelling, tilt and GPS observations. *Journal of Volcanology and Geothermal Research* 177: 405–417.

[52] Allis G and Hunt T (1986) Analysis of exploitation-induced gravity changes at Wairakei geothermal field. *Geophysics* 51: 1647–1660.
[53] Nishijima J, Fujimitsu Y, Ehara S, and Motoyama T (2000) Reservoir monitoring by observation of gravity changes at some geothermal fields in Kyushu, Japan. *Proceedings of the World Geothermal Congress 2000*, pp. 1515–1520. Kyushu-Tohoku, Japan, May–June.
[54] Nishijima J, Fujimitsu Y, Ehara S, *et al.* (2005) Micro-gravity monitoring and repeated GPS survey at Hatchobaru geothermal field, Central Kyushu, Japan. *Proceedings of the World Geothermal Congress 2005*, 5pp. Antalya, Turkey, April.
[55] Eysteinsson H (2000) Elevation and gravity changes at geothermal fields on the Reykjanes peninsula, SW-Iceland. *Proceedings of the World Geothermal Congress 2000*, pp. 559–564. Kyushu-Tohoku, Japan, May–June.
[56] Muffler LPJ and Cataldi R (1978) Methods for regional assessment of geothermal resources. *Geothermics* 7: 53–89.
[57] Rybach L and Muffler LJP (1981) *Geothermal Systems: Principles and Case Histories*, 359pp. Chichester: John Wiley.
[58] Sarmiento ZF and Björnsson G (2007) Reliability of early modelling studies for high-temperature reservoirs in Iceland and the Philippines. *Proceedings of the 32nd Workshop on Geothermal Reservoir Engineering*, 12pp. Stanford University, CA, January.
[59] Williams CF (2007) Updated methods for estimating recovery factors for geothermal resources. *Proceedings of the 32nd Workshop on Geothermal Reservoir Engineering*, 7pp. Stanford University, CA, January.
[60] O'Sullivan MJ, Pruess K, and Lippmann MJ (2001) State of the art of geothermal reservoir simulation. *Geothermics* 30: 395–429.
[61] Bödvarsson GS, Pruess K, and Lippmann MJ (1986) Modeling of geothermal systems. *Journal of Petroleum Technology* 38: 1007–1021.
[62] Axelsson G, Björnsson G, and Quijano J (2005) Reliability of lumped parameter modelling of pressure changes in geothermal reservoirs. *Proceedings of the World Geothermal Congress 2005*, 8pp. Antalya, Turkey, April.
[63] Axelsson G (1989) Simulation of pressure response data from geothermal reservoirs by lumped parameter models. *Proceedings of the 14th Workshop on Geothermal Reservoir Engineering*, pp. 257–263. Stanford University, USA.
[64] Sarak H, Korkmaz ED, Onur M, and Satman A (2005) Problems in the use of lumped parameter reservoir models for low-temperature geothermal fields. *Proceedings of the World Geothermal Congress 2005*, 9pp. Antalya, Turkey, April.
[65] Onur M, Sarak H, Tureyen OI, *et al.* (2008) A new non-isothermal lumped-parameter model for low temperature, liquid dominated geothermal reservoirs and its applications. *Proceedings of the 33rd Workshop on Geothermal Reservoir Engineering*, 10pp. Stanford University, CA, January.
[66] Bödvarsson G (1966) Direct interpretation methods in applied geophysics. *Geoexploration* 4: 113–138.
[67] Axelsson G and Arason Th (1992) LUMPFIT. Automated simulation of pressure changes in hydrological reservoirs. *User's Guide, version 3.1*, September, 32pp.
[68] Bödvarsson *et al.* (1996).
[69] Björnsson G, Hjartarson A, Bödvarsson GS, and Steingrimsson B (2003) Development of a 3-D geothermal reservoir model for the greater Hengill volcano in SW-Iceland. *Proceedings of the TOUGH Symposium 2003*, 12pp. Lawrence Berkeley National Laboratory, Berkeley, CA, USA, 12–14 May.
[70] O'Sullivan MJ, Yeh A, and Mannington WI (2009) A history of numerical modelling of the Wairakei geothermal field. *Geothermics* 38: 155–168.
[71] Axelsson G (2008) The importance of geothermal reinjection. *Proceedings of the Workshop for Decision Makers on the Direct Heating Use of Geothermal Resources in Asia*, 15pp. Tianjin, PR China, May.
[72] Barker BJ (2000) The Geysers: Past and future. *Geothermal Resources Council Bulletin* 29: 163–171.
[73] Goyal KP and Box WT (2004) Geysers performance update through 2002. *Proceedings of the 29th Workshop on Geothermal Reservoir Engineering*, 6pp. Stanford University, CA, January.
[74] Axelsson G (2008) Production capacity of geothermal systems. *Proceedings of the Workshop for Decision Makers on the Direct Heating Use of Geothermal Resources in Asia*, 14pp. Tianjin, PR China, May.
[75] Boisdet A, Ferrandes R, Fouillac C, *et al.* (1990) Current state of exploitation of low-enthalpy geothermal energy in France. *Geothermal Resources Council, Transactions* 14(1): 55–61.
[76] Wang *et al.* (2006).
[77] Kristmannsdóttir H and Ármannsson H (2003) Environmental aspects of geothermal energy utilization. *Geothermics* 32: 451–461.
[78] Bromley CJ, Mongillo M, and Rybach L (2006) Sustainable utilization strategies and promotion of beneficial environmental effects – Having your cake and eating it too. *Proceedings of the New Zealand Geothermal Workshop 2006*, 5pp. Auckland, New Zealand, November.
[79] Cataldi R (1999) Social acceptance: A sine qua non for geothermal development in the 21st century. *Bulletin d'Hydrogéologie* 17: 467–476.
[80] de Jesus AC (2005) Social issues raised and measures adopted in Philippine geothermal projects. *Proceedings of the World Geothermal Congress 2005*, 7pp. Antalya, Turkey, April.
[81] Majer E, Baria R, Stark M, *et al.* (2007) Induced seismicity associated with enhanced geothermal systems. *International Energy Agency Geothermal Implementing Agreement Report (Draft)*, 47pp. http://www.iea-gia.org/documents/ISWPf1MajerWebsecure20Sep06_000.doc.
[82] Stefánsson (1997).
[83] Barker BJ, Koenig BA, and Stark MA (1995) Water injection management for resource maximization: Observations from 25 years at The Geysers, California. *Proceedings of the World Geothermal Congress 1995*, pp. 1959–1964. Florence, Italy, May.
[84] Stark MA, Box WT, Jr., Beall JJ, *et al.* (2005) The Santa Rosa – Geysers recharge project, Geysers geothermal field, California, USA. *Proceedings of the World Geothermal Congress 2005*, 9pp. Antalya, Turkey, April.
[85] Capetti G, Parisi L, Ridolfi A, and Stefani G (1995) Fifteen years of reinjection in the Larderello-Valle Secolo area: Analysis of the production data. *Proceedings of the World Geothermal Congress 1995*, pp. 1997–2000. Florence, Italy, May.
[86] Ungemach P, Antics M, and Papachristou M (2005) Sustainable geothermal reservoir management. *Proceedings of the World Geothermal Congress 2005*, 12pp. Antalya, Turkey, April.
[87] Mainieri A (2000) Costa Rica country update. *Proceedings of the World Geothermal Congress 2000*, pp. 313–318. Kyushu-Tohoku, Japan, May–June.
[88] Seibt P, Kabus F, and Hoth P (2005) The Neustadt-Gleve geothermal power plant – Practical experience in the reinjection of cooled thermal waters into sandstone aquifers. *Proceedings of the World Geothermal Congress 2005*, 9pp. Antalya, Turkey, April.
[89] Malate RCM and O'Sullivan MJ (1991) Modelling of chemical and thermal changes in well PN-26 Palinpinon geothermal field, Philippines. *Geothermics* 20: 291–318.
[90] Mahler A (2000) Geothermal plant with efficient absorption heat pumps driven by incineration CHP plant. Successful injection in sandstone aquifer. Country update Denmark. *Proceedings of the World Geothermal Congress 2000*, pp. 307–312. Kyushu-Tohoku, Japan, May–June.
[91] Seibt P and Kellner T (2003) Practical experience in the reinjection of cooled thermal waters back into sandstone reservoirs. *Geothermics* 32: 733–741.
[92] Seibt P (2008) Practical experience in the reinjection of thermal waters into sandstone. *Proceedings of the Workshop for Decision Makers on the Direct Heating Use of Geothermal Resources in Asia*, 18pp. Tianjin, China, May.
[93] Axelsson G, Björnsson G, and Montalvo F (2005) Quantitative interpretation of tracer test data. *Proceedings of the World Geothermal Congress 2005*, 12pp. Antalya, Turkey, April.
[94] Axelsson G, Björnsson G, Flóvenz ÓG, *et al.* (1995) Injection experiments in low-temperature geothermal areas in Iceland. *Proceedings of the World Geothermal Congress 1995*, pp. 1991–1996. Florence, Italy, May.
[95] Stefánsson V (2000) The renewability of geothermal energy. *Proceedings of the World Geothermal Congress 2000*, pp. 883–888. Kyushu-Tohoku, Japan, May–June.
[96] Axelsson G, Stefánsson V, and Björnsson G (2005) Sustainable utilization of geothermal resources for 100–300 years. *Proceedings of the World Geothermal Congress 2005*, 8pp. Antalya, Turkey, April.
[97] World Commission on Environment and Development (1987) *Our Common Future*, 400pp. Oxford: Oxford University Press.

[98]   Wright PM (1999) The sustainability of production from geothermal resources. *Lectures presented at the United Nations University Geothermal Training Programme*, Report, 42pp. Reykjavík, Iceland, September.
[99]   Rybach L, Megel T, and Eugster WJ (2000) At what scale are geothermal resources renewable? *Proceedings of the World Geothermal Congress 200*, pp. 867–872. Kyushu-Tohoku, Japan, May–June.
[100] Cataldi R (2001) Sustainability and renewability of geothermal energy. *Proceedings of the International Scientific Conference on Geothermal Energy in Underground Mines*, 4pp. Ustron, Poland, November.
[101] Sanyal SK (2005) Sustainability and renewability of geothermal power capacity. *Proceedings of the World Geothermal Congress 2005*, 13pp. Antalya, Turkey, April.
[102] Stefánsson V and Axelsson G (2005) Sustainable utilization of geothermal resources through stepwise development. *Proceedings of the World Geothermal Congress 2005*, 5pp. Antalya, Turkey, April.
[103] O'Sullivan M and Mannington W (2005) Renewability of the Wairakei-Tauhara geothermal resource. *Proceedings of the World Geothermal Congress 2005*, 8pp. Antalya, Turkey, April.
[104] Rybach L and Mongillo MA (2006) Geothermal sustainability – A review with identified research needs. *Geothermal Resources Council Transactions* 30: 1083–1090.
[105] Axelsson G and Stefánsson V (2003) Sustainable management of geothermal resources. *Proceedings of the International Geothermal Conference 2003*, pp. 40–48. Reykjavík, Iceland, September.
[106] Hanano (2003).
[107] Axelsson G (2008) Management of geothermal resources. *Proceedings of the Workshop for Decision Makers on the Direct Heating Use of Geothermal Resources in Asia*, 15pp. Tianjin, China, May.
[108] Axelsson G, Gudmundsson Á, Steingrímsson B, *et al.* (2001) Sustainable production of geothermal energy: Suggested definition. *IGA News*, Quarterly No. 43, January–March, pp. 1–2.
[109] Axelsson G, Bromley C, Mongillo M, and Rybach L (2010) The sustainability task of the International Energy Agency's Geothermal Implementing Agreement. *Proceedings of the World Geothermal Congress 2010*, 8pp. Bali, Indonesia, April.
[110] Lund J, Sanner B, Rybach L, *et al.* (2003) Ground source heat pumps – A world review. *Renewable Energy World* July–August, pp. 218–227.
[111] Rybach L and Eugster W (2010) Sustainability aspects of geothermal heat pump operation, with experience from Switzerland. *Geothermics* In press.
[112] Kohl T, Bächler D, and Rybach L (2000) Steps towards a comprehensive thermo-hydraulic analysis of the HDR test site Soultz-sous-Forêts. *Proceedings of the World Geothermal Congress 2000*, pp. 2671–2676. Kyushu-Tohoku, Japan, May–June.
[113] Sanyal SK, Butler SJ, and RoBertson-Tait A (2005) An analysis of power generation prospects from enhanced geothermal systems. *Proceedings of the World Geothermal Congress 2005*, 6pp. Antalya, Turkey, April.
[114] Axelsson G (2010) Sustainable geothermal utilization – Case histories, definitions, research issues and modelling. *Geothermics* In press.
[115] Axelsson *et al.* (2009).
[116] Ketilsson J, Axelsson G, Björnsson A, *et al.* (2009) Introducing the concept of sustainable geothermal utilization in Icelandic Legislation. *Proceedings of the World Geothermal Congress 2010*, 7pp. Bali, Indonesia, April 2010.

7.03 Geothermal Energy Exploration Techniques

ÓG Flóvenz, GP Hersir, K Sæmundsson, H Ármannsson, and Þ Friðriksson, Iceland GeoSurvey (ISOR), Reykjavík, Iceland

© 2012 Elsevier Ltd.

7.03.1	Importance of the Exploration	52
7.03.2	Geological Exploration	52
7.03.2.1	Geological Maps	53
7.03.2.2	Hydrology and Topography	54
7.03.2.3	Geothermal Mapping	54
7.03.2.3.1	Surface geothermal mapping	54
7.03.2.3.2	Extrapolation of mapping results to subsurface	55
7.03.2.4	Mapping and Outlining of Major Controlling Structures	55
7.03.2.4.1	Rifts and their segmentation	55
7.03.2.4.2	Geothermal systems through time	55
7.03.2.4.3	Mapping of faults	56
7.03.3	Assessment of Geological Hazard	56
7.03.3.1	Volcanic Events	56
7.03.3.1.1	Fault movements	57
7.03.3.2	Gas Fluxes	57
7.03.3.3	Drilling into Molten Rock	57
7.03.3.4	Flooding and Sliding	58
7.03.3.5	Elevation Changes	58
7.03.4	Geochemistry and Geothermometers	58
7.03.4.1	General	58
7.03.4.2	Chemical Geothermometers	59
7.03.4.3	Univariant Geothermometers	59
7.03.4.4	Geothermometers Based on Ratios	59
7.03.4.5	Multiple Mineral Equilibria Approach	60
7.03.4.6	Example of Application	60
7.03.5	Geophysical Methods	61
7.03.5.1	Resistivity Methods	63
7.03.5.1.1	Introduction	63
7.03.5.1.2	Modeling and presenting resistivity soundings	64
7.03.5.1.3	The equivalence problem in 1D inversion	65
7.03.5.1.4	DC methods – Schlumberger soundings	65
7.03.5.1.5	EM measurements	68
7.03.5.1.6	TEM soundings	69
7.03.5.1.7	Comparison of the Schlumberger and the TEM methods	71
7.03.5.1.8	MT soundings	71
7.03.5.2	Resistivity of Rocks	78
7.03.5.2.1	Fluid saturation	78
7.03.5.2.2	Conductivity of the rock matrix	78
7.03.5.2.3	Resistivity of electrolytes	78
7.03.5.2.4	Porosity	78
7.03.5.2.5	Conduction in porous rock	79
7.03.5.2.6	To summarize	81
7.03.5.3	Seismic Methods	83
7.03.5.3.1	Microseismic studies	84
7.03.5.3.2	Seismic waves and physical properties	84
7.03.5.3.3	Seismic networks	84
7.03.5.3.4	Earthquake location	85
7.03.5.3.5	Velocity structure	86
7.03.5.3.6	The brittle–ductile boundary	87
7.03.5.3.7	Source mechanism	87
7.03.5.3.8	Joint interpretation with resistivity data	88
7.03.5.4	Thermal Methods	88
7.03.5.4.1	Heat transport within the Earth	88
7.03.5.4.2	Basic theory of heat flow	88

7.03.5.4.3	Measurements of heat flow	89
7.03.5.4.4	Determination of the thermal conductivity	90
7.03.5.4.5	Heat flow as tool in geothermal exploration	90
7.03.5.4.6	Depth of heat flow boreholes	91
7.03.5.4.7	Pitfalls in heat flow interpretations	92
7.03.5.4.8	Example	92
References		93

7.03.1 Importance of the Exploration

The heat source for most high-temperature geothermal resources suitable for electricity production is hot or even molten magma intrusions at shallow levels in the Earth's crust. These resources are typically located above or near the intrusions, and consist of convecting fluid, usually water or brine, flowing mainly through a network of permeable fractures in hot, low-permeable rock bodies. On the other hand, the low- and medium-temperature fields derive their heat from the normal heat flow toward the Earth's surface. The low-temperature fields are common in sedimentary basins where the heat accumulates in permeable sedimentary layers covered by a roof of poorly thermally conductive material. Low-temperature systems are also found as convective in nature tectonic fault systems in crystalline rocks.

The lithology of geothermal reservoirs can be quite variable, with complex stratigraphic and structural relationships, and the associated igneous and tectonic systems may be still active. Recent fracturing, faulting, or magmatic intrusions create new flow paths for hot or cold fluids, resulting in heating or cooling of the surrounding rocks. Open fractures may also fill over time, due to precipitation of secondary minerals, which reduce the overall permeability of the host rock mass and often produce an impermeable roof above the geothermal system.

The cost of geothermal drilling makes up a considerable part of the investment needed for a geothermal plant. For a typical geothermal power plant, the drilling cost can be considerable. A 3 km-deep geothermal well can cost 5–10 million dollars and the initial risk of failure is often considerable. To reduce this risk, detailed and reliable information on the internal structure of the geothermal systems must be obtained. This is done by geothermal exploration; a group of geoscientific methods that provide extensive information to yield a conceptual model of the system to be tested by exploration drilling.

Effective exploration methods are crucial for successful geothermal development due to the complexity of the subsurface systems. Not only the geological, but also the physical and geochemical characteristics of these systems vary greatly. In contrast to oil and gas industry, where seismic reflection surveys are the main exploration method, no such reliable method has been found for locating and characterizing high-temperature geothermal systems, although electrical resistivity, seismic, magnetic, and gravity techniques are all widely used. Experience has shown that the exploration strategy has to be tailor-made for each geothermal field.

Geothermal exploration should be done with a multidisciplinary approach where geology, geochemistry, and geophysics interact. Geological mapping with emphasis on tectonic structure, stratigraphy, hydrothermal alteration, and the geological history is usually the first step. If hot springs or fumaroles exist, chemical methods are used to evaluate the reservoir temperature and the fluid properties prior to drilling. Geophysical surveys are the most widely used methods to detect subsurface high-temperature systems and to estimate their size and properties. Resistivity soundings, mainly based on transient electromagnetics (TEM) and magnetotellurics (MT) measurements, play the key role, but analysis of natural seismic events, aeromagnetic, and gravity surveys are also helpful [1]. In the case of exploring for low-temperature fields, heat flow measurements are also important as well as geophysical methods to detect water-bearing fractures [2]. The exploratory work leads to a conceptual model of the geothermal system.

This chapter is based on many decades of experience of the authors in worldwide geothermal exploration. Some have partly been published before in lecture notes for the Geothermal Training Programme of the United Nations University (UNU) and at the University of Iceland.

7.03.2 Geological Exploration

High-temperature geothermal fields occur in volcanic terrains. Plate tectonics defines three main categories: one at convergent plate boundaries, another at spreading centers (mainly submarine) or continental rifts, and third, a few at intraplate hotspots. The first step in geothermal exploration is to collect geological information on the proposed geothermal site. Some basic geological information exists for the largest part of the world, including even the most remote geothermal sites. If not, this information must be acquired. Satellite images may provide a first useful overview; however, they lack details. Air photos (stereo pairs) are a very important guide to structures, but ground control of structures is a must. Geological surveys as a rule have information on the mapping status and keep record of boreholes, and thus may provide some subsurface information.

Exploration strategy should be fitted to detect and map the outline of an upwelling geothermal plume and its outflow. The geologist's role is to investigate a variety of features that may shed light on the nature, geological history, and present state of the respective geothermal system with emphasis on the central volcanic focus. Information about the volcanic stratigraphy, structure, and rock composition is needed as a basis for interpreting results of geophysical and geochemical surveys, and helps select sites for drilling. The volcanic history and mode of eruption needs to be known for assessment of volcanic hazard. Most magma involved in the formation of a volcanic system (i.e., a volcano and the associated volcanic and nonvolcanic fissures) does not reach the surface but heats a large volume of underground rock. This is difficult to measure, but has been estimated to be at least 50% of the magma involved. Sheets, dykes, and minor intrusions thus constitute a high percentage of the rock mass at shallow depth (1–3 km) underneath volcanic centers. These constitute a significant part of the heat source. Larger intrusions (magma chambers) formed at greater depth, preferably near the level of neutral buoyancy, act as long-term heat sources [3].

7.03.2.1 Geological Maps

Geological maps are the first data to be collected as they give us a general geological picture of the geothermal site and its possibilities for energy production. We base our first ideas of every potential geothermal system on the geological maps. Existing geological maps are of different quality, and most of them have emphasis on the bedrock type and tectonic structure. Specific items related to geothermal activity are often ignored during mapping and not regarded important for the general geology. Additional basic information must therefore frequently be acquired when geothermal exploration is initiated. The most important information is the tectonic structure, distribution of thermal springs and steam vents, and of alteration minerals in geothermal systems. Specific geothermal maps of the potential geothermal field are recommended. Furthermore, data on the geological history are appreciated, that is, the age of tectonic and volcanic events and other geological processes. Existing geological maps might provide good enough basis for the first prefeasibility assessment, but for further development, extensive mapping with detailed field work is recommended. It should also be pointed out that in addition to the exploitation of geological maps to assess geothermal resources, they form basis for a part of the environmental assessment that is usually required to obtain necessary permits for energy production.

It is also important to have geological maps of different scales. A map scale of 1:100,000 provides the general picture of a large area around the site of interest and puts the geothermal activity in a larger geological perspective which might be important to understand the geological processes that are causing the geothermal activity. Map scale of 1:25,000 or larger are necessary for the detailed structure of the geothermal site. Such maps should give precise location of geological structures like faults, craters, and volcanic fissures as well as hot springs, steam vents, geothermal alteration, and spectacular geological formations that must be preserved.

Figures 1 and **2** show examples of geological maps from the same site in different scales of the Reykjanes geothermal field in Iceland. **Figure 1** shows a map of a larger area in small scale (1:100,000) and places the geothermal field into a regional geological context. **Figure 2** shows a detailed map of the production field with much higher resolution.

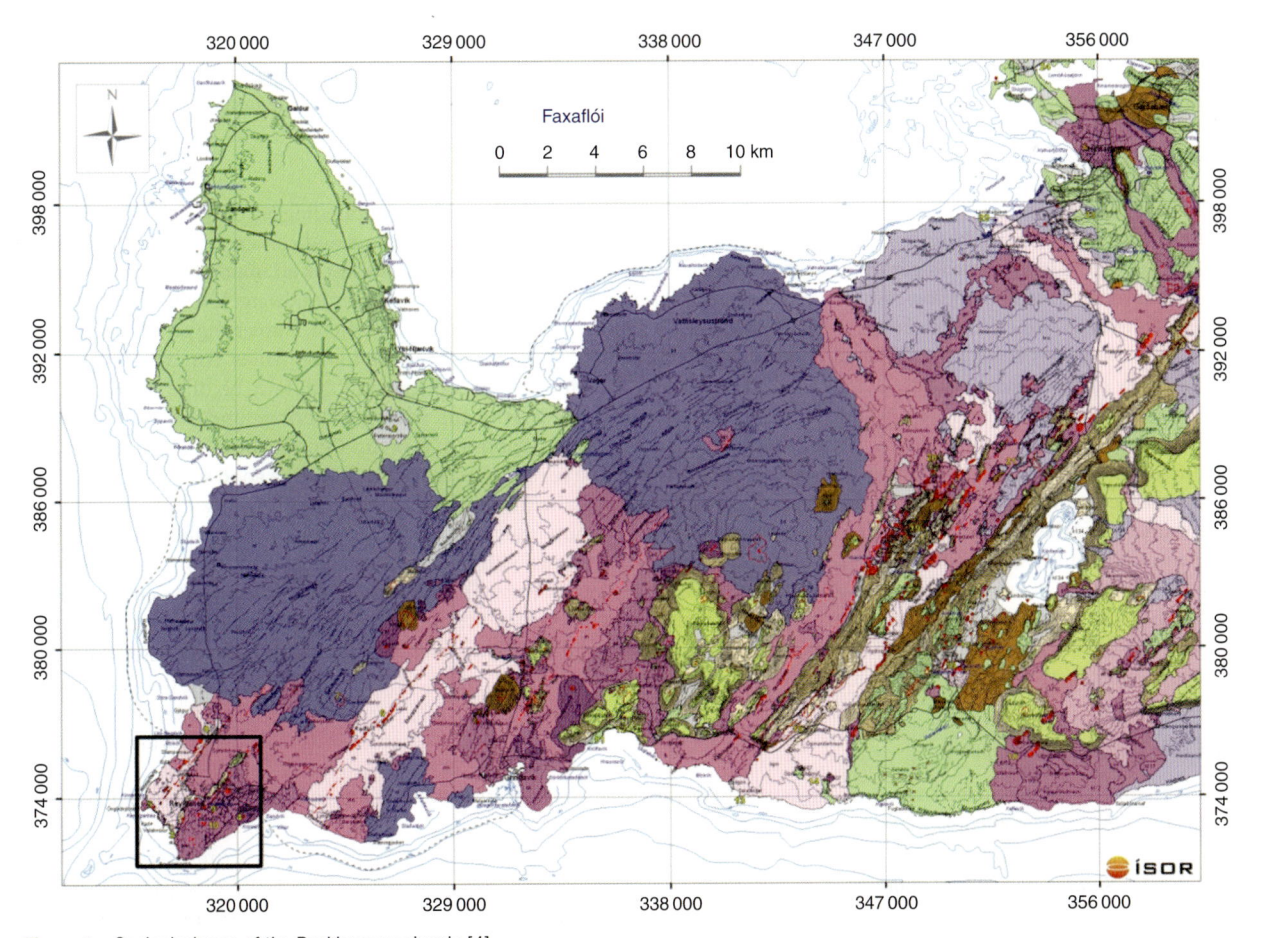

Figure 1 Geological map of the Reykjanes peninsula [4].

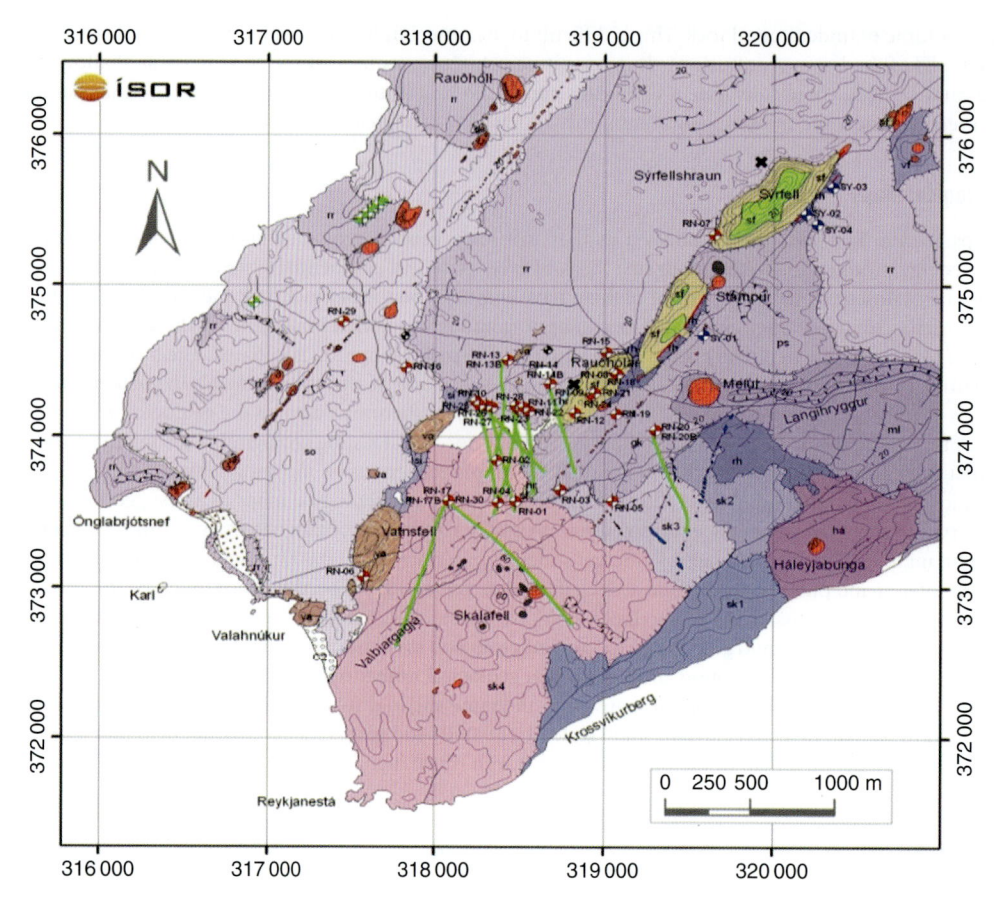

Figure 2 Geological map of the production field at Reykjanes, an area enlarged from Figure 1. Green lines denote directional wells [4].

7.03.2.2 Hydrology and Topography

It is important at an early stage of geothermal prospection to investigate the hydrology of the surrounding region such as precipitation, catchment area (for likely recharge), and depth to the groundwater level, general flow direction, and content of dissolved solids. If available, it should be possible to get access to relevant data from appropriate authorities. The last is an important issue, that is, to avoid locating deep wells in outflow areas too far away from upwelling geothermal plumes. The groundwater level may be very low, that is, at hundreds of meters depth, under lofty volcanic edifices which may host a geothermal system. Harnessing geothermal energy under such conditions is not attractive, even impossible unless by directional drilling from their lower flanks. Fortunately, from the point of view of exploitation, shield volcanoes and stratovolcanoes develop collapse calderas and thus have become accessible.

Fumaroles are an indication of a boiling reservoir. Intensive fumarole activity and widespread hot ground, several hectares in extent, point to a steam zone at shallow depth. At low levels, hot or boiling springs may occur. Deposits from their water must be identified: travertine (tufa) is a bad omen as regards water chemistry and temperature, but silica sinter is a good sign especially if it is the sole or predominant precipitate. Off-flow from high-temperature geothermal areas includes groundwater heated by contact with hot groundwater and/or mixing of deep reservoir water with local groundwater. Commonly, inversion of temperature is found. Aquifers may be either stratabound or fracture-related. Temperature decreases with distance from the source region. The near-surface rocks of a geothermal area are often permeable, especially lavas and pyroclastics. The same applies to faults which may be densely spaced in rift and caldera environments. Permeability decreases downwards as alteration progresses, but secondary permeability may prevail or form later. The possibility of low permeability near-surface layers, alluvial, lacustrine, or mudflow deposits, in particular, must be considered. Such layers may divert water flow laterally.

7.03.2.3 Geothermal Mapping

As high-temperature geothermal resources are associated with volcanism or intrusions of up to batholithic dimensions, it is necessary to plan the geothermal mapping accordingly.

7.03.2.3.1 Surface geothermal mapping

Plain mapping involves fissures and faults (trend, throw, width, hade, sense of motion, and relative age from cross cutting relationships), craters and volcanic fissures (trends, swarming, age relations, and explosivity), and tilting of the ground (most obvious in antithetic fault zones and distinguish between depositional dips and tectonic tilt). Mapping of hydrothermal features, both active and extinct, is important. Active features such as areal distribution, intensity, size and coherence of fumarole fields and hot ground and their efflorescence minerals, and hot and tepid springs and their deposits should be mapped. Directional trends and/or local concentrations will be quickly assessed. As to the extinct features, it is necessary to study the type of alteration. Kaolinite and smectite are typical of recently cooled and little eroded outcrops. Transition from smectite to chlorite, which is temperature-dependent, may be observed if the prospect has suffered erosion. The relationship to unaltered rock or soil nearest to hydrothermally altered rock may show if the feature became recently extinct. Alteration, whether cold or active, may be local or pervasive with the rock altered beyond recognition, or moderate if original structure of rock is preserved. Clayey slopes may constitute a hazard from sliding.

7.03.2.3.2 Extrapolation of mapping results to subsurface

The nature of the subsurface rock needs to be assessed from what is known from the surrounding geology. This is important for borehole design, in particular, casing. Are permeable rocks such as ignimbrite breccias, pillow basalt, sandstone, or limestone likely to occur at depth? Fracture permeability may prevail above 200 °C, dependent on the type of rock. Are fracture-friendly rocks to be expected? These are hard and 'nonyielding', such as igneous and intrusive rock (lavas, dykes, plugs, and laccoliths) and also limestone and indurated sandstone. Fracture-unfriendly rocks are claystone, shale, and the like which react to stress by plastic deformation. Not all fractures contribute to an effective fracture volume. Release joints and tension fractures have a relatively high effective fracture volume contrary to compression fractures. Water contained in matrix pores and microfractures is inaccessible unless pressure decrease due to drawdown causes it to boil which may contribute to the available part of the resource.

7.03.2.4 Mapping and Outlining of Major Controlling Structures

Some of the world's largest geothermal areas are associated with batholithic intrusives, sometimes with minor volcanism but also such that they have erupted huge volumes of ignimbrite. These manifest themselves as fumaroles. The predominating country rock may be sedimentary or metamorphic, constituting the roof of underlying intrusions. Geothermal areas of this type are rare, at least only a few have been recognized. They occur in fold belts. The Philippines, Italy, and the United States exploit geothermal resources of this type. Due to their high potential, these countries are the three foremost in exploitation of high-temperature geothermal energy. The more common type of high-temperature geothermal systems around the world is volcanic. They occur in various tectonic settings, such as rifts, volcanic chains of collision zones, and hotspots. We will dwell on these aspects in the following paragraphs.

7.03.2.4.1 Rifts and their segmentation

Rifts are usually segmented into volcanic systems. They can be recognized and defined from fault trends, crater rows, and rock composition. Individual volcanic systems measure 100 km or more in rifts, and are usually elongated also in the direction of maximum compression at convergent plate margins, best expressed in island arcs. The geologist should try to evaluate volcanic production, eruption frequency, and mode of eruption for the volcanic systems and define rock types. The geologist must try also to estimate, or preferably help measure ground movements, vertical and horizontal, their rate as latent creep, and find out if rifting episodes that would be accompanied by volcanic or intrusive activity occur. From the energy point of view, the intrusion events are important as they recharge the heat source in the roots of the geothermal fields and thereby help to maintain the energy resource. Intrusion events would act beneficially for the geothermal system. Recognition of volcanic systems is widely applied in Icelandic geology and is fairly obvious also in continental rifts such as the Ethiopian and Kenya rifts. This apparently also applies to the hotspot environment, Saõ Miguel, Azores, being an example.

Besides stratigraphic and tectonic mappings, significant features to be defined include volcano type (stratovolcano or shield volcano), dominant rock type (basaltic or acidic), occurrence of silicic rocks (lavas, domes, ignimbrite, and pumice), calderas, incremental or collapse with related volcanics, type of basalt eruptions and their structural control such as unidirectional fissure swarm, radial or circumferential fissures around caldera, and central-vent eruptions. Point-source stresses give rise to inclined sheet swarms, which often form a regular arcuate system of crater rows and dykes (cone sheets) projecting toward magma chambers at depth. Hydrothermal and volcanic explosion craters, their age, distribution, size, and ejecta are important. They indicate nearness to an upflow or a boiling reservoir and are targets for drilling production boreholes. These also constitute a hazard to be assessed properly before siting of surface constructions.

7.03.2.4.2 Geothermal systems through time

It is most informative to study extinct and deeply eroded volcanic centers, the internal volcanic feed system, and their hydrothermal aureoles. The alteration zones can be seen with their characteristic secondary minerals. Dyke complexes can be separated by rock type, distribution, and relative age relationships. Dense dyke complexes correlate with increase in high-temperature mineralization. Retrograde mineralization toward end of activity is seen as overgrowth by zeolites. Deeper roots of hydrothermal systems, including supercritical conditions beyond the depth of drilling, are well known from study of epithermal ore deposits around exhumed intrusive bodies (former magma chambers).

The life time of volcanic systems varies from hundreds of thousands to millions of years. It may be assessed from the study of well-exposed extinct and eroded volcanoes in geologically related terrains. Development through the nearest geological past and history of activity can usually be found out for at least the last few thousand years. Ground movement across volcanic systems during a much longer active period can often be estimated from fault density and throws. With time, a preferred stationary intrusion focus in a rift zone volcanic system would produce an intrusive body, elongated in the direction of stretching (spreading), as calderas also do. Distal parts cool off with time and increasing distance from the active intrusion focus. CO_2 fluxing of marginal parts of geothermal system may correlate with intrusion patterns of this type.

7.03.2.4.3 Mapping of faults

Faults are important features in geothermal mapping. They are not always topographically distinct unless nascent or recently activated. Faults are sometimes smoothed out by lava, leveled by erosion, disguised by vegetation, or draped over by scree, pumice, or other sediment and only visible in erosive channels, quarries, road cuts, or other exposures. Reference markers should be looked for. Various types of faults occur. Normal faults and tension gashes dominate in extensional regimes. Whether listric, planar, or vertical depends on whether they are dry or magma-generated (the vertical ones). Sense of motion may be determined from striations and Riedel shears. Normal and strike-slip faults both occur in transtensional rift zone settings. The two types may be active alternately. Reverse faults occur in the circum-Pacific belt. Volcanic systems in collision zones, preferably in island arcs, may develop fissure swarms that are parallel with the axis of maximum compression and also parallel with the trend of the arc in back-arc settings.

Minor faults or fractures may give a clue to prevailing stress field. The geologist should therefore look for Riedels and striations on fault surfaces wherever exposed. This helps define the local stress field. As a rule, maximum stress axis is near vertical in rift zones.

Point-source stress develops above inflating magma chambers, causing circumferentially arranged volcanic fissures to form, connected via inclined sheets to a magma chamber. This is common in case of caldera volcanoes, indicating incremental caldera growth (Askja, Iceland and Silali, Kenya).

7.03.3 Assessment of Geological Hazard

All high-temperature fields of the world are located at the tectonically active plate boundaries of the Earth and are usually associated with recent volcanic activity like volcanism or intrusive events. Harnessing geothermal resources in such areas involves risk factors that are quite different from most other energy projects like oil or gas. Financial institutions are usually not familiar with the geological hazard involved in geothermal energy production and therefore are reluctant to participate in such projects. This is one of the major obstacles for more extensive worldwide development of geothermal energy resources.

Geohazards need to be taken into account in harnessing of geothermal areas. The issues to be regarded include the type and history of volcanism, definition of segments with most active fault movements, and earthquake activity including microseismicity, slope stability, and possibility of flash floods. Gas fluxes from magma chambers or intrusive activity may cause corrosion problems of production wells. In geothermal systems of restricted recharge, drawdown of the reservoir fluid causes thickening of the overlying steam zone and increased surface geothermal activity. Hazards involved with exploitation of low- and high-temperature geothermal systems, where hosted in sedimentary or thick pyroclastic deposits having limited recharge, may cause ground subsidence and damage to buildings and roads.

The main geological hazard factors in the development of a geothermal field are discussed in the following sections.

7.03.3.1 Volcanic Events

Volcanic events are periods of volcanic unrest where magma is being fed into the roots of the volcano or moving toward the surface. As discussed earlier, the events might either involve volcanic eruption or just an intrusion. For geothermal exploration, the type and history of the volcanic activity in the proposed geothermal field is mapped and traced, both from historical records and field data. It should give information on the eruption frequency, type of eruption, and possible eruptive sites. In many volcanoes, the eruption frequency is quite low with centuries or millennia between or since the last volcanic event. In such cases, the volcanic risk for a geothermal power plant is low when compared with the depreciation time of the investment and other risks like political or economic risks.

The type of eruption is an important issue. On diverging plate boundaries (e.g., rift zones like in Iceland and East Africa), basaltic fissure eruptions with low-viscosity lavas are relatively common, although rare on a human timescale. Voluminous pyroclastic flows may happen and spread over large areas and is followed by caldera collapses. Fortunately, such events are rare, even on a geological scale. At converging plate boundaries (e.g., West Coast of America, Mediterranean, Indonesia, Japan, and New Zealand), island arc volcanism is dominant with large volcanoes where thick and viscous silicic lavas are erupted either as thick flows or domes, restricted in area and volume, or as pyroclastic flows and surges. Air-fall ash and pumice usually accompany the first, forming quite thick deposits in the vicinity of the eruption site, but dispersed far by winds. In order to reduce possible damage caused by an eruption, it is recommended that selection of sites for a powerhouse and other surface installations is based on the best knowledge of the volcanic behavior, even though eruption frequency is low.

Intrusions make themselves felt in two ways. They may form dykes when magma is expelled laterally out of a magma chamber during rifting events. They may also form sheets in the roof of magma chambers both as irregular net veins or regularly inclined as cone sheets as a result of point-source stresses. Dykes have made themselves felt when they cut through and clog boreholes. Examples are known from Krafla, Iceland, where a borehole erupted basalt and several were clogged as became evident from fresh glassy basalt being drilled through when cleared.

7.03.3.1.1 Fault movements

As geothermal fields are located in tectonically active areas, stress release with fault movements and associated earthquakes are to be expected in every geothermal field. The tectonic activity is indeed one of the prerequisites for the existence of a productive geothermal field. It opens and maintains open fractures that are the pathways for the circulation fluid that extracts heat from the hot rock, and permeable fractures are the target during drilling of production wells.

Fault movements may create ground fissures in the epicentral areas of large earthquakes. They would presumably follow the trace of preexisting faults. Earthquakes associated with magmatically driven rifting are not as severe, probably not much over M 5.5. They are associated with dyking. Ruptures associated with tectonic earthquakes would propagate at a rate of kilometers per second as against kilometers per hour, for the latter accompanying dyke propagation. The fissures themselves would cause damage of surface structures where they cross pipelines or cut through boreholes. Needless to say, the mapping of faults is important at the stage of site selection.

7.03.3.2 Gas Fluxes

The magma chambers themselves have an aureole of magmatic gases such as CO_2, SO_2, Cl, and F in a supercritical water phase around them. These may migrate off during times of unrest and pollute the geothermal system (lowering its pH), rendering it partly unexploitable for years, or even decades. The Krafla geothermal system in Iceland is an example being situated in the caldera of a degassing volcano. An informative paper on volatile fluxes from volcanoes at rest is given by Brantley et al. [5].

Sediment-filled deep grabens are targets for oil prospection. Traps containing organic gases like methane are unlikely to occur in their volcanic segments. But farther off, drilling into a sediment-covered prospect should take notice of this.

7.03.3.3 Drilling into Molten Rock

Shallow depth to molten rock may cause problems in geothermal drilling. One possibility is a blowout, not known to have occurred for this reason yet. The reality of drilling into a basaltic melt came up 5 years ago in Hawaii [6] and in late 2008 and 2010 at Krafla, Iceland, in all cases at about 2500 m depth. At Krafla, the yielding wells are located in an area of late Pleistocene and recent explosion craters. In that case, the drill penetrated 50 m into the molten body. It was not recognized as such during drilling, because there had been a total loss of drill fluid which was water. The drill then got stuck as circulation was stopped briefly for a temperature log (showed 386 °C at the bottom of the drill string). The string was blasted apart above the hot part. The drill pipe broke well below. On pulling out, the lowest pipe was found to be plugged by fresh, silicic glass. Even though a feed zone just above the now recognized molten zone was plugged with cement, the well-yielded low-pH fluid which is corrosive. A well that was completed at Krafla toward the end of 2007 ran into a gas-rich fluid at the same depth (**Figure 3**) [7]. That particular feed zone was cemented off and the well is a moderately good producer.

Figure 3 Well KJ-36 blowing at Krafla [7].

7.03.3.4 Flooding and Sliding

Flooding and sliding involve a hazard in areas of steep topography and clayey ground, which is a common feature in high-temperature geothermal fields and heavy, in particular tropical, rain which may cause flash floods. The selection of drill pads, siting of buildings, and layout and construction of steam pipes needs to be considered with regard to such hazard factors.

7.03.3.5 Elevation Changes

Geophysics has the means of measuring accurately the vertical and horizontal displacements by GPS, InSAR, and by leveling. It has been a common practice in volcanology for a long time to measure elevation changes on volcanoes as swelling may indicate magma accumulation. This is also important in surveillance of geothermal fields, which may subside due to exploitation if recharge does not make up for fluid production. In recent years, satellites have made it possible to register horizontal displacements also [8].

7.03.4 Geochemistry and Geothermometers

7.03.4.1 General

Knowledge of reservoir temperature is one of the most important parameters to assess the potential of a geothermal field prior to drilling. Although geological considerations and geophysical measurements can give strong indications of the possible reservoir temperature, the most reliable temperature information comes from chemical geothermometers. To apply them, samples of the geothermal fluid or gases collected from hot springs and steam vents are needed. Chemical geothermometry is also commonly used to assess reservoir temperature in wells. This is of course a major limitation for the use of the chemical geothermometers, as hot springs or steam vents might be absent or have limited spatial coverage.

Chemical geothermometry refers to the use of chemistry to evaluate the temperature in geothermal reservoirs. They are based on a few main assumptions as follows:

1. There exists a temperature-dependent equilibrium between fluids and gases in the porous rock and the rock-forming minerals. Hence, the composition of the geothermal fluids can be depicted as a function of temperature.
2. That the composition of the fluid is not severely changed during its flow from the location of equilibrium to the place where the samples are collected, typically from the geothermal reservoir to the surface in hot springs or steam vents. This means that the velocity of the fluid from the location of equilibrium within the reservoir to the sampling point must be high enough to prevent reequilibrium to occur. This also means that mixing of the fluid with water of other origin on the same pathway must not take place.

One of the fundamental assumptions in the use of chemical geothermometers is that a partial chemical equilibrium is attained in the geothermal reservoir. Dissolved chemical components in geothermal solutions are referred to as either conservative components or rock-forming components. The conservative components, such as Cl^-, are generally not controlled by water–rock equilibria, but their concentration is determined by their initial concentration in the source fluids or dissolution from the rock. The concentrations, or more correctly the activities, of the reactive components are, on the other hand, controlled by equilibria between the fluid and secondary minerals in the rock that are in contact with it. Most of the elements dissolved in geothermal solutions are considered to be reactive components. However, under some circumstances, the assumption of partial equilibrium does not hold for some of the dissolved components. Dissolved silica, for example, is almost universally controlled by equilibrium with quartz in most geothermal systems with the exception of young basalt-hosted geothermal systems at temperatures below ∼180 °C. There the silica is controlled by the solubility of chalcedony, a metastable silica polymorph [9–11]. Similarly, dissolved CO_2 is generally considered a reactive component, but in some volcanic geothermal systems the rate of CO_2 influx from magma may, at least periodically, exceed the capacity of the secondary mineral assemblages to incorporate the CO_2. During such periods of high magmatic gas influx, the concentration of CO_2 is controlled by the flux of gas from magma, and not by chemical equilibria between the fluid and the rocks. Under such conditions, CO_2 cannot be considered a reactive component, and the application of CO_2 geothermometers will give erroneous results. Considering that dissolved silica and CO_2 are involved in the most common chemical geothermometers, it should be clear from these examples that caution must be exercised in the application of chemical geothermometers.

Another fundamental assumption is that the composition of the different geothermal fluids has not been affected by secondary processes, other than boiling, on the way to the surface. While this assumption holds true in some cases, it is by no means a law of nature. Steam may be affected by condensation on the way to the surface, a process that increases the concentration of all the gases in the steam. Similarly, geothermal solutions that boil and/or cool on the way to the surface may react to reequilibrate with the rock under the changing-temperature conditions. There exists, fortunately, a fair number of chemical geothermometers that are affected in different ways by such secondary changes. Consequently, it is very important to use as many geothermometers as possible for any given fluid sample, be it of steam or liquid, as the discrepancy between the results of the different geothermometers may be indicative of the secondary processes affecting the fluid [12].

7.03.4.2 Chemical Geothermometers

A brief discussion is given below on some of the most commonly used chemical geothermometers. This publication does not present an exhaustive literature review of this topic but rather an overview of the application possibilities of geothermometry in geothermal exploration. It is to a large extent based on Ármannsson and Friðriksson [13]. Isotope geothermometers will, for instance, not be discussed in this publication. For thorough literature reviews of chemical geothermometry, the reader is referred to Zhao-Ping and Ármannsson [14], D'Amore and Arnórsson [15], Yock [16], and Zheng-Xilai et al. [17], and for discussion of mixing models, the reader is referred to Arnórsson [18].

7.03.4.3 Univariant Geothermometers

Chemical geothermometers can be univariant, that is, based on the concentration of one reactive constituent (gas or aqueous species) or based on ratios of reactive components. The most widely used univariant geothermometer is probably the silica geothermometer. Univariant gas geothermometers using the concentrations of CO_2, H_2, and H_2S are also common. Several empirical calibrations are available for these geothermometers. The most widely used silica geothermometers are based on equilibrium between quartz and the geothermal solution, but geothermometers for other silica polymorphs (most importantly for chalcedony) have also been published. The quartz geothermometer of Fournier and Potter [19] for boiling springs is given in **Table 1**.

The univariant gas geothermometers are more complicated as several possible assemblages of secondary minerals can be identified as potential buffers of the gas concentrations. Arnórsson et al. [21], for instance, propose two possible mineral assemblages for controlling CO_2 concentrations in geothermal fluids and four different assemblages as buffers for the concentration of H_2 and H_2S in geothermal solutions. Predictions of reservoir temperature based on the different mineral assemblages do, fortunately, agree fairly well with each other, so the choice of reaction does not greatly affect the predicted temperature. Three of the gas geothermometers reported by Arnórsson et al. [21] for CO_2, H_2S, and H_2, based on the assumption of equilibrium with quartz, epidote, prehnite, and calcite in the case of CO_2 and pyrite and pyrrhotite in the case of H_2S and H_2, are listed in **Table 1**.

Simplicity is a benefit of the univariant geothermometers, but they are also susceptible to secondary processes such as dilution and condensation. Errors due to condensation on univariant gas geothermometers can be prevented by using ratios of the reactive gases to conservative gas species such as Ar or N_2. In such cases, the concentration of the conservative gas species is taken to be equal to that of air-saturated water at the recharge conditions.

7.03.4.4 Geothermometers Based on Ratios

The most commonly used geothermometer that utilizes cation ratios is the Na/K geothermometer. Several calibrations have been published, both empirical and theoretical. The Na/K geothermometer of Fournier [20] is shown in **Table 1**. It is commonly assumed that the Na/K ratio in geothermal solutions is constrained by simultaneous equilibria between the geothermal solution and Na- and K-feldspar, described by the following reaction:

$$NaAlSi_3O_8 + K^+ = KAlSi_3O_8 + Na^+$$

However, it has also been postulated that the Na/K ratio may in some geothermal systems just as well be controlled by ion-exchange equilibrium between Na- and K-clay minerals. Cation ratio geothermometers have been calibrated and published for other cation pairs such as K/Mg, Na/Ca, K/Ca, Na/Li, and Li/Mg (for discussion, see Reference 15). A characteristic feature of the Na/K thermometer is that it seems to equilibrate slowly, which can be both an advantage and a disadvantage. For example, a discrepancy between the temperatures predicted by the Na/K geothermometer and other, more rapidly equilibrated thermometers, such as the quartz thermometer, the discrepancy can be indicative of the cooling or heating history of the geothermal fluid. The Na/K/Ca geothermometer proposed by Fournier and Truesdell [22] uses both the Na/K and the Na/$\sqrt{Ca}$ ratios to predict reservoir

Table 1 selected geothermometers

Quartz[a]	$T\ (°C) = -53.5 + 0.11\ 236S - 0.5559 \cdot 10^{-4} S^2 + 0.1772 \cdot 10^{-7} S^3 + 88.39\ \log S$
Na/K[b]	$T\ (°C) = \frac{1217}{1.438 + \log(Na/K)} - 273.15$
CO_2[c]	$T\ (°C) = \frac{\log(CO_2) + 3.28 + 1.5\ \log(a_{pre}) - \log(a_{czo})}{0.0097}$
H_2S[c]	$T\ (°C) = \frac{\log(H_2S) + 6.853 + \frac{2}{3}\log(a_{epi}) - \frac{2}{3}\log(a_{pre})}{0.013\ 43}$
H_2[c]	$T\ (°C) = \frac{\log(H_2) + 4.686 + \frac{2}{3}\log(a_{epi}) - \frac{2}{3}\log(a_{pre})}{0.007\ 962}$

[a] Fournier and Potter [19]; S refers to concentration of SiO_2 (mg kg^{-1}) and applies to solutions boiled to 100 °C; shown as reported by D'Amore and Arnórsson [12].
[b] Fournier [20]; Na and K refer to concentrations (mg kg^{-1}); shown as reported by D'Amore and Arnórsson [12].
[c] Arnórsson et al. [21]; CO_2, H_2S, and H_2 refer to concentrations in steam (mmole kg^{-1} steam); a_{epi} and a_{czo} refer to the activities of the endmembers of the epidote solid solution ($Ca_2FeAl_2Si_3O_{10}(OH)$ and $Ca_2Al_3Si_3O_{10}(OH)$) and a_{pre} refers to the activity of prehnite.

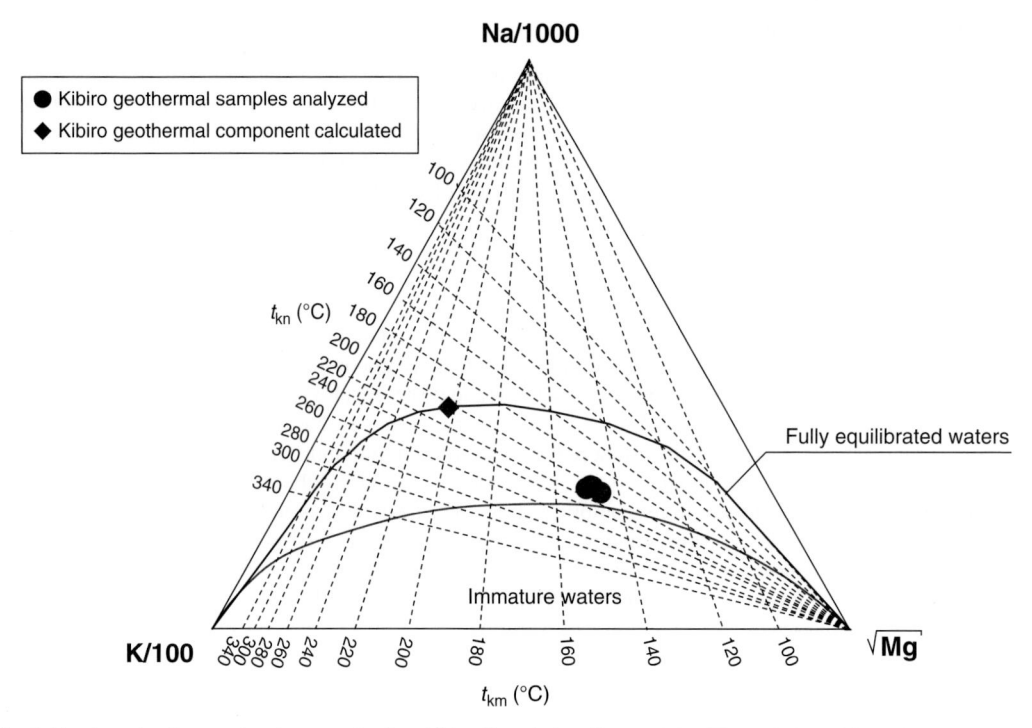

Figure 4 Na–K–Mg triangular diagram showing examples from Kibiro, Uganda (see Chapter **7.04**). The partially equilibrated waters represent a mixture of the geothermal component and local groundwater, whereas the fully equilibrated water represents the geothermal component. With courtesy of ISOR.

temperature. It has been used successfully on many occasions and it has been found to give reliable results at low temperatures, at which the Na/K geothermometers have a tendency to give erroneously high results [15]. Giggenbach [23] proposed a graphical method involving the simultaneous use of an Na/K and K/$\sqrt{Mg}$ ratio geothermometers. The advantage of this method is that it gives both an estimate of the reservoir temperature and indicates the 'maturity' of the geothermal solution by combining the results of the fast equilibrating K/$\sqrt{Mg}$ geothermometer and the slow Na/K geothermometer. An example of an Na–K–Mg ternary diagram is shown in **Figure 4**.

7.03.4.5 Multiple Mineral Equilibria Approach

Reed and Spycher [24] proposed this method for evaluating reservoir temperatures. It is based on computation of the saturation state of typical secondary minerals in geothermal systems over a range of temperatures. The results are presented on a graph showing the saturation state, presented as $\log(Q/K)$, for the different minerals as a function of temperature, where Q is equal to the activity product and K is the equilibrium constant. If the fluid has been in equilibrium with a certain assemblage of secondary minerals, the $\log(Q/K)$ curves for these minerals will intersect at zero, indicating equilibrium. The temperature at which the curves intersect zero is then the reservoir temperature. This method has the advantage of discriminating between equilibrated and nonequilibrated solutions. However, this method is sensitive to the choice of secondary minerals considered, the quality of thermodynamic data for the minerals, and to the quality of analysis of elements such as Mg, Al, and Fe that occur in the geothermal solutions in very low concentrations. As such a diagram is based on alteration minerals, it is desirable to have an idea of such minerals in the system, for example, from a nearby borehole. An example of a multiple mineral equilibria analysis is shown in **Figure 5**.

7.03.4.6 Example of Application

Geothermometers are widely used in the world in geothermal exploration, and examples can be found in most countries with geothermal activity. Ólafsson and Bjarnason [26] report a nice example of the utilization of geochemistry in the Torfajökull high-temperature field in Iceland. This is a large field mostly located within a large caldera. Hot springs and fumaroles are found distributed over large parts of the caldera and have been sampled and analyzed. Various types of gas geothermometers were applied. Examples of the predicted reservoir temperatures based on the CO_2 geothermometer and the ratio of CO_2/N_2 are shown in **Figure 6**. The highest values, up to 350 °C, are found in the southern and southeastern parts of the area. Elsewhere, temperatures of around 300 °C, or a little less, are obtained. This pattern is even more pronounced for the CO_2 geothermometer, which yields temperatures of 350 °C or higher in the south and southeast, but temperatures generally below 280 °C in other parts [27].

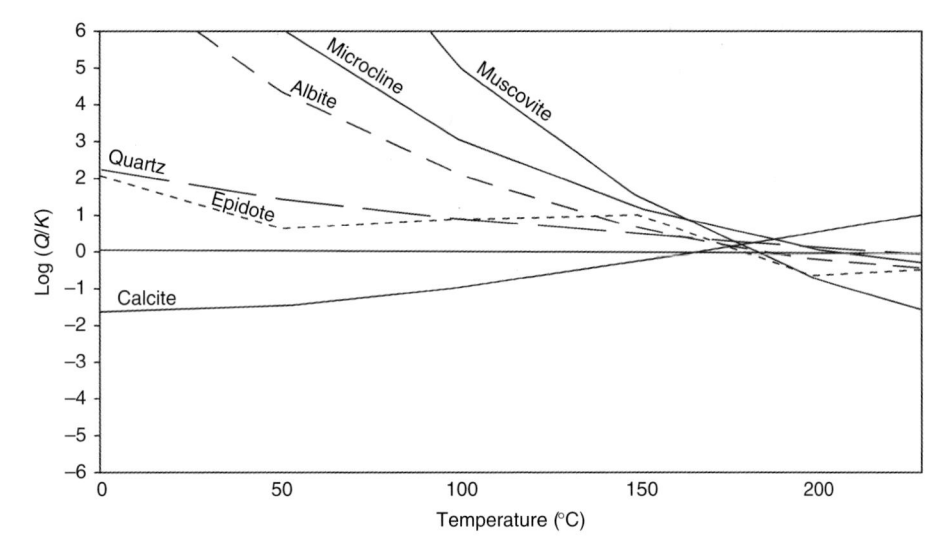

Figure 5 A log(Q/K) diagram for probable alteration minerals in well B-4, Námafjall, Iceland [25]. The saturation temperature and therefore the equilibrium subsurface temperature correspond to log(Q/K) = 0 and this is found at about 160 °C (see Chapter **7.04**). With courtesy of ISOR.

The H_2, H_2S, and H_2S/H_2 geothermometers were also applied in the area. The H_2S geothermometer gives values of about 300 °C in the southern and southeastern parts of the Torfajökull field, and 275–290 °C elsewhere. The H_2 and H_2S/H_2 geothermometers yield temperatures close to 300 °C over the entire field, with a slight trend toward higher values in the south and southeast. The H_2S geothermometer shows more scatter than the other two. Different geothermometers typically yield somewhat scattered results like here. But the picture that emerges here is rather consistent, indicating reservoir temperatures of 300 °C over most of the field except the south and southeast, where temperatures may reach 350 °C [27].

7.03.5 Geophysical Methods

The task involved in geothermal exploration is the detection and delineation of geothermal resources and the understanding of their characteristics, the location of exploitable reservoirs, and the siting of boreholes through which hot fluids at depth can be extracted. Geological and geochemical mapping are usually limited to direct observations on the surface and conclusions and extrapolation that can be drawn about the system and possible underlying structures. Geophysical surface exploration methods are different. They utilize equipment that measures directly some physical parameters on the surface that are directly created by physical properties or processes at depth. Geophysical exploration is a young scientific discipline that developed slowly in the first half of the twentieth century. With large advances in electronics, computer technology, and numerical calculations during the past decades, it developed rapidly.

Oil and gas prospecting have been the main driving force for advances in geophysical exploration methods. This applies mainly to methods that are well suited for oil and gas exploration like seismic methods, but less emphasis has been on methods like resistivity measurements that are more efficient in geothermal exploration. Geothermal has also benefited from tools and methods used for mineral exploration.

Geophysical exploration methods can be classified into several groups like seismic methods, electrical resistivity methods, potential methods (gravity and magnetics), heat flow measurements, and surface deformation measurements. Some of these methods and their application in geothermal exploration are described in this chapter.

Ambiguity of results is a common problem of geophysical methods, that is, each method only gives results of a ratio or multiplication of two or more parameters. There are trade-offs between velocities and thickness in seismology, between density and volume size in gravity, and between the value of resistivity and thickness in resistivity interpretation. This ambiguity must be overcome by imposing some constraint on the parameters from other observations. A classic example is to use seismic methods to constrain gravity interpretation.

Resistivity methods are the most important geophysical methods in geothermal exploration. The reason is that the resistivity is highly sensitive to temperature and geothermal alteration processes and is directly related to parameters characterizing the reservoir. Therefore, the main emphasis here is placed on description of the methods.

Seismic methods utilize the propagation of seismic waves through the Earth. They give information about seismic velocities, attenuation of seismic signals, and location of earthquakes. The physical parameters that can be found from seismic studies are, however, not very sensitive for variations in temperature within the expected temperature range in geothermal systems. They give, however, important structural information that can be directly related to flow of water within a geothermal reservoir. Their spatial resolution at reservoir depths is rather good.

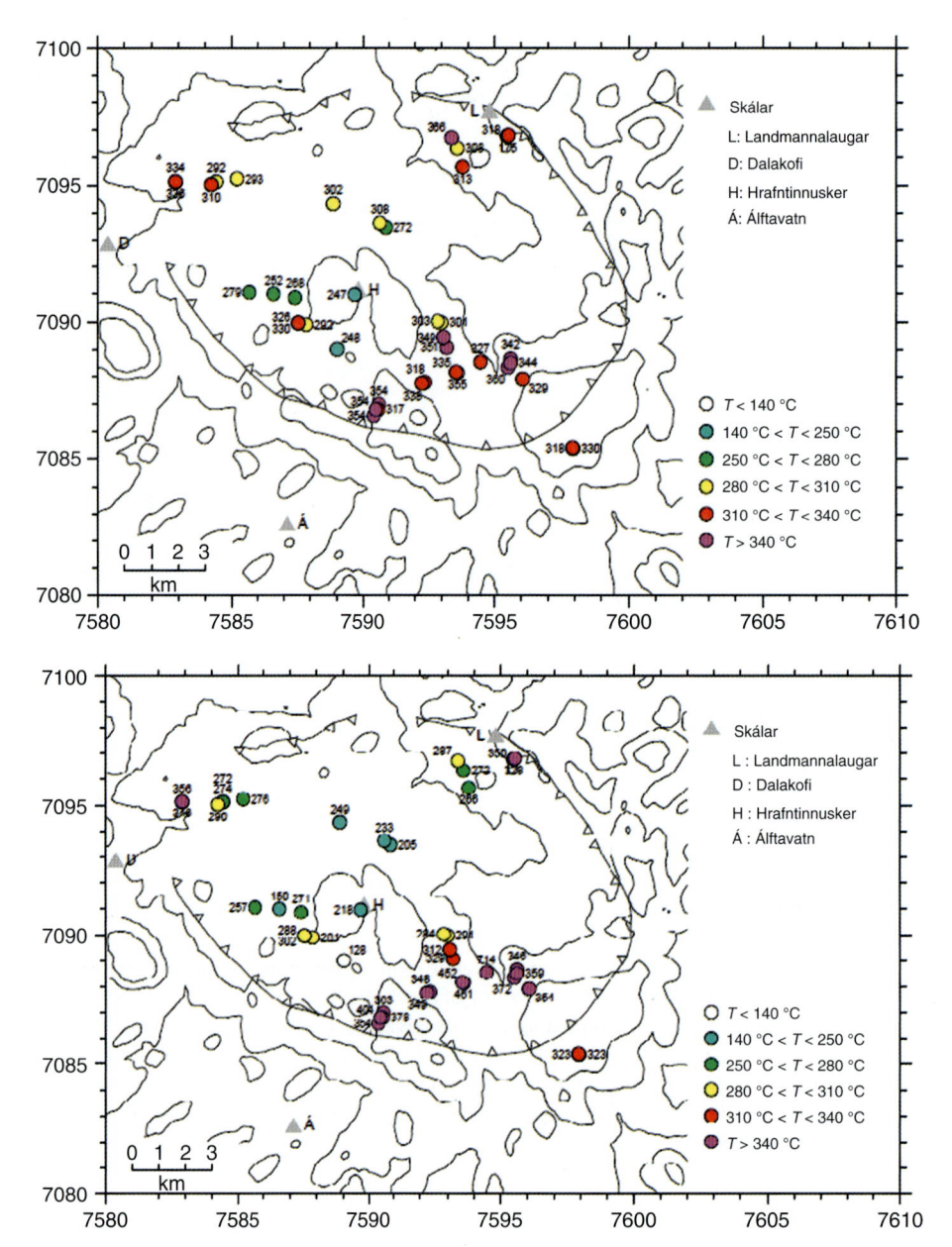

Figure 6 Torfajökull high-temperature field in South Iceland. The dots denote the sampling places, and the temperatures according to geothermometers are indicated by the color [27]. The upper figure shows temperatures computed from a CO_2 geothermometer, whereas the lower figure shows temperatures computed from a CO_2/N_2 geothermometer. With courtesy of ISOR.

The potential methods are gravity and magnetic measurements. In gravity measurements, the spatial variation in the gravity acceleration is measured. After correction for solar and lunar effects, elevation, mass, and topography, a map of gravitational acceleration, the Bouguer map, is presented. It reflects lateral variations of density in the subsurface and is used for structural purposes. Density contrasts may well be related to basement depth variations, rim of caldera, intrusives, rock alteration, porosity variations, faults, or dykes. It should be noted as well that gravity measurements are important as surveillance tool in geothermal production. By measuring gravitation acceleration over time in geothermal area, the net total mass withdrawal from the reservoir can be estimated.

In magnetic measurements, the spatial variations in the strength of the Earth's magnetic field are measured, either on the ground or in an aeromagnetic survey. The resulting magnetic map of the survey area reflects variations in the magnetic properties of the subsurface. They may be related to different magnetic susceptibilities of the rock. Abnormally high-temperature and related alteration processes destroy the magnetic properties of the rock volume. This is clearly observed as an anomaly in magnetic maps in high-temperature areas. Magnetic maps are used for structural purposes, locating intrusives, dykes, faults, buried lava, and hydrothermally altered areas.

Generally, the importance of the potential methods in geothermal exploration is not high; they primarily give information on geological structures rather than on the direct geothermal parameters. Therefore, further details of these methods are not covered here.

Finally, measurements of surface deformation are important to reveal geological processes that are affecting the geothermal fields. The deformation is usually measured with GPS recording instruments on the surface or remotely by satellites, InSAR. The deformation is then related to changes in the subsurface, for instance, by magmatic processes, tectonic movements, or mass withdrawal from the geothermal reservoir. It provides useful information, but is not a priority in geothermal exploration work and is very useful in surveillance of production.

7.03.5.1 Resistivity Methods

Measuring the electrical resistivity, ρ, of the subsurface is the most powerful geophysical prospecting method in geothermal exploration and the main method used for delineating geothermal resources. The electrical resistivity (Ωm) is defined by the Ohm's law, $E = \rho j$, where E (V m^{-1}) is the electrical field and j (A m^{-2}) is the current density. Electrical resistivity can also be defined as the ratio of the potential difference ΔV (V) to the current I (A), across a material which has a cross-sectional area of 1 m^2 and is 1 m long ($\rho = \Delta V/I$).

The electrical resistivity of rocks is controlled by important geothermal parameters like temperature, fluid type and salinity, porosity, the composition of the rocks, and the presence of alteration minerals. The reciprocal of resistivity is conductivity (S m^{-1}). Therefore, it is also possible to talk about conductivity measurements. However, in geothermal research, the tradition is to refer to electrical or resistivity measurements.

A distinction is made between resistivity soundings and resistivity profiling, depending on what kind of resistivity structure is being investigated. Soundings are done at a specified point to sound or measure changes in resistivity with depth at a fixed place, while profiling is done at various points on the surface along a profile to find lateral changes in resistivity and to locate narrow vertical or near-vertical structures. These are often the flow path for geothermal fluid especially in low-temperature geothermal areas.

7.03.5.1.1 Introduction

There exist several different methods to measure the subsurface resistivity. The common principle of all resistivity methods is to create an electrical current within the Earth and monitor, normally at the surface, the signals generated by the current. There are two main groups of resistivity methods, direct current (DC) method and electromagnetic (EM) method (sometimes called AC soundings). In conventional DC methods, such as Schlumberger soundings, the current is injected into the ground through a pair of electrodes at the surface and the measured signal is the electric field (the potential difference over a short distance) generated at the surface. In EM methods, the current is induced in the Earth by an external magnetic field. In MT, alternating current is induced in the ground by natural oscillations in the Earth's magnetic field, and the measured signal is the electric field at the surface. In TEM, the current is created by a man-made time-varying magnetic field generated by a current in a loop on the surface or by a grounded dipole. The monitored signal is the decaying magnetic field at the surface caused by induced currents at depth. It is customary in geophysics to talk about passive and active methods, depending on whether the source is a natural one or a controlled (artificial) one. MT is an example of a passive method, whereas Schlumberger and TEM are active ones.

All geophysical exploration technologies involve four steps: data acquisition, processing of data as an input for inversion or modeling, the modeling of the processed data, and finally the interpretation of the subsurface resistivity model in terms of geothermal parameters.

In the resistivity method, the term apparent resistivity, ρ_a, is used. This denotes the measured or calculated resistivity as if the Earth was homogeneous. It is a sort of an average of the true resistivity of the Earth detected by the sounding down to the penetration depth of the subsurface currents. The measured apparent resistivity is inverted to the true resistivity of the subsurface through modeling.

In all types of resistivity measurements, the final product of the data acquisition and the accompanying processing is a curve normally giving the apparent resistivity as a function of some depth-related free parameter. In the case of DC soundings, the free parameter is the electrode spacing; for TEM soundings, the time after turning off the source current; and the period of the EM fields in case of MT soundings.

Since the apparent resistivity does not show the true resistivity structure of the Earth, it has to be modeled in terms of the actual spatial resistivity distribution, that is, resistivity as a function of the two horizontal directions, x and y, and the vertical direction, z. This is the task of the geophysical modeler, transforming the measured apparent resistivity into a model of the true resistivity structure. The procedures are similar, whether considering DC soundings or EM soundings. In the modeling, geometrical restrictions of the resistivity structure are applied; the modeling is done in a one-, two-, or three-dimensional (1D, 2D, or 3D) way. In the 1D modeling, the resistivity distribution is only allowed to change with depth and is in general assumed to resemble a horizontally layered Earth.

The 2D modeling means that the resistivity distribution changes with depth and in one lateral direction, but is assumed to be constant in the other orthogonal horizontal direction. The last one is the so-called electrical strike direction, which is usually the direction of the main structure or the geological strike in the area. In a 2D survey, soundings are made along a profile line, which should be perpendicular to the strike. Good data density is needed, depending on the required spatial subsurface resistivity resolution, preferably a spacing of less than 1–2 km between soundings. The 2D modeling can account for variations in the topography.

The 3D modeling allows the resistivity to vary in all three directions. For a meaningful 3D interpretation, high data density is needed with a good areal coverage of the soundings, again depending on the required spatial subsurface resistivity resolution, preferably on a regular grid, for example, 1 km between sites. Soundings located well outside the prospected area are necessary to constrain the 3D subsurface resistivity model.

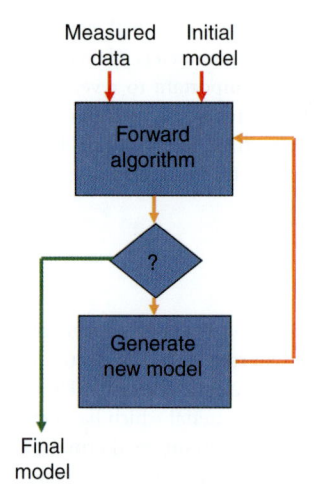

Figure 7 Flow diagram: inversion algorithm improves the model based on the misfit. With courtesy of ISOR.

7.03.5.1.2 Modeling and presenting resistivity soundings

Modeling of resistivity soundings, regardless of the dimension, is either done using forward modeling or through inversion processes (**Figure 7**). In forward modeling, the geophysicist examines the apparent resistivity curve and guesses an initial resistivity model, that he/she believes can explain the measured data. The forward algorithm is then used to calculate the apparent resistivity curve that would have been measured if the subsurface resistivity distribution was like the suggested model and the curve is compared with the measured one. Based on the comparison, the geophysicist changes/improves the model manually and makes a new forward calculation until a reasonable fit has been achieved and the result is found to be satisfactory.

Inversion, on the other hand, starts with the data and an educated guess of an initial model. The inversion algorithm improves the model in an iterative process by calculating adjustments to the model from the difference between the measured data and the response of the model until a satisfactory agreement has been reached. Inversion produces the statistically 'best' solution plus determining estimates of the model parameters, namely, which parameters are well determined and which ones are badly determined and how the estimates may be interrelated. It also indicates which data points contain relatively important information necessary to resolve the model parameters.

In 1D modeling, data from one and only one sounding are supposed to fit the response from a given model. Although a 1D Earth is assumed, in practice there are different 1D models for different soundings within the same survey area – every sounding has its own 1D model. In 2D modeling, data from all the soundings on the same profile line are supposed to fit the response from the same 2D model. In 3D modeling, data from all the soundings in the survey or modeled area are supposed to fit the response from the same 3D model.

Sometimes, the apparent resistivity is presented on pseudosections, for example, where the depth axis in Schlumberger soundings is taken as AB/2. A strong caution should be exercised when evaluating such sections since they do not reveal the actual resistivity structure and can lead to erroneous conclusions. It is strongly recommended never to publish such sections. Apparent resistivity always has to be converted to true resistivity values.

The results of resistivity interpretation are presented in different ways to ease further inspection in geothermal terms, depending on whether the interpretation is 1D, 2D, or 3D. For all cases, data from individual soundings should be shown together with the response from the final model (1D, 2D, or 3D) for comparing the fit and estimate the reliability of the model. These apparent resistivity curves are commonly presented in appendices of scientific reports.

The resistivity models are in most cases published as resistivity maps or cross sections. The maps show the resistivity at different depth level, usually referring to sea level. The cross sections show the modeled resistivity along some arbitrary lines. Examples of both are given later in this chapter (**Figures 8, 21**, and **26**). Information from geological mapping, magnetics, gravity, seismics, wells, and other relevant results is commonly added to these maps and sections to clarify the interpretation in geothermal terms.

For 1D interpretation, the models usually accompany the resistivity curves (**Figures 10, 14**, and **20**). Models from 1D interpretation of individual soundings are usually compiled to make 2D resistivity models, presented as cross sections, and a 3D resistivity model, presented as resistivity maps. However, it should be kept strictly in mind that these are not real 2D and 3D models – but rather pseudo-2D and -3D models. If there are considerable lateral changes in resistivity in or close to the sounding area, this will lead to errors in the 1D interpretation. True 3D models are only produced by 3D inversion of the data. In general, 1D inversion is often a fair approximation to the real resistivity model but might contain serious deviations. However, as will be discussed later, 1D inversion reproduces the basic resistivity structures but smears them out, whereas the 3D inversion sharpens the picture considerably.

The 2D inversion model is presented as a cross section and the 3D inversion model is presented both as cross sections and as resistivity maps.

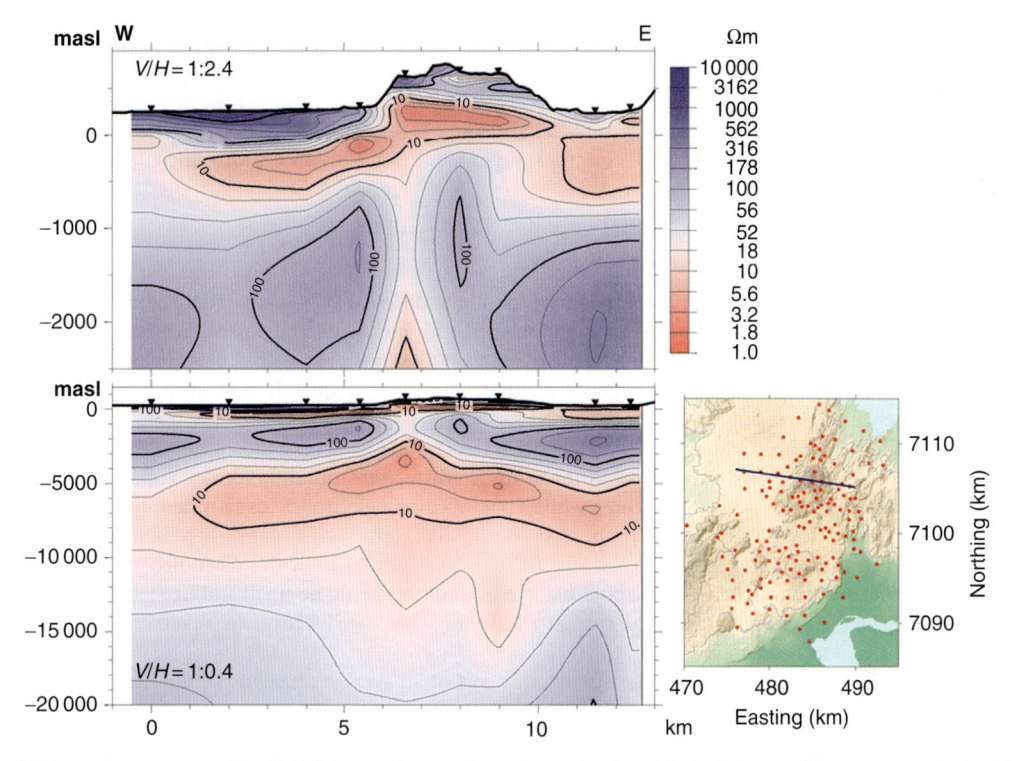

Figure 8 Resistivity section across the Hengill high-temperature geothermal area, Southwest Iceland, for two different ranges obtained from stitched joined 1D inversion of TEM and determinant MT data. Inverted triangles denote MT stations, and V/H is the ratio between vertical and horizontal axes. Section location is shown as a blue line in the map to the right. Red dots in the map denote MT stations [28].

7.03.5.1.3 The equivalence problem in 1D inversion

There are always some inaccuracies involved in the measured data of a resistivity sounding. Therefore, the solution – the subsurface resistivity 1D model derived from the data – is never unique; there are many models whose responses are within the measured error of the data. These models are called equivalent models. If the data were error-free, no measured error would exist and neither would the equivalence. The data could be fitted with one and only one model. This, however, is never the case in real situations and equivalence can be very prominent. There are several ways to handle some of these errors through statistical means. The inversion, described earlier, tells us about the uniqueness of the model, that is, how inaccuracies in measured data are coupled with the determination of the parameters, which parameters are well determined and which ones are badly determined and their interrelationships. Inaccuracies in measured data are not only reflected in inaccuracies in the parameters, but the more serious problem or limitation in the inversion lies in the existence of the so-called equivalence layers.

In Schlumberger and MT soundings, two types of equivalences are most common, where there are layers whose thickness and resistivity are undetermined to a certain extent: a bell-type curve, that is, a resistivity layer which is embedded between two conductive layers, and a bowl-type layer, that is, a conductive layer embedded between two resistive layers (**Figure 10**). For the first case, the only well-determined parameter for the intermediate layer is the transversal resistance, given by the product, $\rho_i d_i = T$. This means that the resistive layer can be thicker and less resistive or thinner and more resistive. For the second case, the only well-determined parameter is the longitudinal conductance, given by the ratio $d_i / \rho_i = S_L$. This means the conductive layer can be thinner and more conductive or thicker and less conductive. This ambiguity is inherent in the method, and it is not possible to distinguish between the different apparent resistivity curves derived from the different equivalent models – they are within the existing error bars. Information from other investigations is needed in order to resolve the equivalence.

For TEM soundings, the depth to a low-resistivity layer is well determined. Similar equivalences apply for TEM as described above for Schlumberger and MT soundings. The equivalence problem must be kept in mind when interpreting the subsurface resistivity models derived from the inversion of resistivity surveying. When comparing the results with other investigations and making a conceptual model of a geothermal system, the limitations of the models must be recognized, that is, which parameters are well known and which are not so well known.

7.03.5.1.4 DC methods – Schlumberger soundings

In DC methods, direct current is injected into the ground through a pair of electrodes at the surface. The current in the Earth produces an electrical field in the surface that is related to the resistivity of the underlying ground. The electrical field is determined from the measured potential difference between a pair of electrodes at the surface.

The basic relationship behind DC resistivity methods is simply the Ohm's law:

$$E = \rho j \qquad [1]$$

where E is the electric field (V m^{-1}), j is the current density (A m^{-2}), and ρ is the resistivity (Ωm), which is a material constant. For a homogeneous Earth and a single current source, the electrical potential, V_r, at a distance r from the current source, I, is given as follows:

$$V_r = \frac{\rho I}{2\pi r} \quad \text{or} \quad \rho = \frac{2\pi r V_r}{I} \qquad [2]$$

This is the key equation for calculating the apparent resistivity for all the different DC configurations. Most configurations rely on two pairs of electrodes: one pair for current transmission and the other for measuring the potential difference. The most common DC method is the Schlumberger method that will be described below. Other methods, with different electrode configurations are, for example, the dipole–dipole method and the Wenner method. They were frequently used in the early days of geothermal exploration, but are rarely used now and will not be discussed further.

Schlumberger soundings have been widely used through recent decades in geothermal prospecting. The electrode configuration is shown in **Figure 9**. The electrodes are on a line, and the setup is symmetric around the center. A pair of potential electrodes (usually denoted by M and N) is kept close to the center, while a pair of current electrodes (usually denoted as A and B) is gradually moved away from the center, for the current to probe deeper into the Earth. The distance between the current electrodes is commonly increased in near-logarithmic steps (frequently 10 steps per decade) until the scheduled maximum separation has been reached. In principle, the distance between the potential electrodes MN should be small and fixed, but in practice, it needs to be enlarged a few times as the spacing between the current electrodes is increased. This is to increase the voltage signal and to maintain an acceptable signal to noise ratio.

The measured resistivity value is the apparent resistivity, ρ_a, a sort of an average resistivity of the material through which the current passes. By using eqn [2], the apparent resistivity can be easily derived from the measured current and potential difference and the geometrical setup parameters (**Figure 9**) as follows:

$$\rho_a = \frac{\Delta V}{I}(S^2 - P^2)\frac{\pi}{2P} = K\frac{\Delta V}{I} \qquad [3]$$

where $S = AB/2$, $P = MN/2$, and K is a geometrical factor.

During the measurement, the apparent resistivity obtained from eqn [3] is plotted as a function of AB/2 on a bilogarithmic scale and then inverted into a resistivity model. For a single sounding, it is done in 1D way, traditionally by assuming that the Earth is

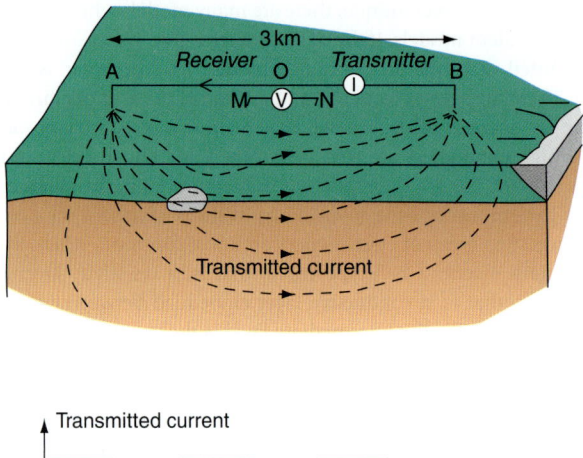

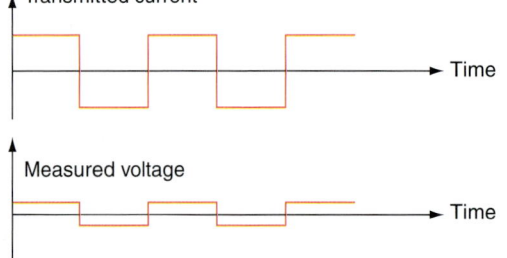

Figure 9 Schlumberger configuration: as the spacing between the current electrodes, A and B, is increased, the current penetrates deeper into the subsurface and the measured potential difference at the surface (between M and N) is affected by the resistivity of deeper-lying layers. The lower part of the figure shows the typical half-duty square wave current and the corresponding potential signal. The typical period of the current signal is 1–2 s. With courtesy of ISOR.

made of horizontal homogeneous and isotropic layers with constant resistivity. The apparent resistivity curve can be inverted to estimate the resistivity and thicknesses of the layers. An example of an apparent resistivity curve and the result of the 1D inversion are shown in **Figure 10**.

Typical soundings for geothermal exploration have a maximum current electrode spacing AB/2 of 1–3 km, but much longer spacings have been used. In practice, very long wire distances can be difficult to handle and the injected current has to be quite large, otherwise the voltage signal will drown in noise. For the depth penetration of the sounding, a rule of thumb says that it reaches down to about one-third of the distance AB/2, but is in fact dependent on the actual resistivity structure.

Due to different potential electrode spacing, the sounding curve consists of a few segments that may not tie in. If local anomalies can be avoided, they might converge (an example is shown in **Figure 11**). This is sometimes called converging shift and is due to large vertical resistivity changes. The depth of penetration depends on the difference $S-P$ but not on S alone. The shift can be corrected for in the modeling itself, which is preferable, or by relying on the values measured with the smallest P and consequently the largest $S-P$.

Another and different shift, which must be taken into account and will be discussed more thoroughly later, is due to resistivity inhomogeneity close to the potential electrodes. These inhomogeneities can provoke constant shifts in the apparent resistivity curve and lead the interpretation astray [30]. The way to handle these shifts is to fix the segment of the curve measured with the largest P used in the sounding, and correct other segments by a factor (multiplication coefficient) that forces the segments to tie in. This assumes that the segment of the apparent resistivity curve measured with the largest P has the least local influence (an example is shown **Figure 12**).

The Schlumberger sounding method cannot detect narrow vertical or near-vertical resistivity structures such as faults, dykes, or fractures. These structures are often the flow path for geothermal fluid, especially in low-temperature geothermal areas. The head-on profiling method has been used successfully for locating these structures [31]. The method has also been used together with Schlumberger soundings for joint 2D interpretation [32]. The head-on arrangement is similar to the Schlumberger array (**Figure 9**) but has an extra fixed current electrode, C, located at a great distance from the other two. The Schlumberger array is moved along the profile, while keeping the distance between the four electrodes fixed. Comparison of the three calculated apparent resistivity curves,

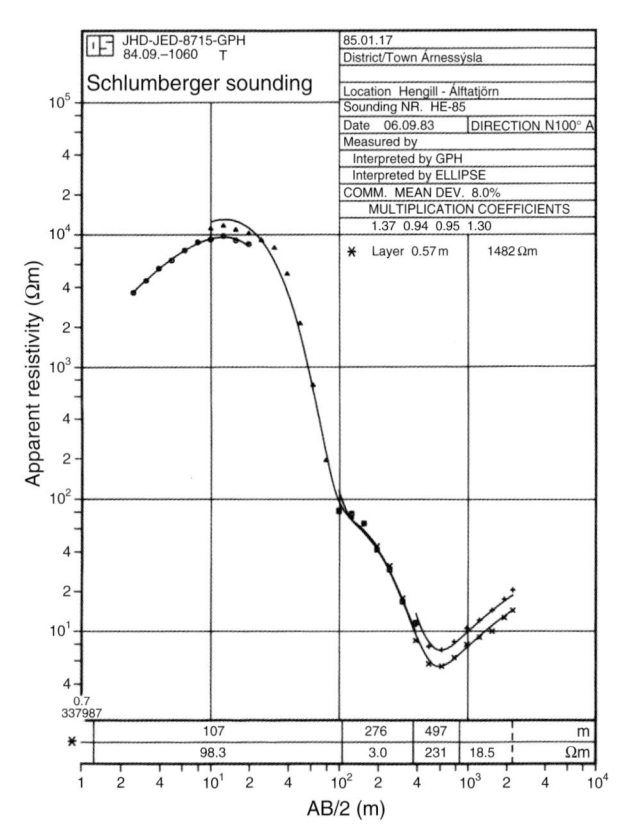

Figure 10 One dimensional inversion (layered earth model) of a Schlumberger sounding from the Hengill high-temperature geothermal area, Southwest Iceland [29]. The data points are black dots and the calculated curve from the final model (the response) is shown as black lines. The final model parameters (resistivity and thickness of layers) are shown at the bottom. The curve shows both converging and constant shifts (notice the multiplication coefficients). The resistive layer (second layer) is an equivalent layer (bell-type curve) and the conductive layer (fourth layer) is also an equivalent layer (bowl-type curve). The resistivity of the conductive layer was fixed at 3 Ωm.

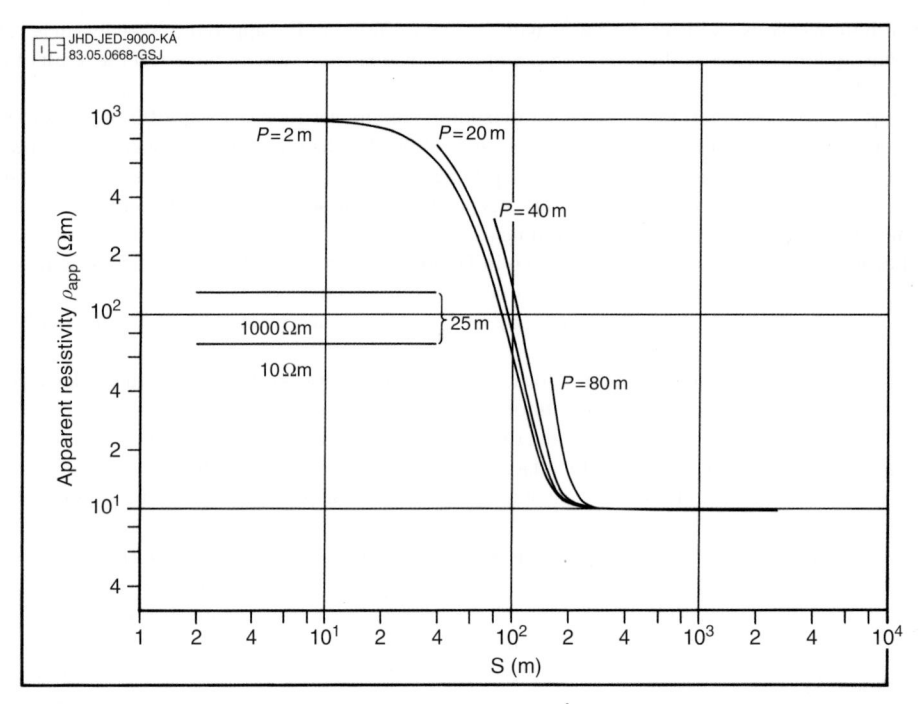

Figure 11 Converging shifts in the apparent resistivity curve for a two-layered model (Árnason, unpublished data). P is half the distance between the potential electrodes ($P = MN/2$).

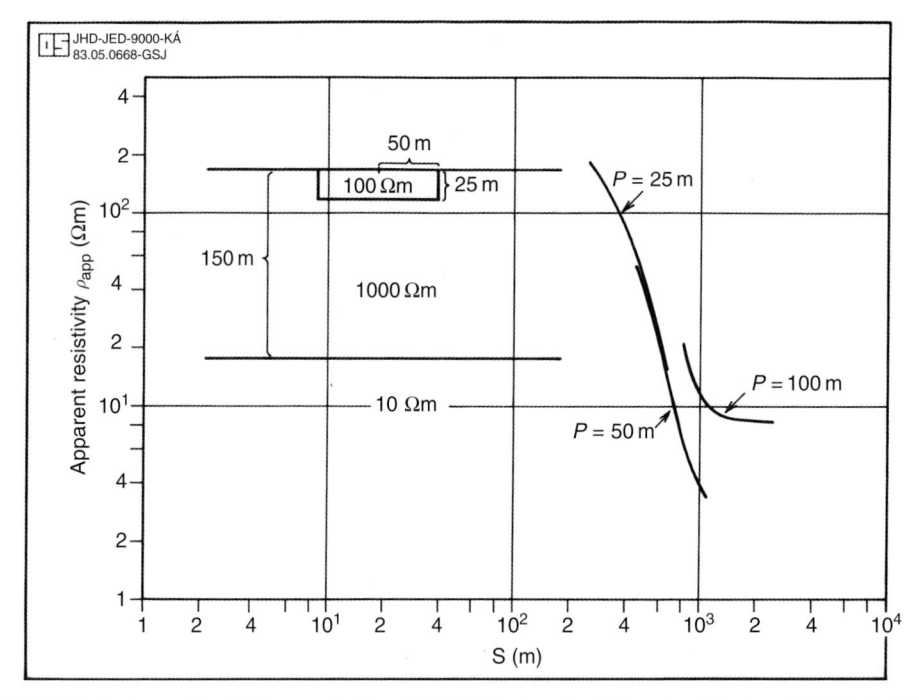

Figure 12 Constant shifts in the apparent resistivity curve due to resistivity inhomogeneity at the center of the array [30]. P is half the distance between the potential electrodes ($P = MN/2$).

resulting from injecting a current between the three pairs of electrodes AB, AC, and BC, gives information on the lateral resistivity changes.

7.03.5.1.5 EM measurements

EM measurements refer to a group of various exploration resistivity methods that have the common feature of using time variations in an EM field to induce currents within the Earth that can be monitored. The most common methods in geothermal exploration are TEM soundings, sometimes called TDEM soundings, and MT soundings. These methods are described here.

7.03.5.1.6 TEM soundings

The TEM method, the theoretical background of which is described in detail in Reference [33], uses a controlled and time-varying man-made magnetic field to induce currents within the Earth. It is an active method, wherein the primary magnetic field is known. A secondary decaying magnetic field from the induced subsurface current is measured. There exist several variations of TEM measurements depending on the type of the source (loop source or dipole source) and the location of the receiver relative to the source. Here we will concentrate on the central-loop TEM sounding method where the receiver is at the center of a source loop and refer to them as TEM.

The TEM method is a fairly recent addition to the resistivity methods used in geothermal exploration, developed and refined since the late 1980s. This is mainly because the TEM response covers a very large dynamic range and advances in electronics were needed, and second, because interpretation of the data is intensive and relatively large computers were needed [34].

The principle of the TEM method is shown in **Figure 13**. A loop of wire is placed on the ground and a constant magnetic field of known strength is built up by transmitting a constant current in the loop. The current is abruptly turned off. The magnetic field is then left without its source and responds by inducing an image of the source loop in the surface. With time, the current and the magnetic field decay and again induce electrical currents at greater depths in the ground. The process can be visualized as if, when the current is turned off, the induced currents, which at very early times are an image of the source loop, diffuse downwards and outwards like a smoke ring (**Figure 13**). The decay rate of the magnetic field with time is monitored by measuring the voltage induced in a receiver coil at the center of the transmitting loop as a function of time, normally at prefixed time gates equally distributed in log time. The decay rate of the magnetic field with time is dependent on the current distribution which in turn depends on the resistivity structure of the Earth. The induced voltage in the receiver loop, as a function of time after the current in the transmitter loop is turned off, can therefore be interpreted in terms of the subsurface resistivity structure.

The transmitter and receiver are synchronized either by connecting them with a reference cable or by high-precision crystal clocks so that the receiver gets to know when the transmitter turns off the current. Turning off the current instantaneously would induce infinite voltage in the source loop. Therefore, the transmitters are designed to turn off the current linearly from maximum to zero in a short but finite time called turnoff time. The zero time of the transients is the time when the current has become zero and the time gates are located relative to this. This implies that the receiver has to know the turnoff time. To reduce the influence of EM noise, the recorded transients are stacked over a number of cycles before they are stored in the receiver memory.

The depth penetration of the TEM method depends on the resistivity beneath the sounding as well as on the equipment and the field layout used (i.e., the setup geometry and the generated current and its frequency). The depth penetration increases with time

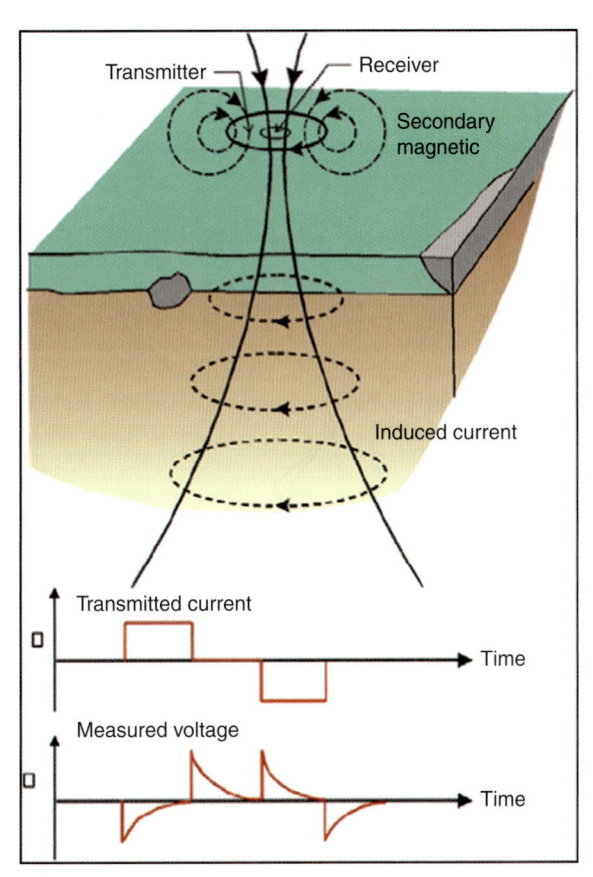

Figure 13 TEM sounding setup; the receiver coil is in the center of the transmitter loop. Transmitted current and measured transient voltage are shown as well. With courtesy of ISOR.

after the current turnoff. Different frequencies of the current signal are therefore used, high frequencies for shallow depths and low frequencies for deep probing. For typical geometries and frequencies, the penetration depth is of the order of or somewhat < 1 km, depending also on the subsurface resistivity.

Typically, the size of the source loop is a 300 m × 300 m-square loop (sometimes 200 m × 200 m, reducing the depth of penetration to around 500 m), and the transmitted current is a half-duty square wave (**Figure 13**) of around 20–25 A with frequencies of 25 and 2.5 Hz (50 Hz electrical environment).

Two receiver loops are used commonly. For both frequencies, a circular loop is used, for example, with an area of 1 m^2 and 100 windings, an effective area of 100 m^2. For the low frequency, for example, a 10 m × 10 m-square loop is used with an effective area of 5640 m^2. The transients are recorded at 30 time gates equally spaced on log scale and stacked over a number of cycles. Usually, several datasets are recorded for processing and stacking to reduce the influence of noise on the data. After analyzing the datasets, omitting outliers and performing stacking, the apparent resistivity is calculated as a function of the square root of time after the current has been turned off (**Figure 13**). Now the data are ready for inversion.

The results of a TEM sounding is, similarly to a Schlumberger sounding, expressed as an apparent resistivity, ρ_a (or more correctly the so-called late-time apparent resistivity), as a function of time after the current turnoff. At late times after the current turnoff, the induced currents have diffused way below the surface and the response is independent of near-surface conditions. The apparent resistivity is a function of several variables, including the induced voltage (V) measured at the time, t, elapsed after the current in the transmitter loop has been turned off; r denotes the radius of the transmitter loop, the effective area (cross-sectional area times the number of windings) of the transmitter loop ($A_s n_s$), and the receiver coil ($A_r n_r$); and the current strength (I_0) and magnetic permeability (μ_0). The apparent resistivity, ρ_a, is given as follows in eqn [4]:

$$\rho_a(t,r) = \frac{\mu_0}{4\pi} \left[\frac{2\mu_0 A_r n_r A_s n_s I_0}{5 t^{5/2} V(t,r)} \right]^{2/3} \quad [4]$$

The apparent resistivity curve is then inverted in terms of a horizontally layered Earth model with homogeneous and isotropic layers to give a 1D model below each sounding. For all the layers in the inversion, both the resistivity and layers' thicknesses can vary. An alternative method for 1D interpretation, and a more commonly one used today, is Occam (minimum structure) inversion [35]. It is based on the assumption that the resistivity varies smoothly with depth rather than in discrete layers. In the Occam inversion, the smooth variations are approximated by numerous thin layers of fixed thickness and the data are inverted for the values of the resistivity (**Figure 14**).

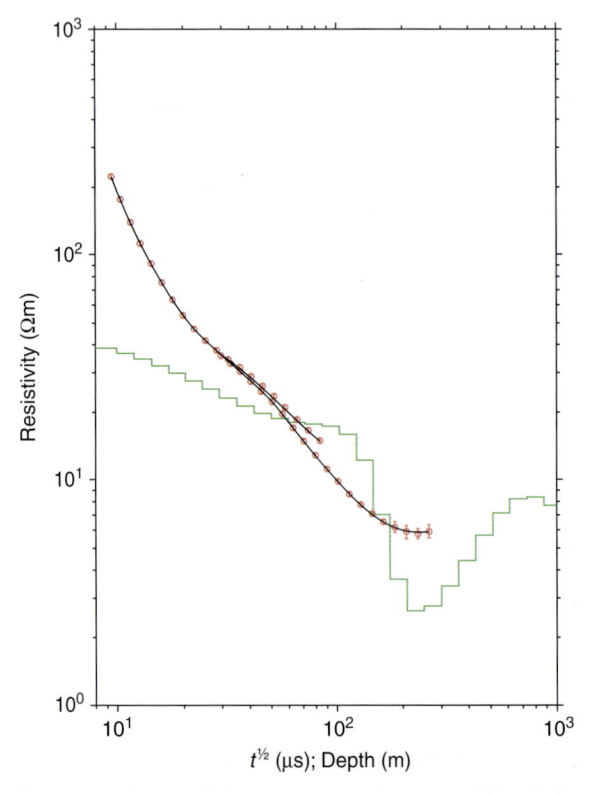

Figure 14 A TEM sounding and its 1D Occam inversion from high-temperature geothermal area Krýsuvík, Southwest Iceland [36]. Red circles: measured late-time apparent resistivities (different datasets for different receiver loop sizes and current frequencies); and black line: apparent resistivity calculated from the model shown in green. Below the name of the TEM station (TEM 472857) at the top of the figure is the misfit function; the root-mean-square difference between the measured and calculated values is $\chi = 0.262$.

Compared with Schlumberger soundings, the TEM soundings have much higher horizontal resolution. The reason is that the current loops used in the TEM soundings are only 300 m × 300 m large, whereas for similar depth penetration the Schlumberger soundings are affected by resistivity inhomogeneities over a 3–4 km distance. It follows therefore that the TEM soundings are much less affected by resistivity irregularities and the 1D interpretation of TEM soundings gives much more reliable information than 2D interpretation of Schlumberger soundings.

7.03.5.1.7 Comparison of the Schlumberger and the TEM methods

The TEM method has few advantages when compared with the Schlumberger sounding method. They relate to several factors, such as the method of generating the signal and the simplicity of the field work. The main advantages of the TEM method are as follows:

- In TEM method, no current has to be injected directly into the Earth and shorter but heavier wires are used. This is important in areas where the contact resistivity in the surface is very high and thus current transmission, in case of DC soundings, is difficult (e.g., in deserts and lava fields), making data collection even possible on snow and ice, or bare rock.
- In TEM method, distortions due to local inhomogeneities are small, since the signals (the downward migrating currents) are at late times independent of near-surface variations.
- Similarly, TEM is much less sensitive to lateral resistivity variations than DC methods. Thus, 1D interpretation is much better justified.
- In DC soundings, the monitored signal is low when surveying over low-resistivity structures like in geothermal areas, but strong in TEM soundings, increasing depth penetration in target areas.
- Finally, TEM field work needs less man power, and measurements are considerably faster to carry out. Thus, it is more cost-effective, or allows collection of data in higher density, consequently giving a more detailed model of the geothermal system.

However, TEM soundings are more sensitive to man-made noise than the Schlumberger soundings. This applies especially to power lines. DC soundings do also have some advantages in their simple and more robust equipment; they have higher transparency of the data, giving confidence in results and they better resolve near-surface features.

7.03.5.1.8 MT soundings

The fundamental theory of MT was initially developed in the 1950s by Cagniard [37] in France and by Tikhonov ([38], reprinted [39]) in the Soviet Union. MT is a passive method where the natural time variations in the Earth's magnetic field, the so-called micropulsations, are the signal source. Variations in the magnetic and the corresponding electric field in the surface of the ground are registered, which are used to reveal the subsurface resistivity distribution.

The MT method has the greatest exploration depth of all resistivity methods, some tens or hundreds of kilometers, depending on the recording period, and is practically the only method for studying deep resistivity structures. Similar to the TEM method, the MT method has, due to developments in the electronic and data industry in recent years, improved tremendously, on both the acquisition side (equipment and the measurement techniques) as well as on data analysis and the inversion of the data. MT has become a standard tool in surface exploration for geothermal resources.

In the MT method, the natural fluctuations of the Earth's magnetic field are used as a signal source. Those fluctuations induce an electric field and hence currents in the ground, referred to as eddy currents, which are measured on the surface in two horizontal and orthogonal directions (E_x and E_y). The eddy currents are also called telluric currents, derived from the Latin word tellus, which means Earth. The magnetic field is measured in three orthogonal directions (H_x, H_y, and H_z). A typical setup for an MT sounding is shown in **Figure 15**. It is customary to have the x direction to the magnetic north. For a homogeneous or layered Earth, the electrical

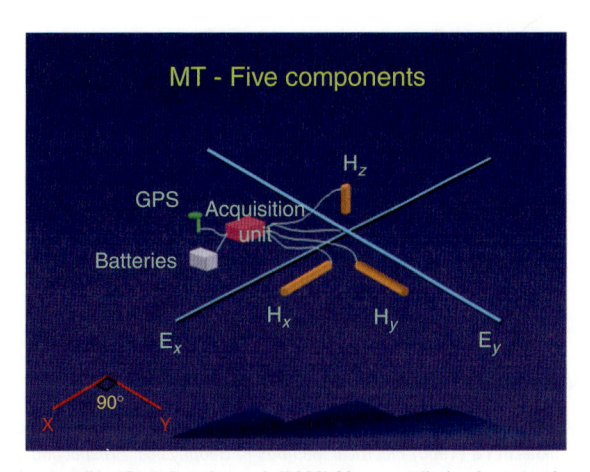

Figure 15 The setup of a magnetotelluric sounding. Based on Jones A (2008) Magnetotellurics for natural resources: From acquisition through interpretation. Dublin Institute for Advanced Studies (DIAS), 17–18 November [40].

field is induced by its orthogonal source magnetic field (i.e., E_x correlates with H_y and E_y with H_x). For more complicated resistivity structures, these relations become more complex. The magnetic field is usually measured with induction coils and the electrical field by a pair of electrodes, filled with solutions like copper sulfate or lead chloride. The electrode dipole length is in most cases 50–100 m. The electric field equals the potential difference between the two electrodes divided by its length. A GPS unit is used to synchronize the data. The digital recording of the EM fields as a function of time is done through an acquisition unit and the time series are saved on a memory card.

MT generally refers to recording time series of electric and magnetic fields of wavelengths from 0.0025 s (400 Hz) to 1000 s (0.001 Hz) or as high as 10.000 s (0.0001 Hz). Audio magnetotellurics (AMT) refers to 'audio' frequencies, generally recording frequencies of 100 Hz to 10 kHz. Long-period magnetotellurics (LMT) generally refers to recording from 1.000 to 10.000 s or even much higher (to 100.000 s). Note that in MT, it is customary to talk both about wavelengths, measured in seconds (s) and its transformation, the frequency (1/T) measured in Hertz (Hz).

The small-amplitude geomagnetic time variations of Earth's EM field contain a wide spectrum (**Figure 16**) generated by two different sources. The low frequencies (long periods) are generated by ionospheric and magnetospheric currents caused by solar wind (plasma) emitted from the sun interfering with the Earth's magnetic field. Higher frequencies, >1 Hz (short periods), are due to thunderstorm activity near the Equator and are distributed as guided waves, known as spherics, between the ionosphere and the Earth to higher latitudes. The natural EM fluctuations of interest here have two relatively low-intensity ranges, the so-called dead-band (**Figure 16**). The MT 'dead-band' is at approximately 0.5–5 Hz (2–0.2 s) and the AMT 'dead-band' is at approximately 1–5 kHz. MT and AMT measurements in these frequency ranges usually suffer from poor data quality, resulting in inaccurate data for a certain depth interval.

The sunspot cycle has been monitored since the mid-seventeenth century. There is a regular cycle over 10–11 years. The last minimum of activity was around 2008 (**Figure 17**). At that time, the MT source spectrum was therefore weak and acquisition of data was relatively difficult, compared with the time around 5 years earlier or presumably later.

MT signals are customarily measured in the frequency range downwards from 400 Hz. Typically, each MT station is deployed for recording one day and picked up the following day. This gives about 20 h of continuous time series per site, and MT data in the range from 400 Hz (0.0025 s) to about 1000 s. The short-period MT data (high frequency) mainly reflect the shallow structures due to their short depth of penetration, whereas the long-period data mainly reflect the deeper structures. Data qualities are to be inspected before moving to the next site and the measurement is redone for another day, if the data qualities are unacceptable – in particular, if the reason is found. In cases where the interest lies in structures at great depths, more than a few tens of kilometers – periods >1000 s – the station should be kept running for several days (LMT).

It has become an industry standard method to keep one MT station recording continuously at a fixed location some tens of kilometers away from the survey area for remote reference data recording [43]. The station is used to get better quality data from the processing, higher signal to noise ratio and to remove the bias caused by local noise sources.

Following the data acquisition, the measured MT time series are Fourier-transformed from the time domain into the frequency domain and the 'best' solution that describes the relation between the electrical and magnetic field is found through the following equation:

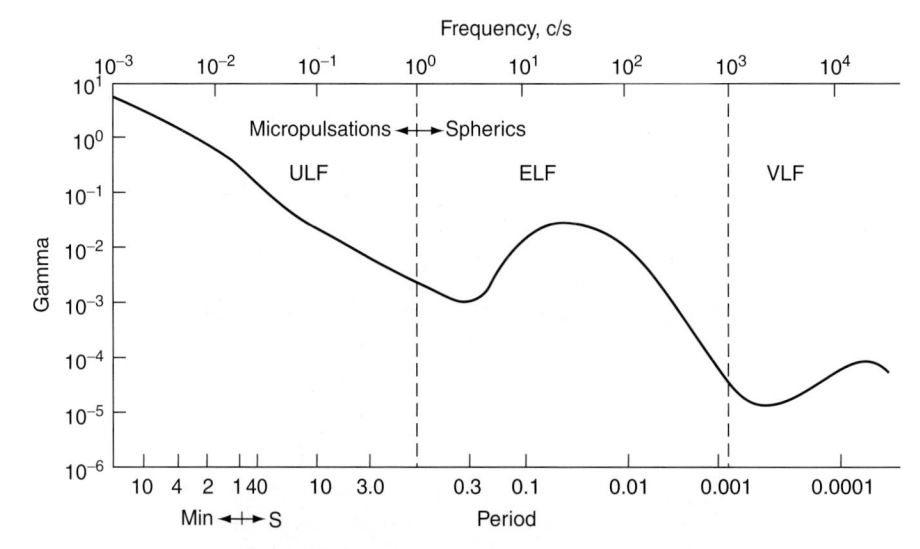

Figure 16 The mean amplitude of the natural magnetic field spectrum in gamma ($\gamma = nT$) as a function of the period – the period decreases to the right on the abscissa. Based on Keller GV and Frischknecht FC (1966) *Electrical Methods in Geophysical Prospecting*, 527pp. New York: Pergamon Press [41]. Note the two local minima of the spectrum: the MT 'dead-band' in the range of approximately 0.5–5 Hz (2–0.2 s) and the AMT 'dead-band' in the range of approximately 1–5 kHz.

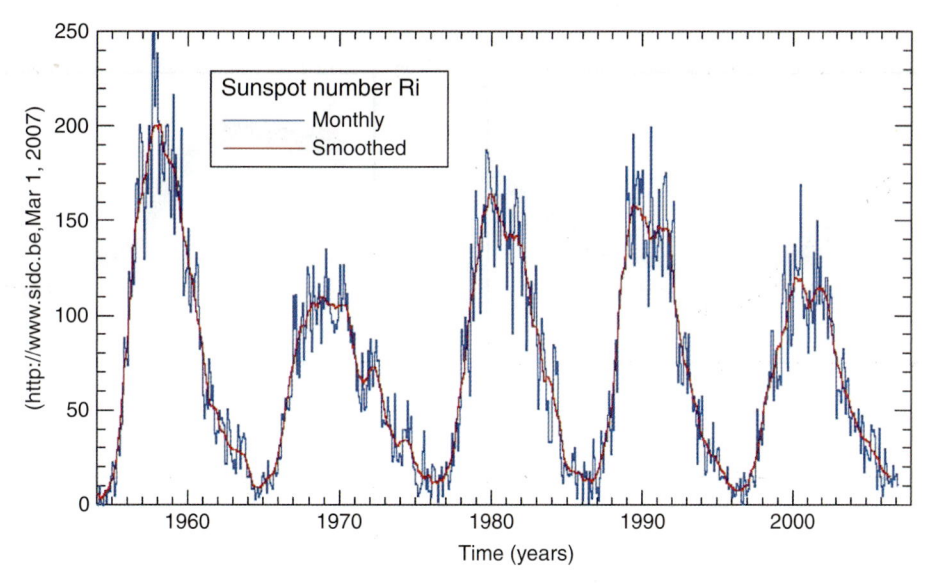

Figure 17 The sunspot cycle over the past 60 years [42].

$$\begin{bmatrix} E_x \\ E_y \end{bmatrix} = \begin{bmatrix} Z_{xx} & Z_{xy} \\ Z_{yx} & Z_{yy} \end{bmatrix} \begin{bmatrix} H_x \\ H_y \end{bmatrix} \quad [5]$$

or in matrix notation:

$$\vec{E} = Z\vec{H} \quad [6]$$

where $\vec{E}$ and $\vec{H}$ are the electrical and magnetic field vectors (in the frequency domain), respectively, and Z is a complex impedance tensor which contains information on the subsurface resistivity structure. The values of the impedance tensor elements depend on the resistivity structures below and around the site. For a homogeneous and 1D Earth, $Z_{xy} = -Z_{yx}$ and $Z_{xx} = Z_{yy} = 0$. For a 2D Earth, that is, resistivity varies with depth and in one horizontal direction, it is possible to rotate the coordinate system by mathematical means, such that $Z_{xx} = Z_{yy} = 0$, but $Z_{xy} \neq -Z_{yx}$. For a 3D Earth, all the impedance tensor elements are different.

From the impedances, the apparent resistivity (ρ) and phases (θ) for each period (T) are calculated according to the following equations:

$$\rho_{xy}(T) = 0.2T|Z_{xy}|^2; \quad \theta_{xy} = \arg(Z_{xy}) \quad [7]$$

$$\rho_{yx}(T) = 0.2T|Z_{yx}|^2; \quad \theta_{yx} = \arg(Z_{yx}) \quad [8]$$

As noted above, $Z_{xy} = -Z_{yx}$, for a homogeneous and 1D Earth, and hence, the xy and yx parameters, ρ_{xy} and ρ_{yx}, and θ_{xy} and θ_{yx} are equal. An example of the processed xy and yx parameters, resistivity, and phase are shown in **Figure 18**.

The depth of penetration of MT soundings depends on the wavelength of the recorded EM fields and the subsurface resistivity structure. The longer the period T, the greater is the depth of penetration and vice versa. The relation is often described by the skin depth or the penetration depth (δ), which is the depth where the EM fields have attenuated to a value of e^{-1} (about 0.37) of their surface amplitude.

$$\delta(T) \approx 500\sqrt{T\rho} \ (m) \quad [9]$$

where ρ is the average resistivity of the subsurface down to that depth.

The xy and yx parameters, both resistivity and phase, are seldom the same, and in cases where they do not, they depend on the orientation of the setup of the measurement. In 1D inversion (layered Earth or Occam inversion), it is possible to invert for either xy or yx parameters, and there have been different opinions through the years which one to use. Nowadays, it is becoming more customary to invert for some rotationally invariant parameter, that is, independent of the sounding setup, which is defined in such a way that it averages over directions. Therefore, one has not to deal with the question of rotation. Three such invariants exist:

$$Z_B = \frac{Z_{xy} - Z_{yx}}{2} \quad [10]$$

$$Z_{\det} = \sqrt{Z_{xx}Z_{yy} - Z_{xy}Z_{yx}} \quad [11]$$

$$Z_{gm} = \sqrt{-Z_{xy}Z_{yx}} \quad [12]$$

All these parameters give the same values for a 1D Earth response. For 2D, $Z_{\det}$ (determinant) and Z_{gm} (geometric mean) reduce to the same value, but Z_B (arithmetic mean) is different. For 3D responses, all these parameters are different.

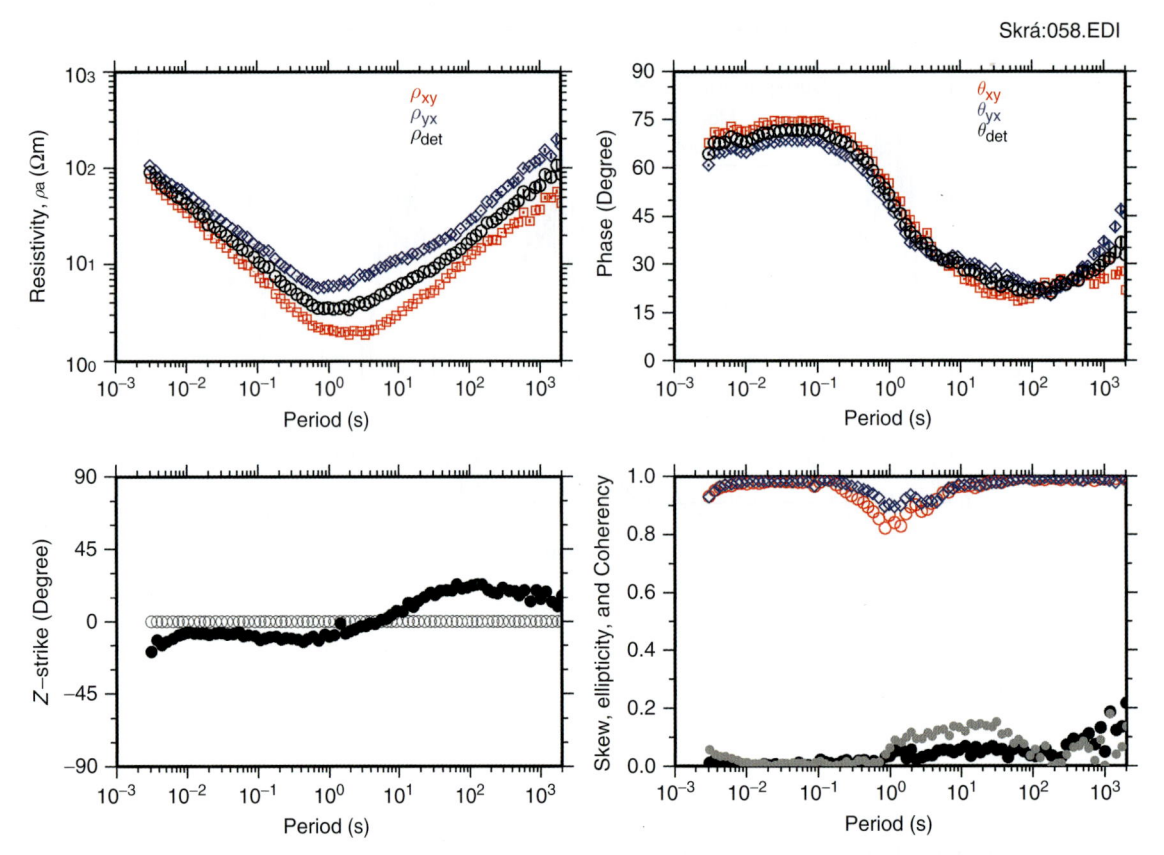

Figure 18 Processed MT data for sounding 058 from the high-temperature geothermal area Krýsuvík, Southwest Iceland [36]. The plots show the apparent resistivity and phase derived from the *xy* (red) and *yx* (blue) components of the impedance tensor and the determinant invariant (black), the Z-strike or swift angle (black dots), and multiple coherency of *xy* (red) and *yx* (blue), and skew (black dots) and ellipticity (gray dots).

There are different opinions on which of the three invariants, if any, is best suited for 1D inversion. However, based on the comparison of model responses for 2D and 3D models, it has been suggested that the determinant invariant is the one to use in 1D inversion [44]. The apparent resistivity and phase calculated from the rotationally invariant determinant of the MT impedance tensor as a function of the period is shown in **Figure 18**.

In **Figure 18**, a few additional useful parameters are shown on the bottom right-hand panel. The multiple coherency of the electrical fields with respect to the horizontal magnetic fields is used as an indicator of the quality of the data, the closer to 1, the better are the data. The coherency should preferably be higher than 0.9. Notice the relatively small coherency values in the dead-band. The calculated skew and ellipticity are indicators of three dimensionality. The skew is rotationally invariant and should be zero for 1D and 2D Earth. A value of zero for both skew and ellipticity is a necessary and sufficient condition for two dimensionality of the data.

Electrical strike analysis of MT data can indicate the directions of resistivity contrasts. These can be geological fractures, not necessarily seen on the surface. As discussed above, the elements of the MT impedance tensor do, in addition to the resistivity structures below and around the site, depend on the orientation of the *x* and *y* directions of the field layout. For a 2D Earth, the resistivity varies with depth and in one horizontal direction. The horizontal angle perpendicular to that direction is called the electrical strike. The angle it makes with geographical north is called the swift angle or Z-strike, Φ. It is possible to rotate the coordinate system by mathematical means and recalculate the elements of the impedance tensor for any desired direction. This equals that the fields (E and H) had been measured in these rotated directions. If the Earth is 2D and the coordinate system of the field layout has one axis parallel to the electrical strike direction, we have that $Z_{xx} = Z_{yy} = 0$, but $Z_{xy} \neq Z_{yx}$. We get two sets of apparent resistivity (ρ_{xy} and ρ_{yx}) and two sets of apparent phases (θ_{xy} and θ_{yx}) as shown above. For a 1D Earth they are equal. The electrical strike, Z-strike, can be determined by minimizing $|Z_{xx}|^2 + |Z_{yy}|^2$ with respect to Φ – the rotation of the coordinate system. There is, however, a 90° ambiguity in the strike angle determined in this way because the diagonal elements of the tensor are minimized as if either the *x*- or *y*-axis is along the electrical strike. There is therefore no way of distinguishing between Φ and $\Phi + 90°$, from the tensor alone.

The depth of investigation increases with period and Z-strike depends on the period because the dominant electrical strike can be different at different depths. The Z-strike is shown as a function of period in **Figure 18**. Another parameter that is often used for directional analysis is the so-called Tipper, *T*, which relates the vertical component of the magnetic field to its horizontal components:

$$H_z = T_x H_x + T_y H_y \qquad [13]$$

where T_x and T_y are the x and y components of the Tipper, respectively. For 1D Earth, the Tipper value is 0, that is, $T_x = T_y = 0$. For a 2D Earth, the coordinate system can be rotated so that the x-axis is in the strike direction, the so-called T-strike, that is, $T_x = 0$, but $T_y \neq 0$. This is done by minimizing $|T_x|$. By proper definition, the T-strike does not suffer the 90° ambiguity of the Z-strike.

Figure 19 is a rose diagram of the Tipper strike for the period interval, 0.1–1 s, corresponding to a depth of around 1 km. Thick, dark-red lines are drawn on the figure indicating zones of different dominant strike directions. However, these lines are by no means unambiguous, and simply an indication. To the west, the T-strike is along the dominant geological strike. To the east, the area can be divided into four zones, two of them showing dominant electrical strike direction perpendicular to the geological strike. These features do contribute to the picture of the subsurface resistivity structure of the area [45].

The MT method, like all resistivity methods that are based on measuring the electric field on the surface, suffer from the so-called telluric or static shift problem [28, 46, 47]. This is a similar phenomenon as the constant shift in Schlumberger soundings discussed earlier in this chapter. It is caused by resistivity inhomogeneity close to the electric dipoles. There are mainly three processes that cause static shift, that is, voltage distortion, topographic distortion, and current channeling [48]. Voltage distortion is caused by a local resistivity anomaly, resistivity contrast at the surface. Topographic distortion takes place where the current flows into the hills and under the valleys, affecting the current density, and current distortion (current channeling) is where the current flow in the ground is deflected when encountering a resistivity anomaly. If the anomaly is of lower resistivity than the surroundings, the current is deflected (channeled) into the anomaly, and if the resistivity is higher, the current is deflected out of the anomaly. If the anomaly

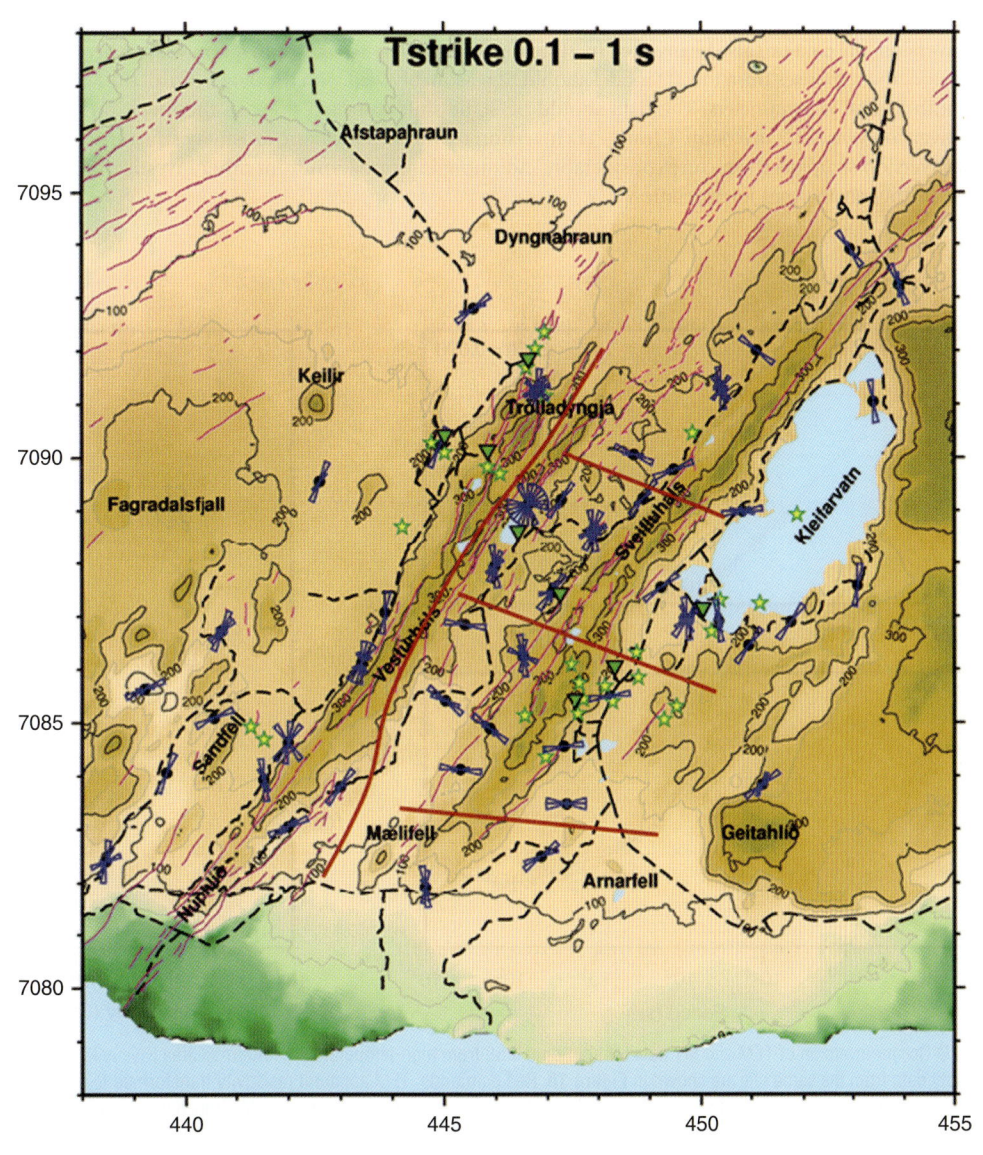

Figure 19 Rose diagram of the Tipper strike for the period 0.1–1 s from Krýsuvík area in Southwest Iceland [45]. Wells are denoted by green-filled triangles, fumaroles by green/yellow stars, and fractures and faults by magenta lines. Thick, dark-red lines indicate zones of different dominant strike directions. Scales in kilometers.

is close to the surface, this will affect the current density at the surface and hence the electric field. Like for the voltage distortion, this effect is independent of the frequency of the current.

These three phenomena are common in geothermal areas in volcanic environment where the surface consists of resistive lavas. Geothermal alteration and weathering of minerals can produce patches of very conductive clay on the surface surrounded by very resistive lavas, producing severe voltage distortion. Similarly, if the conductive clay minerals dome up to shallow depth but not quite to the surface, they can result in extensive current channeling.

The problem is that the amplitude of the electric field on the surface and, consequently, the apparent resistivity is scaled by an unknown dimensionless factor (shifted on log scale) due to the resistivity heterogeneity in the vicinity of the measuring dipole. Static shift can be a big problem in volcanic geothermal areas where resistivity variations are often extreme. Shift factors of the apparent resistivity have been observed as low as 0.1, leading to 10 times too low-resistivity values and about 3 times too small depths to resistivity boundaries [46]. In the central-loop TEM method, the measured signal is the decay rate of the magnetic field from the current distribution induced by the current turnoff in the source loop, not the electric field. At late times, the induced currents have diffused way below the surface and the response is independent of near-surface conditions.

Therefore, TEM soundings and MT soundings can be jointly inverted in order to correct for the static shift of the MT soundings. The shift multiplier may be used in multidimensional inversion of MT soundings, and has been proven in high-temperature geothermal areas to be a necessary precondition. MT data cannot be used to correct themselves for static shifts. Interpretation of MT data without correction by TEM cannot be trusted except, may be, in areas where it is known that little or no near-surface inhomogeneity is present (e.g., thick homogeneous sediments). **Figure 20** shows an example of a 1D joint Occam inversion of TEM and MT data.

Besides 1D inversion, MT data can also be inverted in 2D and particularly in 3D, which in recent years is becoming more practical [49]. In 3D inversion, the responses from the 3D model should fit reasonably well with the data from all the MT soundings from the modeled area, both xy and yx parameters. The data should be static shift-corrected prior to the inversion. **Figure 21** shows an example of 1D inversion versus 3D inversion. Clearly, 1D inversion reproduces the basic resistivity structures but smears them out, whereas the 3D inversion sharpens the picture considerably. Additional information from other investigations has been added to the figure to ease further geothermal interpretation.

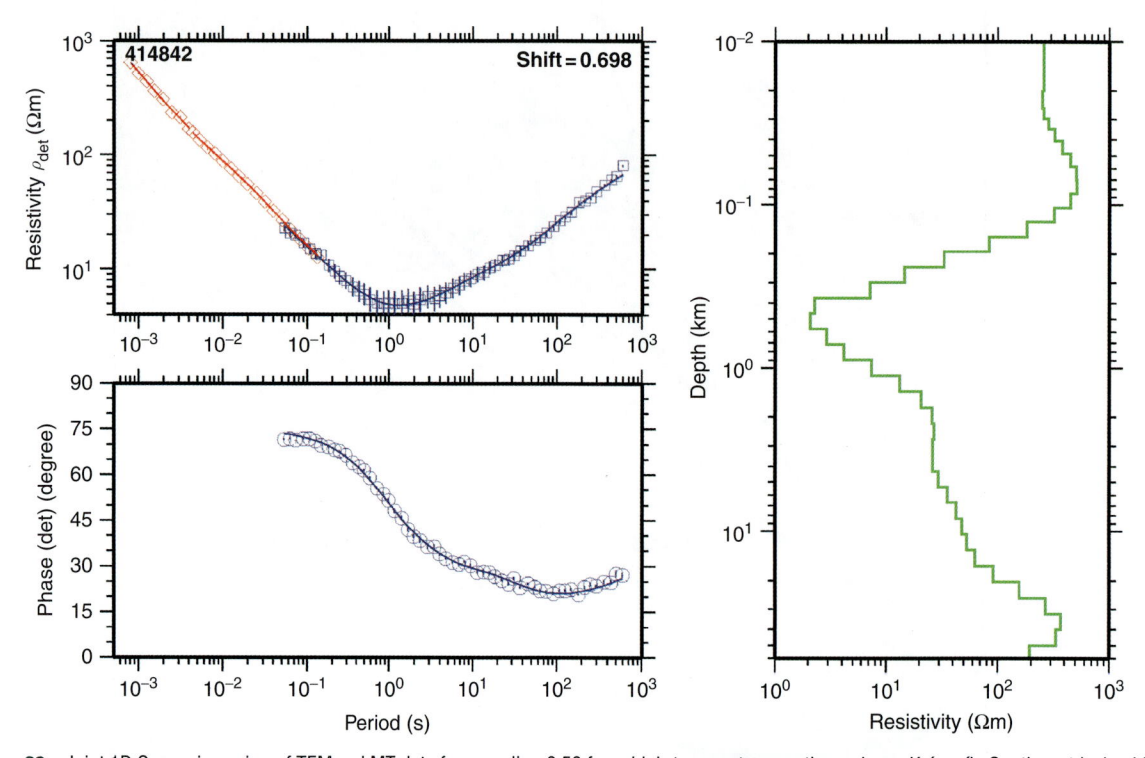

Figure 20 Joint 1D Occam inversion of TEM and MT data for sounding 0.58 from high-temperature geothermal area Krýsuvík, Southwest Iceland [36]. The processed empty data from the same site are shown in **Figure 18**. Red diamonds: TEM apparent resistivity transformed to a pseudo-MT curve; blue squares: measured apparent resistivity; blue circles: apparent phase – both derived from the determinant of MT impedance tensor; green lines: on the right are results of the 1D resistivity inversion model and to the left are its synthetic MT apparent resistivity and phase response. Note the shift value being as low as 0.698 for the MT data to tie in with the TEM data. The misfit function; the root-mean-square difference between the measured and calculated values is $\chi = 1.0479$.

Geothermal Energy Exploration Techniques 77

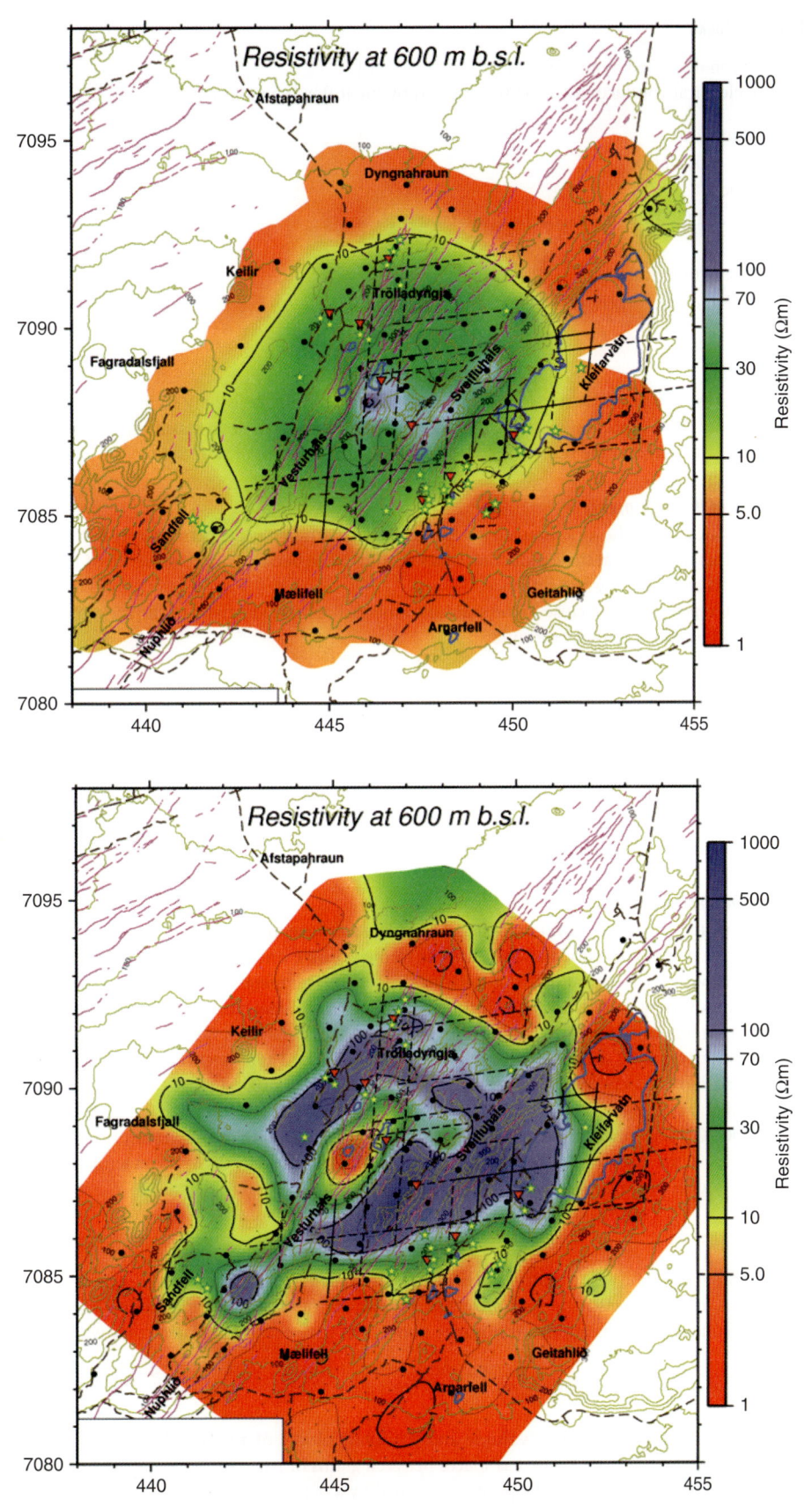

Figure 21 Resistivity models from Krýsuvík, Southwest Iceland [45]: based on 1D model (upper panel), and 3D model using the 1D model as an initial model in the 3D inversion (lower panel). Black dots are MT soundings, wells are denoted by red-filled triangles, fumaroles by green/yellow stars, and fractures and faults by magenta lines. Solid and broken black lines show possible fracture zones, inferred from seismicity.

7.03.5.2 Resistivity of Rocks

Resistivity of rocks has been described by many authors [1, 32, 50–60].

In porous rocks, the electrical conductivity is mainly affected by the following parameters:

- The degree of fluid saturation
- The conductivity of the rock matrix
- Salinity of the pore fluid
- Water–rock interaction and the mineral assemblage, alteration
- Temperature
- Porosity and the pore structure of the rock
- Type of pore fluid similar to the content of water, steam, gas, and oil.

7.03.5.2.1 Fluid saturation

In geothermal areas, the rocks are water or steam-saturated below the water table. Resistivity soundings are frequently used to find the depth to the groundwater table, since water saturation causes a significant decrease in resistivity. Above the groundwater table, the rocks may be partially saturated and the resistivity there depends on the degree of saturation.

7.03.5.2.2 Conductivity of the rock matrix

For most rocks in geothermal systems, the rock matrix itself has very low to extremely low conductivity at reservoir temperature; rock is normally an insulator. This implies that the conduction takes mainly place because of the presence of fluid and ions in the rock and by electrons in minerals at the rock–water interface.

However, at very high temperatures and close to the solidus of the rock, the conductivity of the rock matrix becomes important. The matrix conductivity follows the Arrhenius formula:

$$\sigma_m(T) = \sigma_0 e^{-E/kT} \qquad [14]$$

where σ_m is the matrix conductivity, σ_0 is the conductivity at infinite temperature, E is the activation energy (eV), k is the Boltzmann constant (eV°K^{-1}), and T is the temperature in °K. Laboratory measurements of basalts and related material over the temperature range of 400 °C to 900 °C give typical value of 0.80 for E and 300 for σ_m [61]. This indicates that the matrix resistivity of basaltic rock is in the order of 1000 Ωm at 400 °C and decreases to 10 Ωm at 800 °C. At higher temperature, partial melt will still increase the conductivity. Since temperature exceeding 400 °C can be expected in the root of the geothermal systems, the matrix conductivity will have an increasing impact on the overall conductivity.

7.03.5.2.3 Resistivity of electrolytes

In an aqueous salt solution, the ions of the solid separate and are free to move independently in the solution. In an electric field, cations are accelerated to the negative electrode and the anions to the positive one. A viscous drag force limits the velocity of the ions. The mobility (thermal velocity/electrical field) of the ions depends on temperature (viscosity) and on concentration.

Groundwater may have a variety of salts in the solution. Therefore, equivalent salinity is defined as the salinity of an NaCl solution with the same resistivity as the particular solution. Mobility of the ions does not vary widely and equivalent salinity is therefore close to true salinity. **Figure 22** shows the resistivity of solutions of NaCl as a function of concentration and temperature. It reveals the nearly linear relationship between the salinity and conductivity ($\sigma \approx C/10$, where C (g l^{-1}) is the concentration of NaCl) except at very high salinities, much higher than can be expected in a geothermal reservoir.

At temperatures, 0–200 °C, resistivity of aqueous solution decreases with increasing temperature, due to increasing mobility of the ions caused by a decrease in the viscosity of the water (**Figure 23**). Pore-fluid conductivity, σ_f, at temperatures below 150 °C can be described by the linear model of Dakhnov [63]:

$$\sigma_f(T) = \sigma_f(T_0)[1 + \alpha_f(T-T_0)] \qquad [15]$$

where T_0 is a reference temperature and α_f is a temperature-independent coefficient. The value of α_f was found to be 0.023 °C^{-1} for $T_0 = 23$ °C. Due to changes in density, viscosity, and dielectric permittivity of water for temperatures above 150 °C, affecting the mobility of free charges, conductivity diverges from linearity above this temperature and decreases with increasing temperature higher than 250 °C [64].

7.03.5.2.4 Porosity

Porosity is defined as the ratio between the pore volume and the total volume of a material. There are primarily three types of porosity: 'intergranular', where the pores are formed as spaces between grains or particles in a compact material like sediments and volcanic ash; 'joints–fissures' or fractures, where the pores are formed by a net of fine fissures caused by tectonics or cooling of the rock (igneous rocks, lava); and 'vugular porosity', where big and irregular pores have been formed due to dissolution of material, especially in limestone. Pore spaces must be interconnected and filled with water if fluid conduction is to take place. In all types of

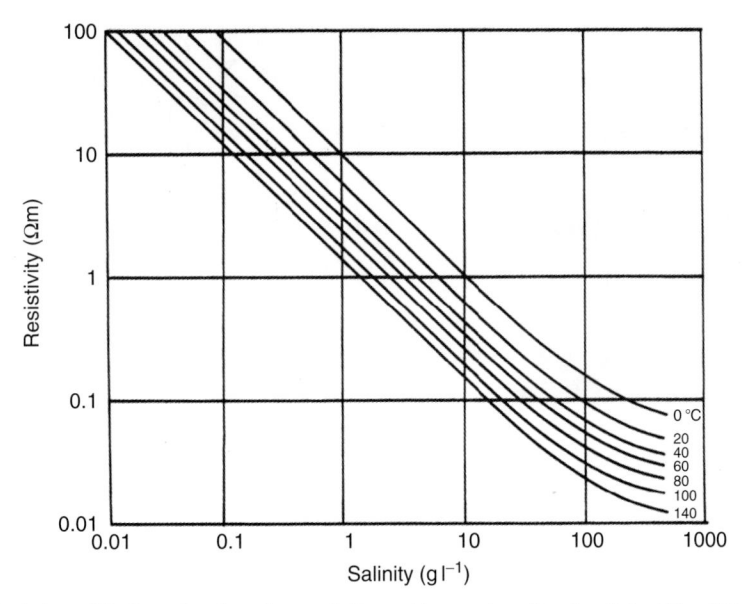

Figure 22 The resistivity of solutions of NaCl as a function of concentration and temperature. Based on Keller GV and Frischknecht FC (1966) *Electrical Methods in Geophysical Prospecting*, 527pp. New York: Pergamon Press [41].

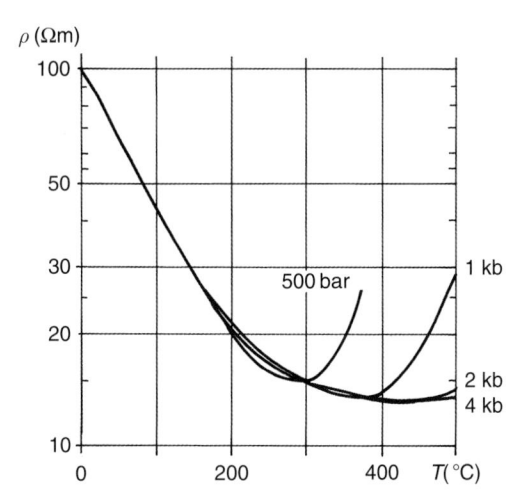

Figure 23 The resistivity of an NaCl solution as a function of temperature [57]. Modified from Quist AS and Marshall WL (1968) Electrical conductances of aqueous sodium chloride solutions from 0 to 800 °C and at pressures to 4000 bars. *The Journal of Physical Chemistry* 72: 684–703 [62].

porosity, there are some isolated voids, called storage pores, and finer connecting pores called fracture pores. Electric conduction in water-saturated porous rocks occurs mainly along the connected pores.

Rocks with fracture porosity, like volcanic rocks, normally contain some isolated saturated pores. They are often spherical, formed by gas bubbles that originally were trapped in the cooling magma. The contribution of fluid in these pores to the overall conductivity of the rock is, however, very small, almost negligible.

Laboratory measurements of porosity are basically accomplished in two different ways. The triple-weighing method is the most common one. It involves drying of the sample under vacuum at elevated temperature, resaturation of the sample under vacuum, and weighing of the dry sample as well as the saturated sample in air and submerged in water. This method only measures the porosity of interconnected pores (intergranular and fracture porosity), but not the total porosity of the rock. The other main method of porosity measurements in laboratories involves crushing of the rock specimen into fine grains and use of a pycnometer to measure the porosity. This method gives the total porosity. Porosity of rock is also frequently measured indirectly in boreholes by various geophysical logging methods. Some of these methods give estimate of the total porosity, whereas others are sensitive to fracture porosity.

7.03.5.2.5 Conduction in porous rock

Conduction of electrical current in the pore space happens in two ways: by ionic conduction through the pore fluid and by conduction on the interface between the pore fluid and the pore walls [51, 52, 58, 65]. The latter is called 'interface' or 'surface

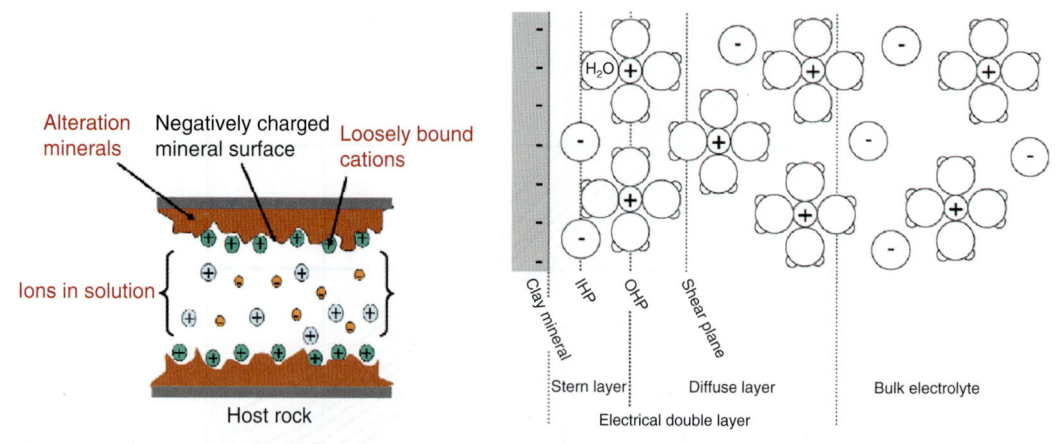

Figure 24 Surface conduction explained [66]. The zone between the surface of a solid clay mineral and the contiguous electrolyte is called the electrical double layer (or triple layer). It is divided into the Stern layer and the electrical diffuse layer. The Stern layer consists of adsorbed ions at the negatively charged mineral surface. Outside the Stern layer a higher concentration of cations than in the remaining electrolyte form the diffusive part of the double layer. The plane of shear defines the boundary where the mobile part of the diffuse layer can move along the charged surface. According to Revil and Glover [58], interface conduction is the sum of (a) conduction in the Stern layer, (b) conduction in the diffuse layer, and (c) a mechanism working directly on the mineral surface.

conduction' and is caused by the highly mobile ions that form a conductive layer on the surface of the pore walls (**Figure 24**). Different rock types have varying ability in forming a conductive layer in the pores. This ability is called cation-exchange capacity (CEC), and it varies greatly between minerals. Clay minerals have variable but high CEC, whereas minerals forming normal volcanic rocks have practically no CEC.

As a first approximation, the two mechanisms act in parallel according to the (modified) Waxman–Smits equation [53] of Rink and Schopper [52]:

$$\sigma_0 = \frac{\sigma_f}{F} + \sigma_S \qquad [16]$$

where σ_0, σ_f, σ_S, and F are bulk conductivity, pore-fluid conductivity, surface conductivity, and formation factor, respectively. If the surface conductivity is negligible, as in case of high-salinity pore fluid, the formation factor is equal to the ratio of the fluid conductivity to the bulk conductivity. On the other hand, the surface conduction will dominate in rocks with low pore-fluid salinity and high CEC. Under these circumstances, the resistivity of the rock is independent of the pore-fluid salinity.

Surface conductivity, σ_S, depends on the surface area of pores, the surface charge density, the valence and mobility of surface ions, temperature, and acidity (pH) ([58], and references therein). For temperatures below 200 °C, the interface conductivity can be approximated as being linear with temperature, that is:

$$\sigma_S(T) = \sigma_S(T_0)[1 + \alpha_S(T-T_0)] \qquad [17]$$

where T_0 is the reference temperature and α_S is a temperature-independent coefficient, as described earlier. Revil and Glover [58] determined a value of α_S being equal to 0.040 °C^{-1} for $T_0 = 25$ °C and Kristinsdóttir et al. [66] report values in the range 0.027–0.160 °C^{-1}. According to these authors, surface conductivity is in general much more temperature-dependent than pore-fluid conductivity.

At temperatures higher than 200–250 °C, the conductivity starts to level off from the linear relationship [66]. Only very few laboratory measurements of water-saturated rocks at *in-situ* conditions exist for volcanic rocks in the temperature range 200–400 °C. Violay et al. [67] reported measurements of saturated basalt in this temperature range. Their results indicate that the conductivity of the saturated rock samples is almost constant over this temperature range. More measurements are, however, necessary to confirm this as a general rule.

It has been observed through laboratory tests that the relationship between resistivity of porous rocks and porosity follows an inverse power law [50] if the salinity of the pore fluid is high, that is, interface conduction is negligible. This empirical law, called Archie's law, describes resistivity dependence on porosity if ionic conduction in the pore fluid dominates other conduction mechanisms in the rocks:

$$\rho = \rho_W a \phi_t^{-n} \qquad [18]$$

where ρ is bulk (measured) resistivity; ρ_W is resistivity of the pore fluid; ϕ_t is fracture porosity as a proportion of the total volume; a is an empirical parameter, which varies from < 1 for intergranular porosity to > 1 for joint porosity, usually around 1; and n is cementing factor, an empirical parameter, usually around 2.

The type of pore fluid also affects the conductivity of porous rock. For geothermal systems, the main issue is whether the pore fluid is liquid water, steam, supercritical fluid, or even gas. The few experiments that exist on the effect of boiling in geothermal systems strongly indicate at least an order of magnitude decrease in conductivity if the liquid water is replaced by steam [68].

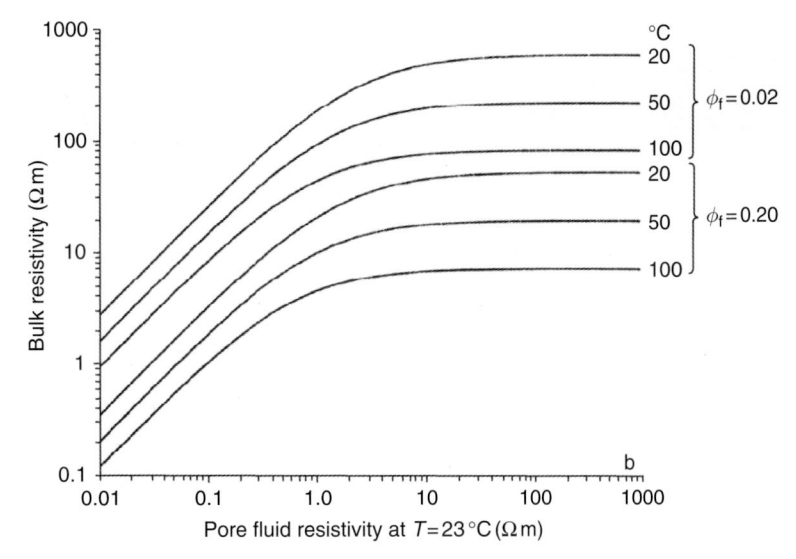

Figure 25 Calculated bulk resistivity as a function of pore-fluid resistivity for different temperatures and porosities [51].

Comparison of conductivity for basaltic rock in Iceland, where interface conduction is dominant over pore-fluid conduction, has shown that an Archie-type relationship also exists between conductivity and porosity [51]:

$$\rho = b\phi_f^{-m} \qquad [19]$$

where ρ is bulk (measured) resistivity; ϕ_f is fracture porosity as a proportion of total volume; b is an empirical parameter, which depends on temperature according to eqn [13]; and m is an empirical parameter, slightly higher than 1.

Figure 25 shows the relationship between the bulk resistivity and the pore-fluid resistivity for different porosities and temperatures for the uppermost basaltic crust of Iceland. It is based on a model put forward by Flóvenz et al. [51]. The model includes both electrolytic and surface/mineral conduction. For pore-fluid resistivity < 2 Ωm, the dominant conductivity is pore-fluid conductivity, and Archie's law applies. For rocks saturated with fluids, having resistivity higher than about 2 Ωm at room temperature, the bulk resistivity is practically independent of the resistivity of the fluid, but dependent on porosity and temperature, the dominant conductivity is surface conductivity. The figure also shows the previously described relationship between resistivity, on the one hand, and temperature and porosity, on the other hand.

7.03.5.2.6 To summarize
At typical geothermal reservoir temperatures, the conduction in the rock matrix is normally negligible. The main contributors to the electrical conduction in geothermal reservoirs are conduction by dissolved ions in the pore fluid (pore-fluid conduction) and conduction by absorbed ions on the pore surface (interface or surface conduction). Both these conduction mechanisms are highly temperature-dependent, especially the surface conduction.

7.03.5.2.6(i) Resistivity structure of high-temperature fields
High-temperature geothermal fields in volcanic areas of the world have in general a similar electrical resistivity structure. A typical resistivity cross section taken from the Nesjavellir high-temperature geothermal system in SW Iceland is given in **Figure 26** [32]. This is where this kind of subsurface resistivity structure was first explained reasonably and was related to the dominant alteration mineralogy and temperature found in boreholes. The rocks in the area are almost entirely composed of basalts in various forms, as lavas, scoria layers, hyaloclastite, or intrusions. No correlation was found between resistivity and lithology in the boreholes. The cross section shows a broad resistivity anomaly consisting of an up-doming conductive cap overlying a resistive core. This type of resistivity structure in volcanic areas of the world has been discussed by several authors [51], such as Árnason et al. [1, 2, 32, 54, 59, 60, 69, 70]. The conductive cap consists of rocks with considerable amount of conductive alteration minerals, like smectite and zeolites that have a high CEC. The resistivity of the cap decreases with temperature until a core of high resistivity is reached. Well logging from different areas shows that the transition from the low-resistivity cap to the high-resistivity core coincides with a change in mineral alteration, that is, from smectite and zeolites to mixed-layered clays, chlorite and epidote.

The increase in resistivity from the smectite alteration zone to the chlorite zone is likely due to the higher CEC of smectite, as compared with chlorite [2]. The CEC is not the same for these two clay minerals; for smectite, the CEC is 0.8–1.5 meq g^{-1} [71], and for chlorite, it is 0.01 meq g^{-1} [72]. This could explain the difference in conductivity between the smectite/zeolite and the chlorite/epidote alteration zones. The resistivity contrast at the top of the smectite zone is due to the onset of interface conduction in the rock [51]. In more silica-rich geological environment, the smectite tends to be replaced by illite with typically lower CEC than that of smectite, often around 0.2–0.30 meq g^{-1}.

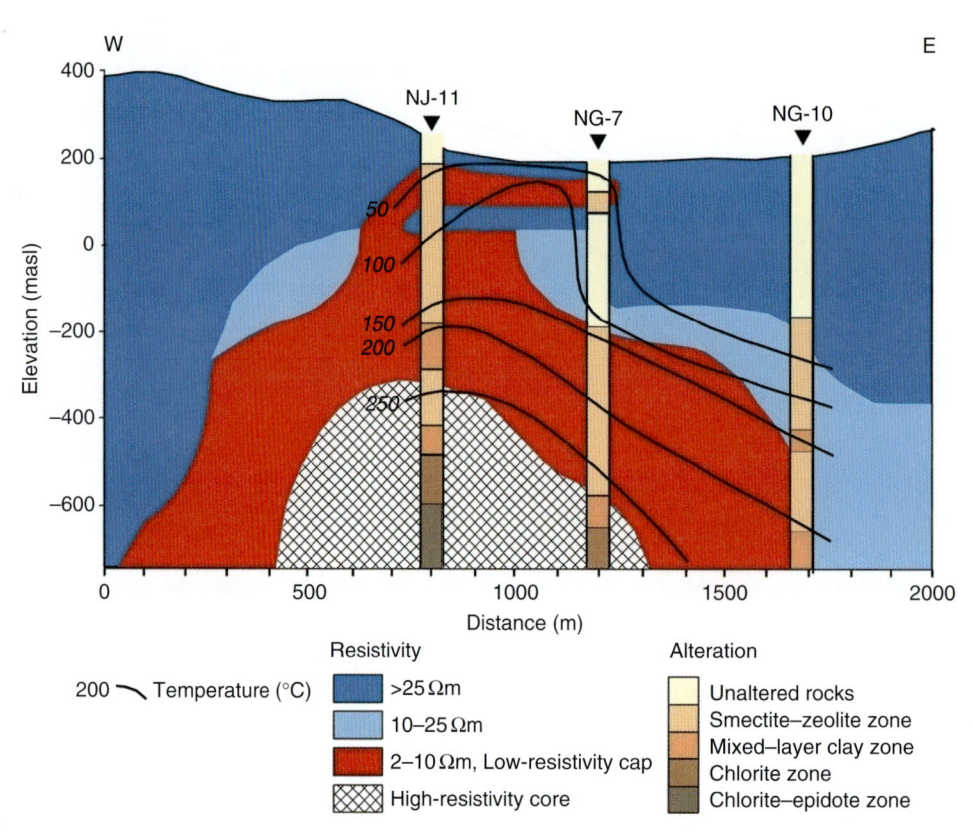

Figure 26 Typical resistivity structure of a high-temperature geothermal reservoir showing a high-resistivity core beneath a low-resistivity cap based on 2D interpretation of a detailed multimethod DC resistivity survey from 1985 and 1986. The figure also shows the alteration minerals in three wells and the isotherms derived from the estimated true formation temperature in each well based on numerous temperature logs obtained during and after drilling. The figure shows a very clear correlation between the subsurface resistivity structure, on the one hand, and the alteration mineralogy and true formation temperature, on the other hand. The section is from the Nesjavellir geothermal field, Southwest Iceland [32].

Figure 27 shows measured normalized conductivity of basaltic rock samples as a function of pore-fluid conductivity for different salinities from different alteration zones in Iceland. For unaltered rocks, the conductivity is dominantly pore-fluid conductivity for all salinities. On the other hand, for smectite-altered rocks, the figure shows near-constant values of conductivity for different salinities (except for one sample), showing dominantly mineral conduction. In the case of chlorite alteration, the conductivity curve lies between these two, showing dominantly pore-fluid and surface conduction. This is also in good agreement with the result in **Figure 26** that shows the correlation between the subsurface resistivity and hydrothermal alteration minerals as revealed in cuttings from boreholes.

The relationship between subsurface resistivity, hydrothermal alteration, temperature, and conduction mechanism is summarized in **Figure 28**. The change from a smectite to chlorite-type alteration assemblage is reported to occur at temperatures close to 230 °C in basaltic geothermal systems [73]. The change to illite seems to occur at somewhat lower temperature, or 180 °C [74]. Permeable geothermal reservoirs with temperatures above 230 °C are of great importance, since they are well suited for electrical generation. Hence, being able to detect the approximate 220–240 °C anomalies with resistivity measurements would help enormously in the search for reservoirs suitable for power generation. However, the apparent change in resistivity appears to be fixed by the type of clay mineral alteration. The boundary between the low- and high-resistivity regions persists, even if the reservoir has cooled down and the measured temperatures no longer exceed 230 °C. Consequently, the top of the high-resistivity zone represents a surface where the temperature may have been approximately above 230 °C at some time in the past, but the present reservoir temperatures may be somewhat lower.

The subsurface resistivity structure in high-temperature geothermal fields therefore reflects the hydrothermal alteration. The primary minerals in the host rock matrix are transformed into different minerals because of water–rock interaction and chemical transport by the geothermal fluids. Formation of alteration minerals depends on temperature and the type of primary minerals and the chemical composition of the geothermal fluid. Porosity and permeability also control the intensity of the alteration. If the alteration and temperature are in equilibrium, the subsurface resistivity structure reflects not only the alteration but also which temperature to expect. This was an important finding, because if the temperature that produced the alteration mineralogy still prevails, the resistivity structure can be used to predict temperature. But if cooling occurs, the alteration remains and so does the resistivity structure. The resistivity structure can therefore in most cases be regarded as a 'maximum thermometer'. However, it has occurred that alteration minerals have indicated lower temperature than measured in the wells. This has been interpreted as being due to a young system being heated up and the alteration is lagging behind, still not in equilibrium with the temperature.

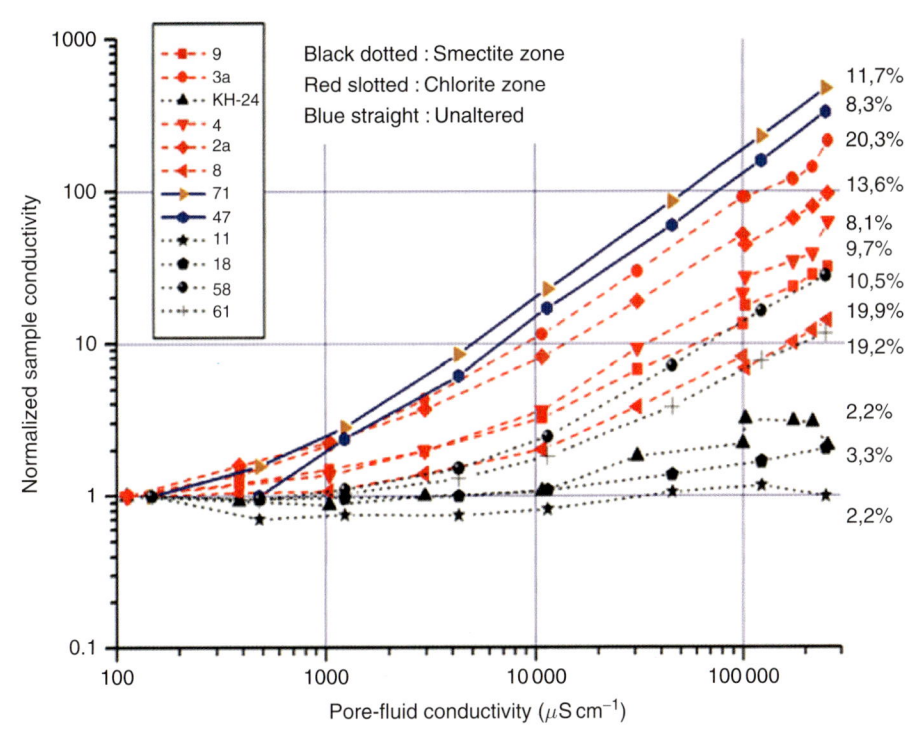

Figure 27 Normalized resistivity as a function of saturating fluid conductivity for different alteration zones in Icelandic rocks [54].

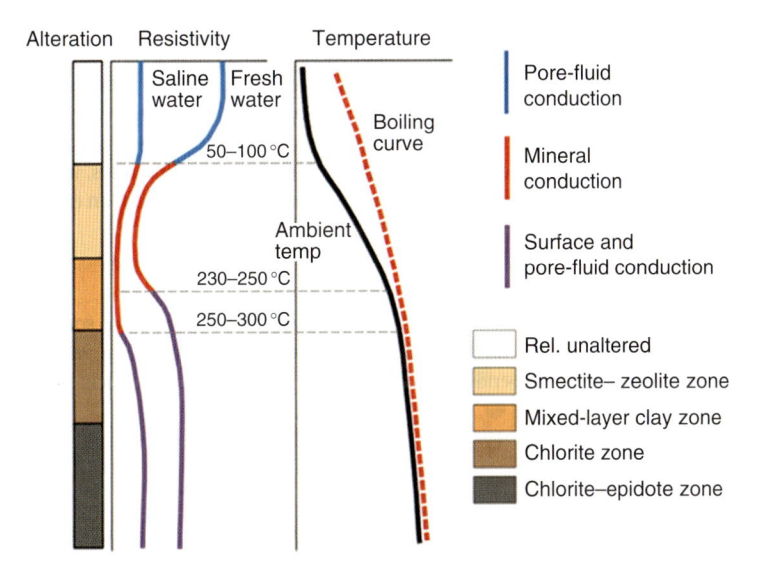

Figure 28 The general resistivity structure and alteration of the basaltic crust in Iceland summarized [54].

For geothermal exploration, it is important to be able to establish prior to drilling whether the resistive core has cooled. Presently, the only method to do that is to use chemical geothermometers, provided reliable fluid samples from hot springs or fumaroles are available; otherwise, drilling is the only option. Drilling is expensive, and therefore development of geophysical methods to resolve this problem is highly desirable as it could significantly reduce the cost of geothermal energy development.

7.03.5.3 Seismic Methods

Seismic exploration methods are traditionally divided into two main categories, passive and active seismics. Passive methods utilize natural seismic earthquakes to get information on the interior of the geothermal systems. They are usually referred to as microseismic studies since earthquakes in geothermal systems are generally of small magnitude on the Richter scale. Active seismic methods use artificially induced seismic signals, typically by use of explosives and air guns.

86   Geothermal Energy Exploration Techniques

When an earthquake occurs, displacement takes place on an existing fault or a new fault is formed. Some of the faults are permeable and might be a target in geothermal drilling. They might also be zones where cold water intrudes the geothermal systems. It is therefore of great importance to locate as precisely as possible the active faults within a geothermal reservoir. This is done with the technique of relative locations and can be applied to events that occur within short time interval on the same fault. This technique is based on comparison of travel times of two or more different events that occur almost at the same site so the seismic waves travel almost along the same path from the hypocenter to the recording stations. The method reduces the errors in relative locations of individual small earthquakes to a few tenths of a meter. It also improves the determination of the dip and strike of the fault but leaves behind the absolute location of the fault as whole. An example of relative location is shown in **Figure 30**.

7.03.5.3.5 Velocity structure

If data coverage is good enough, a catalog of all located seismic events over long time, including possible results from seismic refraction experiments, can be used as an input in tomography. Favorable event and station distributions are further prerequisites for that. The result is a 3D velocity model consisting of blocks which during iteration are changed until best fit is obtained for the entire data collection. The algorithm solves simultaneously for the velocity in the blocks and the location of the events. The output is a 3D velocity model for P and S wave velocities and their ratio. The resulting model can be used to conclude about the physical and geothermal properties of a geothermal field.

Since the P wave velocity is proportional to the density of the rock material, density anomalies will appear as velocity anomalies. Solid gabbroic intrusions in volcanic systems are of high density and can be detected as high-velocity anomalies. Soft rock-like tuffs and sediments like those found in caldera fillings will show up as low-velocity anomalies. Gravity surveys also reveal density anomalies. Joint interpretation of results from seismic tomography and gravity surveys will enhance the modeling results.

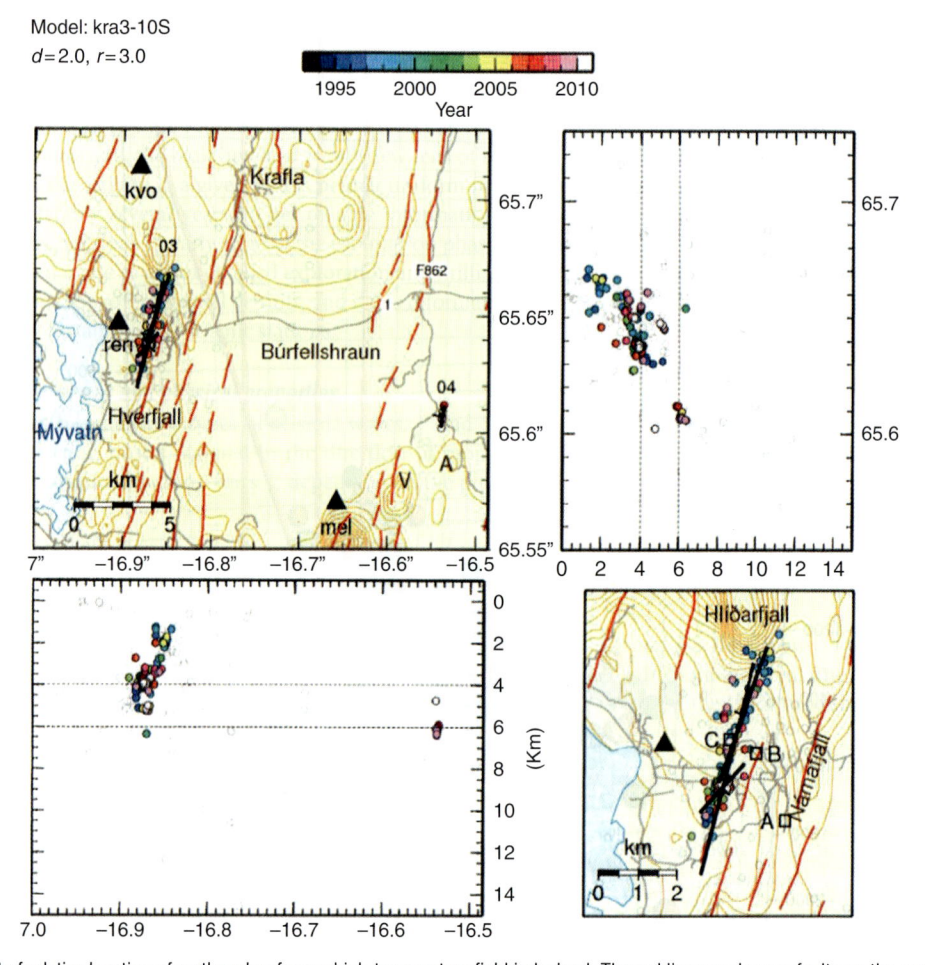

Figure 30 Result of relative location of earthquakes from a high-temperature field in Iceland. The red lines are known faults on the surface. The dots are epicenters and colors indicate the year of the quakes. The upper map shows the epicentres, but the lower one shows a blow up of the upper one. The maps show clearly how the epicenters are bound to just one of the faults and this fault is known to be a flow path for geothermal water. The upper cross section shows a north–south cross section of the hypocenters, whereas the lower one shows a east–west section. Note the westward dip of the fault and the deepest earthquakes are at 6 km depth, suggesting temperature close to 700 °C [75].

Since porosity of the rock is one of the main parameters affecting density of rocks, both Vp and Vs are strongly porosity-dependent. The pore-fluid properties are also important. If the fluid is in a gaseous phase (air or steam), the incompressibility is considerably more reduced than the shear modulus. This means that abnormally low Vp/Vs ratio will be observed where the pores are saturated with steam or gas. Similar effect is supposed in the case of supercritical pore fluid.

Experiments show that the seismic velocities are only slightly reduced with temperature until close to solidus of the rock. Near melting point the shear modulus is strongly reduced, as the rock loses its shear strength. When melting starts, the shear modulus becomes zero, which means that the S waves do not propagate in fluids. This means that molten rock in intrusions or magma chambers appears as an S wave shadow zone and a high Vp/Vs ratio will be observed close to the solidus of the rock.

7.03.5.3.6 The brittle–ductile boundary

A condition for stress to build up in the crust is that the rock is brittle and behaves elastically. If the rock is ductile, it will creep as a consequence of external stress and no earthquakes will occur. The boundary between the brittle and ductile crust depends not only on the type, temperature, and pressure of the rock but also on the strain rate. If the strain rate is high, earthquakes can occur at a higher temperature than for low strain rates. In principle, the boundary between the brittle and the ductile crust can be regarded as an isotherm, at least for a given strain rate and depth. This isotherm is close to 450 °C in continental crust [76] but 650–800 °C in basaltic material [77]. By mapping the lower limits of the depth distribution of the earthquakes in a geothermal field, the depth to the brittle–ductile boundary can be located and the temperature at this depth estimated. This can be valuable since it is often difficult to estimate the evolution of temperature with depth below the deepest boreholes, typically below 2–3 km depth. By this method it is possible to get information about the deeper parts of the geothermal system as well as their roots and heat sources.

An example of mapping of depth distribution of earthquakes is shown in **Figure 31**. It shows how the bottom of the seismogenic crust rises up by 2 km below the Menengai caldera and geothermal field, indicating that at least 400 °C can be expected at 4 km depth.

7.03.5.3.7 Source mechanism

The criterion for an earthquake is that the differential stress within the Earth exceeds the mechanical strength of the rock and a failure occurs. The stress field at a point within the Earth can be described as a stress tensor with one vertical and two horizontal components, called the minimum and maximum horizontal stresses. The most common type of earthquakes is the so-called double-couple earthquakes where the only motion in the quake is a slip along a fault plane. Depending on the orientation of the differential stress, three types of faults can be generated: a normal fault, a strike-slip fault, and a reverse fault. A normal fault occurs when the vertical stress is higher than both the horizontal maximum and minimum stresses. These happen typically in extensional tectonic environment. A strike-slip fault happens when the horizontal stresses are the largest and smallest. Reverse fault occurs when the vertical stress is least. The last type is typical for tectonic compressive environment.

When a fault plane is ruptured, the fault surface will not appear as a sharp plane but rather as a zone of broken or brecciated material that in principle should give rise to fluid permeability. In reality, it depends on the type of earthquake and how effective the formation of permeability is. In normal earthquakes, the environment is extensional and that favors increased permeability, whereas in reverse quakes, the environment is compressional which tends to reduce the permeability. The case for strike-slip faults is intermediate.

Detailed analysis of focal mechanisms in recent years has shown that non-double-couple earthquakes occur within geothermal fields [79]. The cause of these events is unknown but they might be related to fluid or magmatic processes like sudden phase changes.

The above discussion leads to the conclusion that the information on focal mechanism of earthquakes in geothermal fields can provide important information about their internal physical processes. Calculation of the focal mechanism of an earthquake requires a number of seismic stations with good geographical coverage around the epicenter. Traditionally, analysis of the polarity of the first motion in an earthquake at different stations gives the fault plane solution, that is, the orientation of the fault plane and the slip vector. By analysis of the entire seismic waveforms, it is possible to calculate a moment tensor for the quake and from it derive the focal mechanism and the stress within the geothermal system.

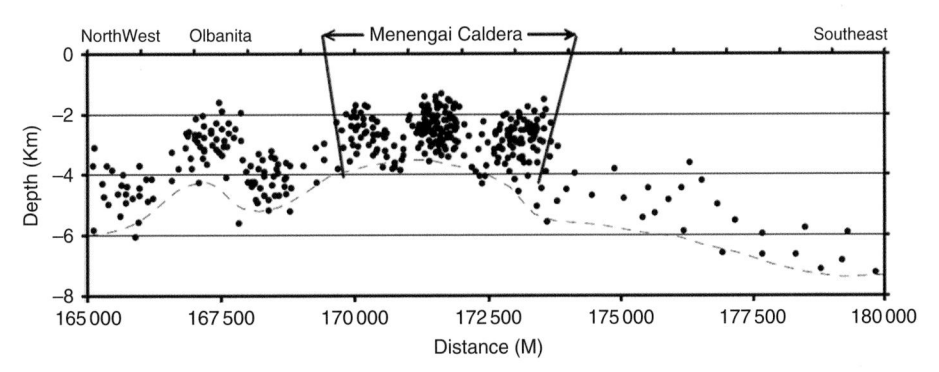

Figure 31 A cross section showing seismic hypocenters across the Menengai caldera and geothermal field in the East-African Rift Valley in Kenya. The lower boundary of the seismic activity defines the brittle–ductile boundary in the crust, possibly the 450 °C isotherm [78].

7.03.5.3.8 Joint interpretation with resistivity data

The individual geophysical methods give quite useful information on the interior of the geothermal fields and their physical state. However, no single method gives sufficient and accurate enough information to avoid drilling of unsuccessful boreholes. A deep geothermal borehole can easily cost 5–10 million dollars, so this should in principle be a strong incentive for improvements of geothermal exploration methods.

The way to advance geothermal exploration technology is not straightforward. For the time being, the emphasis is on joint application of various geophysical methods, especially resistivity and seismic methods. This involves joint inversion or interpretation of both methods. Joint inversion implies that there must exist some kind of a functional relationship between seismic velocities or other seismic properties and resistivity so that the inversion process can invert for both simultaneously. This is, however, almost certainly not the general case for a whole geothermal system but might apply to parts of the systems. For example, a molten magmatic heat source has low-resistivity and low seismic velocities, so joint inversion of that volume might enhance the location of such a body. On the contrary, no change in seismic properties occurs across the major resistivity anomaly caused by the transition from the smectite to the chlorite alteration zone. A joint inversion of the volumes containing this boundary will obviously not lead to any progress. Joint interpretation is a different thing. It involves comparison of the model results from the inversion of the individual measurements followed by comparison and joint interpretation of the results. To make such a comparison easy, it would be necessary to use the same model grid for inversion of both parameters. Such a comparison could then lead to identification of bodies with certain seismic and electrical characteristics that could be related to geothermal processes or physical state.

7.03.5.4 Thermal Methods

By its nature, geothermal systems are characterized by disturbances in the Earth's heat flow, where high heat flow is to be expected. Measurements of heat flow are therefore an important method for exploring geothermal fields.

7.03.5.4.1 Heat transport within the Earth

The internal heat of the Earth is continuously produced by decay of radioactive isotopes. The concentration of radioactive minerals is highest in the crust, mainly in the continental crust. The average rate of radioactive heat production rate in the continental crust is $0.8\,\mu\text{W m}^{-3}$ [80] compared with 0.2–$0.3\,\mu\text{W m}^{-3}$ [81] in the oceanic crust. Considerable chemical reactions occur within the crust that affect the heat budget. These can either be exothermic or endothermic. In addition to the heat produced in the crust, there is constant heat flow from the mantle into the crust. Thus, the heat balance of the crust can be rather complicated.

The internal heat is primarily transported toward the surface in two ways: as thermal conduction or through fluid flow or advection. If the crust was completely impermeable, no fluid transport would occur and all the internal heat would flow toward the surface by thermal conduction. The advective heat transport is either by fluid transport to the surface or in the form of magma that either is emplaced at shallow depth as intrusions or escapes to the oceans and the atmosphere. Convective transport is typical for geothermal systems where water is convecting and disturbing the temperature field produced by conduction. The convection results in heat flow anomalies at the surface. Where the crust is of low permeability, fluid-driven heat transport is negligible and the observed heat flow is only the background heat flow, that is, the general conductive heat flow toward Earth's surface.

7.03.5.4.2 Basic theory of heat flow

In the case of conductive heat flow within the Earth, the temperature distribution is described by the heat flow equation:

$$\frac{\partial T}{\partial t} = \alpha \nabla^2 T + \frac{H}{\rho c} \quad [22]$$

where T is the temperature, $\alpha = \kappa/\rho c$ is the thermal diffusivity, κ is thermal conductivity in $\text{W m}^{-1}\,°\text{K}^{-1}$, H is the rate of heat generation per unit volume, ρ is the density, and c is the specific heat capacity in $\text{J kg}^{-1}\,°\text{K}^{-1}$. In case of homogeneous and isotropic material, the thermal diffusivity is a constant, but if not, it is described by a 3D tensor.

In the case of a steady-state condition (i.e., no time-dependent variations) and assuming only vertical heat flow, eqn [16] reduces to

$$\kappa \frac{d^2 T}{dz^2} = -H \quad [23]$$

where z is positive downwards. By integration we get

$$\frac{dT}{dz} = a - \frac{H}{\kappa} Z \quad \text{and} \quad T = T_0 + az - \frac{H}{2\kappa} Z^2 \quad [24]$$

This implies that based on the above assumptions the temperature gradient will decrease with depth unless the heat production rate is zero. Hence, we can only extrapolate a measured surface temperature gradient linearly into the Earth if we assume zero heat production rates. In case of no heat production, the integration constant, a, is equal to the temperature gradient.

Conductive heat flow in the Earth material depends on the temperature gradient and the thermal conductivity of the rock formation:

$$q = \kappa \frac{dT}{dz} \quad [25]$$

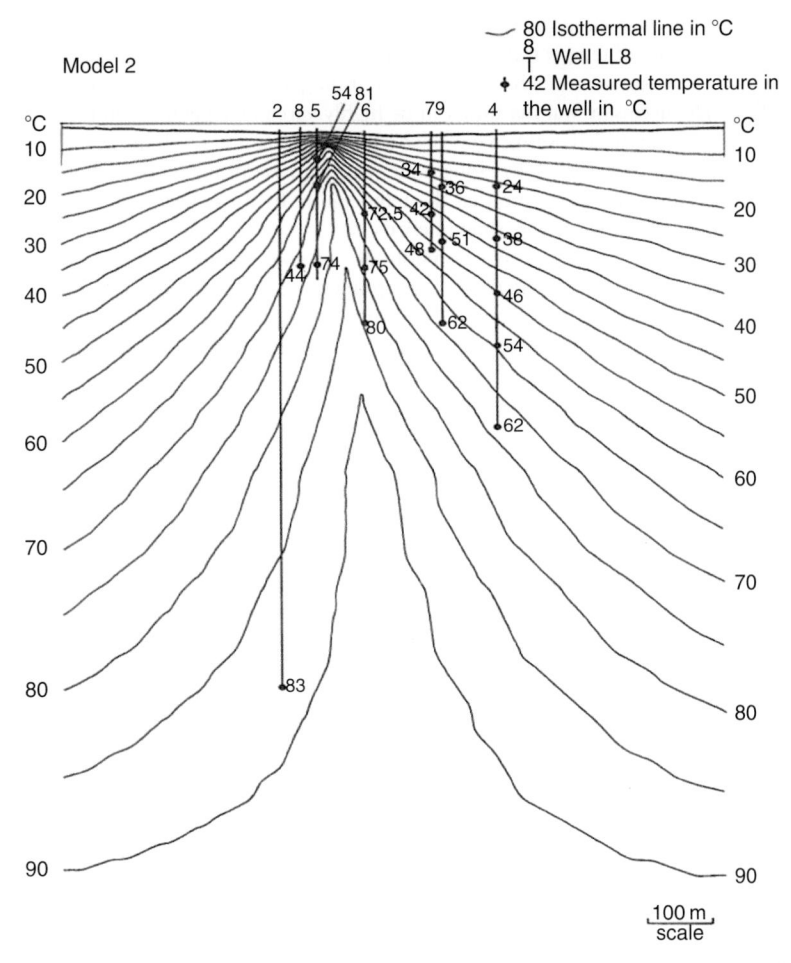

Figure 32 Calculated temperature isolines around a dipping permeable dyke with upflowing geothermal fluid and comparison with borehole data [85].

where q is the heat flow in $W\,m^{-2}$ and dT/dz is the temperature gradient. Hence, to measure the heat flow, we need to drill a hole and measure the temperature gradient and the thermal conductivity of the rock.

Heat flow is usually given in $mW\,m^{-2}$. Earlier the unit HFU (heat flow unit) was commonly used. Calculations based on worldwide near-surface heat flow measurements show that average heat flow of the Earth is $87\,mW\,m^{-2}$, $101\,mW\,m^{-2}$ for the oceanic crust, and $65\,mW\,m^{-2}$ for the continental crust (Pollack et al., 1993). More recently, it has been argued that these numbers are too high for the oceanic crust. According to Hofmeister and Criss [82], the values are similar for the oceanic and the continental crust. However, large variations occur in these values depending on the age of the rock and geological settings.

Conventional geothermal systems are characterized by convective transport of fluid, normally in permeable fractures and also in permeable layers within the sedimentary basins. Outside the permeable zones the heat transport is almost purely conductive. Therefore, the presence of a convective system is accompanied by temperature disturbances of the surrounding impermeable material that give rise to anomalies in conductive heat flow. **Figure 32** shows a simple case for the temperature field around a buried convective geothermal fracture embedded in nonpermeable rock. If we would drill shallow holes far away from the fracture, the heat flow will just be the normal background heat flow. As we approach the fracture on the surface, the vertical heat flow will increase and peak just above the fracture.

7.03.5.4.3 *Measurements of heat flow*

Measurements of heat flow from the Earth require two parameters, the vertical temperature gradient and the value of thermal conductivity in the rock where the gradient is measured. The result will of course rely on the quality of the data. The determination of the temperature gradient relies on the equipment used and the conditions of the borehole. Usually, the temperature logging equipment is not a problem and precision of the measurements is typically of the order of $0.01-0.1\,°C$. However, absolute values in real logging often have considerable lower accuracy, but that is not a problem since we are primarily interested in the gradients. The conditions in the boreholes are much more critical. When we measure the heat flow, we assume that the temperature everywhere in the borehole is exactly the same as the temperature of the bedrock was prior to drilling. This means that the temperature field must have recovered the disturbance caused by the drilling. We must also be sure that there is no internal flow in the well, and third, we must be sure that the heat transfer in the rock surrounding the well is purely conductive, that is, no heat is transferred by mass flow of fluid. **Figure 33** shows few examples of temperature logs from temperature gradient boreholes under different conditions.

To ensure that temperature field around the well has relaxed after drilling, we must do our temperature logging late enough after the completion of the drilling. The necessary waiting time can be highly variable depending on the method and duration of the drilling. As an indication, if the well was drilled during a day or so by using air hammer drilling, the relaxation time is only a couple of days. On the other hand, if the drilling time was very long, water was used as drilling fluid, probably with circulation losses, the relaxation might take months (**Figure 34**). To ensure that the temperature field has been equilibrated, it is recommended that several logging runs are made in each well at suitable time intervals.

Internal flow in a well can be prevented by proper borehole design and drilling procedures. The best wells for heat flow measurements are cased all the way to the bottom and the casing is properly cemented to the surrounding bedrock. However, this is rarely the case since construction of cemented casing is quite expensive. Therefore, the geothermist has usually to live with partly or even uncased wells but use the temperature logs themselves to conclude about possible internal flow. In such cases, he/she has to conclude which data points are most likely to represent the true formation temperature and use these data points to estimate the average temperature gradient. In the worst cases, only the bottom-hole temperature is known with confidence and the average gradient is estimated from that and the average surface temperature.

To account for the problems of advective heat transport, the well must be sited in an area where the rock permeability is low enough to prevent considerable advection effect. This is usually done by selecting the drill site properly in sound bedrock and if necessary casing the well through permeable near-surface layers.

7.03.5.4.4 Determination of the thermal conductivity

The thermal conductivity of real rock varies from roughly $0.2-5.0$ mW m^{-1} °K^{-1}, depending on the rock material and the porosity. Therefore, it is obvious that it is not enough to rely on measurements of temperature gradient to predict a subsurface geothermal field as variations in the thermal conductivity alone might create anomalies in temperature gradient. There exist several methods to measure the thermal conductivity in boreholes and measurements can either been made on cores or cuttings from the borehole or directly in the borehole itself. Description of the various methods can be found in geophysical textbooks and papers [83].

7.03.5.4.5 Heat flow as tool in geothermal exploration

Typical values for temperature gradients measured in geothermal exploration can vary from nearly 0 to 500 °C km^{-1}. Common values of the thermal conductivity of rocks are in the range $1.5-3.0$ Mw °K^{-1}, and corresponding heat flow values can therefore range from almost 0 to 1.5 mW m^{-2}. In areas of homogeneous geology, the thermal conductivity may be regarded as constant. In that case, it can be justified to omit the measurements of the thermal conductivity of the rock, and using maps of temperature gradient instead of maps of heat flow can be justified. This reduces the cost of the survey but adds some uncertainty to the results.

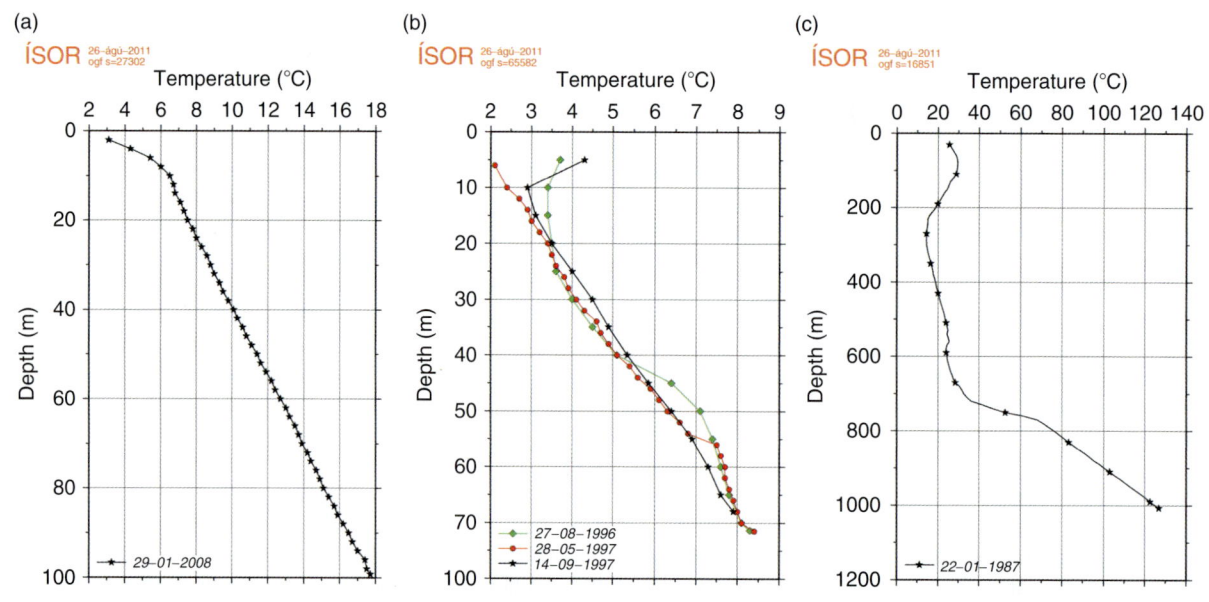

Figure 33 Various types of temperature logs from heat flow wells. (a) A 100 m-deep well showing almost constant gradient apart from seasonal effects above 20 m. (b) An 80 m-deep well showing internal flow disturbing the gradient in the first two logs. The third log is measured after casing with a plastic pipe that prevents the internal flow and results in nearly constant gradient. (c) A 1000 m-deep well in porous rock in high-temperature area. The uppermost permeable zone shows a cold and irregular thermal regime. The well penetrates low-permeability rock at 800 m depth where conductive heat transport occurs. In order to use heat flow measurements under these circumstances, 1000 m-deep wells would be needed. With courtesy of ISOR.

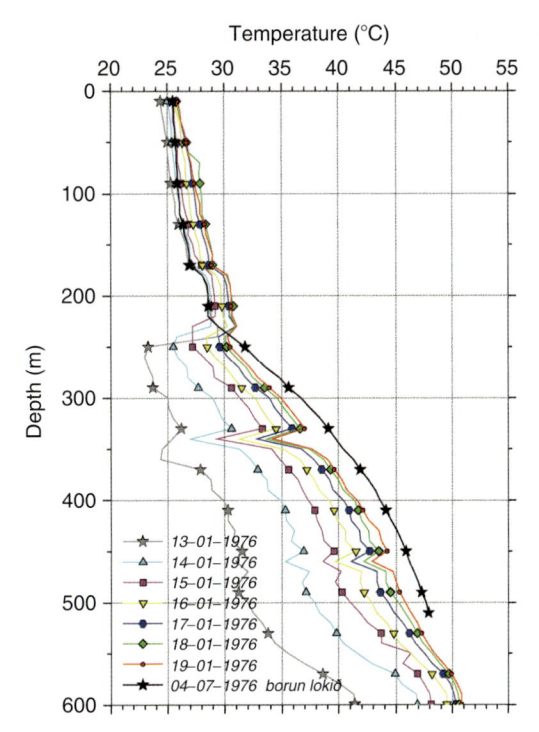

Figure 34 Post-drilling relaxation of temperature after drilling. After a week from drilling completion, the well is still not in thermal balance. With courtesy of ISOR.

The application of heat flow in geothermal exploration involves drilling of shallow wells distributed over the research area, and maps of the near-surface heat flow or temperature gradient are produced. Heat flow anomalies may be of varying scale, both in amplitude and lateral extent. In general, it can be concluded that wide anomalies of low amplitude are caused by a deeply buried heat source, whereas high-amplitude anomalies of small lateral extent have a shallow origin.

Heat flow surveys may be carried out in different scales, either on regional or local scale. In case of regional surveys, the boreholes are distributed over a large area to explore for the possible existence of an unknown geothermal field and estimate its size. In this case, we get the value of the background heat flow and then look for some deviations from it which are caused by geothermal activity. Typically, spacing of the heat flow wells is of the order of one or few kilometers. In this kind of survey, aliasing of the data may occur as a consequence of too large spacing between the heat flow wells. Aliasing is a phenomenon that causes true anomalies of small lateral extent to appear on maps as anomalies of large extent and can lead to misinterpretation of the data. To avoid this, a survey with more dense spacing of heat flow wells must be carried out around the well with anomalous heat flow.

Local survey of heat flow is usually carried out around and within a known heat flow anomaly in order to map it in details of look for permeable, near-surface fracture that commonly are targeted in drilling of exploratory wells. This method is very powerful to map shallow geothermal fractures in rock of low permeability.

It is important to keep in mind that heat flow survey in geothermal exploration is always a comparison study, where we compare the heat flow in specific wells with the known or expected background heat flow. If we only know a heat flow value from a single well and not the background value, we are hardly able to conclude if the measured value indicates an underlying geothermal system or not. Normally, there is random noise in heat flow maps caused by near-surface local disturbances. As a rule of thumb, a heat flow value that is twice the background value can be regarded as real anomaly.

7.03.5.4.6 Depth of heat flow boreholes

It depends mainly on geological and environmental factors how deep one must drill to obtain reliable values of the temperature gradient. The main criterion is that the well penetrates deep enough into the rock with conductive heat flow to allow a good estimate of the temperature gradient and deep enough not to be affected by annual variations in temperature. Consequently, the necessary depth can vary from a few meters to 1–2 km.

At the ocean bottom, heat flow is often measured by a device that penetrates only a few meters into the sea bottom sediments. This is possible because of the stable conditions in the deep ocean. In low-permeable areas on land with thin soil cover, the common depth of heat flow wells is 60–100 m, but specific geological conditions like permeable layers may require deeper holes. In high-temperature fields where young permeable volcanic rocks prevail, it might be necessary to drill down to 1–2 km to enter rock with low enough permeability to allow reliable estimate of conductive heat flow. A consequence of this is that measurements of heat flow are hardly an acceptable tool in exploration for high-temperature fields because of the high drilling cost. Therefore, heat flow measurements are mainly a useful exploration tool in low- and medium-temperature areas.

7.03.5.4.7 Pitfalls in heat flow interpretations

Analysis of heat flow maps is not always straightforward as a number of factors other than an underlying geothermal system can create anomalies in the heat flow.

'Topographic effects' are typically seen in heat flow data due to deviation from vertical heat flow as the heat always flows the easiest way to the surface. These effects appear as relatively high heat flow on valleys compared with values in hills or mountains. There exist simple models to evaluate the topographic effect [84] and programs can be found on the Internet to perform the correction.

'Fluid flow', either as groundwater flow in the bedrock or fractures close to a heat flow well or internal flow in the well, can seriously affect the measured temperature gradient. There are no ways to correct for this, but anomalous values must be examined carefully to estimate possible effects of fluid flow.

'Temporary effects' on the heat flow must be accounted for. This applies especially to annual variations in atmospheric temperature that propagate into the Earth and disturb the heat flow to a depth of several tens of meters. These effects are more serious in areas of low heat flow and high seasonal variations in surface temperature. The same applies to ancient climate variations like the Little Ice Age. Effects from the atmospheric cooling during this period have been seen in heat flow wells at several places. This effect is however rather small.

'Man-made effects' can affect the heat flow determination. Actions like deforestation and reforestation or asphalting of large areas change the boundary conditions at the surface. Deforestation opens the way for the sunshine to the surface resulting in heating of it. Asphalting of the streets will further increase the heating of the surface. This will lead to a relative increase of the shallow temperature and cause an underestimate of the heat flow.

'Rapid erosion and sedimentation rate' can seriously disturb the regional gradient. In case of rapid sedimentation, the measured heat flow will be lower than the corresponding background flow. In the case of rapid erosion, as happened during the Ice Age, the measured heat flow will be higher than the background heat flow. Simple methods exist for estimating the size of these effects.

7.03.5.4.8 Example

The village of Stykkishólmur on the Snæfellsnes peninsula in West Iceland was one of the villages in Iceland that did not have geothermal district heating. There were no known signs of geothermal activities at the surface within dozens of kilometers from the

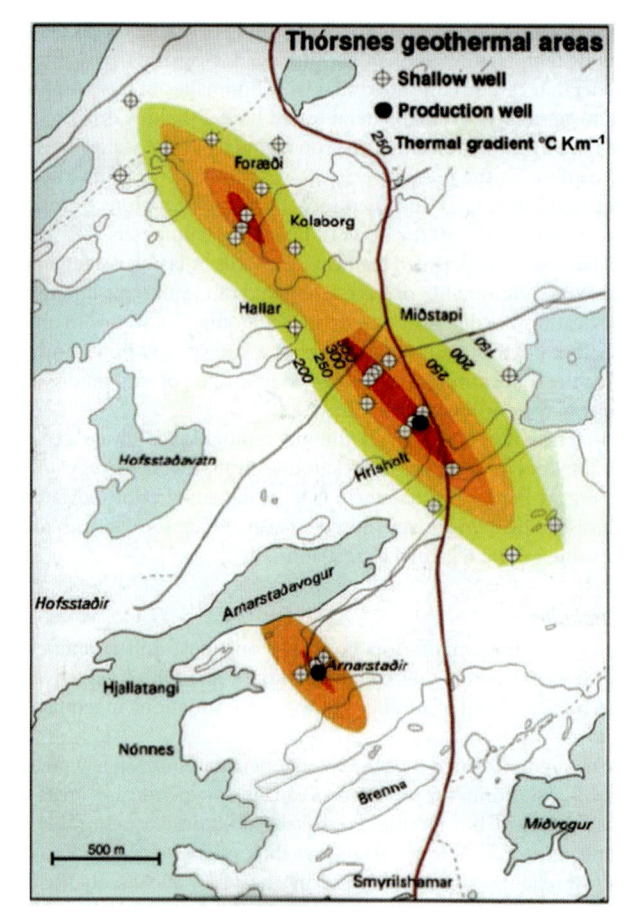

Figure 35 A local anomaly in temperature gradient indicates an underlying geothermal fracture that is a target for deeper drilling. With courtesy of ISOR.

village. The area is located in basaltic rock of Tertiary age that has low permeability due to secondary mineralization. The geological structure of the area is a rather complicated mixture of flow basalts, dykes, large intrusions, rhyolite, and complex tectonic pattern of various ages. The most recent ones are related to some postglacial volcanism on NW-trending fissures.

In order to explore for geothermal energy, a regional survey was carried out and shallow temperature gradient wells were spread over large area around the village with spacing of 1–2 km. These wells showed background temperature gradient of 80 °C km^{-1}, but on the Thorsnes peninsula close to the village, higher values were found, far away from any recent volcanism. The result of a local survey at this site is shown in **Figure 35**. An anomaly appeared that shows up to 400 °C km^{-1} along a NW–SE elongated structure. No signs of geothermal activity were seen on the surface but the strike of the anomaly is in accordance with the strike of the most recent volcanic fissures in the area. Production drilling was carried out at the center of the anomaly and led to discovery of a small 80 °C geothermal system that now satisfies the needs for heating in the village of Stykkishólmur.

References

[1] Árnason K, Karlsdóttir R, Eysteinsson H, et al. (2000) The resistivity structure of high-temperature geothermal systems in Iceland. *Proceedings of the 2000 World Geothermal Congress*. Kyushu-Tohoku, Japan, pp. 923–928.
[2] Árnason K and Flóvenz Ó.G (1992) Evaluation of physical methods in geothermal exploration of rifted volcanic crust. *Geothermal Resources Council Transactions* 16: 207–214.
[3] Walker GPL (1989) Gravitational (density) control of volcanism, magmatic chambers and intrusions. *Australian Journal of Earth Sciences* 36: 149–165.
[4] Sæmundsson K, Jóhannesson H, Hjartarson Á, et al. (2010) *Geological Map of Southwest Iceland, 1:100.000*. Iceland GeoSurvey, Reykjavík, Iceland.
[5] Brantley SL, Agustsdottir AM, and Rowe GL (1993) Crater lakes reveal volcanic heat and volatile fluxes. *Geological Society of America Today* 3: 173–178.
[6] Stolper EM, DePaolo DJ, and Thomas DM (2009) Deep drilling into a Mantle Plume volcano: The Hawaii scientific drilling project. *Scientific Report*. doi:10.2204/iodp.sd.7.02.2009.
[7] Thorhallsson S, Palsson B, and Ingason K (2008) The Iceland deep drilling project, drilling plans. http://www.iddp.is.
[8] Stamps DS (2008) A kinematic model for the East African Rift. *Geophysical Research Letters* 35: L05304.
[9] Arnórsson S (1975) Application of the silica geothermometer in low-temperature hydrothermal areas in Iceland. *American Journal of Science* 275: 763–784.
[10] Gíslason SR, Heaney PJ, Oelkers EH, and Schott J (1997) Kinetic and thermodynamic properties of moganite, a novel silica polymorph. *Geochimica et Cosmochimica Acta* 61: 1193–1204.
[11] Stefánsson A and Arnórsson S (2000) Feldspar saturation state in natural waters. *Geochimica et Cosmochimica Acta* 64: 2567–2584.
[12] D'Amore F and Arnórsson S (2000) Geothermal manifestations and hydrothermal alteration. In: Arnórsson S (ed.) *Isotopic and Chemical Techniques in Geothermal Exploration, Development and Use*. Vienna, Austria: International Atomic Energy Agency.
[13] Ármannsson H and Friðriksson T (2009) Application of geochemical methods in geothermal exploration. *Short Course on Surface Exploration for Geothermal Resources*. Ahuachapan and Santa Tecla, El Salvador, 17–30 October, San Salvador, El Salvador: UNU-GTP and LaGeo.
[14] Zhao P and Ármannsson H (1996) Gas geothermometry in selected Icelandic geothermal fields with comparative examples from Kenya. *Geothermics* 25: 307–347.
[15] D'Amore F and Arnórsson S (2000) Geothermometry. In: Arnórsson S (ed.) *Isotopic and Chemical Techniques in Geothermal Exploration, Development and Use*. Vienna, Austria: International Atomic Energy Agency.
[16] Yock A (2009) Geothermometry. *Short Course on Surface Exploration for Geothermal Resources*. Ahuachapan and Santa Tecla, El Salvador, 17–30 October. San Salvador, El Salvador: UNU-GTP and LaGeo.
[17] Xilai Z, Ármannsson H, Youngle L, and Hanxue Q (2002) Chemical equilibria of thermal waters for the application of geothermometers from Guanzhong basin, China. *Journal of Volcanology and Geothermal Research* 113: 119–127.
[18] Arnórsson S (2000) Mixing processes in upflow zones and mixing models. In: Arnórsson S (ed.) *Isotopic and Chemical Techniques in Geothermal Exploration, Development and Use*. Vienna, Austria: International Atomic Energy Agency.
[19] Fournier RO and Potter RW, II (1982) A revised and expanded silica (quartz) geothermometer. *Geothermal Resources Council Bulletin* 11: 3–9.
[20] Fournier RO (1979) A revised Na/K geothermometer. *Geothermal Resources Council Transactions* 3: 221–224.
[21] Arnórsson S, Stefánsson A, and Bjarnason JÖ (2007) Fluid-fluid interactions in geothermal systems. *Reviews in Mineralogy & Geochemistry* 65: 259–312.
[22] Fournier RO and Truesdell AH (1973) An empirical Na–K–Ca geothermometer for natural waters. *Geochimica et Cosmochimica Acta* 37: 1255–1275.
[23] Giggenbach WF (1988) Geothermal solute equilibria. *Geochimica et Cosmochimica Acta* 52: 2749–2765.
[24] Reed MH and Spycher NF (1989) SOLVEQ: A computer program for computing aqueous-mineral gas equilibria. *A Manual*. 37pp. Eugene, OR: Department of Geological Sciences, University of Oregon.
[25] Tole MP, Ármannsson H, Pang Z, and Arnórsson S (1993) Fluid/mineral equilibrium calculations for geothermal fluids and chemical geothermometry. *Geothermics* 22: 17–37.
[26] Ólafsson M and Bjarnason JÖ (2000) Chemistry of fumaroles and hot springs in the Torfajökull geothermal area, South Iceland. *Proceedings of the 2000 World Geothermal Congress*, pp. 1547–1552. Kyushu–Tohoku, Japan, 28 May–10 June.
[27] Bjarnason JÖ and Ólafsson M (2000) In Torfajökull Glacier. Material in geothermal steam and hot water. *National Energy Authority, Report* OS-2000/080, 94pp. (in Icelandic).
[28] Árnason K, Eysteinsson H, and Hersir GP (2010) Joint 1D inversion of TEM and MT data and 3D inversion of MT data in the Hengill area, SW Iceland. *Geothermics* 39: 13–34.
[29] Hersir GP, Björnsson G, Björnsson A, and Eysteinsson H (1990) Volcanism and geothermal activity in the Hengill area. Geophysical exploration: Resistivity data. *Orkustofnun Report* OS-90032/JHD-16 B, p. 89 (in Icelandic).
[30] Árnason K (1984) The effect of finite potential electrode separation of Schlumberger soundings. *54th Annual International SEG Meeting*, pp. 129–132. Atlanta, GA, Extended Abstracts.
[31] Flóvenz ÓG (1984) Application of the head-on resistivity profiling method in geothermal exploration. *Geothermal Resources Council Transactions* 8: 493–498.
[32] Árnason K, Haraldsson GI, Johnsen GV, et al. (1987) Nesjavellir-Ölkelduháls, surface exploration 1986. *Orkustofnun, Reykjavík, Report* OS-87018/JHD-02, 112pp. + maps (in Icelandic).
[33] Árnason K (1989) Central loop transient electromagnetic sounding over a horizontally layered earth. *Orkustofnun, Reykjavík, Report* OS-89032/JHD-06, 129pp.
[34] Christensen A, Auken E, and Sorensen K (2006) The transient electromagnetic method. *Groundwater Geophysics* 71: 179–225.
[35] Constable SC, Parker RL, and Constable CG (1987) Occam's inversion: A practical algorithm for generating smooth models from electromagnetic sounding data. *Geophysics* 52: 289–300.
[36] Hersir GP, Vilhjálmsson AM, Rosenkjær GK, et al. (2010) The Krýsuvík geothermal area. Resistivity soundings 2007 and 2008. *ÍSOR – Iceland GeoSurvey, Reykjavík, Report* ÍSOR-2010/25, 263pp. (in Icelandic).
[37] Cagniard L (1953) Basic theory of the magneto-telluric method of geophysical prospecting. *Geophysics* 18: 605–635.
[38] Tikhonov AN (1950) The determination of electrical properties of the deep layers of the Earth's crust. *Doklady Akademii Nauk SSSR* 73: 293–297 (in Russian).

[39] Tikhonov AN (1986) On determining electrical characteristics of the deep layers of the Earth's crust. In Vozoff K (ed.) *Magnetotelluric Methods: Society of Exploration Geophysics*, pp. 2–3. New York: Cambridge University Press.
[40] Jones A (2008) Magnetotellurics for natural resources: From acquisition through interpretation. Dublin Institute for Advanced Studies (DIAS), 17–18 November.
[41] Keller GV and Frischknecht FC (1966) *Electrical Methods in Geophysical Prospecting*, 527pp. New York: Pergamon Press.
[42] Arizona Master Naturalist News Web Log (2007) Astronomy note for March 2007. http://blog.ltc.arizona.edu/azmasternaturalist/2007/03/ (accessed 29 August 2011).
[43] Gamble TD, Goubau WM, and Clarke J (1979) Magnetotellurics with a remote magnetic reference. *Geophysics* 44: 53–68.
[44] Park SK and Livelybrook DW (1989) Quantitative interpretation of rotationally invariant parameters in magnetotellurics. *Geophysics* 54: 1483–1490.
[45] Hersir GP, Árnason K, and Vilhjálmsson A (2011) 3D inversion of MT data from Krýsuvík, SW Iceland. *ÍSOR – Iceland GeoSurvey, Reykjavík, Report* ÍSOR-2011/072, 165pp.
[46] Árnason K (2008) The magneto-telluric static shift problem. *Iceland GeoSurvey, Reykjavík, Report* ÍSOR-2008/08088, 17pp.
[47] Sternberg B, Washburne JC, and Pellerin L (1988) Correction for the static shift in magnetotellurics using transient electromagnetic soundings. *Geophysics* 53: 1459–1468.
[48] Jiracek GR (1990) Near-surface and topographic distortions in electromagnetic induction. *Surveys in Geophysics* 11: 163–203.
[49] Siripunvaraporn W (2010) Three-dimensional magnetotelluric inversion: An introductory guide for developers and users. *Abstract from the 20th IAGA WG 1.2 Workshop on Electromagnetic Induction in the Earth.* Giza, Egypt, 18–24 September.
[50] Archie GE (1942) The electrical resistivity log as an aid in determining some reservoir characteristics. *Transactions of the American Institute of Mining, Metallurgical, and Petroleum Engineering* 146: 54–67.
[51] Flóvenz ÓG, Georgsson LS, and Árnason K (1985) Resistivity structure of the upper crust in Iceland. *Journal of Geophysical Research* 90-B12: 10136–10150.
[52] Rink M and Schopper JR (1976) Pore structure and physical properties in porous sedimentary rocks. *Pure and Applied Geophysics* 114: 273–284.
[53] Waxman MH and Smits LJM (1968) Electrical conductivities in oil-bearing shaly sands. *Transactions of the Society of Petroleum Engineers* 343: 315–330.
[54] Flóvenz ÓG, Spangenberg E, Kulenkampff J, et al. (2005) The role of electrical conduction in geothermal exploration. *Proceedings of the 2005 World Geothermal Congress*, 9pp. Antalya, Turkey.
[55] Árnason K, Flóvenz Ó, Georgsson L, and Hersir GP (1987) Resistivity structure of high temperature geothermal systems in Iceland. *International Union of Geodesy and Geophysics (IUGG) XIX General Assembly*, p. 477. Vancouver, BC, Canada, August, Abstract V.
[56] Hersir GP and Árnason K (2009) Resistivity of rocks. *Short Course on Surface Exploration for Geothermal Resources*, 8pp. Ahuachapan and Santa Tecla, El Salvador, 17–30 October. San Salvador, El Salvador: UNU-GTP and LaGeo.
[57] Hersir GP and Björnsson A (1991) Geophysical exploration for geothermal resources. *Principles and Applications*, 94pp., Report 15. Iceland: UNU-GTP.
[58] Revil A and Glover PWJ (1998) Nature of surface electrical conductivity in natural sands, sandstones, and clays. *Geophysical Research Letters* 25: 691–694.
[59] Uchida T (1995) Resistivity structure of Sumikawa geothermal field, North-Eastern Japan, obtained from magnetotelluric data. *Proceedings of the 1995 World Geothermal Congress*, pp. 921–925. Florence, Italy.
[60] Ussher G, Harvey C, Johnstone R, and Anderson E (2000) Understanding the resistivities observed in geothermal systems. *Proceedings of the 2000 World Geothermal Congress*, pp. 1915–1920. Kyushu, Tohoku, Japan, 28 May–10 June.
[61] Scarlato P, Poe BT, and Freda C (2004) High-pressure and high-temperature measurements of electrical conductivity in basaltic rock from Mount Etna, Sicily, Italy. *Journal of Geophysical Research* 109-B02210: 11p.
[62] Quist AS and Marshall WL (1968) Electrical conductances of aqueous sodium chloride solutions from 0 to 800 °C and at pressures to 4000 bars. *The Journal of Physical Chemistry* 72: 684–703.
[63] Dakhnov VN (1962) Geophysical well logging. *Colorado School of Mines* 57-2: 445pp.
[64] Ucok H, Ershaghi I, and Olhoeft GR (1980) Electrical resistivity of geothermal brines. *Journal of Petroleum Technology* 32: 717–727.
[65] Pezard P (1990) Electrical properties of mid-ocean ridge basalt and implications for the structure of the upper oceanic crust in hole 504B. *Journal of Geophysical Research* 95(B6): 9237–9264.
[66] Kristinsdóttir LH, Flóvenz ÓG, Árnason K, et al. (2010) Electrical conductivity and P-wave velocity in rock samples from high-temperature Icelandic geothermal fields. *Geothermics* 39: 94–105.
[67] Violay M, Gibert B, Azais P, et al. (2010) A new cell for electrical conductivity measurements on saturated samples at upper crust conditions. *Transport in Porous Media*.
[68] Milsch H, Kristinsdóttir LH, Spangenberg E, et al. (2010) Effect of the water-steam phase transition on the electrical conductivity of porous rocks. *Geothermics* 39: 106–114.
[69] Anderson E, Crosby D, and Ussher G, 2000. Bulls-eye!: Simple resistivity imaging to reliably locate the geothermal reservoir. *Proceedings of the 2000 World Geothermal Congress*, pp. 909–914. Kyushu, Tohoku, Japan, 28 May–10 June.
[70] Kulenkampff J, Spangenberg E, Flóvenz OG, et al. (2005) Petrophysical parameters of rocks saturated with liquid water at high temperature geothermal reservoir conditions. *Proceedings of the 2005 World Geothermal Congress*, Paper 1610, 9pp. Antalya, Turkey, 24–29 April.
[71] Ellis DV (1987) *Well Logging for Earth Scientists*, 532pp. New York: Elsevier.
[72] Thomas EC (1976) Determination of Qv from membrane potential measurements on shaly sands. *Transactions of the American Institute of Mining, Metallurgical, and Petroleum Engineering* 261: 1087–1096.
[73] Kristmannsdóttir H (1979) Alteration of basaltic rocks by hydrothermal activity at 100–300 °C. In: Mortland MM and Farmer VC (eds.) *International Clay Conference 1978*, pp. 359–367. Amsterdam, The Netherlands: Elsevier Scientific Publishing Co.
[74] Chi MA and Browne PRL (1991) Alteration mineralogy of sediments in the Huka falls formation of the Te Mihi area, Wairakei. *Proceedings of the 13th New Zealand Geothermal Workshop 1991*. pp. 185–191.
[75] Hjaltadóttir S and Vogfjörð K (2011) Mapping of fractures at Theistareykir and Bjarnarflag using high resolution locations of microearthquakes. *Iceland Meteorological Office, Report* VI2011/016, ISSN 1670-8261, 44pp.
[76] Dragoni M (1993) The brittle-ductile transition in tectonic boundary zones. *Annali di Geofisica* 36(2): 37–44.
[77] Ágústsson K and Flóvenz ÓG (2005) The thickness of the seismogenic crust in Iceland and its implications for geothermal systems. *Proceedings of the 2005 World Geothermal Congress*. Antalya, Turkey, 24–29 April.
[78] Simiyu SM (2008) Application of micro-seismic methods to geothermal exploration: Examples from the Kenya Rift. *Short Course III on Exploration for Geothermal Resources*, 27pp. Lake Naivasha, Kenya, October 24–November 17. UNU-GTP and KenGen.
[79] Miller AD, Julian BR, and Foulger GR (1997) Three-dimensional seismic structure and moment tensors of non-double-couple earthquakes at the Hengill–Grensdalur volcanic complex, Iceland. *Geophysical Journal International* 133: 309–325.
[80] Uyeda S (1988) Geodynamics. In: Haenel R, Rybach L, and Stegena L (eds.) *Handbook of Terrestrial Heat-Flow Density Determination*, pp. 317–352. Dordrecht, Holland: Kluwer Academic Publishers.
[81] Flóvenz ÓG and Sæmundsson K (1993) Heat flow and geothermal processes in Iceland. *Tectonophysics* 225: 123–138.
[82] Hofmeister AM and Criss RE (2005) Earth's heat flux revised and linked to chemistry. *Tectonophysics* 395: 159–177.
[83] Milicevic B (1990) Interpretation and modelling of the temperature distribution at Laugaland in Thelamörk, N-Iceland. *Geothermal Training in Iceland 1990, Report* 10, 36pp. Reykjavik, Iceland: UNU-GTP.
[84] Beardsmore GR and Cull JP (2001) *Crustal Heat Flow. A Guide to Measurements and Modeling*, 324p. New York: Cambridge University Press.
[85] Lees CH (1910) On the shapes of isogeotherms under mountain ranges in radioactive districts. *Proceedings of the Royal Society of London, A* 83: 339–346.
[86] Smithsonian list of volcanoes (in various countries) available on the internet.

7.04 Geochemical Aspects of Geothermal Utilization

H Ármannsson, Iceland GeoSurvey (ISOR), Reykjavik, Iceland

© 2012 Elsevier Ltd. All rights reserved.

7.04.1	Introduction	95
7.04.2	Collection of Liquid and Gas Samples	95
7.04.3	Characterization of Solids	97
7.04.4	Analysis of Fluids	100
7.04.5	Classification of Water	101
7.04.6	Alteration	103
7.04.7	Tracing the Origin and Flow of Geothermal Fluids	108
7.04.8	Speciation and Reaction Path Calculations	128
7.04.9	Geothermometry	134
7.04.10	Applications during Production	141
7.04.11	Case History. Exploration of a Geothermal Area. Theistareykir, NE Iceland	155
References		163

7.04.1 Introduction

Geochemistry is used at all stages of geothermal utilization, from preliminary exploration to production of geothermal energy. The major goals of geochemical exploration are to obtain the subsurface composition of the fluids in the system and use this to obtain information on temperature, origin, and flow direction, which help in locating the subsurface reservoir. Equilibrium speciation is obtained using speciation programs and simulation of processes such as boiling and cooling to get more information in order to predict potential deposition and corrosion. Environmental effects are foreseen and the general information is used as a contribution to the model of the geothermal system.

Prediction and analysis of scaling and corrosion become more important at later stages, although studies on changes in characteristics of geothermal systems such as temperature and origin still remain important. Geochemistry is also an important tool in environmental management and monitoring.

Geochemical work generally consists of

- collection of samples
- chemical analysis of samples
- interpretation of analytical results

In this chapter sampling and chemical analysis will be discussed before going on to interpretation of the results first in exploration and then during production. Case histories will be used to illustrate the methods.

7.04.2 Collection of Liquid and Gas Samples

General. The collection of samples for chemical analysis is the first step in a long process, which eventually yields results that provide building blocks in the model of a geothermal system. It is imperative that this step be properly carried out because all subsequent steps depend on it.

There are several hidden dangers inherent in the collection of geothermal samples. The terrain may be treacherous and dangerous chemicals need to be handled.

Thus, there is an obvious need for well-trained personnel with insight into possible errors and interferences in order to carry out this task.

The most common mistakes made during sampling involve the use of improper containers, improper cleaning, and a lack of or improper treatment for the preservation of samples.

Containers. For lightness, ruggedness, and tolerance of bumps in the field, plastic bottles are the best. Most plastics are, however, relatively permeable and let atmospheric air easily through, possibly setting off oxidation reactions, and liquids may easily evaporate through them causing concentration of constituents and possible oversaturation. Many plastics are also rife with possible adsorption sites for sample constituents and may thus decrease their concentrations.

Glass is fragile and relatively heavy, but can fairly easily be made airtight. Thus, glass containers are preferable for the preservation of constituents affected by atmospheric air. Constituents that are sensitive to light are collected into amber bottles.

If containers have not been specifically precleaned and prepared for a certain task, they should be rinsed at least three times with the sample fluid prior to collection.

Sample preservation. Some constituents will not survive intact from sample collection to analysis without special precautions. Common reasons for concentration changes are interaction with suspended matter, adsorption on the walls of the containers, biological activity, redox reactions, polymerization, and precipitation. Different preservation methods are needed for the various processes and therefore the total sample will comprise several subsamples. Preservation methods may be physical or chemical and the more common ones are listed in **Table 1**.

It is desirable that samples be kept relatively cool apart from the inconvenience of handling boiling hot water and steam. Fluid that is well above ambient temperature is therefore cooled to ambient temperature using a cooling device, usually a cooling coil immersed in cold water, during collection. Steam samples collected into NaOH in double-port bottles may bypass the cooling device and the bottle itself be cooled in cold water.

Collection. The collection of samples of nonboiling water can be divided into two categories: samples from natural springs and samples from hot water wells. When collecting samples from hot springs it is desirable that the water be free-flowing from the sample spot. If not, a sampling pump is needed. Water temperature and discharge as well as wellhead pressure if available are reported.

The collection of representative samples from high-temperature drill holes is done either by using the separator on the wellhead separating the whole discharge or with a small Webre separator. Natural steam discharge may occur in many different forms, such as gentle discharge from a large area of hot ground or major discharge from large fumaroles. The most useful information is often obtained from steam discharged from powerful fumaroles.

It has been shown that the most representative samples are collected from the flow of a two-phase well at about 1.5 m distance from the T-joint at the well top.

The various subsamples collected are described in detail in **Table 2**, but the total procedure for collection from high-temperature wells is shown in **Figure 1**. Samples are collected into plastic bottles unless otherwise specified.

The vents on the Webre separator are opened and the fluid is allowed to flow from the borehole through the separator. Care is taken that the pressure in the separator does not deviate much from that of the wellhead. For the collection of the vapor phase, the water level inside the separator is kept low until preferably a mixture of water and steam issues through the water vent. A blue cone should form at the steam vent showing that dry steam is being issued. To check the efficiency of the separation, a small sample of condensed steam may be drawn and the concentration of a nonvolatile component such as Na or Cl determined, compared with the concentration of the same component in the liquid phase, and the percentage of carryover calculated. If $t < 70\,°C$, it may be desirable to determine the dissolved oxygen concentration of the water to estimate its corrosion potential. This determination is carried out during sampling as described below.

When sampling fumaroles, care has to be taken that a discrete, directed outflow is chosen and diffuse ones avoided at all costs. A good guide to the suitability of an outflow for sampling is sulfur deposits. A funnel is placed atop the outflow and care taken that no atmospheric air is drawn in. The funnel is connected to a titanium or a silica rubber tube, which is directed to a lower point where the sample is collected. When sampling springs care has to be taken to obtain a sample as near to the outflow as possible. An indicator such as ink may be used if it is difficult to find. Normally the water sample will be drawn with a pump into an evacuation flask. The filtering apparatus is fitted between the sample and the pump when appropriate. If a gas sample is required, two evacuated flasks, one with taps on both ends below and a double-port gas bottle containing 40% NaOH above, are

Table 1 Preservation methods for geothermal samples

Type	Method	Purpose	Used for
Physical	Filtration	Prevent interaction with suspended matter	Anions, cations
	Freezing	Prevent biological activity	Nutrients
	Airtight container	Prevent interaction with atmospheric air	Volatiles
	On-site analysis	Prevent reactions of reactive constituents	Reactive constituents
Chemical	Base addition	Absorption of acid gases	CO_2, H_2S in steam, $\delta^{34}S$ in H_2S in vapor
	Acidification	Prevent adsorption on walls of containers	Cations
	Precipitation	Prevent a constituent from reaction to change the concentration of another	Sulfide to preserve sulfate
	Sterilization	Prevent biological activity, using HgCl or formaldehyde	$\delta^{34}S$ and $\delta^{18}O$ in SO_4, prevents biological oxidation of sulfide
	Dilution	Prevent polymerization and precipitation	Silica
	Redox	To change oxidation state of a volatile constituent to make it less volatile	Hg
	Ion exchange	Concentrate and further prevent adsorption on walls of container of trace constituents	Trace cations
	Extraction	Concentrate and further prevent adsorption on walls of container of trace constituents	Trace cations

Table 2 Treatment and subsamples from geothermal sampling

Phase	Treatment	Specification	To determine
Vapor	None; amber glass bottle	Ru	$\delta^2 H$, $\delta^{18}O$
	0.5 ml 0.2 M ZnAc$_2$ added to sample in 100 ml volumetric glass flask to precipitate sulfide	Rp	SO$_4$
	None	Ru	Anions
	0.8 ml conc. HNO$_3$ (Suprapur) added to 200 ml sample	Ra	Cations
	Added to 50 ml 40% NaOH in evacuated double-port bottle	Gas sample, Ai	CO$_2$, H$_2$S in NaOH, residual gases in gas phase, δ^{34}S in H$_2$S in vapor
Liquid	None	Ru	Mg, SiO$_2$ if <100 ppm
	Dilution; 10–50 ml of sample added to 90–50 ml of distilled, deionized water	Rd (1:10 to 1:1)	SiO$_2$ if >100 ppm
	None; amber glass bottle with ground glass stopper	Ru	pH, CO$_2$, H$_2$S (if not in field)
	Filtration (0.45)	Fu	Anions
	Filtration; 2 ml 0.2 M ZnAc$_2$ added to sample in 100 ml volumetric glass flask and ≥10 to ≥500 ml bottle containing ≥25 mg SO$_4$ to precipitate sulfide	Fp, Fpi	SO$_4$, δ^{34}S and δ^{18}O in SO$_4$
	Filtration; one 60 ml and two 1000 ml amber glass bottles, with ground glass stoppers	Fui, Fuc, Fut	δ^2H, δ^{18}O, ^{13}C, ^{3}H
	Filtration; 0.8 ml conc. HNO$_3$ (Suprapur) added to 200 ml sample	Fa	Cations

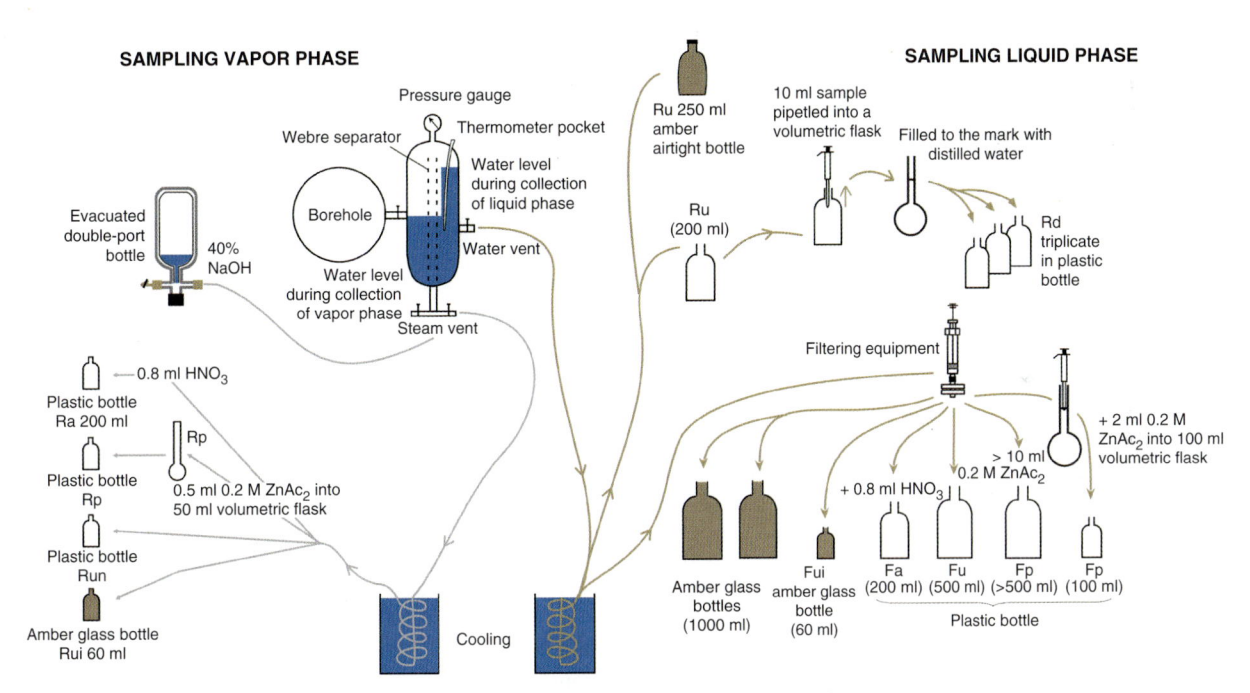

Figure 1 Overview of collection of a sample from a two-phase geothermal well for chemical analysis.

arranged in series. The taps are opened slowly, first on the two-ended flask, and care taken that water does not enter the double-port bottle (**Figure 2**). Sampling techniques are described in more detail by Ármannsson and Ólafsson [1].

Summary. For proper sampling clean containers of appropriate material are needed. Care has to be taken that appropriate preservation techniques for particular constituents are applied. Thus, each sample will be composed of several sample fractions ready for analysis. Volatile and urgent constituents are analyzed in a field laboratory or upon sampling.

7.04.3 Characterization of Solids

Solid samples are characterized during drilling either cuttings or core samples. Similar methods are employed to characterize samples of deposits and corrosion products formed during production. The latter are either collected from their formation sites or coupons of similar material as the pipes are inserted into the flow for a known period of time and the material formed characterized by weighing and analysis. The most common techniques of solid characterization are described below. The interpretation of the analysis of the fluids is in fact dependent on knowledge of the alteration minerals present.

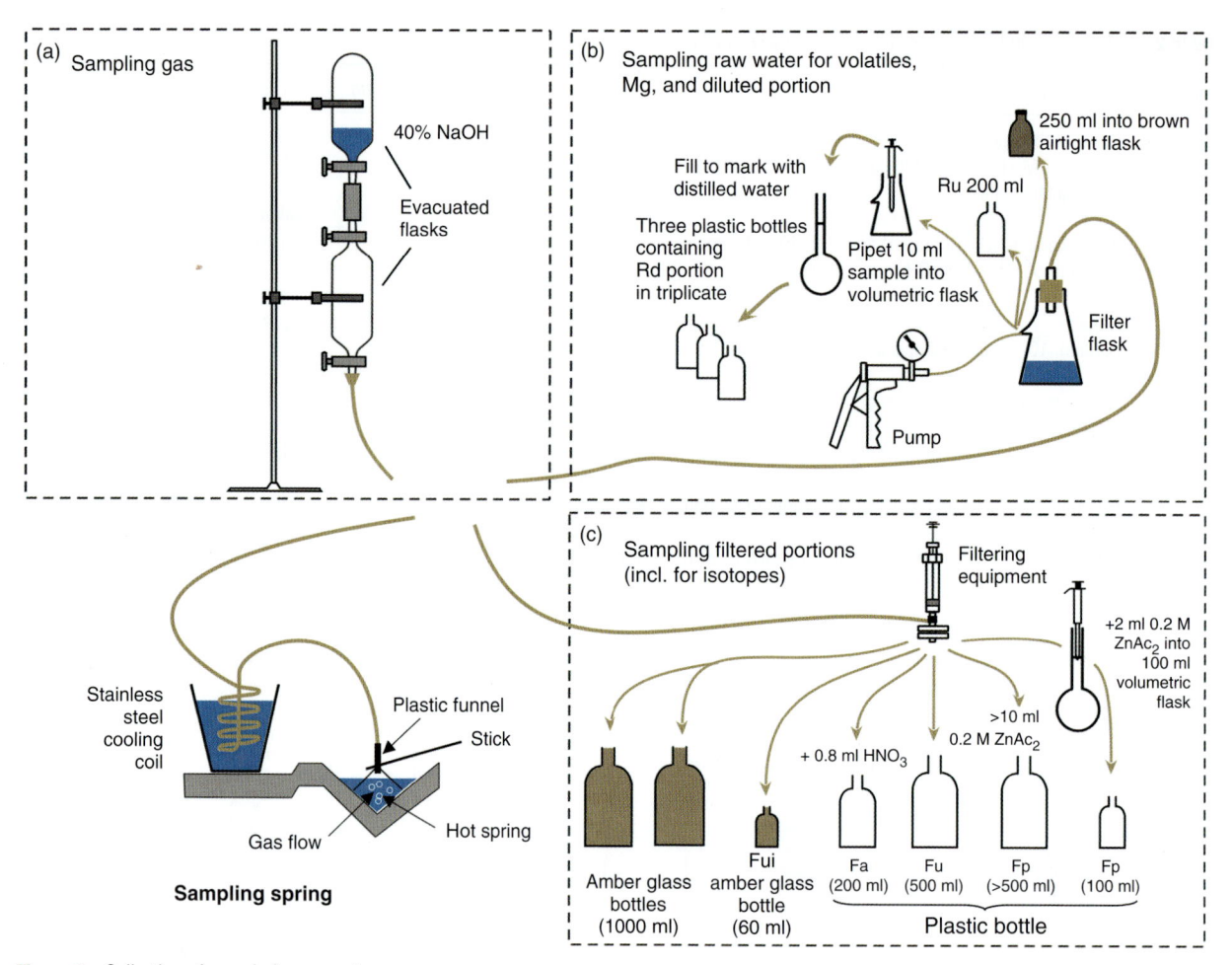

Figure 2 Collection of sample from a spring.

'Microscopy' is the technical field of using microscopes to view samples or objects. There are three well-known branches of microscopy: optical, electron, and scanning probe microscopy.

'Optical and electron microscopy' involve the diffraction, reflection, or refraction of an electromagnetic radiation/electron beam interacting with the subject of study and the subsequent collection of this scattered radiation in order to build up an image. This process may be carried out by wide-field irradiation of the sample (e.g., standard light microscopy and transmission electron microscopy, TEM) or by scanning of a fine beam over the sample (e.g., confocal laser scanning microscopy and scanning electron microscopy (SEM)).

In SEM an incident beam of electrons strikes the sample and both photon and electron signals are emitted. The signals most commonly used are the secondary electrons, the backscattered electrons, and X-rays.

Electron signals are collected by a secondary detector or a backscatter detector, converted to a voltage, and amplified. Amplified voltage is applied to the grid of a cathode ray tube (CRT) and causes the intensity of the spot of light to change. The image consists of thousands of spots of varying intensity on the face of the CRT and corresponds to the topography of the sample.

Scanning probe microscopy involves the interaction of a scanning probe with the surface or object of interest.

X-ray methods. Emission, absorption, scattering, fluorescence, and diffraction of magnetic radiation are measured and an idea of deceleration of high-energy electrons or electronic transition of electrons in inner orbitals of atoms obtained. The possible wavelength range is $10^{-5}-10^{2}$ Å, but in conventional X-ray spectroscopy it is 0.1–25 Å. A metal target is bombarded with a beam of high-energy electrons and the substance exposed to a primary X-ray beam to obtain a secondary beam of X-ray fluorescence (XRF). A radioactive source whose decay process results in X-ray emission, for example, a synchrotron radiation source, is deployed.

X-ray diffraction (XRD). An X-ray tube with suitable filters is deployed to obtain a pattern by automatic scanning. The source is commonly an X-ray tube with suitable filters. A powdered sample is mounted on a goniometer or a rotatable table that permits variation in the angle θ between the crystal and the collimated beam. In some instances the sample holder may be rotated in order to increase the randomness of the orientation of the crystals. The diffraction pattern is obtained by automatic scanning. Specific interpretation is empirical based on massive existing libraries. A computer search is extremely useful. Each mineral has its characteristic spectral pattern so that if a crystalline mineral is present it can be characterized individually. This method is *inter alia* very important in recognizing alteration minerals in borehole cuttings.

XRF. Absorption of X-rays sends excited atoms to their ground state by transition of electrons from higher energy levels. Excited ions are sent to their ground states via series of electronic transitions characterized by X-ray emission (fluorescence) of same wavelength (λ_f) as excitation. Absorption removes electrons completely, but emissions give rise to transition of electrons from a higher energy level within the atom. An X-ray tube with high enough voltage for λ_0 to be shorter than the absorption edge of the element is deployed. Three types of X-ray sources are used:

- *X-ray tube*. A highly evacuated tube with a W filament cathode and a massive anode. The target material may be various metals. The filament is heated and the electrons accelerated, thus controlling the X-ray intensity. The voltage determines the energy or the wavelength. This is an inefficient source.
- *Radioisotopes*. A given isotope is used for a range of elements giving a simple spectra. This has proved to be a powerful source.
- *Secondary fluorescent sources*. The fluorescence spectrum of an element is excited by an X-ray tube.

The successful application of XRF depends on the fact that they are powerful for all but the lightest elements; for nine elements in granitic rocks and sediments, precision <0.1% has been obtained. It is easily deployed for materials collected on filters and natural water samples collected on ion exchange resins. The main advantages to using XRF are that the spectra are simple, spectral line interference is unlikely, the technique is nondestructive, it is independent of sample size, and it can be applied with speed to multielement analysis with accuracy and precision. The main disadvantages are that it is not very sensitive, yet expensive and not applicable to lighter elements. This method has *inter alia* been used with great success to characterize scales formed in boreholes.

Microprobe. X-ray emission is stimulated on the surface of a sample by a narrow, focused beam of electrons. The resulting X-ray emission is detected and analyzed with either a wavelength or an energy-dispersive spectrometer. A wealth of both qualitative and quantitative information on the physical and chemical nature of the surfaces is obtained. This method has been deployed to characterize scales formed and in cores obtained from boreholes.

Energy-dispersive X-ray spectroscopy (EDS) is one of the variants of XRF. It relies on the investigation of a sample through interactions between electromagnetic radiation and matter, analyzing X-rays emitted by the matter in response to being hit with charged particles. Capabilities are due in large part to the fundamental principle that each element has a unique atomic structure allowing X-rays that are characteristic of an element's atomic structure to be identified uniquely from one another. To stimulate the emission of characteristic X-rays from a specimen, a high-energy beam of charged particles such as electrons or protons or a beam of X-rays is focused onto the sample being studied. The incident beam may excite an electron in an inner shell, ejecting it from the shell while creating an electron hole where the electron was. An electron from an outer, higher energy shell then fills the hole, and the difference in energy between the higher energy shell and the lower energy shell may be released in the form of an X-ray. The number and energy of the X-rays emitted from a specimen can be measured by an energy-dispersive spectrometer, allowing the elemental composition of the specimen to be measured.

There are four primary components of the EDS setup: the beam source, the X-ray detector, the pulse processor, and the analyzer. A number of free-standing EDS systems exist. However, EDS systems are most commonly found on scanning electron microscopes (SEM-EDS) and electron microprobes. SEMs are equipped with a cathode and magnetic lenses to create and focus a beam of electrons, and since the 1960s they have been equipped with elemental analysis capabilities. A detector is used to convert X-ray energy into voltage signals; this information is sent to a pulse processor, which measures the signals and passes them onto an analyzer for data display and analysis. This method has been used for most types of geological samples and proves useful when a total analysis is required.

Differential Thermal Analysis (DTA). The sample is heated up and characteristic changes observed. The method is useful in studies of alteration. Little sample preparation is needed and it is found to be sensitive to sulfides and carbonates and subtle differences in the thermal characteristics of clays.

Infrared spectrometry (IR). A major advantage is that a small sample is needed. The method has been found to be useful for identifying clay, zeolite, and feldspar minerals. It can be developed as a quantitative tool too.

Fluid inclusion geothermometry. Fluid inclusions are heated or cooled under a microscope and homogenization temperatures on double polished crystals are obtained. To obtain the original system salinity, a freezing stage is included.

Wet chemical analysis. H_2O is determined by heating and CO_2 by ascarite absorption and gravimetry or coulometry. If silica is included in the analysis, solution (a) is prepared by fusion with sodium hydroxide and Si determined by UV/Vis spectrophotometry, for example, ammonium molybdate α-complex, atomic absorption spectrophotometry (AAS), or in inductively coupled plasma (ICP) by mass spectrometry (MS) or atomic emission spectrometry (AES), and Al by UV/Vis spectrophotometry, for example, alizarin red, AAS, or ICP (MS or AES). If silica is not included in the analysis, solution (b) is prepared after removal of SiO_2 by fuming HF. Ti is determined by spectrophotometry, for example, Tiron, or ICP (MS or AES); P by UV/Vis spectrophotometry or ICP (MS or AES); and other metals by AAS or ICP (MS or AES). This method has proved its worth in studies of scales and in total rock analysis.

Coulometry. Carbon in cuttings is determined by automated coulometry.

Combination of techniques. Neither full chemical analysis nor crystal characterization gives the full picture in studies of solids and the most powerful method is based on combining the two, for example,

- The crystalline phases are determined by XRD and the amorphous phases by SEM.
- Total elemental analysis is obtained by EDS or wet chemical methods.

- The total composition of the phases is then calculated, for example, if zinc, lead, and copper sulfides have been found to be significant but iron sulfides and silicates are observed as well as amorphous silica the zinc, lead, and copper are assumed to combine with sulfide only, the rest of the sulfide to combine with Fe, then the rest of the Fe to combine with silicate (Fe:Si 3:4), and the rest of the silica is assumed to be amorphous silica.

7.04.4 Analysis of Fluids

Main laboratory. The choice of an analytical technique depends on several factors, that is, the availability of instruments, potential servicing facilities for different types of instruments, the presence of trained personnel, and the speed, reliability, and cost of the different methods.

Field laboratory. In a field laboratory facilities for the determination of volatile constituents (pH, CO_2, H_2S, NH_3, and O_2), urgent constituents (e.g., SiO_2), constituents used for separation efficiency checks (Na or Cl), and apparatus for specific tests if required (e.g., analytical balance, drying oven) and a supply of deionized water are needed.

Gas analysis. The most important techniques for gas analysis are titrimetry, gas chromatography, MS, and radiometry. CO_2 and H_2S are determined titrimetrically in a solution of a strong alkali (NaOH or KOH), by an alkalinity titration with HCl, but by either iodometry or with mercuric acetate using dithizone as an indicator. Gases that are not absorbed by the strong alkali (N_2, H_2, CH_4 (higher hydrocarbons if present), O_2, Ar, and He) are determined by gas chromatography. Gas chromatographs are usually designed for their specific function. The University of Iceland/Iceland GeoSurvey instrument is a Perkin-Elmer Arnel 4019 Analyzer designed for the analysis of geothermal gases. Its most important features are three carrier flow sources, dual and single thermal conductivity detectors, four valves, five analytical columns, and three auxiliary carrier gas sources. It combines into three analytical channels and employs N_2 and He as carrier gases. Its special capability are the separations of H_2 and He and of O_2 and Ar. Trace noble gases (Ne, Kr, and Xe) are determined by MS and radioactive gases (e.g., Rn) by radiometry.

CO_2 flux measurements. The closed chamber method [2, 3], using a closed chamber CO_2 flux meter equipped with a single-path, dual-wavelength, nondispersive infrared gas analyzer, is deployed. Flux measurements are usually made using a chamber with known total internal volume and basal area. The flux measurement is based on the rate of CO_2 increase in the chamber. If φ_{CO_2} through the soil is moderate, the CO_2 concentration increase is generally linear for several minutes, allowing for relatively precise flux determinations.

Determination of volatile constituents in water. It is recommended that analysis for oxygen and hydrogen sulfide be carried out in the field.

Oxygen is determined colorimetrically using ampoules from CHEMetrics, Inc., containing Rhodazine D for concentrations 0–100 ppb, but Indigo carmine for higher concentrations, but may also be determined by a Winkler iodometric titration. Hydrogen sulfide is determined titrimetrically using mercuric acetate and dithizone [1]. Mercury can behave as a volatile constituent. Even though it is usually present as Hg^{2+} it is easily reduced to elemental Hg, which is extremely volatile. Therefore, it is recommended that an oxidizing agent such as $KMnO_4$ be added upon collection to samples for mercury analysis, which is carried out by reduction, gold amalgamation of elemental mercury, heating, and flameless AAS [4].

Cation analysis. AAS (flame for major cations, carbon furnace for minor cations), flame emission spectrometry (FES) (major cations), ion chromatography (IC, major cations), and ICP with atomic emission spectrometry (ICP/AES) or mass spectrometry (ICP/MS) (major and minor cations, respectively) are all widely used techniques for cation analysis. Specific applications include fluorometry for Al^{3+}, spectrophotometry for field determinations of Fe^{2+} and the determination of ammonia in saline water, and ion-selective electrode for the determination of ammonia in dilute water.

Anion analysis. IC is the most convenient technique for chloride, bromide, and sulfate. Sulfide has to be removed from the sample upon collection by precipitation with zinc acetate before sulfate determination. Fluoride can also be determined by IC if care is taken to separate its peak from the chloride peak, but it is more conveniently determined using an ion-selective electrode. Boron and silica can both be determined easily by spectrophotometry and ICP. It is also fairly common to determine sulfate by colorimetry (CO) and turbidometry (TU). In **Table 3** the results for the three methods used by laboratories taking part in a comparative exercise are compared and for the two samples the best results are obtained by IC.

Isotope analysis. Stable isotope ratios are determined by MS in comparison with a standard, but radioactive isotopes by radiometry. The most common stable isotopes determined during geothermal work are ^2H, ^{18}O, ^{13}C, and ^{34}S but the most common radioactive isotopes ^3H and ^{14}C used for dating, and ^{222}Rn. Due to interferences such as that of water vapor in MS, the compounds containing the IC, CO, and TU isotopes to be determined are converted to constituents that do not interfere. Thus, H_2O is converted to H_2 for ^2H analysis and CO_2 for ^{18}O analysis. H_2S and SO_4 are converted to SO_2 for ^{34}S analysis and SO_4 to CO_2 for ^{18}O determination. The reduction of H_2O to H_2 has been problematic. Originally hot uranium was used [6] but that is too dangerous. Zn metal [7] has been widely used, but the general experience shows that for unexplained reasons the only reagent that seems to work is zinc shot from British drug houses (BDH). Equilibration using a Pt catalyst [8] has given some useful results but only works for some samples. Those that give erroneous results generally contain H_2S. More recent developments involve the use of hot Cr for the reduction [9, 10]. Oxygen is generally equilibrated with carbon dioxide according to the method of Epstein and Mayeda [11]. Hydrogen sulfide is converted to SO_2 by precipitation as Ag_2S followed by oxidation with Cu_2O or V_2O_5 [12]. $BaSO_4$ is precipitated either directly from high-sulfate solutions or following ion exchange from low-sulfate solutions and then reduced with graphite to

Table 3 Comparison of results for different methods of sulfate determination in the IAEA laboratory comparison 2001

Sample no.	Method	Number of labs	Mean ($mg\,l^{-1}$)	RSD (%)
1	IC	8	22.3	10.0
	CO	16	24.2	27.0
	TU	11	26.9	38.2
	Reference		23.2	
3	IC	8	31.5	6.4
	CO	17	32.5	8.8
	TU	11	30.4	24.2
	Reference		31.8	

By Alvis-Isidro R, Urbino GA, and Pang Z (2002) Results of the 2001 IAEA inter-laboratory comparison. IAEA Report, 57pp [5].

Table 4 Methods used for selected constituents by laboratories in IAEA interlaboratory comparison 2003

Method	Cl	SO_4	SiO_2	K	Mg
Co	2	16	14		
Tm	23				1
IC	5	5		2	2
TU		9			
AA			9	24	21
ICP/MS			1		
ICP/AES			3		3
FE				1	

Co, colorimetric; Tm, titrimetry; IC, ion chromatography; TU, turbidometry; AA, atomic absorption; ICP/MS, inductively coupled plasma/mass spectrometry; ICP/AES, ICP/atomic emission spectrometry; FE, flame emission
After Urbino GA and Pang Z (2004) 2003 Inter-laboratory comparison of geothermal water chemistry. IAEA Report, 42pp [14].

obtain CO which then is converted to CO_2 used for ^{18}O determination [13]. The reduced sulfide is precipitated as Ag_2S and converted to SO_2 using the above procedure. The radioactive isotopes are determined by liquid scintillation counting.

Quality control. The precision of methods can be checked by repeated analysis of the same sample or by duplicates or triplicates of several samples. To obtain an idea of the accuracy of the determinations several approaches are possible, that is, the use of standard additions to sample to obtain % recovery, carrying out determinations of the same constituent by different methods, using standards or reference samples that are run with each batch of samples determined, checks on ionic balance, that is, whether the sum of anions determined is close to the sum of cations determined, or a check on mass balance, that is, whether the sum of constituent concentrations matches that of the result of the determination of total dissolved solids.

One of the most useful checks is an interlaboratory comparison in which samples whose composition is known are sent to a number of laboratories that use different methods for the determination of each sample. Thus, each laboratory can measure itself against others in the same field. Examples are the interlaboratory comparisons for the determination of major constituents of geothermal fluids organized by the International Atomic Energy Agency [5], from which the results presented in **Table 3** are obtained. It is interesting to find out which methods were used by the various laboratories that took part in the 2003 exercise [14] presented in **Table 4**.

Summary. Analysis for most anions is usually best performed in the home laboratory, but cations and most trace constituents may be advantageously analyzed in a commercial laboratory applying ICP techniques. A survey of 30 laboratories taking part in an IAEA laboratory comparison exercise showed that AAS, spectrophotometry, and titrimetry were the techniques most widely employed.

7.04.5 Classification of Water

Subsurface waters. It has proved difficult to obtain a generic classification of subsurface waters. The waters that have been studied in detail are mostly those that are of economic interest as potable water. Water also tends to flow away from its point of origin and also undergo water–rock interaction during its travels, making it increasingly difficult to decipher its origins. White's [15] classification is followed here.

Meteoric water: circulates in the atmosphere, coexisting with near-surface, uncemented sediments, can circulate in subsurface rocks and dissolve constituents, for example, evaporites.

Ocean water: partly evaporated products of meteoric water.

Evolved connate water: forms in young marine sediments. It is initially 10–50% oceanic or pore water mixed with combined water. Upon increased burial depth more interaction takes place at modest temperatures, and compaction leads to lower pressure environments. Variable salinity is observed and may be due to filtration, evaporation, or dissolution of evaporites.

Metamorphic water: contained in or driven from rocks undergoing metamorphic dehydration reactions. Being overpressured at depth, it may escape in response to lithostatic load.

Magmatic water: derived from oceanic and evolved connate waters subducted along with oceanic crust into the mantle. At deep crustal level it is mostly due to rocks undergoing metamorphism.

Juvenile water: classified as water that has never circulated in the atmosphere. If it exists it must be extremely rare. Juvenile ^{3}He and CO_2 of mantle origin exist and thus suggest that juvenile H_2O may exist too, but it has not yet been identified conclusively.

Geothermal waters. In most cases geothermal waters are either meteoric or ocean waters. Giggenbach [244] has, however, shown that so-called andesitic waters that are found in subduction zones encompass at least partly evolved connate water which mixes with magmatic steam and water. Ellis and Mahon [16] classified geothermal water into four categories based on major ions:

Alkali chloride water: pH. 4–11, least common in young rocks, for example, Iceland. These are mostly sodium and potassium chloride waters although in brines Ca concentration is often significant.

Acid sulfate water: These waters arise from the oxidation $H_2S \rightarrow SO_4$ near the surface and most of its constituents are dissolved from surface rock. Thus, such water is generally not useful for prediction of subsurface properties. The sulfate in acid sulfate waters occurring in andesitic systems [244] is, on the other hand, considered to be derived directly from magmatic SO_2.

Acid sulfate-chloride water: Such water may be a mixture of alkali chloride water and acid sulfate water or it can arise from the oxidation $H_2S \rightarrow SO_4$ in alkali chloride water or dissolution of S from rock followed by oxidation. Sulfate-chloride waters need not be very acid and may then reflect subsurface equilibria and be used for prediction of subsurface properties.

Bicarbonate water: Bicarbonate water may derive from CO_2-rich steam condensing or mixing with water; it is quite common in old geothermal waters or on the peripheries of geothermal areas in outflows. They are commonly at equilibrium and may be used to predict subsurface properties.

A good way of distinguishing the differences between the different types of geothermal water is the use of the chloride–sulfate–bicarbonate ternary diagram described by Giggenbach [243]. An example from Uganda is seen in **Figure 3**, where the geothermal water from one area, Kibiro, is a typical alkali chloride water, the water from another, Buranga, is a relatively alkaline

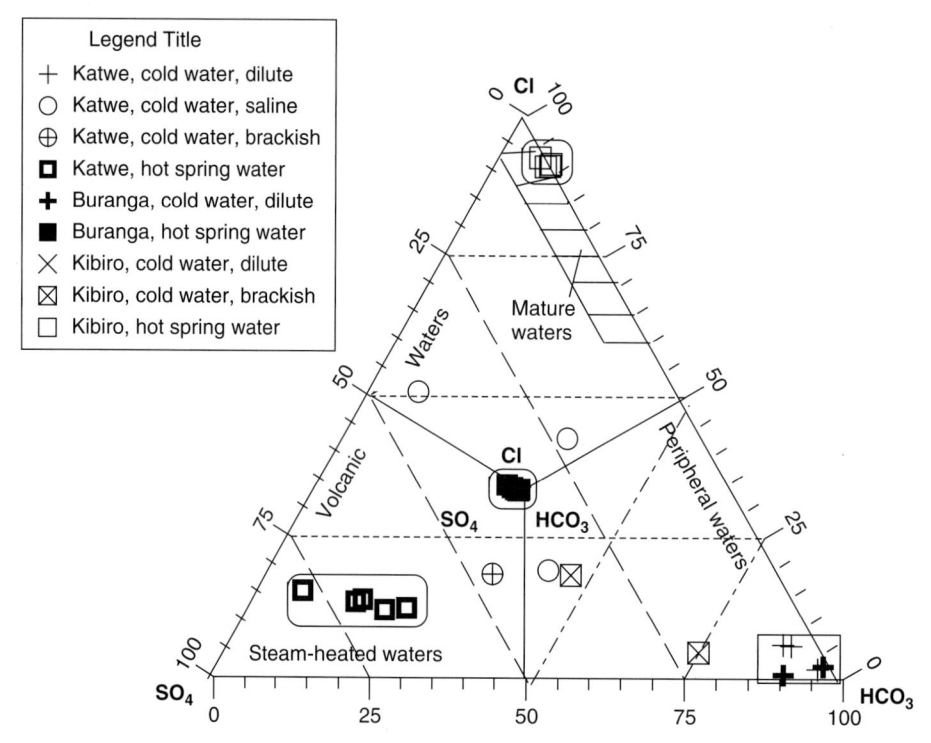

Figure 3 A ternary Cl–SO$_4$–HCO$_3$ diagram showing the characteristics of waters from different Ugandan geothermal systems.

chloride–sulfate–bicarbonate water, but the geothermal water from the third one, Katwe, is a sulfate water. The cold groundwater in the areas is scattered.

The dissolved constituents of geothermal water may originate in the original meteoric or oceanic water, but more likely they are the result of water–rock interaction and possibly modification by magmatic gas. They are divided into 'rock-forming constituents', for example, Si, Al, Na, K, Ca, Mg, Fe, and Mn, and 'incompatible or conservative constituents', for example, Cl, B, and Br.

Summary. Subsurface waters are divided into six categories but have mostly at one time or another circulated in the atmosphere. In areas of spreading the origin of geothermal waters is almost exclusively meteoric or oceanic but in subduction areas components of evolved connate and magmatic water are found. Geothermal water has been divided into four groups according to their major ion composition, that is, alkali chloride, acid sulfate, acid sulfate-chloride, and bicarbonate waters.

7.04.6 Alteration

Products of geothermal alteration are controlled by temperature, pressure, chemical composition of water (e.g., CO_2, H_2S), original composition of rock, reaction time, rate of water and steam flow, permeability, and type of permeability, and these products in turn control the chemical composition of the fluid. Some of the effects are that the silica concentration depends on the solubility of quartz/chalcedony; temperature-dependent equilibria of Al-silicates control Na/K, Na/Rb ratios; pH is controlled by salinity and Al-silicate equilibria involving hydrogen and alkali ions, while Ca^{2+} and HCO_3^- concentrations depend on pH and CO_2 concentration; F^- and SO_4^{2-} concentrations are related to that of Ca^{2+}, limited by solubility of fluorite and anhydrite and temperature; and salinity-dependent silicate equilibria control a very low Mg^{2+} concentration. The results of alteration studies show that the chemical composition of geothermal fluids originates in controlled reactions dependent on temperature, pressure, and rock composition. Therefore, it is possible to deduce the properties of subsurface water from the chemical composition of water which has been collected at the Earth's surface. In studies of hydrothermal alteration a distinction is made between the 'intensity' of alteration, which is a measure of how completely a rock has reacted to produce new minerals, and alteration 'rank', which depends upon the identity of the new minerals and is based on their significance in terms of subsurface conditions, for example, when considering permeability and temperature [250].

Basic chemical reaction processes. Processes taking place on the surface of the Earth are usually referred to as weathering, those taking place in the top layers of the crust (0–4 km) as alteration, but those taking place at greater depth as metamorphism.

The basic progress of chemical weathering can be described as primary minerals + O_2 + H_2O → secondary minerals. The reactions involve acid dissolution, iron oxidation, and hydration, and the higher the temperature the greater is the rate of reaction and where the runoff is large the transport of chemical components is fast. Ca and Mg are dissolved from the rock and will combine with CO_3^{2-} as the runoff mixes with seawater and contributes to the deposition of $CaCO_3$ and thus depletion of CO_2 from seawater, which in turn favors the dissolution of CO_2 from atmospheric air. The main solid products are noncrystalline clay minerals and hydrated iron oxides. Soil formation is an essential consequence of the process.

High-temperature geothermal areas are commonly characterized by acid sulfate alteration manifested by clay, yellow sulfur, gray FeS_2, and red hematite. Hydrogen sulfide is oxidized to sulfuric acid in the following process:

$$H_2S + \frac{1}{2}O_2 \leftrightarrow S + H_2O \quad [1]$$

$$H_2S + 2O_2 \leftrightarrow H_2SO_4 \quad [2]$$

The H_2SO_4 dissolves primary minerals and leaches elements such as Na and K, whereas other elements, for example, Ti, Al, and Fe, will be bound in secondary minerals. The approximate order of mineral formation is smectite, kaolinite, amorphous silica, and anatase (+S, FeS_2, and $CaSO_4$).

The process of alteration is represented by primary mineral + groundwater → dissolved solid → secondary mineral. The secondary minerals replace primary minerals or form amygdales. The nature of the primary mineral, the extent of the contact surface of rock and water, and temperature control the 'intensity' (a measure of how completely a rock has reacted to produce new minerals (0–100%)) and 'rank' (which depends upon the identity of new minerals based upon their significance in terms of subsurface conditions) of alteration. The volume of rock is increased. The most common secondary minerals formed are quartz, chalcedony, calcite, zeolites, celadonite, apophyllite, chlorite, and epidote. The alteration minerals are classified according to the anion but if necessary by structure as is the case with silicates. The most important types are as follows:

- *Carbonates*: calcite, aragonite, siderite
- *Sulfates*: anhydrite, alunite, soda alunite, barite
- *Sulfides*: pyrite, pyrrhotite, marcasite, sphalerite, galena, chalcopyrite
- *Oxides*: hematite, magnetite, leucoxene, diaspore
- *Silicates*: *Ortho, ring*: sphene, garnet, epidote; *sheet*: illite, biotite, pyrophyllite, kaolin, montmorillonite, prehnite; *framework*: adularia, albite, quartz, cristobalite, mordenite, laumontite, wairakite

Information on alteration is used in studies of the thermal stability of the field. Mineral temperatures are compared to measure and obtain the thermal history of the system. Such information can also be applied to infer the subsurface permeability and thus may be useful in deciding the casing depth of wells during drilling. Furthermore, it can give early indications of the nature of the fluid composition in the geothermal system such as whether it is CO_2 rich, H_2S rich, acid, single or two phase, whether there is boiling in formation or inside the well, and also of the depth of recharge and/or discharge zones. A hot, impermeable zone tends to have alteration of high rank but low intensity, whereas the alteration in a cold, permeable zone is of low rank but high intensity. Browne (1984) has thus divided the alteration observed in basalts and rhyolites in wells in Olkaria, Kenya, according to rank as shown in **Table 5**, which is used as a general guide to permeability in geothermal systems.

One of the most important processes of alteration is replacement of primary rock minerals by alteration minerals. The rate of replacement is variable and depends upon permeability. Sometimes incomplete replacement takes place. Such reactions are preserved in cores and are visible under the microscope. They are easily distinguished in volcanic reservoir rocks but with more difficulty in sedimentary or low-grade metamorphic rocks as many of the latter's primary minerals are also stable in geothermal environments. It is important to note that minerals control composition but not the salinity of water. Thus, the ratios of elements may be controlled by alteration in fluids at different salinities with temperature as the controlling parameter and this is the basis for many geothermometers. Hydrothermal alteration involves changes in density, porosity, permeability, magnetic strength (usually decreased), and resistivity (reduced) inflicted on the host rock. Events which may be related or unrelated to alteration, for example, faulting and formation of joints, may affect the alteration process. In the event of replacement it can proceed isochemically, but constituents may still be added or removed. The data in **Table 6** on the behavior of major elements are compiled from Browne (1984) for typical behavior and Franzson *et al.* [17] on their behavior in Icelandic systems.

The factors that control alteration are temperature which affects the stability of OH groups and bound water, for example, in clays, zeolites, prehnite, and amphibole; pressure which controls the depth at which boiling occurs; reservoir rock type because its texture controls permeability; the reservoir permeability; fluid composition with pH and relative constituent concentrations being most important; and finally the duration of the activity which is related to the kinetics of the reactions.

Effect of temperature on clays. In the kaolin group, acidic waters interact to produce kaolin and at <120 °C, kaolinite + (halloysite) becomes dickite, but at >250 °C pyrophyllite will be formed from dickite. In the chlorite group, for example, at Reykjanes, Iceland, smectite is observed at <200 °C, it is interlayered with chlorite at 200–270 °C, but at >270 °C it has gone over to chlorite (nonswelling). In many geothermal systems, montmorillonite, illite, and interlayered montmorillonite/illite are observed at

Table 5 Alteration in Olkaria (Kenya) basalts and rhyolites

Rank	Minerals
0	No hydrothermal alteration minerals
1	Traces of calcite, montmorillonite, pyrite, quartz
2	Fresh primary feldspars, partially altered ferromagnesium minerals
3	Fresh primary feldspars, completely altered ferromagnesium minerals
4	Partially altered primary feldspars, completely altered ferromagnesium minerals
5	Completely altered primary feldspars, trace of hydrothermal albite
6	Host rock altered, lots of hydrothermal albite
7	Lots of hydrothermal albite, less adularia
8	Adularia, less albite
9	Adularia only feldspar
10	Adularia all over host rock and porphyritic alteration

Table 6 Behavior of major constituents during alteration [250]

Oxide	Typical	Icelandic	Hydrothermal minerals
SiO_2	Added	Added	Quartz, cristobalite, silicates
TiO_2	Unchanged	Unchanged/(removed)	Sphene, leucoxene
Al_2O_3	Added/removed	Added	Silicates, oxides
FeO, Fe_2O_3	Added/removed	Added	Chlorite, pyrite, pyrrhotite, siderite, epidote, hematite
MnO	Unchanged	Added	MnO
MgO	Removed	Added	Chlorite, biotite
CaO	Added/removed	Unchanged (added/removed)	Calcite, wairakite, epidote, prehnite, anhydrite
Na_2O	Added/removed	Added/removed	Albite
K_2O	Added	Added/removed	Adularia, illite, alunite, biotite
CO_2	Added	Added	Calcite, siderite
S, SO_3	Added	Added	Anhydrite, alunite, pyrite, pyrrhotite, barite
H_2O	Added	Added	Clay, epidote, prehnite, zeolites, diaspore, pyrophyllite, amphibole
P_2O_5	Unchanged/removed	Unchanged	Apatite
Cl	Removed		
F	Added/unchanged		Fluorite

<140 °C; at 140–220 °C montmorillonite and interlayered montmorillonite/illite are common, but at >220 °C illite is predominant. Illite is not common in Icelandic geothermal systems, but is seen in or near acid and intermediate rocks. In the Icelandic systems, chlorite starts appearing at about 230 °C. Biotite is most common as a primary mineral but has been observed as a hydrothermal mineral in Ngawha, New Zealand, and Tongonan, the Philippines, at >220 °C but only appears in Cerro Prieto, Mexico, at >325 °C.

Effect of temperature on calc-silicates. At <110 °C low-temperature zeolites such as chabazite, mesolite, scolecite, and stilbite are frequently observed, but epidote is a reliable guide to temperatures >250 °C. In New Zealand prehnite occurs at >220 °C but at >300 °C in Cerro Prieto, Mexico, probably due to differences in the pH and Ca concentration of the circulating fluids. Kristmannsdóttir [18] has compiled **Figure 4**, which shows how the occurrence of different minerals may serve as a guide to the rock temperature of a geothermal system.

Alteration geothermometry. Vitrinite reflectance geothermometry has been used successfully for sedimentary rocks with abundant organic matter.

Fluid inclusion geothermometry. Upon the growth or recrystallization of hydrothermal minerals tiny growth irregularities may trap fluid and form primary inclusions. A single phase will separate into vapor and liquid at a lower temperature. Heating the inclusion will separate the single-phase fluid at its homogenization temperature. Quartz, calcite, and anhydrite inclusions are most suitable for such geothermometry, but epidote, wairakite, and sphalerite inclusions have also been deployed successfully. The inherent assumptions are that the inclusion is single phase and that no volume change and no leakage have taken place. It is an advantage of this method that it is not only the temperature that is obtained but also information on whether the system is cooling down or heating up.

An example of the use of fluid inclusion geothermometry is a study of the Ohaki-Broadlands geothermal system in New Zealand. Two-phase water inclusions in quartz and sphalerite were studied and proved to have primary inclusions in clear tips of euhedral crystals but tiny secondary inclusion near their base. The primary inclusions suggested temperatures from 201 to 293 °C, which was on average +8 °C from the measured temperature with a range from –13 to +37 °C. A wider spread was observed for the secondary inclusions, but the average was –6 °C off the measured temperature. Differences due to pressure and temperature changes and changes in fluid composition (CO_2) were shown to have lowered the boiling temperature, but the conclusion was that Ohaki-Broadlands is a thermally stable geothermal system, that is, it is neither heating up nor cooling down. The fluids in the high-temperature systems found in the Reykjanes peninsula, Iceland, show increasing salinities toward the tip of the peninsula. A fluid inclusion study on alteration minerals in three of these systems, Svartsengi, Eldvörp, and Reykjanes, shows a range of salinities from freshwater to salinities slightly above the respective fluids of the systems, and their formation and homogenization temperatures indicate that the Svartsengi and Eldvörp systems are gradually cooling, but the Reykjanes system shows comparable homogenization and formation temperatures on most parts, suggesting that its temperature has remained constant during its lifetime [19].

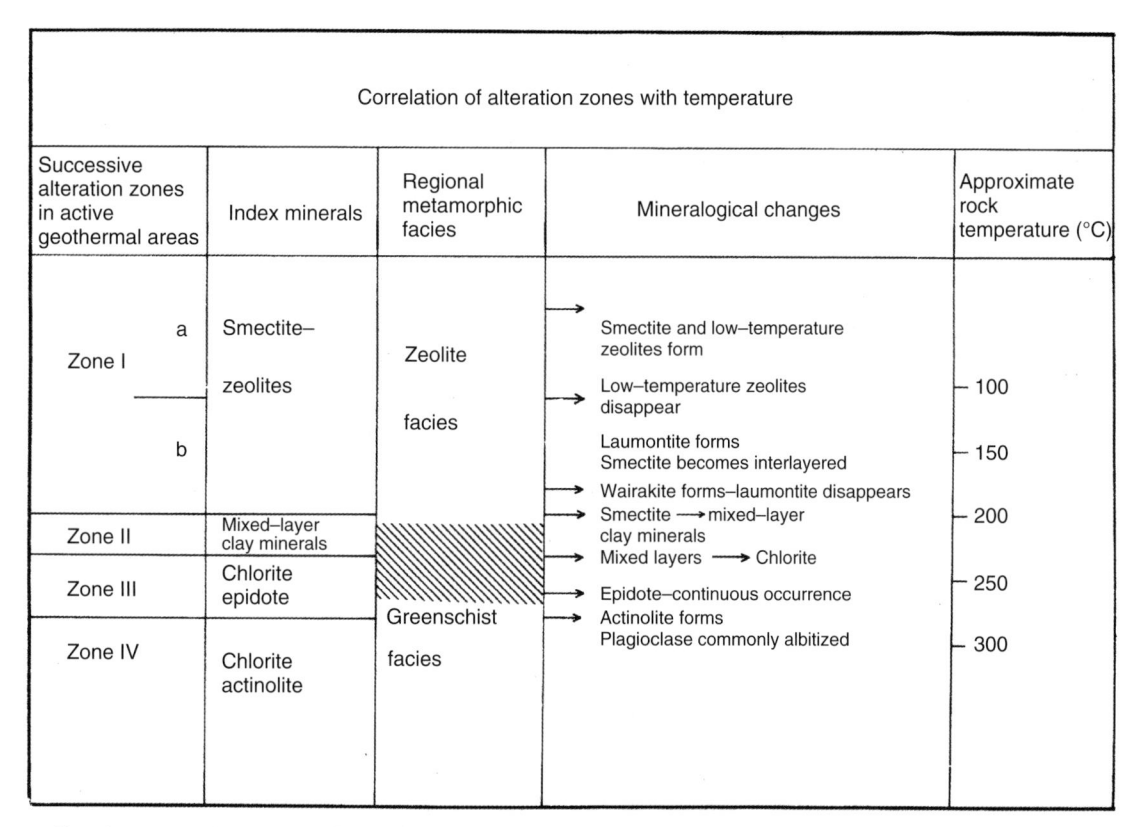

Correlation of alteration zones with temperature

Successive alteration zones in active geothermal areas	Index minerals	Regional metamorphic facies	Mineralogical changes	Approximate rock temperature (°C)
Zone I a	Smectite– zeolites	Zeolite facies	→ Smectite and low–temperature zeolites form → Low–temperature zeolites disappear	100
Zone I b			Laumontite forms Smectite becomes interlayered	150
			→ Wairakite forms–laumontite disappears → Smectite → mixed–layer clay minerals	200
Zone II	Mixed–layer clay minerals	Greenschist facies	→ Mixed layers → Chlorite	
Zone III	Chlorite epidote		→ Epidote–continuous occurrence → Actinolite forms Plagioclase commonly albitized	250
Zone IV	Chlorite actinolite			300

Figure 4 Alteration zones and temperature. From Kristmannsdóttir H (1978) Alteration of basaltic rocks by hydrothermal activity at 100–300°. In: Mortland M and Farmer VC (eds.) *International Clay Conference*, pp. 359–367. Amsterdam: Elsevier Scientific Publishing Company.

Effect of boiling. The most important effects of boiling on alteration are deposition and gas loss. In the kaolin/K-feldspar/muscovite system the pH of the boiling fluid determines which potassium mineral will precipitate. In the Na$_2$O-SiO$_2$-Al$_2$O$_3$-H$_2$O-HCl system albite and/or paragonite should precipitate but do not, possibly for some kinetic reason. Boiling is a self-limiting process because of the resultant cooling and reduction in permeability due to mineral deposition.

Boiling zones may be recognized by adularia veins formed as a result of raised pH of the liquid, deposition of calcite crystals with bladed morphology due to CO$_2$ loss, abundant quartz deposited due to cooling, and vapor and two-phase fluid inclusions in the same samples although liquid-rich inclusions can still form.

Effect of reservoir rock type. The texture of the rocks controls permeability, but the initial mineralogy of the host rocks has little effect on alteration assemblages in the discharge zones. At 260 °C albite, quartz, chlorite, epidote, calcite, ±pyrite, ±adularia, and ±illite will be found whether they derive from andesite, calc-alkaline rhyolites, alkaline lavas, or sediments. Icelandic basalts contain small amounts of K-mica or K-feldspar, but adularia has been found in Geitafell, Hornafjörður (a fossil system), and to a small extent elsewhere (e.g., at Nesjavellir). At lower temperatures, the nature of the parent material clearly influences the alteration product. High-silica zeolites, for example, mordenite, are common in rhyolitic fields whereas lower silica zeolites, for example, chabacite, thomsonite, and scolecite, occur in Icelandic basalt and the andesites of Kamchatka. The quantity of the mineral may reflect the nature of parent rock, for example, in Kizildere, Turkey, and Ngawha, New Zealand, where hydrothermal calcite is present and the reservoir rocks include limestone. Substitution may occur and a hydrothermal mineral thus reflects the composition of the mineral it replaces, but there is insufficient evidence for this. The rock mineralogy in the recharge parts of the system controls the fluid composition, for example, the Ngawha greywackes and argillites, which have a primary mineralogy consisting of quartz, K-feldspar, albite, K-mica, epidote, calcite, and pyrite. The deep waters of, for example, the New Zealand systems, have been found to be of a very similar composition with significant variations only in CO$_2$, B, and Cl and the above minerals precipitate with others in the discharge zones of the same fields.

Effect of fluid composition. In acid (pH < 3) conditions, surface alteration causes the precipitation of sulfur, alunite, and kaolin, but near neutral alkali chloride water precipitates silica sinter. Andydrite tends to be precipitated from sulfate-bearing fluids (e.g., seawater). In areas where the concentration of ammonia is high NH$_4$-bearing minerals may be precipitated, for example, in Ketetahi, New Zealand. Lepidolite has been found to precipitate from fluorine-rich water with a high Li/K ratio in the Yellowstone Park, USA, fluorite from fluorine-rich water in Olkaria, Kenya, and datolite from boron-rich water in Larderello, Italy. CO$_2$ and H$_2$S in the fluid have a direct effect on carbonate and sulfide precipitation. However, absolute concentration of dissolved constituents is much less important than the ratios of the activities of the major ions, for example, Salton Sea brines whose total dissolved solids concentration amounts to 250 000 ppm and fluids from fields whose total dissolved solids concentration is < 3000 ppm at 260 °C react with their reservoir rocks to produce an assemblage consisting of quartz, calcite, epidote, K-feldspar, albite, K-mica, and chlorite.

Activity diagrams are useful tools for summarizing the relationship between hydrothermal minerals and fluids, for example, the log ion activity ratios which are plotted in the presence of excess silica at a useful temperature. Boundaries are drawn where two or more phases coexist in equilibrium. Their positions are determined by experiments, calculations, and observations of mineral relations in geothermal fields. An example of such a diagram is given in **Figure 5**, which is an activity diagram for sodium and potassium in the presence of quartz at 260 °C in terms of ion activity ratios [251].

The diagram shows that equilibrium constants determined for a range of minerals, for example, a_{K+}/a_{H+} for the K-mica–K-feldspar reaction, create a boundary, but the $a^3_{Na+}/(a_{K+} \cdot a^2_{H+})$ constant for the albite–K-mica reaction suggests a slope, not an exact position. The effect of pressure is seen to be small but significant for, for example, 1–1000 bar. The value of such

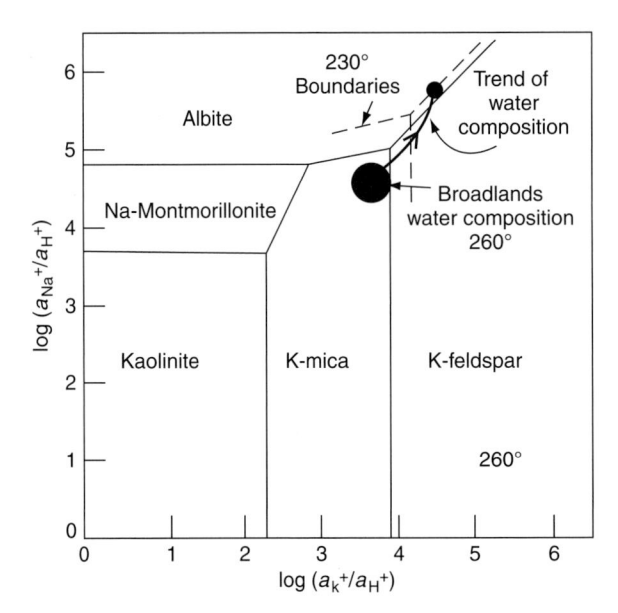

Figure 5 Activity diagram for Na and K in the presence of quartz at 260 °C [251].

diagrams is that activity of ions in geothermal fluid can be plotted and the alteration products predicted as has been done for Ohaki-Broadlands fluid in **Figure 5**, and K-mica is predicted to be the stable Na/K mineral. In such diagrams interlayered clays are not treated as a single phase. Similarly predictions can be made for other constituent systems, for example, the CaO-Al_2O_3-SiO_2-K_2O-H_2O ± CO_2 system. Ca minerals are common in active geothermal fields, and CO_2 is a very important component giving rise to the ions HCO_3^- and CO_3^{2-}. It has been found that for a particular value of mCO_2, a horizontal line on an activity diagram with a_{Ca+2}/a^2_{H+} as an axis represents a value at which calcite precipitates and above which calcium silicates cannot precipitate. This has a very important practical consequence because calcium silicates are rarely deposited in drill pipes whereas calcite does and thus calcite deposits are dealt with. The oxidation state of iron minerals in different geothermal systems has also been studied with the aid of activity diagrams. The stabilities of pyrite and pyrrhotite have been found to be related to P_{H_2S} and P_{H_2} and temperature, and a study of the relative abundance of sulfides and oxides can give an idea of the H_2S concentration in the reservoir fluids. In Olkaria, Kenya, El Tatio, Chile, and the El Salvador areas, hematite is common (but may coexist with sulfides) but hardly ever occurs in New Zealand systems, implying relatively oxidized systems with low H_2S contents in the former areas.

The dominant hydrothermal alteration indicates that the geothermal system reached a peak during the last glaciation, but has since then been gradually cooling. The evidence suggests that Holocene volcanic fissure eruptions opened up new flow paths and locally intensified the geothermal system.

Another example of the use of phase diagrams is shown in **Figure 6** (Arnórsson et al. [20]) where the saturation state of calcite and aragonite in the natural waters in Skagafjördur, North Iceland, with respect to the reaction quotient (Q_{CaCO_3}) for the reaction

$$CaCO_3 + H^+ \leftrightarrow Ca^{2+} + HCO_3 \qquad [3]$$

for individual water samples as a function of temperature as well as the equilibrium constants for calcite (solid curve) and aragonite (dashed curve) is calculated using SUPCRT92 [21]. The figure shows that nearly all surface waters are undersaturated with respect to calcite and aragonite whereas the groundwater is generally at or slightly above calcite saturation. Some of the groundwater samples are close to saturation with respect to aragonite below ≈40 °C but slightly undersaturated with respect to this mineral at higher temperatures. The persistent saturation or supersaturation of groundwaters with respect to calcite is consistent with the common occurrence of that mineral as a secondary mineral in Icelandic geothermal systems [22, 23]. Aragonite is not nearly as common a secondary mineral as calcite in Icelandic basalts but has been found in several locations [24].

Effect of permeability. High permeability and high porosity tend to give extensive alteration and *vice versa*. CO_2 and H_2S may be added from the solution as mineral reactions are rarely isochemical. The primary minerals break down close to major veins, but may persist to a high temperature at low permeability. A relationship has been established for minerals and permeability in some geothermal systems, for example, in Wairakei, New Zealand, the order is andesine, albite, albite + adularia, adularia with increased permeability. In Tongonan, the Philippines, prehnite, abundant laumontite, and sphene without epidote, smectite, and illite/smectite at >230 °C indicate low permeability, but anhydrite, illite, quartz, calcite, adularia, pyrite, and wairakite indicate high permeability. In the Taupo volcanic zone of New Zealand, the area surrounding veins in wells producing >20 kg s^{-1} steam is found to be characterized by adularia, in those producing 5–15 kg s^{-1} by albite + adularia, but in poor or nonproducers by albite and/or andesine. The Na_2O/K_2O ratio has been suggested to be a good guide to permeability. High K_2O/Na_2O ratio (>4) indicates good production zones, K_2O/Na_2O = 0.5–4 average production zones, but if K_2O/Na_2O < 1 the zone is usually nonproducing. In bores containing abundant illite or interlayered illite/montmorillonite the K_2O/Na_2O ratio is not as reliable a guide to production.

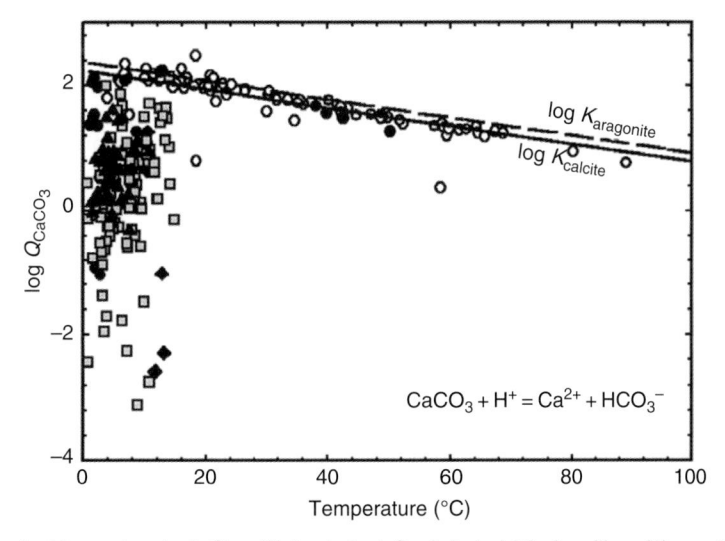

Figure 6 The saturation state of calcium carbonates in Skagafjördur, Iceland. Symbols depict the logarithm of the reaction quotient for the dissolution reaction of calcium carbonate shown in the figure. The solid curve represents the log K for the dissolution of calcite, and the dashed curve represents the log K for the dissolution of aragonite. Waters that have log Q values lower than the log K at a given temperature are undersaturated with respect to the mineral. From Arnórsson S, Gunnarsson I, Stefánsson A, et al. (2002) Major element chemistry of surface- and ground waters in basaltic terrain, N-Iceland. I: Primary mineral saturation. *Geochimica et Cosmochimica Acta* 66: 4015.

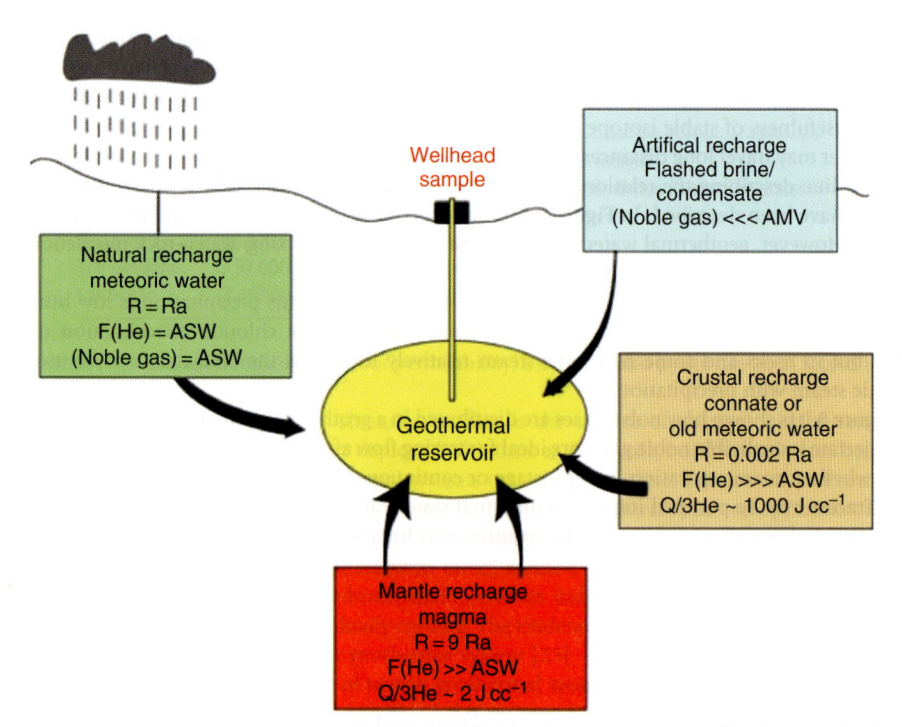

Figure 8 The distribution of noble gases between the various parts of a producing geothermal system. (R = ^{3}He/^{4}He; Ra = ^{3}He/^{4}He in the atmosphere; F = fugacity; ASW = air-saturated water, Q = enthalpy). Provided by B.M. Kennedy.

Dating. One way of studying the origin of geothermal water is by dating. For this, two types of methods have been used, that is, determination of radioactive materials and chlorinated fluorocarbons. Of radioactive substances ^{3}H with a half-life of 12.43 years has been extremely useful for relatively young water. It is measured in tritium units (1 TU = 1.185 Bql^{-1}). The natural cosmogenic level in precipitation is a few TU but rose to ≈2000 TU from the 1950s to 1963/1964 but is down to ≈10 TU at present. For older waters dating with ^{14}C with a half-life of 5730 years has been used. It is present in atmospheric CO_2, the living biosphere, and hydrosphere after production by cosmic radiation, but underground production is negligible and therefore it cannot be used for carbon from a magmatic source. The ^{14}C content is often presented as % modern carbon (pMC), grown in 1950. Fallout ^{14}C (in CO_2) has been used to date water with mean residence time less than 150 years.

Organic compounds of chlorine and fluorine are man-made and first appeared in 1928. They are unreactive and nontoxic. CFC-11, CFC-12, and CFC-113 are the most common of these. The release of CFC-11 and CFC-12 to the atmosphere rose in the 1930s. Deviations in the release were first noted following 1974, when possible ozone depletion by chlorine-containing species was first announced, but much more significant ones after the signing of the Montreal Protocol in 1987. Release of CFC-113 increased significantly through the early and mid-1980s until the Montreal Protocol was signed, after which production significantly diminished. The lifetimes of the most commonly used CFCs are given in **Table 8**.

Potential water pollution. Several constituents of geothermal water are potential pollutants if the effluent water is discharged directly into a lake, a stream, or lava fissures. Hydrogen sulfide may be poisonous and in fluids from some fields there are dangerously high concentrations of arsenic. Mercury and other trace metals may be present at unacceptable levels and ammonia may be a nuisance. Boron in high concentrations is harmful to plants and, for example, in Turkey the Kizildere power plant is shut down during irrigation time to avoid contamination by boron. One way of disposal is collecting the effluents into a pond and let it gradually seep away, but ponds become sealed by silica and increase in area to unacceptable size. The Blue Lagoon in Svartsengi,

Table 8 Atmospheric lifetime of chlorinated fluorocarbons

CFC	Lifetime (years)
CFC-11	45 ± 7
CFC-12	87 ± 17
CFC-113	100 ± 32

Iceland, was originally such a pond, but after the curative properties of the brine were discovered it has been converted to a huge tourist attraction. Treatment processes designed for geothermal effluent have not yet been found economic chiefly because it is very difficult to remove boron from the liquid. Reinjection is by far the most effective way of getting rid of the effluent and it also helps maintain the geothermal system.

Example of monitoring geothermal effluent water, Krafla and Bjarnarflag, Northeast Iceland. Lake Mývatn (37 km^2) is situated in North Iceland at an altitude of nearly 300 m. It is divided into two main basins, the North Basin (8.5 km^2) and the South Basin (28.2 km^2) (**Figure** 9). The eastern part of the South Basin is frequently described as a separate basin (the East Basin) on geographical and ecological grounds. It is much influenced by inflowing cold spring water. Extensive areas in the South Basin are between 3 and 4 m deep, maximum depth is about 4 m. In the North Basin a large bottom area has been dredged, which has increased the depth from about 1 to 2–5.5 m. Water enters the lake almost exclusively from springs along its east shore. Most of the springs are about 5 °C, but springs in the North Basin are warmer, generally warmest at Helgavogur where up to 23.6 °C was found in 1971–1976 [28], and this increased to at least 32.5 °C during the Krafla fires [29] but had gradually cooled to 25.6 °C in 1998 [30]. The average duration of ice cover is about 190 days [252]. Lake Mývatn was formed about 2300 years ago following a major volcanic eruption [31–33]. The South Basin of the lake lies in a shallow depression in an extensive lava field produced by the eruption. Another lake existed at the same site before the eruption, but it appears to have been wiped out by the lava. The North Basin was formed by the same volcanic eruption as the South Basin, but by damming at the edge of the lava field. The geology of the area has been described by Thórarinsson [34] and Sæmundsson [32]. Primary production has been estimated to be 3800 kcal m^{-2} yr^{-1} [35], of which 600 kcal m^{-2} yr^{-1} comes from phytoplankton. Most of the primary production therefore takes place on the bottom of the lake, mainly by diatoms. Average sediment thickness in the South Basin is about 4.3 m. Diatom frustules comprise about 55% and minerogenic material (mostly tephra) about 30% of the dry weight of the sediment in the North Basin [36]. The ecology of the lake is described by Einarsson *et al.* [37].

The River Laxá leaves Lake Mývatn in three main branches that merge a short distance downstream to form a single swift river which flows on a bed of lava rock and sand. The Lake Mývatn area is sparsely populated, with 10–15 farms, traditionally based on sheep farming and fishing. In the last three decades the human population has grown as a result of industrialization (diatomite production and power production from the Krafla geothermal plant) and increased tourism, and a village has been built up at the north end of the lake. The total number of inhabitants now is about 480. Human impact on the ecosystem was mostly felt through the diatomite mining operation as it interfered with the nutrient and sedimentation dynamics of the lake. Grazing by sheep maintains an open landscape and may have contributed to excessive soil erosion in a large area south and east of the lake [38]. The decision to discontinue the operation of the diatomite plant was made in 2005 so that dredging the bottom of the lake has ceased.

The catchment of Lake Mývatn is covered by highly permeable, sparsely vegetated lava terrain, partly covered with aeolian and waterborne sand [39]. There is little surface runoff so the extent and subdivisions of the catchment can only be determined by indirect methods. Based on Árnason [40], who used spatial variation in the deuterium ratio in precipitation to trace groundwater origin, the catchment area has been estimated at about 1400 km^2 [41, 254]. only about 17% of the catchment area has organic topsoil with vegetation [41]. The spring water discharge entering Lake Mývatn is about the same as the outflow from the lake

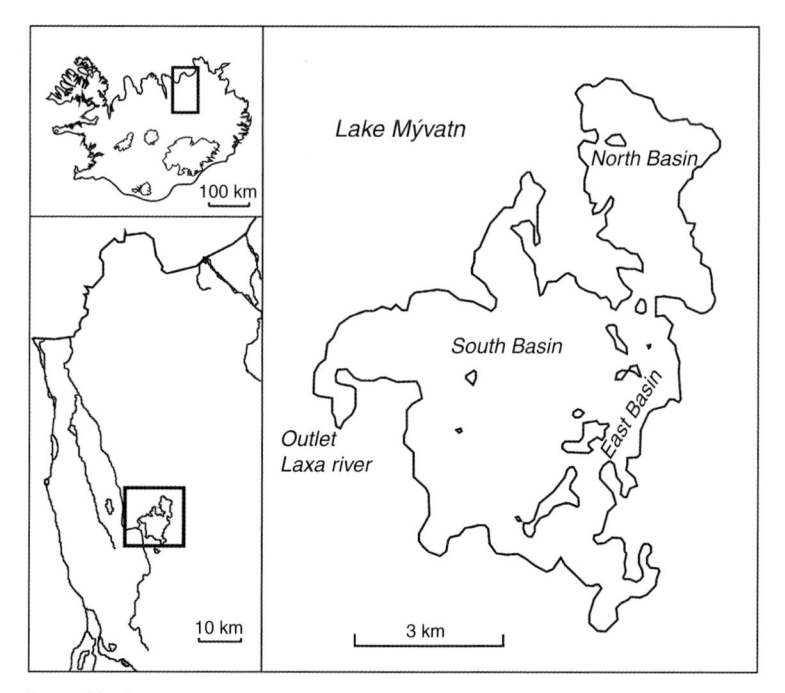

Figure 9 Lake Mývatn. Location and basins.

($32-33\,m^3\,s^{-1}$) since surface runoff is negligible. Of the spring water, $8.3\,m^3\,s^{-1}$ (24%) enters the North Basin and flows via the South Basin on the way to the outlet. The springs in the SE corner of the lake contribute about $14.6\,m^3\,s^{-1}$ (44%). Grænilækur, a river flowing a short distance from the spring-fed Lake Grænavatn and entering the southeast part of Lake Mývatn, has a discharge of $6.4\,m^3\,s^{-1}$. The remaining $3.7\,m^3\,s^{-1}$ emerge along the other parts of the shore. The springs on the eastern shore of Lake Mývatn have a high pH, relatively high concentrations of phosphate, some nitrate, and high concentrations of silicate, especially the warm springs, resulting in inputs of P, N, and Si amounting to 0.05, 0.14, and $12\,mol\,m^2\,yr^{-1}$, respectively [28, 42]. Nitrogen in the groundwater is mostly in the form of nitrate from precipitation in the catchment area of the lake. The mean phosphate concentration of 1.62 µM in groundwater entering Lake Mývatn [42] is more than twice the world average lake concentration of 0.65 µM [43]. The high pH and phosphate concentrations of groundwater feeding the lake are due to the highly reactive basaltic bedrock and the sparse vegetation in the catchment area. Thus, the groundwater, with its constant flow and temperature, acts as a stable source of dissolved constituents [44].

Lake Mývatn is unique in its productivity and biodiversity for a lake at its latitude and altitude. Therefore, the area has been protected by a special law since 1974 and it is listed as an important habitat for birds in the RAMSAR convention on wetlands. There has been some concern that the effluent from the Krafla power station, the diatomite plant, and the small power plant in Bjarnarflag, as well as the proposed 90 MW$_e$ Bjarnarflag power plant might affect the inflow to Lake Mývatn and therefore the groundwater near Lake Mývatn has been thoroughly studied concurrent with the construction of the power plant in Krafla and more recently as part of the environmental impact assessment of the Bjarnarflag (Námafjall) power plant.

Sulfur was mined in the Námafjall area with intervals for centuries using traditional methods, the last period of such mining being during World War II. During the 1950s there were plans to drill for sulfur and erect a modern factory. Several wells were drilled in the Hverarönd part of the Námafjall field at the time but these were abandoned. The remains of some of them still exist as hot springs that are a much praised tourist attraction. Instead interest grew in a diatomite plant using diatomites from the bottom of Lake Mývatn and geothermal steam for drying. The diatomite plant was erected during the 1960s with 10 geothermal wells drilled from 1963 to 1965. These were to a large extent damaged by magmatic activity in 1977 and two make-up wells were drilled outside the most active area in 1979 and 1980. There are few records of hydrological studies or the possible fate of effluent water from this early activity except that Sæmundsson [45] stated that the water level in Bjarnarflag wells remained very constant but that earlier records showed the water level in a well east of Námafjall to oscillate between 321 and 345 m asl.

The Krafla 60 MW$_e$ power plant, comprising two turbines, was commissioned in 1975 on the basis of surface exploration and the drilling of two exploratory wells. Progress was hampered by the Krafla fires during 1975–1984 so to start with only one of the 30 MW turbines was installed at the time. The first 7 MW went on line in early 1978 when 11 wells had been drilled. One more well was drilled in 1978, but after further surface exploration it was decided to drill two more wells in the old drilling area of Leirbotnar but at the same time try drilling in a new area, Sudurhlídar, that seemed less affected by volcanic activity. Later it was decided to test yet another drilling area, Hvíthólar, seemingly unaffected by the volcanic activity. From 1980 to 1983 two wells were drilled in the Leirbotnar area, six wells in the Sudurhlídar area, and three wells in the Hvíthólar area and sufficient steam had been obtained to fully utilize the installed 30 MW turbine. A make-up well was drilled in 1988 and two exploratory wells in 1990–1991, all in Leirbotnar. In 1996 Landsvirkjun (the National Power Company) decided to complete the installation of unit 2 and to drill for additional steam to reach fully rated power on the plant. The project has been successfully completed and the plant has been running on full load since 1998. For completion five wells were drilled in Leirbotnar, two wells in Sudurhlídar, and one well in a new drill field, Vesturhlídar. Several additional wells have been drilled as is described in the section on acid fluids in Section 7.04.10 on production problems. **Figure 10** gives an overview of the wells and wellfields in Krafla.

It has been estimated that from the beginning over 200 million tons of effluent have been discharged into the lavas from Krafla and Bjarnarflag. The early results for the exploration in Krafla suggested that the field was water dominated and its utilization would involve vast quantities of effluent [46]. This aspect of the utilization was therefore thoroughly studied during the early stages of the project. Ármannsson [47] has given a detailed overview of these studies.

Sigbjarnarson et al. [255] estimated that the effluent flow from the then proposed plant would become about $0.6\,m^3\,s^{-1}$ and the major environmental effects steam cloud and silica deposits. They proposed to discharge the effluent into Búrfellshraun lava, this being the cheapest way, the dilution would be great and the water would take a long time to reach Lake Mývatn if ever. Shallow wells should be drilled in the lava to monitor the effluents' progress. If a potential danger were identified the water could be cooled and dangerous substances precipitated, it could be directed to the catchment area of river Jökulsá or it could be reinjected. Sæmundsson et al. [46] suggested that the effluent be cooled and directed into a lagoon, preferentially located in the valley Thríhyrningadalur. VST and Virkir [48] showed that locating the lagoon in the valley Hlídardalur was financially and technically a better option. Arnórsson and Gunnlaugsson [49] divided the Krafla area into three catchment areas: I, II, and III (**Figure 11**). One more catchment area can be defined to the west of these: catchment area IV. The stream Hlídardalslækur which would receive any effluent outflow thus has a catchment area of 21–41 km². In September 1975 the flow from the springs that feed the stream was $871\,s^{-1}$. Water from Thríhyrningadalur lagoon was expected to flow into the valley Hlídardalur or to the west of Mt. Dalfjall about 15 km from Lake Mývatn and most likely flow beneath the bottom of the lake. Model calculations by Ingimarsson et al. [50] suggested that the greatest changes in groundwater level and also the greatest likelihood of the water flowing back into the geothermal system would be obtained if a lagoon were to be formed in Thríhyrningadalur. If the water flowed along the shortest possible path it would take 30 years to reach Lake Mývatn.

Jóhannesson [51, 52] suggested that the major groundwater flow was from the Dyngjufjöll area, 60–80 km to the south, but a part of the current that is heated up rises to the surface and flows back south in the Námafjall area, and that this current joins a local

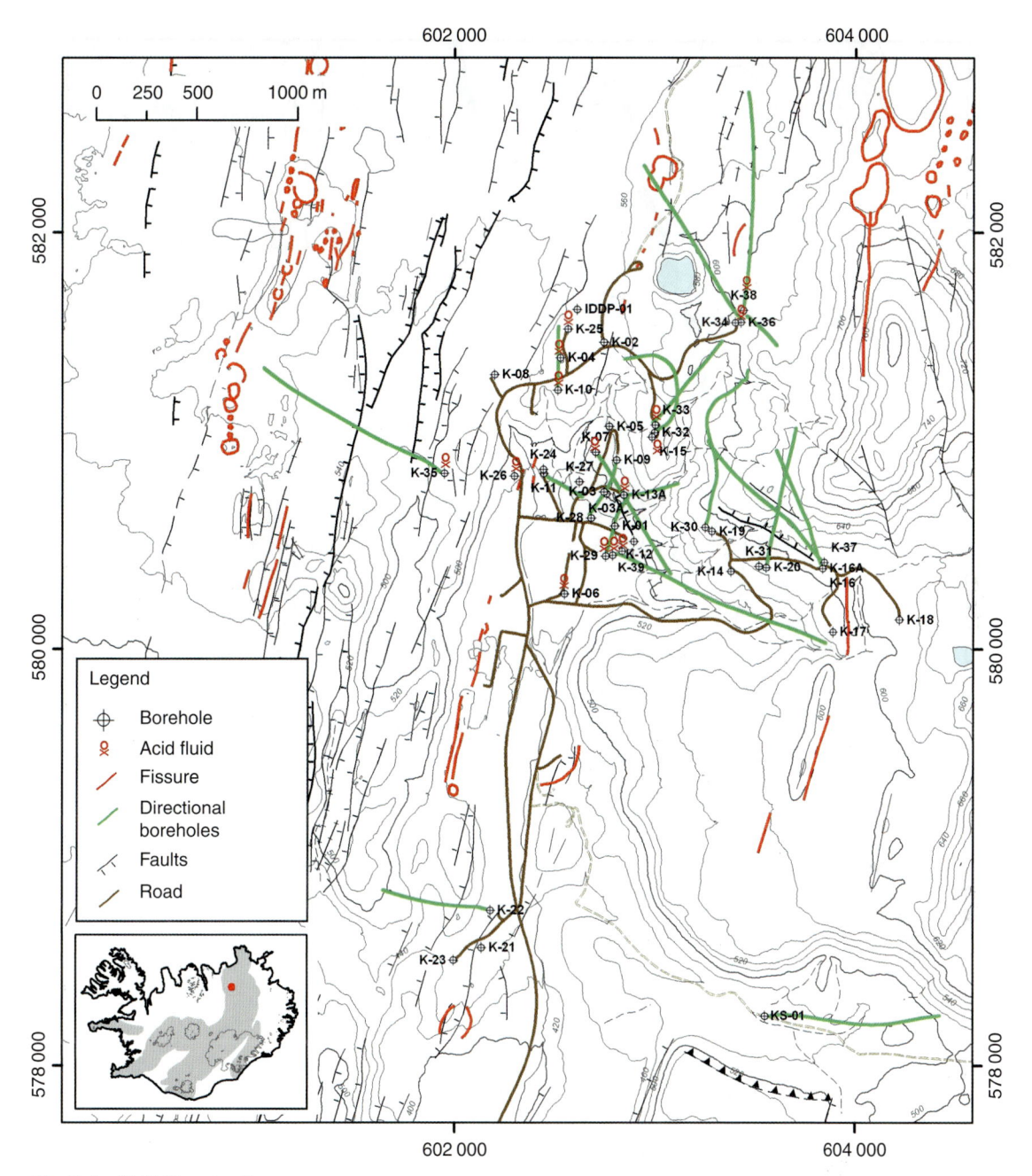

Figure 10 Krafla. Wellfields and wells.

current flowing from Krafla south to Lake Mývatn. This is the macrostructure that has been used for later models of flow in the area into which local detail has been added [30, 53, 54]. Darling and Ármannsson [55] using stable isotope ratios confirmed that this could be the pattern, and using their results in conjunction with those of Árnason [40] and Jóhannesson [51, 52], Hjartarsson et al. [56] have constructed an overall view of the origin of the flow to the area (**Figure 12**). Any effluent from the Námafjall area would thus be likely to be discharged into the 8.3 m^3 s^{-1} flow entering the North Basin and if effluent water from Krafla were to reach Lake Mývatn it would be as part of that same flow.

The drilling results at Krafla revealed a higher enthalpy geothermal system than had been predicted, and presently the amount of effluent from there is a little over 100 l s^{-1}, about half of which is being reinjected. The enthalpy of the two wells drilled in Bjarnarflag in 1979 and 1980 was higher than of the previous ten. The effluent from the early wells had not affected Lake Mývatn and therefore it was decided that it was not likely to affect the lake to discharge these relatively small quantities directly into the lavas.

Several tracer tests have been carried out to establish the flow pattern and dilution of the effluent when it has mixed with the groundwater. In 1980 fluorescein was added to a downflow about 190 m to the NE of well AB-02 in Búrfellshraun lava (**Figure 13**),

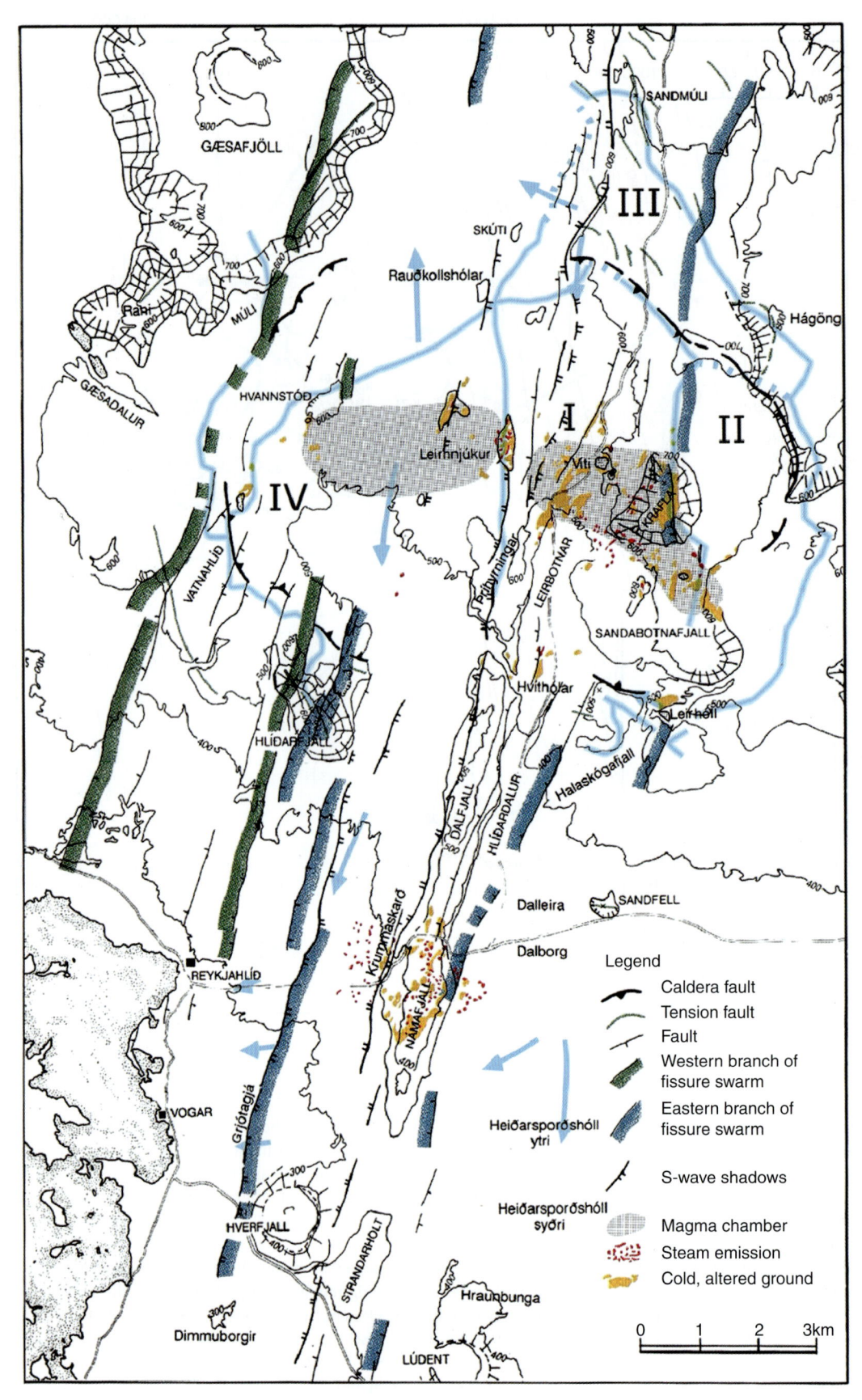

Figure 11 Krafla and Námafjall catchment areas. From Arnórsson S and Gunnlaugsson E (1976) The catchment of the stream Hlídardalslækur and effluent from the Krafla Power Station (in Icelandic). National Energy Authority OS JHD 7602, 13pp.

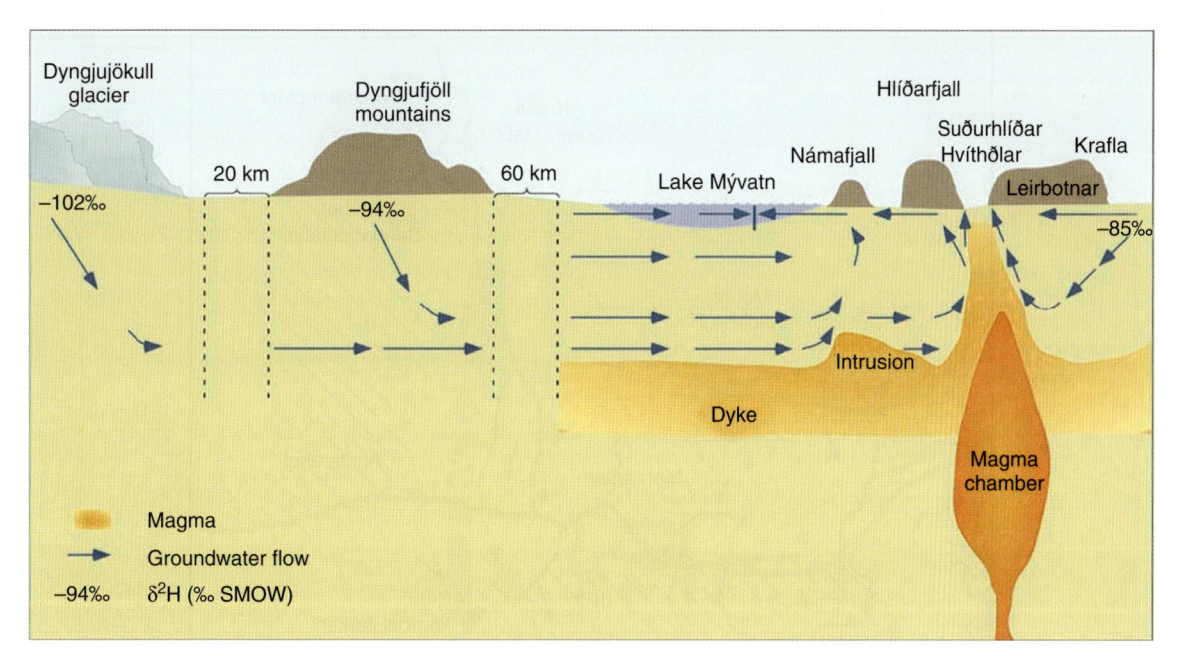

Figure 12 Possible origin and flow of groundwater in the Lake Mývatn area.

most of which was recovered from the well within 40 days (J. Ólafsson, personal communication). During the next 2 years fluorescein was added to effluent from the diatomite plant pumping station at Helgavogur, most of which was recovered in the springs at Helgavogur with traces recovered from Stóragjá and Kálfstjörn, but it was argued that very little or anything could be transported via Grjótagjá to Langivogur (**Figure 13**) [53]. In 1998–1999 several tests were run both from the Hlídardalslækur downflow and the Bjarnarflag lagoon downflow using fluorescein, potassium iodide, and rhodamine WT, the only result being a faint response to the iodide and a very faint one to fluorescein in Grjótagjá, about 4 months after their addition to the Bjarnarflag lagoon downflow [57]. A more detailed test with potassium iodide in 2002 showed the first signs of tracer return in Grjótagjá 2 km to the south of the Bjarnarflag lagoon downflow, 2 months after its addition to it, reaching a peak after 5 months. A smaller trace was recovered from a spot in the same fissure about 1 km further south. The dilution from the downflow to Grjótagjá is 100 millionfold [58].

Reinjection of several types has been considered for effluent from the Krafla power plant. Shallow reinjection into a permeable fissure in eastern or western Hlídardalur valley has been estimated as likely to be effective but would probably involve unacceptable damage to vegetation [59]. Reinjection was tested in the Hvíthólar area and the reinjected effluent was soon recovered from a nearby well so the reinjection would have to be designed differently by injecting the fluid at a great depth so that it does not enter the production aquifer. A reinjection test involving injecting effluent from the separator plant at Krafla into well KG-26 (**Figure 10**) has been in progress since January 2002 and results seem promising. An earlier test with cold groundwater had blocked the well, but the geothermal effluent has removed the blocking and increased the volume received by the well from 10–20 to about $60\,\mathrm{l\,s^{-1}}$. The injectate has not been detected in nearby wells. A tracer test was carried out in which 450 kg potassium iodide dissolved in 3000 l water was pumped into well KG-26 with the injectate in December 2007 and 484 samples collected from 9 nearby wells on a regular basis until August 2007. In no sample was a significant increase of iodide observed. This suggests that there is a large fluid flow through the system and that the reinjection is not likely to change the enthalpy of the fluid [60]. Part of the explanation of the nonreturn could be the two-phase nature of the geothermal system and that a vapor-seeking tracer such as SF_6 or isopropanol might be needed to ensure the tracer's return. Preliminary work suggests that the concentrations of and ratios between noble gases in conjunction with stable isotopes may be used as natural tracers for the injectate (B. Christenson, personal communication). Two tracer tests were conducted by the BRGM during the summer of 2009 (June 1–September 1): one from the reinjection well KG-26 using 1,5- and 2,6-naphthalene disulfonate (1,5-nds and 2,6-nds) and the second from the IDDP borehole using 1,6-nds. The monitoring of the tracer concentrations took place in two steps: (1) analysis on-site using a spectrofluorimeter; (2) analysis by HPLC4 with a fluorescence detector in the BRGM laboratory. During the first step the main breakthrough peaks and interferences in several wells were highlighted, but it was not possible to quantify the concentrations of the tracers. The main breakthrough peaks in the KG-26 test were observed in wells KJ-15 and KJ-37 (**Figure 10**) whose bottoms are relatively close to that of KG-26 and all three are aligned on a west–east line. Such a direction of groundwater flow is perpendicular to the already known N–S direction. Compared with previous tracer tests, the apparent linear velocity ($14\,\mathrm{m\,h^{-1}}$) of the tracer breakthrough was relatively high and the recovery rate (around 0.5%) very low. Even lower recoveries were obtained in the test on well IDDP-1, but again the most significant responses were observed in wells KJ-15 and KJ-37 [61]. On the whole the returns from these tracer tests are so small that it is difficult to draw conclusions about the flow in the Krafla geothermal system based on them.

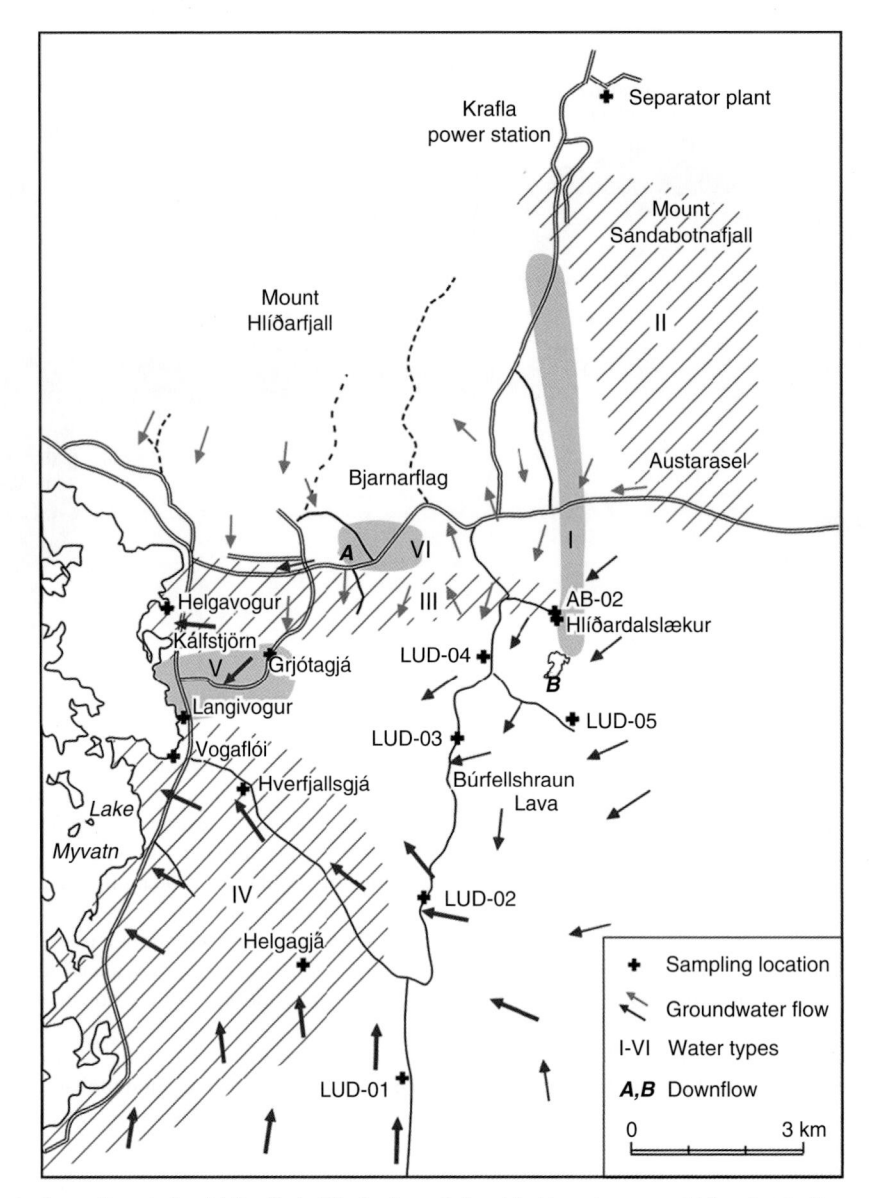

Figure 13 Groundwater flow patterns in the vicinity of Lake Mývatn. Areas distinguished by water groups I–VI, and wells, fissures, and springs sampled are shown.

Groundwater studies, including the chemistry, are described in detail by Kristmannsdóttir and Ármannsson [62]. The water table in the Krafla and Námafjall geothermal systems is at a great depth and in natural circumstances only steam will reach the surface from them. Heated groundwater can be accessed in some fissures and springs in the Námafjall area close to Lake Mývatn. Early records compared with present day ones do not suggest an increase in undesirable components [42, 63, 64]. There were, however, some changes in composition, especially increases in chloride and silica in some of these fissures and springs coincident with an increase in temperature, recorded during the Krafla fires, but these have gradually returned to the previous values [29, 65].

On the basis of δ^2H and $\delta^{18}O$ values waters in the Lake Mývatn area have been divided into six distinct groups [65, 66], which can also be distinguished geographically (**Figure 13**). Groups I ($\delta^{18}O = -80.4$ to -80.7), II ($\delta^2H = -83.0$ to -86.9), and III ($\delta^2H = -87.7$ to -88.9) are local water groups, whereas the water found in groups IV ($\delta^2H = -91.5$ to -94.8) and V ($\delta^2H = -90.9$ to -93.5%) originate from the inland far to the south. Water in group I is discharge from the Krafla power plant and water in group VI is effluent water from Námafjall geothermal field. Oxygen shift due to water–rock interaction suggesting geothermal influence is observed in group V ($\delta^{18}O = -11.58$ to -11.92), which thus differs from group IV ($\delta^{18}O = -12.72$ to -13.03) and constitutes groundwater significantly influenced by geothermal effluent. Oxygen shift is observed in groups I, V, and most prominently in group VI. The Icelandic meteoric line differs slightly from the WML [40, 256]. The grouping of the Mývatn groundwater based on δ^2H and $\delta^{18}O$ values is confirmed by the relationship of Cl and B [66].

In 1978–1979 well AB-02 in the Búrfellshraun lava was drilled to monitor underground flow from the Krafla effluent downflow from the Hlídarsdalslækur stream. Since then the location of the downflow has moved further south and it is thought that the location of this well is now probably not right for monitoring this flow. Samples from the above-mentioned fissures and springs give valuable information but in many cases for rather distant locations. To obtain more representative distribution of results five wells LUD-01–LUD-05 (**Figure 13**) were drilled and sampled. As tracer tests had proved expensive and difficult it was felt desirable to find out whether any natural tracers could be found, that is, constituents that were present in a large concentration in the geothermal effluent but in a small concentration in the groundwater. Constituents that are characteristic of geothermal fluid such as SiO_2, Al, Mo, and As seem possible candidates. One of the difficulties here is that the springs feeding Lake Mývatn are geothermal in their own right, that is, the water is heated by a heat source close to the springs. Thus geothermal constituents such as SiO_2 may be diluted to start with but then replenished by this second geothermal heat source. Therefore, the task is to find a constituent that is characteristic for high-temperature geothermal water but dissolves slowly at lower temperatures. In **Table 9** there is a survey of possible natural tracers in water from selected sampling locations. The conclusion was that As was probably the most useful natural tracer for high-temperature geothermal effluent, but results for Al and Mo would provide support. This is also convenient as As is the only constituent whose concentration in the groundwater may exceed permitted concentrations (**Table 10**). The chemical composition from fluids of the downflows, springs, fissures, and wells is shown in the latest report on monitoring of fluids [69] and that of the downflows and the springs that feed Lake Mývatn and may receive water from the effluent in **Table 11**.

In light of the 200 million tons of effluent that already has entered the groundwater under the lavas in the Lake Mývatn area during the last 40 years without causing harm and the relatively small amount of effluent water due to the high enthalpy of the borehole fluids in the Krafla and Námafjall geothermal areas, it is considered relatively safe to permit continued release of effluent from the Krafla power plant, its enlargement, and the proposed Bjarnarflag power plant into the lava in the vicinity of Lake Mývatn.

Continued experiments with reinjection at Krafla are recommended as this is the most efficient means to dispose of effluent and also extend the lifetime of the geothermal system. It is also suggested that if the proposed Bjarnarflag power plant becomes as large as producing 90 MW_e reinjection is desirable so as to avoid undue strain upon the system [56].

The size of the Bjarnarflag lagoon and the Hlídardalslækur downflow pond should be monitored annually using aerial photography. The water table of the wells in Búrfellshraun lava should similarly be monitored twice per year and samples for total chemical analysis collected once per year and samples for trace metal analysis twice per year from the following locations: Hlídardalslækur downflow; wells AB-02, LUD-02, LUD-03, and LUD-04; Bjarnarflag downflow; Grjótagjá fissure; and the springs at Langivogur and Vogaflói by Lake Mývatn (**Figure 13**). This monitoring scheme is in progress and annual reports are issued.

Geothermal gases. The origins of geothermal gases are diverse and can be magmatic, in rock dissolution, organic, atmospheric, and radiogenic. Studies of isotopes, inert gases, and thermodynamic calculations help elucidate the origin in each case. The $\delta^{13}C$ signatures for CO_2 of different origins are magmatic −10 to −1‰, marine limestone −2 to +2‰, organic <−20‰, and atmospheric

Table 9 Geothermal constituents in samples from selected locations 2002–2003 (Ármannsson and Ólafsson [30, 67])

Location	SiO_2 (mg l^{-1})	Al (mg l^{-1})	Mo (μg l^{-1})	As (μg l^{-1})
Hlídardals-lækur downflow	285	0.706	4.18	25.1
LUD-04	28.4	0.418	1.75	5.69
Langivogur	69.0	0.0017	0.36	0.15
Bjarnarflag lagoon	227	0.735	0.30	157
Helgavogur	77.4	0.0081	1.30	0.16
Grjótagjá	156	0.0098	0.19	0.17

Table 10 Environmental limits for some chemicals in surface water for biological protection

Limit (μg l^{-1})	I	II	III	IV	V
Cu	≤0.5	0.5–3	3–9	9–45	>45
Zn	≤5	5–20	20–60	60–300	>300
Cd	≤0.01	0.01–0.1	0.1–0.3	0.3–1.5	>1.5
Pb	≤0.2	0.2–1	1–3	3–15	>15
Cr	≤0.3	0.3–5	5–15	15–75	>75
Ni	≤0.7	0.7–1.5	1.5–4.5	4.5–22.5	>22.5
As	≤0.4	0.4–5	5–15	15–75	>75

I, negligible or no risk; II, very small risk; III, effects on sensitive biota; IV, effects expected; V, always intolerable [68].

Table 11 Spring and effluent water chemical composition

Constituent	Hlídardalslækur, downflow	Bjarnarflag downflow	Vogaflói spring	Langivogur spring
pH/°C	9.20/22	7.68/24	8.62/23	8.54/23
CO_2 (mg l^{-1})	87.3	35.9	66.9	84.7
H_2S (mg l^{-1})	1.26	0.11	<0.03	<0.03
B (mg l^{-1})	0.69	3.11	0.06	0.31
Cond. µScm^1/25 °C	850	813	210	443
SiO_2 (mg l^{-1})	285	227	21.4	122
TDS (mg l^{-1})	894	1098	118	362
Na (mg l^{-1})	151	144	21.5	69.0
K (mg l^{-1})	16.0	21.3	1.74	5.63
Mg (mg l^{-1})	6.30	0.364	6.26	3.50
Ca (mg l^{-1})	18.6	1.92	10.9	13.4
Sr (mg l^{-1})	0.0302	0.0112	0.0127	0.0160
F (mg l^{-1})	0.80	0.84	0.22	0.38
Cl (mg l^{-1})	35.9	59.0	4.89	15.6
SO_4 (mg l^{-1})	233	191	19.6	78.6
Ba (µg l^{-1})	2.60	0.84	0.33	1.69
Mo (µg l^{-1})	4.180	0.499	0.739	0.356
Al (µg l^{-1})	706	119	7.8	1.7
Cr (µg l^{-1})	0.677	0.033	1.450	0.355
Mn (µg l^{-1})	37.9	1.47	0.182	<0.03
Fe (µg l^{-1})	73.1	6.0	2.8	0.9
Cu (µg l^{-1})	1.15	0.687	1.48	0.30
Zn (µg l^{-1})	8.06	2.65	1.77	0.56
As (µg l^{-1})	25.1	157	<0.01	0.154
Cd (µg l^{-1})	0.0394	0.004	0.0503	0.0065
Hg (µg l^{-1})	0.008	0.0124	<0.002	<0.002
Pb (µg l^{-1})	0.073	0.233	<0.01	0.023
Ni (µg l^{-1})	0.627	0.239	0.308	0.108
Co (µg l^{-1})	0.120	<0.005	0.034	0.018
P (mg l^{-1})	0.0091	0.00558	0.0621	0.0499
δD‰	−73.9	−88.0	−91.6	−90.8
δ^{18}O‰	−8.42	−6.24	−12.66	−11.64

−5 to −8‰; δ^{34}S for H_2S leached from rock < 0‰, magmatic ≈0‰, and marine >0‰; δ^{2}H in H_2 leached from rock or sediments −300 to −450‰ and magmatic <−450‰. In biogenic hydrocarbons δ$^{13}C_{CH_4}$ is <−55‰ in thermogenic (wet) gas, higher in thermogenic (dry) gas of terrestrial origin, but lower in such gas of marine origin. It is rather high in magmatic gas and expected at −20 to 10‰ in hydrocarbons of inorganic origin. The relationship between the δ^{13}C signatures of CO_2 and CH_4 in some Icelandic areas is shown in **Figure 14**, suggesting a magmatic origin except in Öxarfjörður where it might be sedimentary. This relationship also gives an idea of the temperature from where the gas is derived. The very high temperatures at Lýsuhóll and Geysir suggest a direct flow from magma. The presence of higher hydrocarbons suggests a sedimentary origin. In Kibiro, Uganda, the bulk of the gas is hydrocarbons, but in other areas such as Öxarfjörður, Iceland, they constitute a small fraction only.

Darling and co-workers [70–72] have studied hydrothermal hydrocarbon gases worldwide and come to the conclusion that apart from isotopic differences hydrothermal hydrocarbons differ from sedimentary hydrocarbons in possessing tendencies toward a relative excess of CH_4, higher normal/iso ratios for butane and pentane, and relatively large amounts of C_6 gases. They, however, originate in thermal degradation of organic matter at a relatively shallow depth, that is, their origin is crustal, thermogenic.

Giggenbach (1991) has suggested that the relationship between N_2, He, and Ar can be used to delineate the origin of geothermal gases in geothermal systems and has applied this to several systems (**Figure 15**).

As is described below, CO_2 emanations through soil are an important route to the atmosphere. The measurement of CO_2 through soil is thus a powerful tool to detect upflows in geothermal areas and aid in locating boreholes.

Possible environmental impact of geothermal gases. Hydrogen sulfide is toxic at high concentrations besides causing an unpleasant smell that is a common cause for complaint, and in many geothermal plants an elaborate cleaning mechanism is installed to minimize the nuisance caused by its emission. Several methods have been used for hydrogen sulfide abatement. The following methods are most widely applied:

- *Reinjection:* A simple, inexpensive method. Hydrology and chemistry studies are needed prior to the process. Long-term effects are not known.

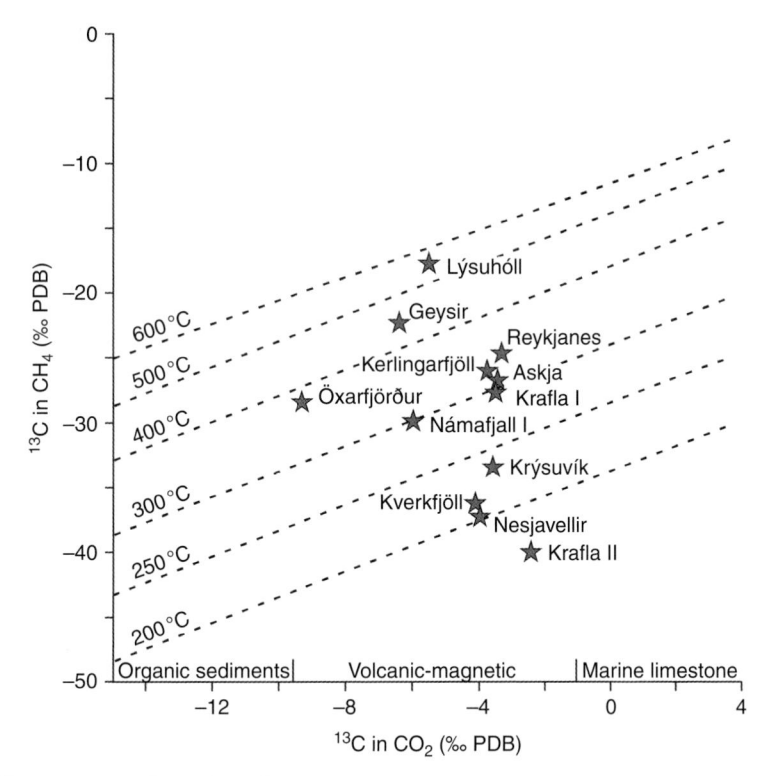

Figure 14 $\delta^{13}C_{CH_4}$ vs. $\delta^{13}C_{CO_2}$ in Icelandic geothermal areas.

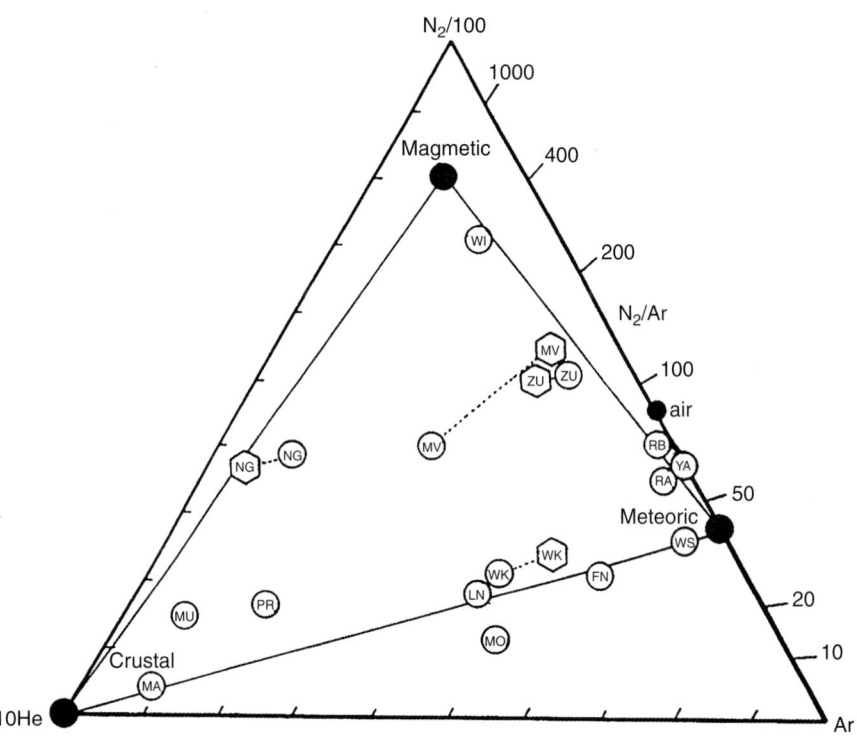

Figure 15 Relative N_2, He, and Ar contents of geothermal discharges on molar basis, suggesting origin. (WI, White Island, New Zealand, spring; MV, Miravalles, Costa Rica, vent; ZU, Zunil, Guatemala, well; NG, Ngawha, New Zealand, well, pool; RB, Ruiz, Colombia, neutral spring; YA, Yazur, Vanuatu; RA, Ruiz, Colombia, acid spring; WS, Waitengi, New Zealand, soda spring; WK, Wairakei, New Zealand, well, fumarole; FN, Fang, Thailand, spring; LN, Lake Nyos, Cameroon, dissolved gas; PR, Paraso, Solomon Islands, spring; MU, Maui, New Zealand, gas well; MO, Morere, New Zealand, spring; MA, Manikaran, India) [243].

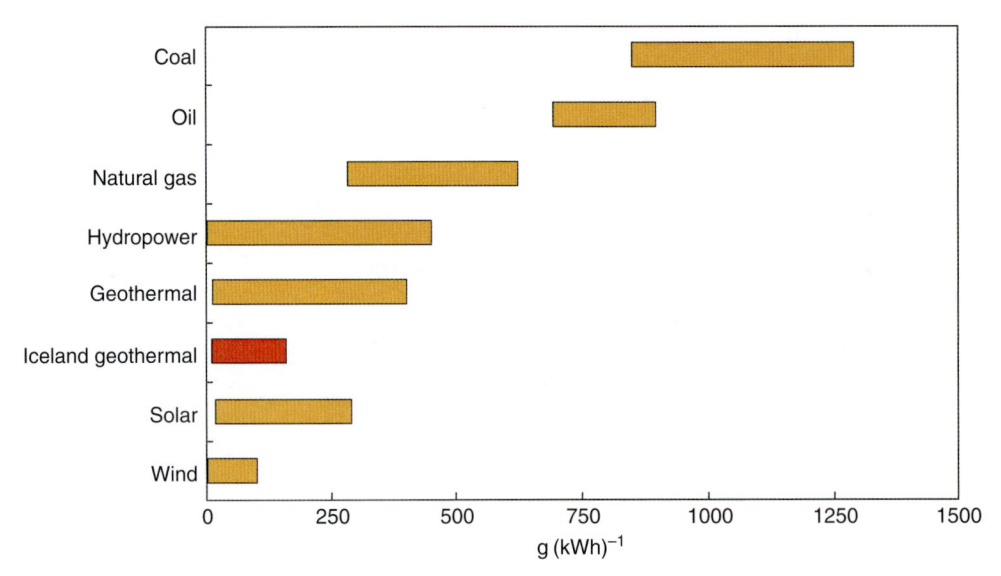

Figure 16 Greenhouse gas emissions from various types of power plants.

- *Claus Selectox chemical oxidation:* A labor-intensive method, there is uncertainty regarding design as H$_2$S concentration may change with time and a risk due to H$_2$S in the apparatus. It was found most attractive of 12 oxidation processes considered for abatement in the Nesjavellir power plant [73]. There are two possibilities regarding the fate of the product.
  Product buried: A small initial cost, but expensive operation as excavation work is needed.
  Products marketed: Profit is a possibility, but there is a large initial cost, and the economics of the process are uncertain. It was, however, considered a better choice than burying in Nesjavellir report [73].
- *Bacterial oxidation (THIOPAC):* An inexpensive and convenient process which has been demonstrated for plants with relatively small H$_2$S emissions but there is uncertainty about plants with large H$_2$S emissions such as Nesjavellir [270].
- *FeCl hybrid process:* This process may be economic especially if hydrogen which may be used as a fuel is a product.

Carbon dioxide and methane are greenhouse gases and their emissions to the atmosphere are considered negative environmental effects of geothermal production. Methane is usually a relatively minor gas in geothermal production, but carbon dioxide is the major gas and thus its emissions tend to be carefully monitored.

Carbon dioxide emissions, however, compare favorably with those from fossil fuels such as can be seen in **Figure 16**. In the figure ranges are shown and the highest values for hydroelectric plants have been observed when forests have been drowned to form dams and large quantities of methane, which is about 20 times more effective greenhouse gas than carbon dioxide, have been formed. Greenhouse gas emissions from hydroelectric plants in Iceland are for instance negligible. The reason why solar and wind plants emit carbon dioxide is that wind and sun are not in constant supply and most such plants burn natural gas to overcome this.

Recent studies of CO$_2$ emissions from geothermal/volcanic systems have demonstrated that vast quantities of CO$_2$ are released naturally and that natural emissions far exceed emissions from power production in many cases (e.g., Refs 73, 246, and 256). Consequently, the validity of considering CO$_2$ emissions as a negative environmental impact of power production in systems where emissions due to power production are negligible in comparison to natural emissions has been challenged in a report published by the International Geothermal Association (2002). In this report it was suggested that the natural emission rate predevelopment be subtracted from that released from the geothermal operation, citing Larderello as an example of a field where a decrease in natural release of CO$_2$ has been recorded and suggested to be due to development. Geothermal flux is commonly of magmatic origin, but CO$_2$ may also be derived from depth where it is mainly produced by metamorphism of marine carbonate rocks. There is often a large flux through soil, but CO$_2$ dissolves in groundwater, where this is present, usually reaching saturation where the flux is sufficiently large. Processes of natural generation are independent of geothermal production. The output is very variable but usually quite substantial. Estimated output from several volcanic and geothermal areas is shown in **Table 12**. Estimates of the fractions of CO$_2$ emitted through groundwater, soil, and fumaroles in three areas are listed in **Table 13** and suggest that emissions through soil are the most extensive.

The CO$_2$ emissions from Icelandic geothermal plants have been recorded since the early 1980s when it was 48 000 t yr^{-1} up to now. In 2009 it was 163 000 t (Í. Baldvinsson, personal communication). In the early years power production was very low, but the relatively high CO$_2$ emission was due to a gas pulse in Krafla associated with the Krafla fires [89].

In 1984 a steam cap developed in the Svartsengi geothermal system, South Iceland, with one well being produced from it to start with, but in 1993–2001 three wells were drilled into it, the discharge of each one causing a sharp rise in CO$_2$ emissions from the field. Natural steam emissions and thus gas emissions through soil also increased at the same time. Since the formation of the steam cap the concentration of CO$_2$ in the steam produced from the steam cap has decreased gradually and is now about half of what it

Table 12 CO$_2$ output from some volcanic and geothermal areas

Area	Megaton (10^9 g) per year	References
Pantellera Island, Italy	0.39	Favara et al. [75]
Vulcano, Italy	0.13	Baubron et al. [76]
Solfatara, Italy	0.048	Chiodini et al. [2]
Ustica Island, Italy	0.26	Etiope et al. [77]
Popocatepetl, Mexico	14.5–36.5	Delgado et al. [74]
Yellowstone	10–22[a]	Werner and Brantley [78]
Mammoth Mountain, USA	0.055–0.2	Sorey et al. [79], Evans et al. [80], Gerlach et al. [81]
White Island, New Zealand	0.95	Wardell and Kyle [82]
Mt. Erebus, Antarctica	0.66	Wardell and Kyle [82]
Taupo Volcanic Zone, New Zealand	0.44	Seaward and Kerrick [247]
Furnas, Azores, Portugal	0.01	Cruz et al. [83]
Midocean Volcanic System	30–100	Gerlach [84], Marty and Tolstikhin [85]
Reykjanes, Iceland	0.005	Fridriksson et al. [86]
Total	200–1000	Delgado et al. [74], Marty and Tolstikhin [85], Mörner and Etiope [87], Kerrick [88]

[a] Diffuse degassing only.

Table 13 Relative CO$_2$ emission through different conduits from three areas [75, 79–81, 86]

	Pantelleria Island	Furnas Volcano	Mammoth Mountain	Reykjanes, Iceland
Soil (%)	81	49[1]	63–90[a]	97.4
Focused degassing (%)	7			
Fumarole (%)	0.0004			1.7
Bubbles (%)	3			
Groundwater (%)	9	51	10–37	0.9

[a] Total flow directly to atmosphere.

Table 14 CO$_2$ and S (expressed as SO$_2$) emission per kWh from Iceland's major geothermal power plants in the year 2000 [90]

	Power production only		Total production	
Plant	CO$_2$ (g (kWh)$^{-1}$)	S as SO$_2$ (g (kWh)$^{-1}$)	CO$_2$ (g (kWh)$^{-1}$)	S as SO$_2$ (g (kWh)$^{-1}$)
Krafla	152	23	152	23
Svartsengi	181	5	74	2
Nesjavellir	26	21	10	8

was in 1984. Continued production from the steam cap will result in further lowering of the concentration of CO$_2$ in the steam, eventually leveling out as the CO$_2$ in the liquid resource has reached equilibrium.

In **Table 14** CO$_2$ and sulfur (expressed as SO$_2$) emissions from Krafla, Svartsengi, and Nesjavellir in grams per kWh of electrical energy and total energy production (the sum of electrical and thermal energy from direct use applications) are listed. CO$_2$ emissions from Krafla and Svartsengi are a little above the world average for geothermal plants when only electrical power production is considered; however, a very small amount of CO$_2$ is emitted from Nesjavellir. The value for Svartsengi is much improved when space heating is accounted for, illustrating the environmentally mitigating effect of cascading uses of geothermal energy.

Ármannsson et al. [91] estimated the CO$_2$ flux from basaltic magma emplaced in the Icelandic crust as 1.2×10^9 kg yr^{-1}. This value represents an estimate of the input into the Icelandic geothermal systems. The CO$_2$ input is in the long term equal to the output but possible CO$_2$ output processes include calcite precipitation and discharge of CO$_2$ into groundwater in addition to atmospheric emission.

In some countries geothermal energy production is significant and to them the discussion of the significance of addition of CO$_2$ emissions to the atmosphere from geothermal power plants is extremely important. In one such country, Italy, the Larderello power station has been producing for over 100 years and thus it has been possible to establish a database on gas emissions over a long period [257]. The conclusion is that all gas discharge due to power production is balanced by a reduction in natural emissions and the resultant change is insignificant and it is concluded that as a rule, power plant CO_2 emissions are small compared with natural CO_2 emissions. A significant increase in CO_2 emissions is reported to be observed with production but that it is balanced to some extent by a decrease in natural CO_2 emissions and this balance is apparently different between areas. Using heat flow measurements as a proxy for gas flow measurement [258], on the other hand, suggest that exploitation of the Wairakei geothermal system, New Zealand, has resulted in significantly increased diffuse CO_2 discharge from the field of the same order as from the power station itself. Studies in Iceland suggest that the situation there is somewhere between these two extremes.

Ways of abating CO_2 emissions have mostly centered on subsurface storage and sequestration. Proposed CO_2 storage techniques include the injection of anthropogenic CO_2 into deep geologic formations due to their large potential storage capacity and geographic ubiquity. Three types of sequestration have been suggested, that is, first 'geological sequestration' in which CO_2 is injected into and stored in underground geological formations whose potential storage capacity is large and they are geographically ubiquitous [92–96]. It has, for example, been shown that deep saline aquifers in sedimentary basins are promising candidates for geological sequestration of CO_2 and laboratory experiments; studies of well fluids and numerical modeling have shown that porosity and permeability of sandstone reservoirs would increase as a consequence of CO_2 injection [97, 253]. The effectiveness of this CO_2 storage and sequestration method depends strongly on the retention time, reservoir stability, and the risk of leakage [93, 98, 99]. Second, 'ocean sequestration' has been suggested, that is, bringing the CO_2 into solution in ocean water as different anions. The environmental effects of such storage have generally been found undesirable. Lastly, 'mineral sequestration' in which CO_2 is bound as carbonate in subsurface rocks has been studied. In Iceland sequestration by basalts has been considered and there is an ongoing project in the Hellisheidi area, South Iceland, involving the injection of CO_2 into basalt layers. The project has been described by Gíslason et al. [100] and the following description is based on their account. Carbon dioxide could be injected into deep geologic formations on land as a separate supercritical fluid. One way to enhance the long-term stability of injected CO_2 is through the formation of carbonate minerals. Carbonate minerals provide a long-lasting, thermodynamically stable, and environmentally benign carbon storage host. Mineral carbonation of CO_2 could be enhanced by injecting it fully dissolved in water and/or by injection into silicate rocks rich in divalent metal cations. Mineral carbonation requires combining CO_2 with metals to form carbonate minerals. The most abundant cation sources for this process are silicate minerals and glasses. The dissolution of the silicate minerals and glasses releasing the divalent cations is the rate-determining step. Natural waters in basaltic terrains and experimental solution in contact with basalt are typically saturated with respect to calcite at intermediate to high temperatures [101, 102]. CO_2 will dissolve in water and the product dissociate, lowering the pH as follows:

$$CO_2 + H_2O \leftrightarrow H_2CO_3 \qquad [4a]$$

$$H_2CO_3 \leftrightarrow \frac{1}{4} HCO_3^- + H^+ \qquad [4b]$$

CO_2 solubility increases, and thus the amount of water required for its dissolution decreases, with increasing CO_2 partial pressure, lower temperature, and lower salinity. Basaltic rocks are rich in divalent cations such as Fe, Ca, and Mg which could react with CO_2 to precipitate carbonate minerals as follows:

$$(Fe, Ca, Mg)^{2+} + CO_2 + H_2O \leftrightarrow (Fe, Ca, Mg)CO_3 + 2H^+ \qquad [5]$$

Reaction [4] suggests that 2 mol of protons are produced for each mole of carbonate mineral produced. This reaction will only proceed to the right if the H^+ ions are consumed in a different reaction such as dissolution reactions in a basalt [101, 103–107] including

$$Mg_2SiO_4 + 4H^+ \leftrightarrow 2Mg^{2+} + 2H_2O + SiO_2(aq) \qquad [6]$$

$$CaAl_2Si_2O_8 + 8H \leftrightarrow Ca^{2+} + 2Al^{3+} + 2SiO_2(aq) + 4H_2O \qquad [7]$$

$$SiAl_{0.36}Ti_{0.02}Fe(III)_{0.02}Ca_{0.26}Mg_{0.28}Fe(II)_{0.17}Na_{0.08}K_{0.008}O_{3.36} + 6.72H^+$$
$$\leftrightarrow Si^{4+} + 0.36Al^{3+} + 0.02Ti^{4+} + 0.02Fe^{3+} + 0.17Fe^{2+} + 0.26Ca^{2+} + 0.28Mg^{2+} + 0.08Na^+ + 0.008K^+ + 3.36H_2O \qquad [8]$$

In addition to advancing carbonate precipitation by proton consumption, reactions [5]–[7] also provide divalent metal cations to further promote this precipitation. In situ mineralization is believed to be effective in basalt or ultramafic rocks [106, 108, 109]. Storage in basalts is now considered to be among the most promising of the options for CO_2 storage [110, 111].

The course of this process is shown in **Figure 17**.

Mineral storage is thus facilitated by the dissolution of CO_2 gas into the aqueous phase. The water density increases, once the gas is fully dissolved, minimizing its tendency to flow toward the Earth's surface.

Example of the presence of higher hydrocarbons, Öxarfjörður, Northeast Iceland. Organic gases have been discovered in geothermal boreholes in Öxarfjörður, Northeast Iceland. Hitherto, methane was the only hydrocarbon that had been confirmed in geothermal gases in Iceland and natural emissions, for example, from Lake Lagarfljót.

Öxarfjörður is at the junction between the NE–SW Iceland spreading zone and the Tjörnes fracture zone, a right-lateral transform zone within which the thickest known sedimentary sequence in Iceland is found on- and offshore, covering an area 140 km long (N–S) and 40 km wide (E–W), up to 4 km thick and possibly accumulating since the Miocene. The uppermost sediments in the Öxarfjörður area are due to a glacial river delta and formed during the last 10 000 years. Several wells have been drilled in the

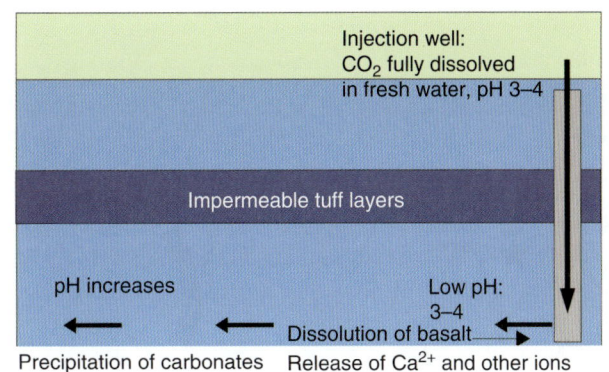

Figure 17 Overall process of carbon dioxide fixation.

Skógarlón area, the deepest one to 450 m depth. Later, deeper wells were drilled further south at Bakki, but their fluids did not contain more hydrocarbon gases and the discussion here will concentrate on the Ærlækjarsel wells. The gas concentrations have been put into context with the analytical results for organic remains in the sediments as well as compared to hydrocarbon gas composition in other locations. The results were described in detail by Ólafsson et al. [112].

Methane from different sources has different characteristics as is apparent from **Table 15**. Generally methane is found in high-temperature wells and fumarole fluids and in some low-temperature well waters and cold emissions which are also known in Iceland (**Table 16**). The locations of the latter's principal sites are shown in **Figure 18**.

Classification of hydrocarbons. The origin of hydrocarbon gases may be studied in three ways, that is, by the proportion of higher hydrocarbons (C_{2+}) which tend to be relatively abundant in thermogenic gases but absent in biogenic gases, by studying their stable isotope ratios, that is, $\delta^{13}C$ in CH_4 and C_{2+} which range from highly depleted in biogenic gases to more enriched in thermogenic and magmatic gases, δD in CH_4 which tends to be relatively depleted in biogenic and wet thermogenic gases but enriched in dry thermogenic gases, and lastly by tentative age determinations, for example, using ^{14}C, which reveal that thermogenic gas tends to be older than biogenic gas.

Three analyses from each of the three wells at Ærlækjarsel, Skógarlón, are reported in **Table 17**. If the hydrocarbons only are considered the percentage of C_{2+} varies from 3.6 to 17, clearly suggesting a thermogenic gas, probably wet gas (**Figure 19**). There is a considerable variation in the $\delta^{13}C_{CH_4}$ values. None of the results are depleted enough for a biogenic gas but they can be divided into two groups, one with values close to –40‰ and another with values ranging from –22.5 to –31.9‰. The two lower values of the

Table 15 Characteristics of methane from different outflows

Type[a]	Main gas	CH_4 (vol.%)	$\delta^{13}C_{CH_4}$ (‰)
C	CH_4	88–98	–73 to –81
L	N_2	0.05–0.8	
L/I	CO_2	0.03–0.05	–17.8
I	N_2	0.8–0.9	
H_{II}	CO_2	0.2–4/4–20[b]	–36 to –40
H_I	CO_2	0–0.2	–22 to –36

[a] C, cold gas flow; L, low temp. geothermal (<100 °C); I, intermediate temp. (100–180 °C); H_{II}, high temperature, lower range (≈200 °C); H_I, high temperature, higher range.
[b] After magmatic event.

Table 16 Gas composition of methane containing natural gas from different sources in Iceland (vol.%)

Location	Type	CO_2	H_2S	H_2	CH_4	O_2+Ar	N_2
Krafla, well 7	h.t.	86.96	4.64	7.33	0.09	0.04	0.93
Lake Urriðavatn, well 7	l.t.	0.25			0.24	2.08	95.40
Lake Lagarfljót	c.e.	1.24			96.65	0.59	1.52

h.t., high-temperature geothermal area; l.t., low-temperature geothermal area; c.e., cold emission.

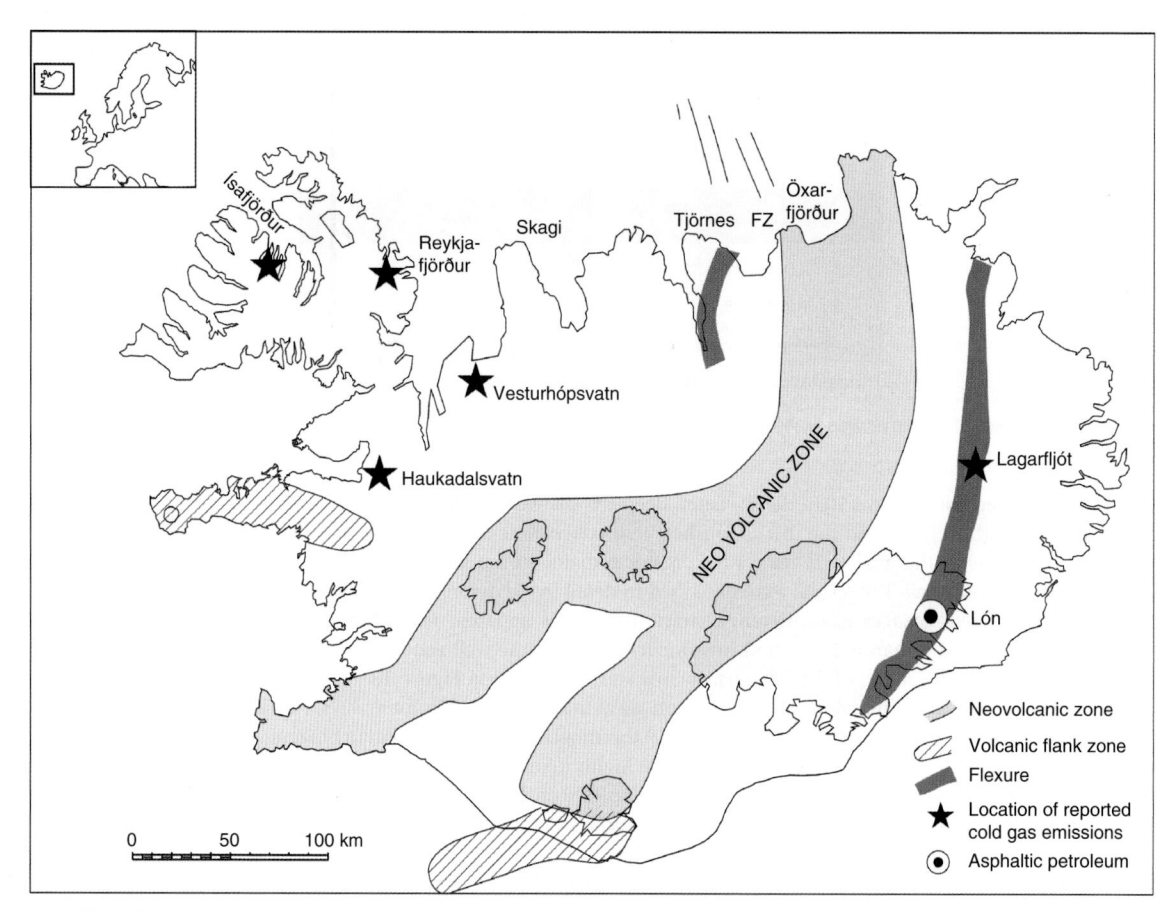

124 Geochemical Aspects of Geothermal Utilization

Figure 18 Volcanic zones and principal sites of cold methane emissions and asphaltic petroleum in Iceland.

Table 17 The chemical composition of gas from boreholes at Skógarlón, Öxarfjörður (vol.%)

Well no	ÆR-04	ÆR-04	ÆR-04	ÆR-03	ÆR-03	ÆR-03	ÆR-01	ÆR-01	ÆR-01
Sample no.	94–200	91–209	91–189	90–237	89–087	88–149	88–088	88–211	87–119
Mode	Sep.	Sep.	Direct	200 m	Direct	Direct	Direct	Direct	Direct
N_2	83.80	86.20	92.80	81.00	93.40	95.90	92.80	93.80	94.60
$O_2 + Ar$	4.26	0.10	0.10	18.40	1.10	1.80	1.20	1.70	2.70
H_2		0.07	0.25	0.06	0.02	0.02	0.07	0.23	0.00
He		0.00	0.00	0.00	0.00	<0.01	0.00	0.03	0.00
CO_2	3.51	7.88	0.91	0.05	0.02	<0.05	0.00	0.05	0.04
CH_4	4.33	5.70	5.80	0.45	5.20	3.60	5.60	4.00	2.22
C_2H_6	0.30	0.082	0.120	0.0015	0.230	0.150	0.300	0.200	0.218
C_3H_8	0.085	0.074	0.083	0.002	0.047	0.050	0.057	0.092	0.156
$i\text{-}C_4H_{10}$	0.0107	0.0088	0.011		0.0066	0.0088	0.0076	0.0164	0.0251
$n\text{-}C_4H_{10}$	0.0169	0.024	0.031	0.0034	0.0093	0.0110	0.0100	0.0208	0.0280
$neo\text{-}C_5H_{12}$					0.0002		0.0030		
$i\text{-}C_5H_{12}$	0.0021	0.0019	0.0052	0.0002	0.0016	0.0035	0.0027	0.0123	0.0147
$n\text{-}C_5H_{12}$	0.0031	0.0042	0.0170		0.0018	0.0058	0.0036	0.0152	0.0132
$i\text{-}C_6H_{14}$		<0.0001	0.0007	0.0002	Trace		Trace		
$n\text{-}C_6H_{14}$		0.0010	0.006						
C_6H_6	0.0080	0.0195	0.0044						
ΣC_{2+}	0.426	0.196	0.274	0.021	0.297	0.229	0.384	0.357	0.455
$\delta^{13}C_{CH_4}$ (‰)	−28.6	−38.9	−40.0	−26.6	−31.9	−29.6	−29.0	−29.0	−22.5
δD_{CH_4} (‰)	−222				−138		−154		

Sep., steam separated with separator; Direct, direct from wellhead, 200 m (depth); $\delta^{13}C$ (PDB); δD (SMOW)

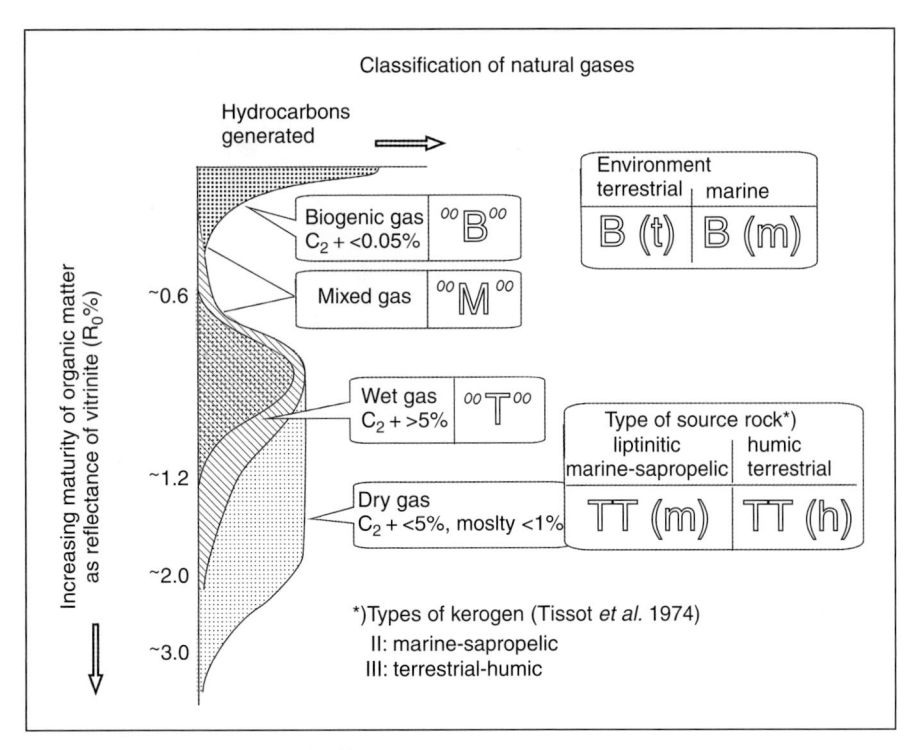

Figure 19 Classification of natural hydrocarbon gases [113].

first group were only observed in gas from the deepest well, ÆR-04, and the highest value was observed in gas from the shallowest well, ÆR-01. The δD values are somewhat ambiguous but suggest that there may be two types of gas, one shallow with δD_{CH_4} values of the order of −150 below −200‰ (SMOW), suggesting a relationship with the $\delta^{13}C_{CH_4}$ results. The values for $\delta^{13}C_{C_2H_6}$, $\delta^{13}C_{C_3H_8}$, and $\delta^{13}C_{CO_2}$ were found to be −26.9, −25.4, and −9.3‰ (PDB), respectively, in sample no. 94-200 from well ÆR-04. The values for ethane and propane are typical for thermogenic gases. The value for CO_2 suggests a geothermal gas. The variation in $\delta^{13}C_{CH_4}$ suggests that there may be a mixture of geothermal and thermogenic methane present. The idea has been put forward that the thermogenic gas is a result of breakdown of lignite at a fairly high temperature. Lignite has not been found in the Öxarfjörður wells, but a few layers are known in Tjörnes to the west of the area (**Figure 20**). Also, one hypothesis is that, due to faulting, sediments of the same origin as those at Tjörnes are preserved below the present drilling area. $\delta^{13}C$ has been determined in three samples of lignite from the Tjörnes sediments (**Table 8**). The only oil that has been found in Iceland is an asphaltic petroleum found in Skyndidalur in Lón, Southeast Iceland (**Figure 18**), which was interpreted as formed by thermal breakdown of lignite [114]. The $\delta^{13}C$ values of the lignites from the two areas, one on each side of the neovolcanic zone (see **Figure 49**), and that of the petroleum are strikingly similar (**Table 18**). Therefore, it is likely that lignite in the area has a $\delta^{13}C$ value in the range −27 to −28‰ (PDB), and by comparison with experiments reported by Des Marais et al. [116] most values obtained for gas from the wells studied could be due to gas produced by such pyrolysis. The depleted values of around −40‰ for early samples from ÆR-04 and the enriched value of −22.5‰ obtained for a sample from well ÆR-01 suggest gases of different origins. The $\delta^{13}C_{C_2H_6}$ and $\delta^{13}C_{C_3H_8}$ values obtained for gas from well ÆR-04 in 1994 are, however, quite compatible with an asphaltic origin. The $\delta^{13}C_{CH_4}$ of geothermal gas in Iceland has been found to vary from −17.8 to −40.4 ([117, 118]; S. Arnórsson, personal communication). Ármannsson et al. [117] argued that in Krafla, which is on the same fissure swarm as the area under study, methane with relatively low $\delta^{13}C_{CH_4}$ is derived from the decomposition of organic matter whereas that with a higher $\delta^{13}C_{CH_4}$ could be derived from basalt at magmatic conditions.

No alkenes have been detected so the gas is probably not an inorganic gas produced by reaction between CO_2 and H_2 at high temperature [119]. Relationships such as $\delta^{13}C_{CH_4}$ versus ΣC_{2+} and δD_{CH_4} versus $\delta^{13}C_{CH_4}$ suggest a thermogenic gas bordering on dry and wet gas (**Figure 19**). Significant amounts of organic carbon were not detected in the sediments above 450 m and at least the uppermost 350 m is less than 10 000 years old. ^{14}C dating of the gas suggested that it was more than 20 000 years old. It is therefore suggested that the gas originates in deeper sediments hitherto not drilled into.

Thus, organic gases have been encountered during drilling into sediments in NE Iceland. They are older than the upper sediments that are deltaic and less than 1000 years old. The composition of the gases is consistent with an origin in breakdown of lignite although oil-associated gases from relatively old sediments at depth are not ruled out.

Example of natural CO_2 emissions from a geothermal area, the Krafla area, Northeast Iceland. Several workers have estimated the total CO_2 emissions from Icelandic geothermal systems to be of the order of 1–2 Mt yr^{-1} [91, 120, 121]. Fridriksson et al. [86] measured the natural CO_2 emissions at Reykjanes, South Iceland, and found that of the ~5000 t yr^{-1} that are emitted, >97% are released through soil environment as diffuse degassing. Natural CO_2 emissions from the Krafla system and determinations of the amount of

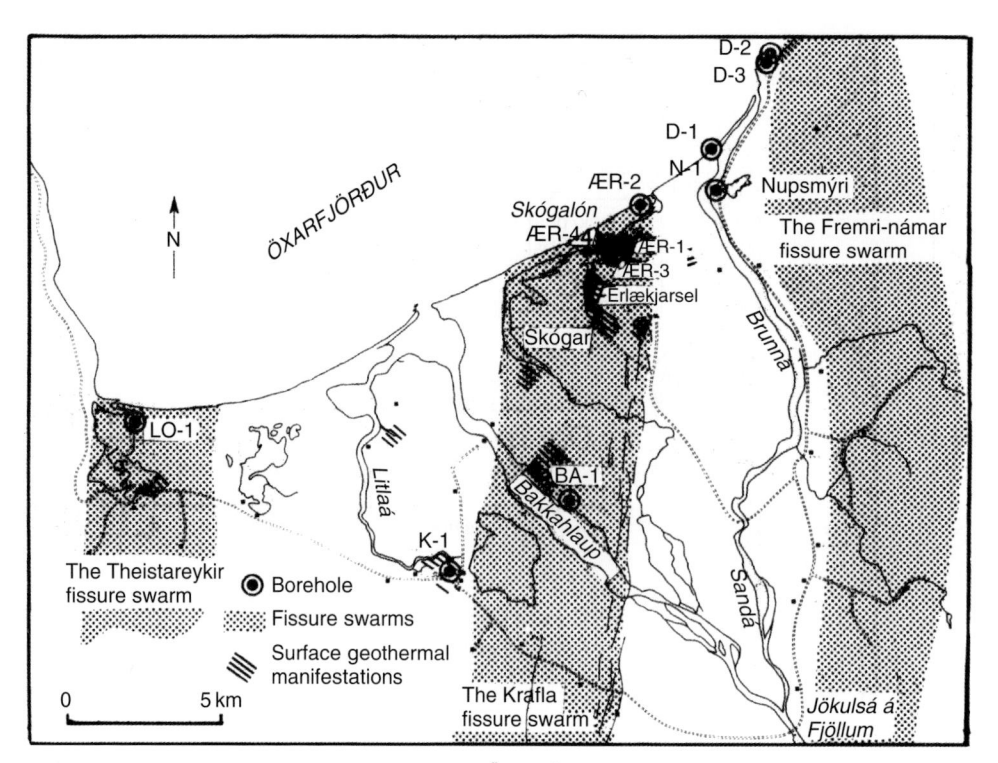

Figure 20 Fissure swarms, geothermal manifestations, and boreholes in Öxarfjörður.

Table 18 $\delta^{13}C$ of lignites from Tjörnes and Lón and of asphaltic petroleum from Lón

Sample type and location	Lignite Tjörnes (mean)	Lignite Lón	Asphaltic petroleum Lón
$\delta^{13}C$ ‰ (PDB)	−27.8	−27.1	−27.7

CO_2 fixed in the bedrock of the system have been reported by Ármannsson et al. [122] who also discussed the relative importance of these two geochemical sinks for geothermal CO_2.

Geology. The Krafla high-temperature geothermal system is located in Northeastern Iceland (**Figure 21**). The geology of the area is characterized by an active central volcano containing a caldera and a magma chamber at 5–8 km depth [123]. The volcano is crosscut by an active fissure swarm that extends tens of kilometers to the north and the south [32]. The volcanic activity at Krafla is episodic, occurring every 250–1000 years, each episode lasting 10–20 years. The last eruptive period from 1975 to 1984 resulted in 21 tectonic events and 9 eruptions. The magma chamber is the heat source of the geothermal system [124]. Three separate upflow channels for geothermal fluids have been identified, the major one associated with the Hveragil fissure. The recharge is essentially local in origin according to isotopic ratios [55], although the Suðurhlíðar and Hvíthólar subfields may be recharged from far south (see **Figure 12**; [56, 125]).

Chemical composition of fluids. Wells have been drilled in three separate subfields (**Figure 22**), which differ considerably in size and characteristics. Temperatures of at least 350 °C have been encountered at 2 km depth. During the volcanic activity magmatic gases invaded the geothermal reservoir and contaminated two upflow zones causing deposition and corrosion in wells (Ármannsson et al. [89, 117]). Surface activity and properties of well fluids suggest four subfields, Leirhnúkur, Leirbotnar, Sudurhlíðar, and Hvíthólar. Leirhnúkur and Leirbotnar were affected by magmatic gas during the volcanic activity. This was most pronounced in 1977–1979, but has been decreasing since. The magmatic gas signal seemed to wane sooner in Southern Leirbotnar and Leirhnúkur than in Northern Leirbotnar near Víti [117]. The gas concentrations and the temperature profiles for the individual subfields were instrumental in constructing a conceptual model of the Leirbotnar and Sudurhlíðar subfields (**Figure 23**). The fluids are dilute with close to neutral pH. Bicarbonate is the major anion [126]. Attempts to simulate the geothermal fluid composition by titrating Krafla rock with local groundwater suggest that the geothermal fluid composition cannot be derived from water and rock interactions alone; volcanic gas must have been added too [127].

The CO_2 flux through soil was measured at a total of 2559 points within the Krafla caldera, the vast majority on two 25 by 25 m grids in Leirhnúkur (0.2 km^2) and in the southern and western slopes of Mt. Krafla (1.1 km^2), but several hundred measurements were also carried out all over the eastern part of the caldera, covering a total of about 20 km^2. Sequential Gaussian simulations were used to generate maps of CO_2 flux from the areas that were sampled on a grid. The graphical statistical (GS) method of Sinclair [128]

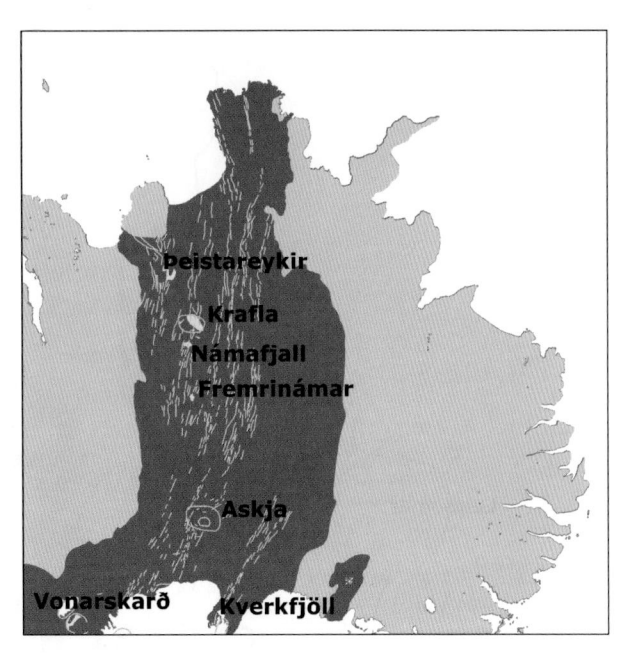

Figure 21 High-temperature areas of Northeastern Iceland

was used to identify different CO_2 flux populations, determine their mean flux value, and relative extent. All data points outside the grid were used for this analysis, plus a small, randomly selected fraction (< 5%) from the grids. The amount of carbon fixed in the bedrock was determined by analysis of drill cuttings from 10 wells. The cuttings samples were selected from a complete suite of drill cuttings collected every 2 m during drilling. Typically, 15–30 samples were selected from each well. The samples covered the entire depth range of the wells, from the surface to about 2000 m depth in some cases.

The grids for the gas flux measurements and the resulting gas flux models are shown in **Figure 23**. The total CO_2 flux from the gridded areas in Leirhúkur and Mt. Krafla was 12 and 8 kt yr^{-1}, respectively. The results (**Figure 23**) illustrate a tectonic control over soil gas emissions in the slopes of Mt. Krafla. Two main trends are apparent: a NNE–SSW trend, parallel to the local normal faults, and a WNW–ESE trend. The relationship between soil gas emissions and structural geology is less obvious in Leirhnúkur, possibly due to the small area of the flux measurement grid. The results of the GS analysis indicate that the mean flux of the geothermal population is about 115 g m^{-2} day^{-1} and it emanates from about 10% of the total area. Two background populations were identified, referred to as background and low background, 6 and 1.6 g m^{-2} day^{-1}, respectively. They covered 80 and 10% of the total area, respectively. The total CO_2 flux from the eastern Krafla caldera is about 120 kt yr^{-1} and about 70% of that is of geothermal origin. This can be considered as an upper limit to the CO_2 flux from Krafla as sampling is skewed toward areas with visible geothermal manifestations. As a result, the relative proportion of the geothermal population might be overestimated, but the mean flux from that population is considered realistic. Significant soil diffuse CO_2 degassing was not found outside the grids with the exception of two fumarole fields around the Víti crater lake and one area of a very limited extent in Leirbotnar, east of Hveragil. Most flux measurements in Leirbotnar were conducted on geothermally altered ground; nevertheless, with the exception of the small area mentioned above, none of the results were above background values.

The CO_2 concentration of cuttings from boreholes in Krafla ranges from 0.0 to 430 kg m^{-3}. The CO_2 concentrations in the bedrock are high near the surface and decrease steadily toward almost zero at a depth of about 1300 m below surface. The maximum CO_2 concentrations in bedrock occur in some wells at the surface but in others at about 200 m depth. As the concentration of fixed CO_2 in the bedrock has reached zero at about 1300 m below the surface, it is possible to compute the total amount of CO_2 fixed in the bedrock per unit surface area by finite element integration over the CO_2 depth profile for each well. The fixed CO_2 is about 90 t m^{-2} in wells 25 and 32, but the average for the 10 wells is about 70 t m^{-2}. If this is representative of the 20 km^2 eastern Krafla caldera, total CO_2 fixed in bedrock there is of the order 1400 Mt. Significantly less CO_2 seems to be fixed in the bedrock in the southern slopes of Mt. Krafla (**Figure 23**) than in the bedrock west of the Hveragil fault, but this needs to be verified by analysis of cuttings from more wells.

A negative correlation between CO_2 diffuse degassing and CO_2 fixation in the bedrock is suggested (**Figures 22 and 24**). CO_2 degassing through soil appears to be more prominent east of the Hveragil fault, whereas significantly more CO_2 appears to be fixed in the bedrock west of the fault. One possible explanation of this apparent negative correlation is that conditions for CO_2 fixation are more favorable west than east of the fault. East of the Hveragil fault, the temperature is higher and the deep steam and the CO_2 rise from depth without interaction with colder groundwater or geothermal fluids, whereas on the western side the deep steam is condensed when it comes into contact with subboiling fluids in the upper reservoir. Upon its condensation the CO_2 dissolves in the fluid, interacts with the bedrock, and precipitates as calcite. This is consistent with the conceptual model (**Figure 23**). However, other causes, such as the eastward migration over time of the geothermal activity in the Krafla system, cannot be excluded.

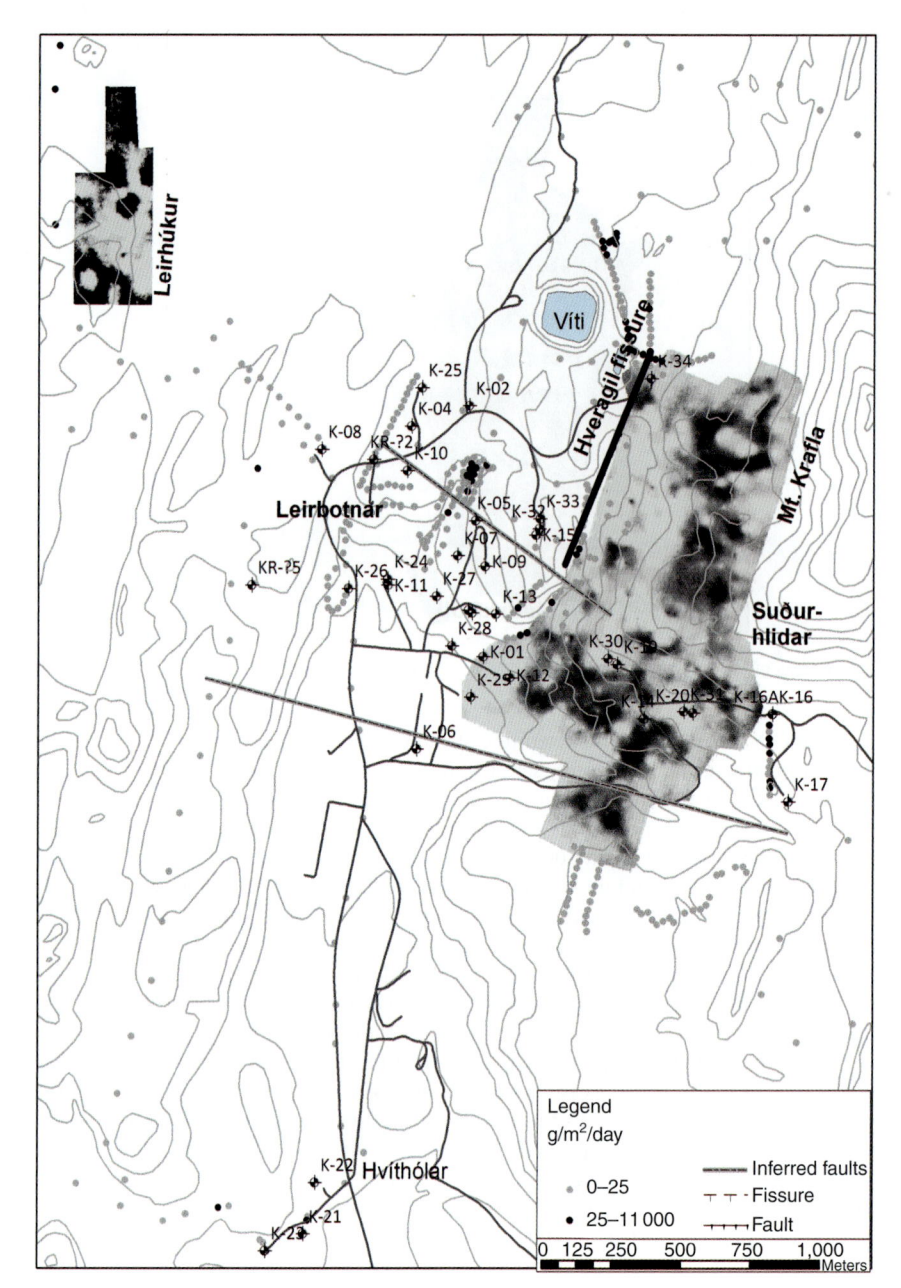

Figure 22 Krafla subfields and CO_2 diffuse degassing through soil.

The age of the Krafla geothermal system is estimated to be between 110 and 290 kyr (K. Saemundsson, personal communication). Assuming that the 1400 Mt of CO_2 that is fixed in the Krafla bedrock has accumulated at a constant rate over the lifetime of the system, the long-term average accumulation rate is between 12.7 and 4.8 kt yr^{-1}. This accumulation rate is relatively small compared with the observed, present day natural CO_2 emission rate from geothermal activity in Krafla, which is of the order of 84 kt yr^{-1}. The corresponding ratio of CO_2 emissions to CO_2 bedrock fixation is between 7:1 and 17.5:1. Thus, the fixation of CO_2 in carbonates is a relatively small, but not insignificant sink for geothermal CO_2.

7.04.8 Speciation and Reaction Path Calculations

As samples are collected at the surface of the Earth, the main interest is in reconstructing the chemical composition of the fluid in the geothermal system. Determination of physical parameters such as temperature, pressure, and enthalpy helps in establishing steam fraction at depth when well samples are considered. But such information is not available for samples collected from springs and fumaroles. When the subsurface composition has been established it can be used to establish the temperature of the geothermal

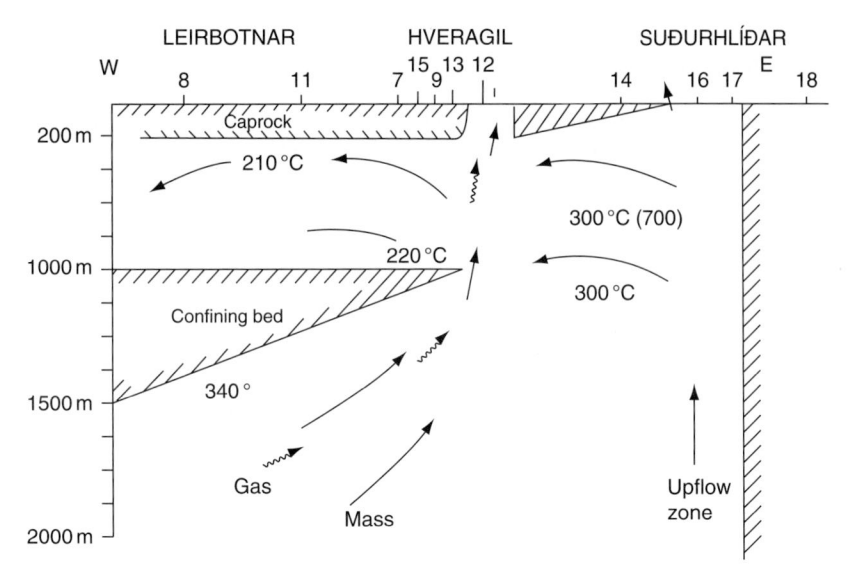

Figure 23 Leirbotnar–Suðurhlíðar. Conceptual model.

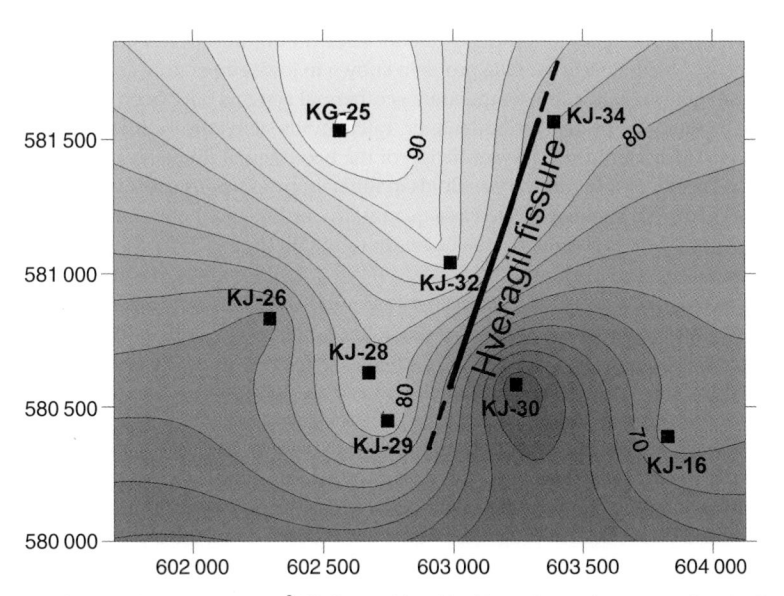

Figure 24 CO_2 fixed in bedrock. Contour lines show tons m^{-2}. Wells considered in this study are shown as well as the Hveragil fissure.

system and elucidate whether problems such as deposition and corrosion may result if the fluid is utilized. Furthermore, it may be desirable to find out what would ensue if the fluid were subjected to changes such as mixing, boiling, condensation, cooling, heating, and reactions with rock.

Several computer programs are available to aid in such calculations. Generally they are of two types, that is, speciation programs that are used to establish which chemical species are present in the geothermal fluid at a preset temperature usually what is thought to be the temperature of the subsurface fluid and may be obtained by measurement, geothermometry, or conjecture using data from the vicinity, and reaction path programs that take over when the speciation has been established and are used to calculate how it changes upon mixing, boiling, condensation, cooling, heating, or reactions with rock.

The progress is similar in most speciation programs, that is, pH is determined at a recorded temperature, the pH at the desired subsurface temperature calculated, the activity coefficients of all potential species at that temperature simulated with the aid of the Debye–Hückel equation, and the speciation thus obtained. When dealing with the chemistry of well fluids, the result of the determination of enthalpy is used to obtain the liquid and vapor fractions of the fluid. Equilibrium constants are used to establish whether the solution is saturated, undersaturated, or supersaturated with respect to the various species. In reaction path programs components are changed, new speciation obtained, and species with which the solution is supersaturated thrown out.

There are several uncertainties inherent in the use of such programs. The chemical analyses may not be sufficiently accurate. The species in the dataset used may not all be the important ones. The equilibrium constants used are not necessarily accurate enough.

The activity coefficients may not have been calculated accurately. There is the question whether kinetic rate constants and rate laws apply. It is also possible that the assumed nature of equilibrium is not appropriate. Finally there is the crucial question whether the conceptual model is correct.

The history of speciation programs may be said to start with HALTAFALL which was originally written by Ingri et al. [129] for laboratory operations. More recently, it has been modified and used to calculate speciation of seawater and estuarine waters. Another modification of HALTAFALL is SOLGASWATER [130] designed for higher temperature calculations. The REDEQL series was originally written by Morel and Morgan [131], but has undergone numerous modifications and spawned many other programs, for example, REDEQL2, MINEQL, and MICROQL (see, e.g., Ref. [132]), some of which are also path programs. PHREEQE [259] was written at the USGS and revised in the early 1980s (and is also a reaction path program). The WATEQ series was started by Truesdell and Jones [133] but later revised and modified to give WATEQ2, WATEQ3, WATEQF, and WATSPEC. SOLMINEQ88 [134] is a revision of an earlier program SOLMINEQ [135] developed parallel to WATEQ, which handles geothermal waters at high temperature and pressure. EQ3 is the largest speciation program of all, with the largest database, often used in conjunction with the reaction path program EQ6 [136–139]. SOLVEQ has been under development by Reed and co-workers since the mid-1970s [140, 141, 249]. A new version SOLVEQ-XPT [142] has been presented recently. WATCH was developed in Iceland during 1975–1980 [143] and rewritten and modified with a merger 1990–1992 [144].

The first reaction path program PATH1 was developed by Helgeson et al. [145]. PHREEQC has been developed from PHREEQE by USGS and can be downloaded from the Internet free of charge. EQ6 is the very large reaction path program that comes with EQ3. CHILLER has been developed by Reed and co-workers along with SOLVEQ [140, 141]. A new version CHIM-XPT has recently been presented [146].

Example of programming the consequences of mixing geothermal fluids. Problems arising from mixing fluids of different origins in distribution systems are well known. In geothermal utilization in Iceland, the most severe problems of this kind have arisen from the formation of magnesium silicates upon mixing of relatively cold magnesium-rich fluids and warmer silica-rich fluids or from heating the former (e.g., [147, 148]). Their crystal structures and those of aluminum silicates formed in similar situations have been studied by Kristmannsdóttir et al. [149]. Another scaling problem known in low-temperature geothermal fields is calcite scaling. The conditions causing calcite scaling in Icelandic low-temperature geothermal systems have been studied (e.g., [150]).

Such problems may be avoided by using thermodynamic calculations at relatively low temperatures using reaction path programs such as CHILLER [151] for prediction. The speciation of the two original fluids is calculated using a speciation program such as SOLVEQ [151] and the result used to mix the two fluids in different proportions using CHILLER. Thus, the temperature and chemical composition of the mixture is obtained as well as a quantitative estimate of potential deposits from the various mixtures. If unacceptable deposition is predicted, experiments may be set up to obtain the kinetics of the deposition at different conditions (mainly varying the temperature and pH).

A space heating system that was founded in 1981 has been using wells from the same geothermal area, Laugaland in Holt, South Iceland (**Figure 25**), ever since, but there are strong signs that this water supply will be exhausted within a few years with unchanged use. Therefore, exploration has been underway for several years and now a new potential area, Kaldárholt, has been discovered, 9–10 km north of Laugaland in Holt [152]. The fluid composition in the two areas is different (**Table 19**), and it was thought advisable to calculate the effect of mixing water from the two geothermal systems.

Both the waters from Laugaland and Kaldárholt show a slight supersaturation with respect to calcite. The experience in Iceland is that at such slight supersaturation deposition does not take place in heating systems presumably due to slow reaction time. At Laugaland no deposition has been observed over the years in spite of the slight supersaturation. As supersaturation was lower in Kaldárholt water and in the mixed waters than in Laugaland water, it was decided that the danger of deposition was extremely small if the water groups were mixed and the company advised to go ahead with mixing the two [149]. Suppressing the calcite from the mixing calculation showed the possibility that a trace of tremolite might form. This mineral has not been found in deposits from Icelandic low-temperature systems and is regarded as extremely unlikely to form. This advice was heeded and the heating system has been using a mixture of the two waters for some years now without any problems due to the mixing. In the year 2000, however, two strong earthquakes shook the area and in their wake some relatively Mg-rich cold groundwater invaded the Laugaland system resulting in magnesium silicate deposition [153].

Example of programming reactions of geothermal fluids with rock and gas. An example of how such programs can be used to study reactions with rock is the following study in which the objective was to endeavor to establish how the composition of the fluid in the Krafla geothermal system, Northeast Iceland, has evolved starting with groundwater from the vicinity, rocks in the geothermal system, and volcanic gas [127].

Calculations have been carried out using water from Austarasel spring (**Figure 26, Table 20**) titrated with rock from Krafla ([154]; N. Óskarsson, personal communication) (**Table 21**) at different temperatures, and as it seemed unlikely that the composition of the geothermal fluid could be due to the interaction of water and rock only, attempts were made to add volcanic gas of basic composition like that of Surtsey gas [155] with additional information on the Cl_2 and F content of gas from the Krafla area from N. Óskarsson (personal communication) (**Table 22**). Volcanic gas had been known to enter the geothermal systems during the Krafla fires during 1975–1984 [126, 155].

The Austarasel springs are situated close to the Krafla and Námafjall geothermal areas (**Figure 26**). Studies of flow and of stable isotopes suggest that their water may feed the Námafjall system but is unlikely to feed the Krafla system [66]. Its composition is, however, very similar to that of Sandabotnar springs, which are located in the Krafla area (**Table 7**) and are quite likely to be of the type feeding the Krafla system.

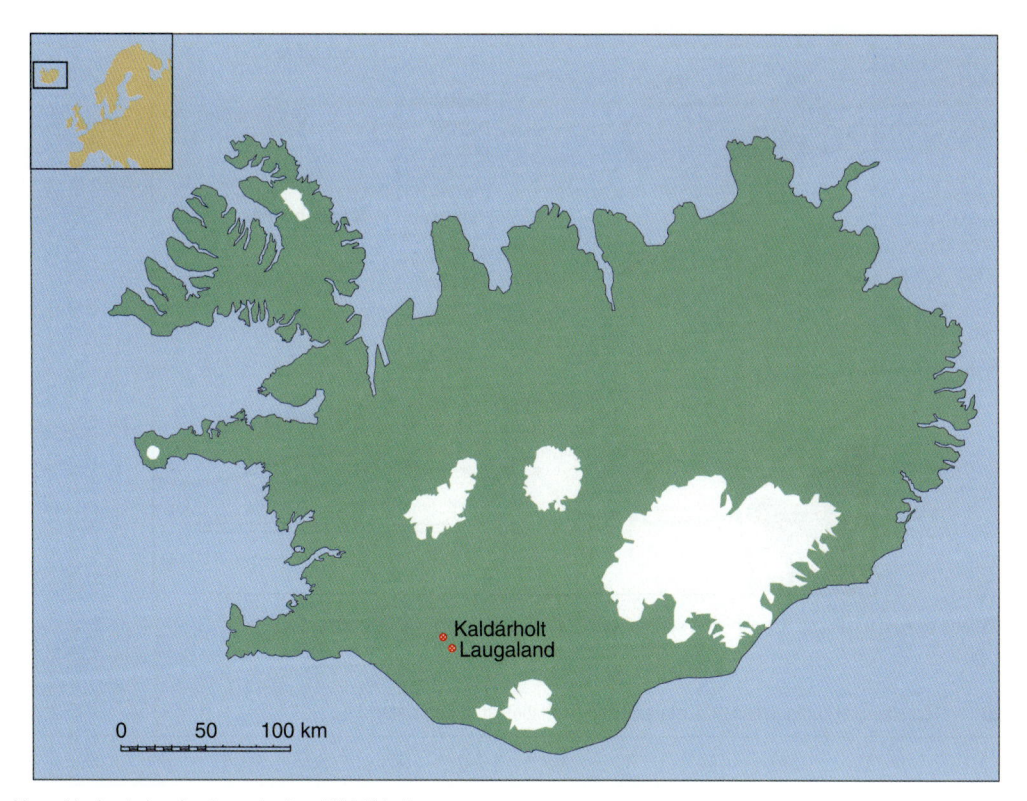

Figure 25 Map of Iceland showing Laugaland and Kaldárholt.

Table 19 Laugaland and Kaldárholt waters mixed. Resulting composition, temperatures, and potential deposits

Property	L:0 K:1[a]	L:1 K:0	L:1 K:0.2[b]	L:1 K:0.5[b]	L:1 K:1[b]
pH/°C	10.4/22.5	9.8/22	8.9/93.5	9.0/89.2	9.1/84.9
SiO_2 (mg l^{-1})	89.0	97.2	95.9	94.6	93.3
Na (mg l^{-1})	68.0	92.8	89.5	86.2	83.0
K (mg l^{-1})	0.77	1.7	1.5	1.4	1.2
Ca (mg l^{-1})	2.27	3.0	2.7	2.5	2.2
Mg (mg l^{-1})	0.012	0.003	0.00008	0.00006	0.00005
CO_2 (mg l^{-1})	13.8	21.0	20.6	20.2	19.9
SO_4 (mg l^{-1})	26.7	65.9	59.4	52.9	46.4
H_2S (mg l^{-1})	0.13	0.13	0.13	0.13	0.13
Cl (mg l^{-1})	18.0	46.5	38.5	33.3	28.1
F (mg l^{-1})	2.24	0.86	1.11	1.35	1.6
Temp. (°C)	67	98.4	93.5	89.2	84.9
Deposit type	Calcite: 97.35%, tremolite: 2.65%	Calcite: 99%, tremolite: 1%	Tremolite	Tremolite	Tremolite
Deposit (mg)	2.690	3.347	0.02	0.03	0.04

[a] L, water from Laugaland; V, water from Kaldárholt.
[b] Calcite suppressed.

Thus, it was not deemed necessary to perform separate calculations for Sandabotnar spring water.

The calculations were carried out for 205 °C which is considered a likely base temperature for the upper part of the Leirbotnar field in Krafla and 295 °C which is close to inflow temperatures of many Krafla wells drawing from the lower part of the Leirbotnar field and the Suðurhlíðar field in Krafla and the hottest wells in Námafjall. The cooler Námafjall wells, the Hvíthólar, and some other wells in Krafla have inflows with intermediate temperatures [126, 156]. The speciation program SOLVEQ and the reaction path program CHILLER [151] were used for the calculations based on the database SOLTHERM [157]. Results for these conditions are compared with the composition of fluid and observed minerals from four Krafla and Námafjall wells calculated using the speciation program WATCH [143, 144] in **Table 23**. Adding sulfur to the rock in the form of pyrite (0.0002%) and gypsum (0.0001%) [161] caused profound matrix changes at W/R ≈ 1245. A comparison between samples containing and not containing sulfur (**Table 23**) suggests only a slight difference in the resulting fluid concentration of the sulfur species.

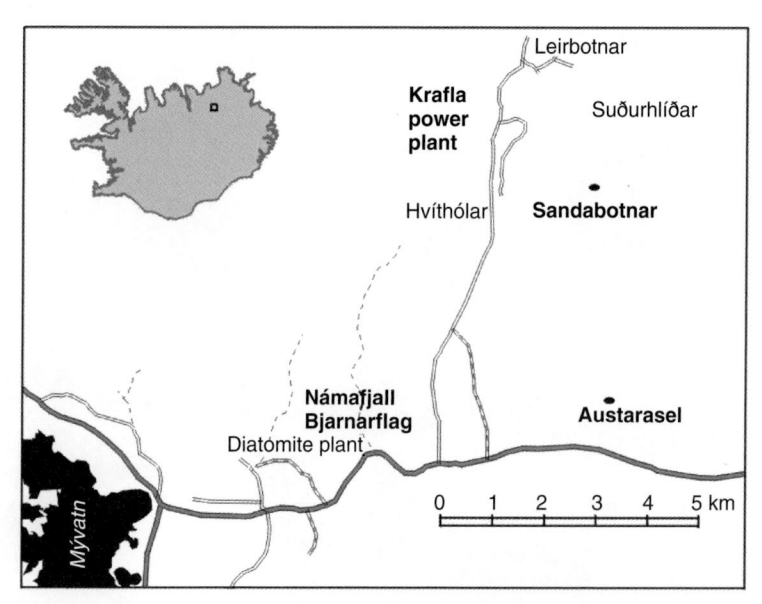

Figure 26 Locations of Austarasel and Sandabotnar springs and Krafla and Námafjall geothermal areas.

Table 20 The chemical composition of Austarasel and Sandabotnar spring water

Spring	pH/°C	SiO_2	Na	K	Ca	Mg	CO_2	SO_4	H_2S	Cl	F	TDS[a]
Austarasel	7.62/23	26.4	7.8	1.1	8.7	5.0	40.0	5.7	0.00	2.9	0.05	164
Sandabotnar	7.10/22	29.4	11.5	1.2	13.8	6.3	70.2	5.6	0.00	3.0	0.12	93

[a] TDS, total dissolved solids.

Table 21 Chemical composition of rock used for the titration (%)

SiO_2	Al_2O_3	Fe_2O_3	FeO	MnO	MgO	CaO	Na_2O	K_2O	H_2O	$CaCl_2$	CaF_2
50.0	13.7	5.0	7.0	0.1	6.0	10.0	3.0	0.15	3.0	0.005	0.006

Table 22 Chemical composition of gas (mol.%) used for the titration

CO	CO_2	HCl	H_2	H_2O	H_2S	SO_2	S_2	HF
0.70	9.54	0.10	2.78	81.56	0.76	3.64	0.19	0.05

The effect of water–rock ratio and gas addition at W/R = 10 at 205 and 295 °C on which minerals and gases are present in the matrix is shown in **Figures 27** and **28**, respectively, and the controlling reactions in **Table 24**. At 205 °C the gases H_2O, CO_2, H_2S, HCl, HF, SO_2, and S_2 are present in the matrix from W/R = 10^6 to 468 but then disappear from it and do not reappear when volcanic gas is added. No gases are ever present in the matrix at 295 °C. The addition of gas has more effect on the composition of the water than raising temperature from 205 to 295 °C.

No gases are in the matrix at W/R = 10, whether gas is added or not. Thus, it can be concluded that at these conditions the concentrations of Cl^-, HCO_3^-, and F^- are solely dependent on their solubility at the respective temperatures. Other components of the solution are dependent on the minerals and equilibria shown in **Table 24**.

The chloride values with gas added (steam fraction 0.07) are close to those observed in well fluids. Fluoride is clearly not so soluble in the actual geothermal fluid as the results of the calculations suggest, indicating there may be controls on its solubility.

The origin of sulfur in the geothermal fluid is most likely to be in volcanic gas. The low sulfide values need further consideration. The sulfate values for the Krafla fluids are of the right order but those for the Námafjall fluids are a little high, inviting speculation on the relative sulfate and sulfide values in that geothermal system. Boiling may be the cause of the relatively low concentrations of HCO_3^- and HS^- in the fluid sampled. Quartz exerts major control on the silica concentration, but other minerals may contribute explaining the lower silica concentrations after the addition of gas.

Table 23 Minerals in matrix and chemical composition (in ppm) of fluid at selected stages of simulation and in fluid from selected Krafla and Námafjall wells [158–160]

Sample	Rock, incl. py+gy	Rock, no py+gy	Rock, no py+gy	Rock, no py+gy	Rock, no py+gy	Rock, no py+gy	Krafla KG-8	Krafla KJ-13	Námafjall B-6	Námafjall BG-10
t (°C)	205	205	205	205	295	295	205	310	254	280
W/R	1245	1000	10	10	10	10				
Gas fraction	0	0	0	0.07	0	0.07				
Minerals in matrix	Andradite, gros-sular, clinochlore14/2, daphnite14/2, clinozoisite, epidote-ord, magnetite, rhodonite, tremolite, actinolite	Andradite, grossular, clinochlore14/2, daphnite14/2, clinozoisite, epidote-ord, rhodonite	Albite-low, clinochlore14/2, daphnite14/2, epidote-ord, microcline-max, prehnite, quartz, rhodonite, tremolite, actinolite	Albite-low, clinochlore14/2, epidote-ord, hematite, muscovite, paragonite, pyrite, quartz, rhodonite	Albite-low, clinochlore14/2, clinozoisite, epidote-ord, magnetite, microcline-max, quartz, rhodonite, tremolite, actinolite	Albite-low, anhydrite, clinochlore14/2, epidote-ord, hematite, muscovite, paragonite, pyrite, quartz, rhodonite	Calcite, epidote, prehnite, pyrite, quartz	Epidote, prehnite, pyrite, quartz, wollastonite, actinolite	Calcite, chlorite, epidote, actinolite	Calcite, chlorite, epidote, actinolite
pH	7.49	7.11	6.85	7.48	7.83	6.76	7.17	7.83	7.44	7.61
Cl	2.93	2.92	6.06	19.89	6.06	41.4	26.35	27.4	65.71	58.47
SO$_4$	2.54	4.71	0	208.5	2.86	179.2	194.1	134.7	27.89	69.48
HCO$_3$	43.90	27.38	55.43	700	55.40	7099	327.6	43.85	209.0	450.0
HS	1.01	0.25	2.03	5.39	0.98	11.8	58.4	294	182.1	253.5
SiO$_2$	202.1	42.95	302.4	251.5	602.4	564.7	383.6	523.4	621.0	617.8
Al	0.29	0.27	1.22	0.38	1.77	4.28	1.15	0.74	1.18	0.48
Ca	0.14	3.49	0.02	0.41	0.006	0.45	1.42	0.42	1.33	0.99
Mg	0.00007	0.0005	0.00001	0.0003	0.00004	0.0015	0.027	0.001	0.038	0.008
Fe	0.0001	0.00008	0.0004	0.0001	0.0002	0.0008	0.024	0.013	0.008	0.008
K	2.11	1.24	5.80	24.51	6.68	10.6	20.03	18.7	23.78	29.27
Na	22.44	6.82	74.64	299.9	36.0	187.6	193.2	134.4	152.2	173.3
F	0.07	0.05	2.94	6.25	2.94	11.4	0.95	0.71	1.71	0.46

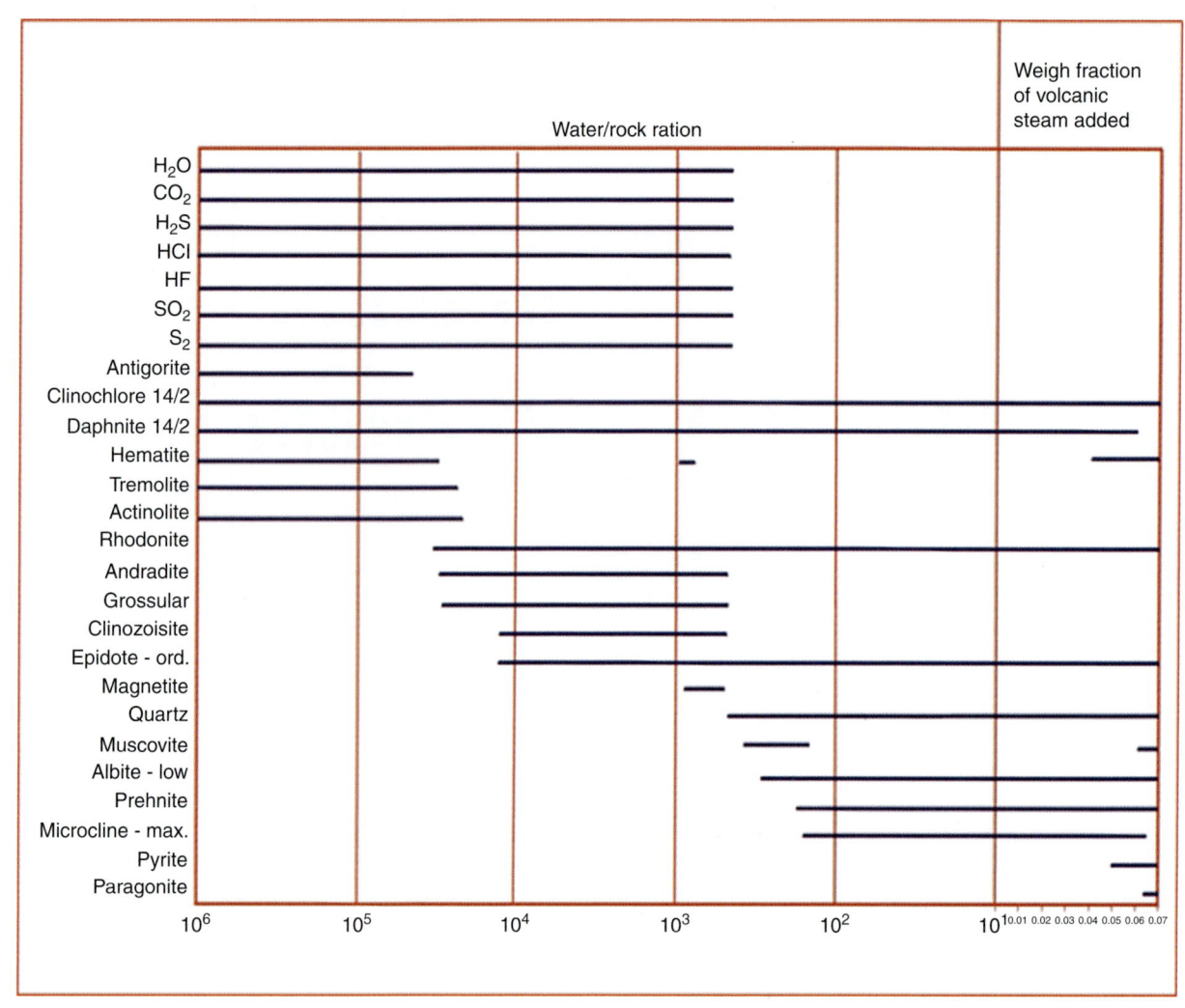

Figure 27 Minerals in matrix at W/R = 10⁶–10 and steam fraction 0–0.07 when W/R = 10 at 205 °C.

Addition of gas seems to facilitate the dissolution of Ca and Mg from the rock. Sodium and potassium concentrations are reasonable with gas added.

The minerals and equilibria controlling the composition of key components at W/R = 10 at 205 and 295 °C of the hydrothermal solution are listed in **Table 25**.

7.04.9 Geothermometry

General. Many reactions in geothermal systems are temperature dependent, but their kinetics are not fast at lower temperatures so that their equilibrium characteristics are preserved even though the waters rise to the surface and cool down. Thus the concentrations of surface geothermal fluids may be determined and the subsurface temperature determined. Reactions in the liquid phase and in the vapor phase as well as isotope exchange reactions in both phases have been used this way for geothermometry. Geothermometers may be univariant, for example, SiO_2, CO_2, H_2S, and H_2, with the disadvantage of sensitivity to secondary changes such as dilution, steam loss, and condensation. They may be global involving the assumption that a number of constituents are simultaneously at equilibrium and that their present concentrations can be used to obtain the equilibrium temperature and thus depend on analytical reliability and thermodynamic data. Third, equimolar and equicoulombic ratios, for example, Na/K, CO_2/H_2, can be used for geothermometry. Such geothermometers often overcome the disadvantage of univariant geothermometers, but equilibrium and rate conditions limit their value. Combinations of alkali and alkaline earth metal concentrations may as well as providing subsurface temperatures be used to evaluate whether the water is at equilibrium with the prevalent alteration minerals in the rock, for example, by using the Na-K-Mg diagram shown in **Figure 29** [243]. The points in the diagram are from the Kibiro area, Uganda, and the partially equilibrated waters represent a mixture of the geothermal component and local groundwater whereas the fully equilibrated water represents the geothermal component. For equilibrium calculations which are needed to obtain

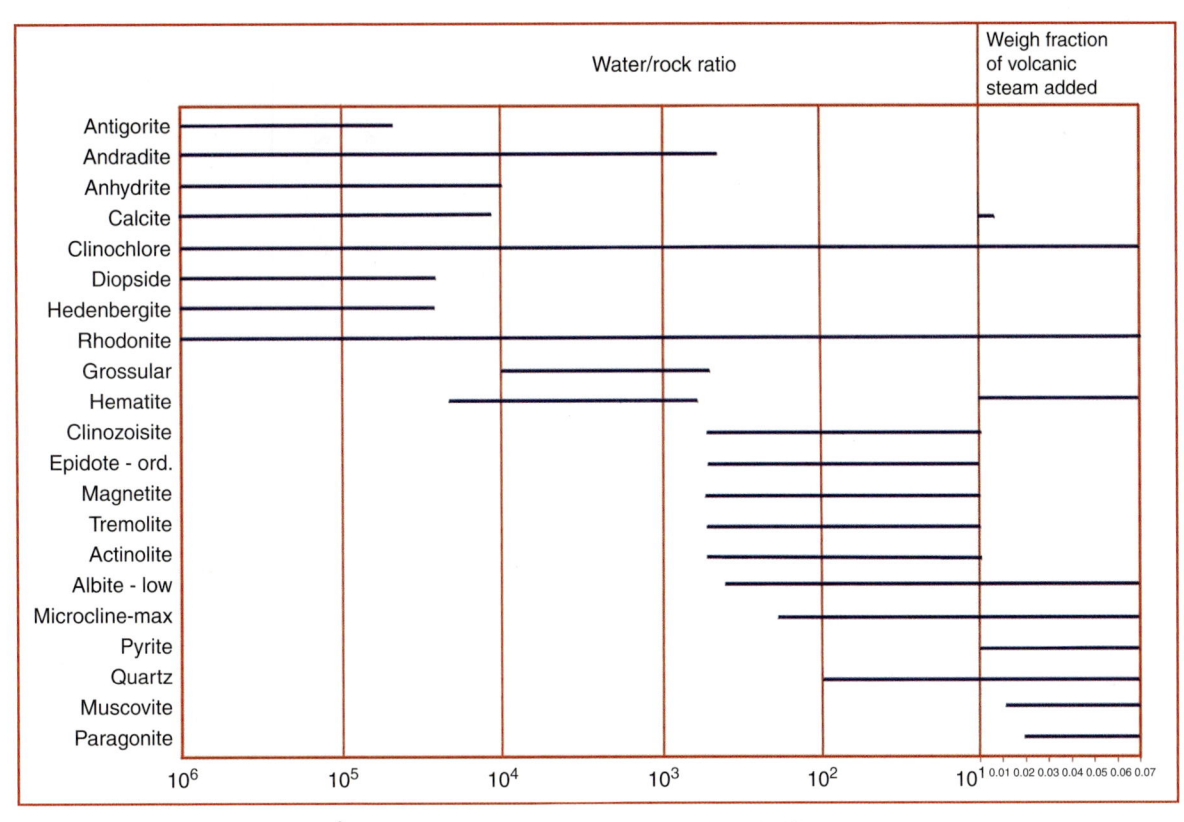

Figure 28 Minerals in matrix at W/R = 10^6–10 and steam fraction 0–0.07 when W/R = 10 at 295 °C.

Table 24 Mineral-controlling reactions

Albite-low: Alb-lo + 4H$^+$ ↔ Na$^+$ + Al^{3+} + SiO$_2$ (aq) + 2H$_2$O [1]
Anhydrite: Anhy ↔ Ca^{2+} + SO$_4^-$ [2]
Clinochlore: Clchl14/2 + 8H$^+$ ↔ 2.5 Mg^{2+} + Al^{3+} + 1.5SiO$_2$ (aq) + 6H$_2$O [3]
Daphnite: Daph14/2 + 8H$^+$ ↔ 2.5Fe^{2+} + Al^{3+} + 1.5SiO$_2$ (aq) + 6H$_2$O [4])
Clinozoisite: Clz + 13H$^+$ ↔ 2Ca^{2+} + 3Al^{2+} + 3SiO$_2$ (aq) + 7H$_2$O [5]
Epidote: Ep-ord + 11.875H$^+$ + 0.125HS$^-$ ↔ 2Ca^{2+} + 2Al^{3+} + 3SiO$_2$(aq) + 1.25SO$_4^-$ + Fe^{2+} + 6.5H$_2$O [6]
Hematite: Hem + 3.75H$^+$ + .25HS$^-$ ↔ 2H$_2$O + .25SO$_4^-$ + 2Fe^{2+} [7]
Magnetite: Magn + 5.75H$^+$ + 0.25HS$^-$↔.25SO$_4^-$ + 3H$_2$O + 3Fe^{2+} [8]
Microcline: Micr-max + 4H$^+$ ↔ K$^+$ + Al^{3+} + 3SiO$_2$ (aq) + 2H$_2$O [9]
Muscovite: Musc + 10H$^+$ ↔ K$^+$ + 3Al^{3+} + 3SiO$_2$ (aq) + 6H$_2$O [10]
Paragonite: Par + 10H$^+$ ↔ Na$^+$ + 3Al^{3+} + 3SiO$_2$ (aq) + 6H$_2$O [11]
Prehnite: Pre + 10H$^+$ ↔ 2Ca^{2+} + 2Al^{3+} + 3SiO$_2$ (aq) + 6H$_2$O [12]
Pyrite: Py + H$_2$O ↔Fe^{2+} 0.25SO$_4^-$ + 1.75HS$^-$ + 0.25H$^+$ [13]
Quartz: Qz ↔ SiO$_2$ (aq) [14]
Rhodonite: Rh + 2H$^+$ ↔ SiO$_2$ (aq) + H$_2$O + Mn^{2+} [15]
Tremolite: Tr + 14H$^+$ ↔ 2Ca^{2+} + 5Mg^{2+} + 8.5SiO$_2$ (aq) + 8H$_2$O [16]
Actinolite: Act + 14H$^+$ ↔ 2Ca^{2+} + 5Mg^{2+} + 8SiO$_2$ (aq) + 8H$_2$O [17]

temperatures from global geothermometers speciation programs (see Chapter **7.05**) are used. An example is shown in **Figure 30** in which the temperature of well 4 in Námafjall, Iceland, has been estimated by calculating log (Q/K) where Q is the activity quotient but K is the equilibrium constant over a range of temperatures. The saturation temperature and therefore the equilibrium subsurface temperature corresponds to log (Q/K) = 0 and this is found at about 160 °C in the present example.

Solute geothermometers. The silica geothermometer was first suggested by Böðvarsson [260], but two functions relating the solubility of the mineral quartz, valid for 120–330 °C based on extensive experimental work, were presented by Fournier and Rowe [163]. Arnórsson [164] argued that at lower temperatures (<150 °C) the solubility of the mineral chalcedony was the controlling parameter. Fournier [165] presented a Si-enthalpy mixing model in which the subsurface temperature of a geothermal fluid that had mixed with cold groundwater could be elucidated. Other such mixing models are based on enthalpy and chloride [166], in which mixing and boiling are accounted for, and on silica and carbonate [167], the advantage of which is that it can be used to find out whether the mixed water has been cooled by boiling or conduction and can then be applied to find the temperature

Table 25 Minerals and equilibria controlling the composition of specific components of the fluid generated by water–rock reaction and volcanic gas addition at W/R = 10 and temperatures 205 and 295 °C

Component	205 °C, gas fraction 0 Minerals	205 °C, gas fraction 0 Reactions	205 °C, gas fraction 0.07 Minerals	205 °C, gas fraction 0.07 Reactions	295 °C, gas fraction 0 Minerals	295 °C, gas fraction 0 Reactions	295 °C, gas fraction 0.07 Minerals	295 °C, gas fraction 0.07 Reactions
Na^+	Albite	(1)	Albite, paragonite	(1, 11)	Albite	(1)	Albite, paragonite	(1, 11)
K^+	Microcline	(9)	Muscovite	(10)	Microcline	(9)	Muscovite	(10)
Ca^{2+}	Epidote, prehnite, tremolite, actinolite	(6, 12, 16, 17)	Epidote	(6)	Clinozoisite, epidote, tremolite, actinolite	(5, 6, 16, 17)	Anhydrite, epidote	(2,6)
Mg^{2+}	Clinochlore, tremolite, actinolite	(3, 16, 17)	Clinochlore	(3)	Clinochlore, tremolite, actinolite	(3, 16, 17)	Clinochlore	(3)
Fe^{2+}	Daphnite, epidote	(4, 6)	Epidote, hematite	(6, 7)	Epidote, magnetite	(6, 8)	Epidote, hematite	(6, 7)
Mn^{2+}	Rhodonite	(15)	Rhodonite	(15)	Rhodonite	(15)	Rhodonite	(15)
Al^{3+}	Albite, clinochlore, daphnite, epidote, microcline prehnite	(1, 3, 4, 6, 9, 12)	Albite, clinochlore, epidote, muscovite, paragonite	(1, 3, 6, 10, 11)	Albite, clinochlore, clinzoisite, epidote, microcline	(1, 3, 5, 6, 9)	Clinochlore, epidote, muscovite, paragonite	(1, 3, 6, 10, 11)
$SiO_2(aq)$	Albite, clinochlore, daphnite, epidote, microcline, prehnite, quartz,	(1, 3, 4, 6, 9, 12, 14)	Albite, clinochlore, epidote, muscovite, paragonite quartz	(1, 3, 6, 10, 11, 14)	Albite, clinochlore, clinzoisite, epidote, microcline quartz	(1, 3, 5, 6, 9, 14)	Albite, clinochlore, epidote, muscovite, paragonite quartz	(1, 3, 6, 10, 11, 14)
HS^-	Epidote	(6)	Epidote, hematite, pyrite	(6, 7, 13)	Epidote	(6)	Epidote, hematite, pyrite	(6, 7, 13)
SO_4^-	Epidote	(6)	Epidote, hematite, pyrite	(6, 7, 13)	Epidote	(6)	Anhydrite, epidote, hematite, pyrite	(2, 6, 7, 13)

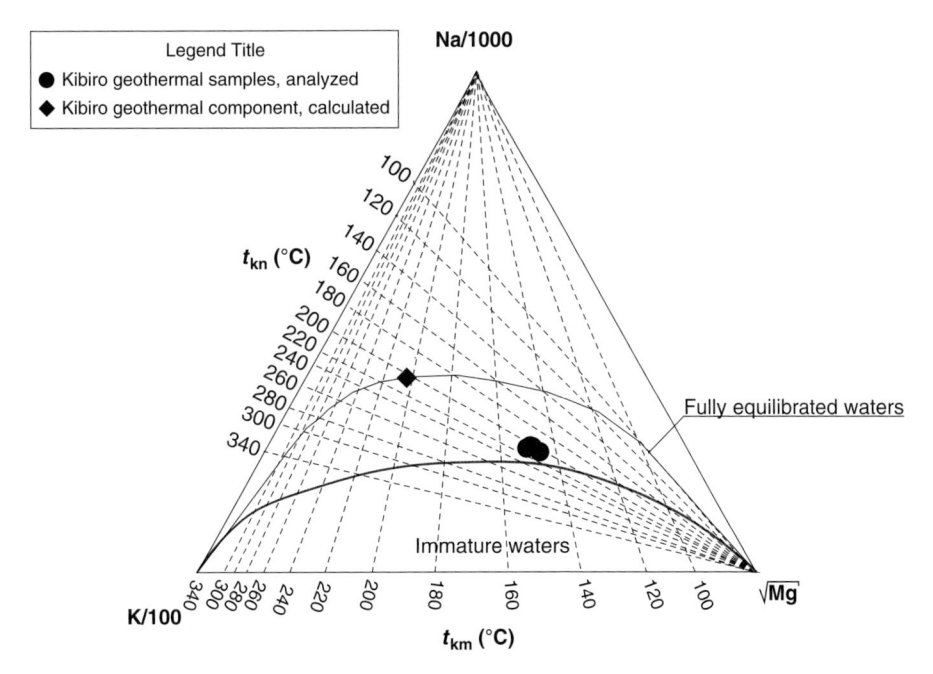

Figure 29 Na-K-Mg triangular diagram, showing examples from Kibiro, Uganda.

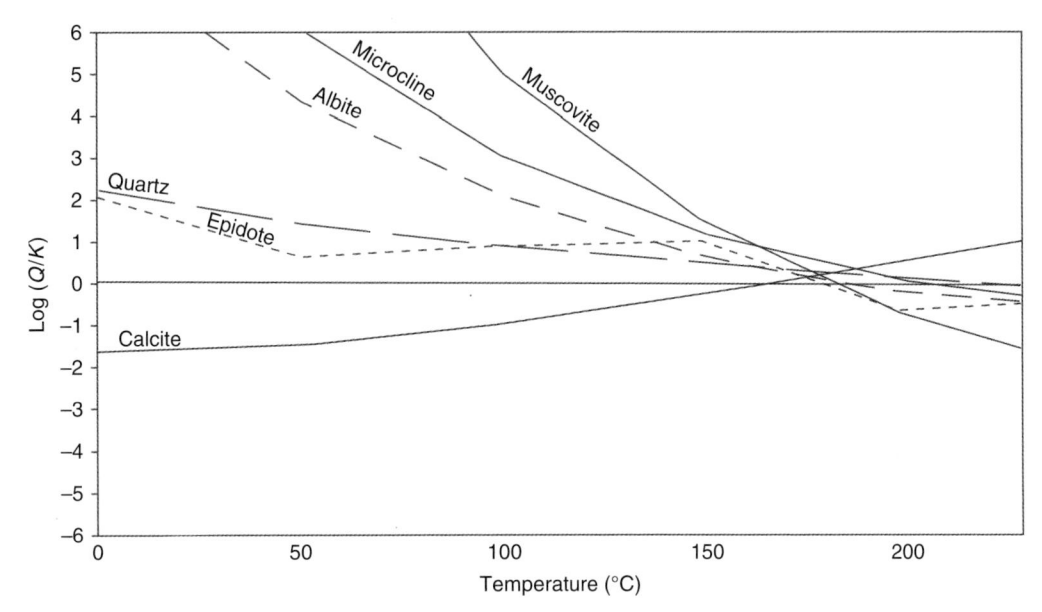

Figure 30 A log (Q/K) diagram for probable alteration minerals in well B-4, Námafjall, Iceland [162].

of hot water component of the water if it is unboiled. Fournier and Potter [168, 169] presented a new equation for quartz temperature, valid for 20–330 °C, in which salinity was accounted for. Gíslason et al. [170] came to the conclusion that chalcedony consisted of morganite and fine-grained quartz which is more soluble than quartz but is gradually altered to quartz.

Silica geothermometry suffers from several limitations. It is affected by temperature range. Steam separation during upflow will cause high results. Polymerization may interfere in the analytical determination of silica and deposition during upflow will cause low results. As shown above different minerals may control the silica concentration at different temperatures. Quartz usually controls it at >180 °C but chalcedony at <120 °C. For solutions from recently formed rocks, the chalcedony geothermometer may be valid up to 180 °C but quartz down to 120 °C or lower in solutions in old rocks. In basic solution H_2SiO_3 is ionized,

$$H_2SiO_3 \leftrightarrow H^+ + HSiO_3^- \qquad [9]$$

and too high values may be obtained. This can be corrected for by using the thermodynamic ionization constant for silicic acid. Lastly, dilution with cold groundwater may result in too low values for the subsurface fluid temperature, but a fair approximation may be obtained by using mixing models (see above).

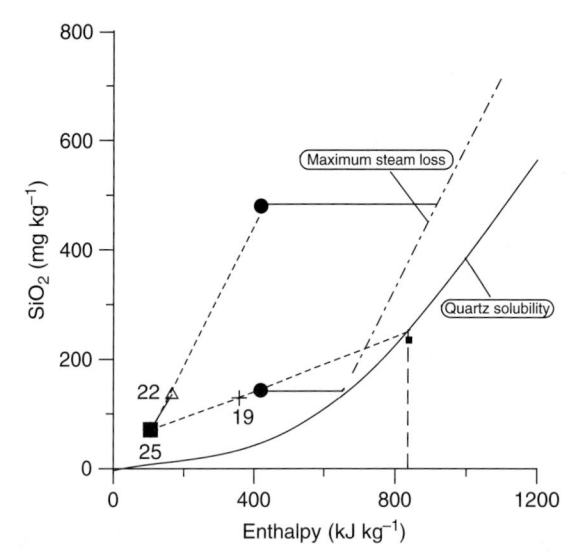

Figure 31 Silica enthalpy mixing model applied to waters from Kibiro, Uganda. Sample 19 is unboiled water, but sample 22 is boiled water.

To overcome problems associated with univariant geothermometers, mixing models have been applied. The most widely applied are the silica enthalpy model [165], the enthalpy chloride model [166], and the silica-carbonate model [167]. The silica enthalpy model does not account for conductive cooling after mixing but can be used for both boiled and unboiled water as is illustrated in **Figure 31**. The quartz solubility curve is drawn and the line joining the silica concentration of local cold groundwater and the spring sample is extended to the curve. If there is evidence that the water has boiled, the line is extended to the enthalpy at the boiling point of water and a horizontal line drawn to the quartz solubility curve for maximum steam loss.

Mixing and boiling are both accounted for in the chloride enthalpy model. This model is empirical, based on the results of chloride determinations on the geothermal fluids, and is applicable if it is significantly higher than that of the local cold groundwater. The final concentration of a component after single-stage separation is given by

$$C_l = C_i \times \frac{(H_s - H_f)}{(H_s - H_i)} \quad [10]$$

where C_i is the initial concentration before boiling, H_i is the enthalpy of the initial liquid before boiling, and H_f and H_s are the enthalpies of the final liquid and steam at t_f. For salinities $< 10\,000$ mg kg^{-1} steam tables can be used to solve the equation. For higher salinities, enthalpies of NaCl solutions (e.g., Ref. [261]) can be used. A graphical solution is demonstrated in **Figure 32**. If the enthalpy and the concentration of a conservative constituent x such as chloride are known prior to boiling (point A), its final concentration in the residual liquid can be obtained by extending a line from the enthalpy at the final steam separation temperature through point A to the enthalpy of the remaining liquid water after boiling. Thus, point B gives the concentration of x in the residual liquid after steam separation if the final steam separation takes place at 100 °C, but point C if it took place at 200 °C. For mixing, a line can be extended from the concentration and enthalpy points for x in cold groundwater in the area and any one of points A, B, and C and the results for determinations of x in the fluid from other manifestations fitted and their boiling and mixing history constructed.

The silica-carbonate model is most usefully applied to separate water cooled by boiling and conduction. Thus, if the CO_2 concentration at the measured temperature of the mixed sample plots to the left of the curve in **Figure 33** the water is boiled and thus depleted in carbon dioxide. It can of course also be applied to find the temperature of hot water component in unboiled water. In **Figure 34** it is applied to samples from Kibiro, Uganda, which are shown to be unboiled and the hot water component is 191 °C if data from Ragnarsdóttir and Walther [172] are used, but 221 °C using data from Fournier and Potter [168, 169].

The theoretical basis for cation geothermometry is equilibria ion exchange reactions between cations such as the following:

$$M_AAlSi_3O_8 + M_B{}^+ \Leftrightarrow M_BAlSi_3O_8 + M_A{}^+ \quad K = \frac{[M_A{}^+]}{[M_B{}^+]} \quad [11]$$

or

$$(M_A)AlSi_3O_8 + \frac{1}{2}M_C{}^{2+} \Leftrightarrow (M_C)_{1/2}AlSi_3O_8 + M_A{}^+; \quad K = \frac{[M_A{}^+]}{[M_C{}^{2+}]^{1/2}} \quad [12]$$

where $[M_X]$ = activity of ion X and the assumptions that activity of solids is 1 and the activity of a solute is equal to its concentration.

The cations most used in geothermometry are Na^+, K^+, Li^+, Ca^{2+}, and Mg^{2+}. The drawbacks in using Li are that its concentration tends to be small and small changes can lead to large changes in ratios to major constituents, and that its behavior is relatively conservative. CO_2 concentration affects Ca^{2+} concentration, especially at low temperatures which hampers the use of Ca^{2+} in

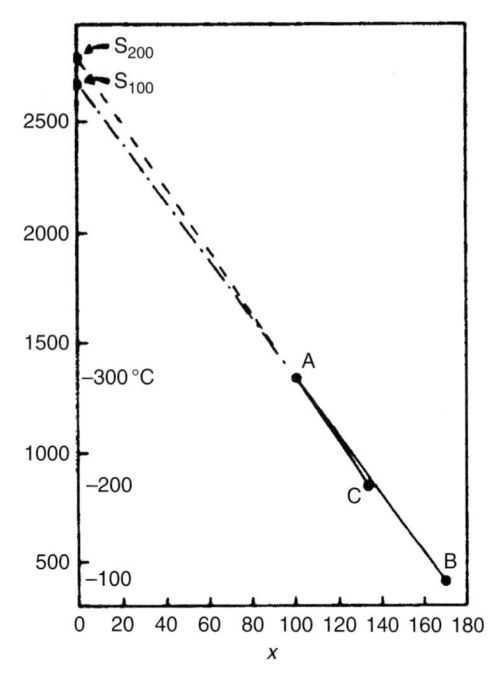

Figure 32 Enthalpy–composition diagram. Points S100 and S200 show the enthalpies of steam at 100 and 200 °C, respectively. X is dissolved material concentration in arbitrary units [171].

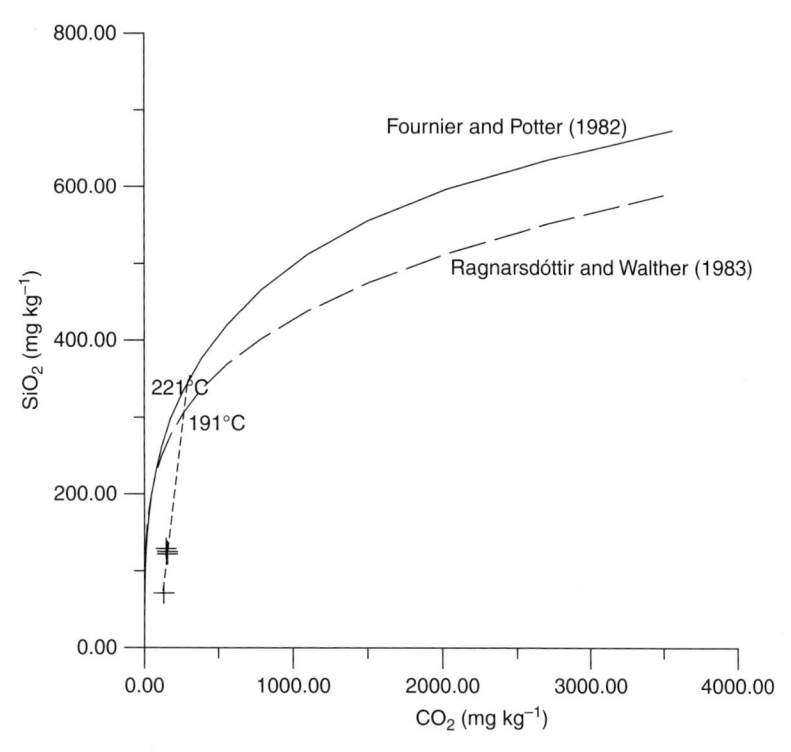

Figure 33 SiO_2–CO_2 mixing model applied to samples from Kibiro, Uganda. The sample with the lowest silica concentration is of cold groundwater from the area.

geothermometry although corrections have been devised. For the same reason Ca^{2+} can be used as an aid in determining the partial pressure of CO_2 in a geothermal system.

The Na/K geothermometer is relatively slow to reach a new equilibrium during cooling and ascent and is thus very useful in elucidating temperatures in deep parts of geothermal systems. A number of empirical formulae have been proposed and give different results especially at low temperatures. This is because different minerals participate in the cation exchange reactions

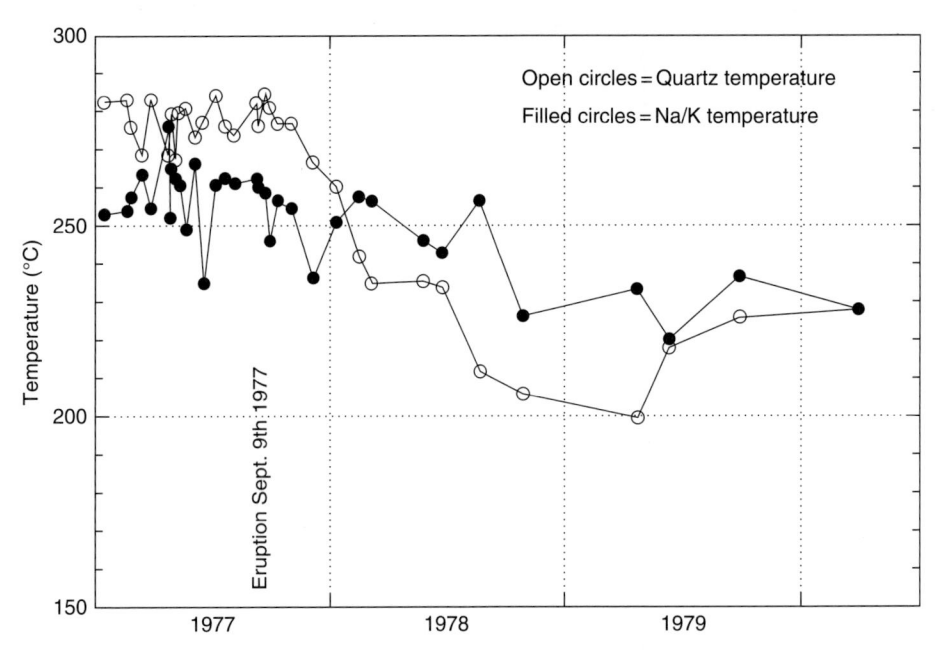

Figure 34 Changes in quartz and Na/K temperatures in well BG-10, Námafjall, upon flow of cold groundwater into the geothermal system as a result of a magmatic intrusion during the Krafla volcanic eruption in September 1977.

in different geothermal systems and it is not necessarily correct to base the geothermometer on the same equilibrium reaction in different areas. Theoretical studies have shown that waters above 200 °C have closely approached equilibrium with microcline and low albite, but even at temperatures as low as 50 °C Na and K ion activities may be controlled by these two feldspars but surface and nonthermal groundwater are usually undersaturated. Stefánsson and Arnórsson have devised a theoretical Na/K geothermometer which could overcome such problems.

The Na-K-Ca geothermometer is based on an empirical formula [173] and often gives good results, especially at >200 °C. There are, however, problems due to sensitivity to CO_2 concentration, especially at low temperatures [262]. Too high values are obtained for Mg-rich water at low temperatures. An Mg correction from Fournier and Potter [174] has been used, but is cumbersome; the use of Giggenbach's [175] Na-K-Mg diagram (**Figure 5**) is a simpler way of overcoming this problem.

Gas geothermometers. Several theoretical gas geothermometers have been suggested such as those reported by Nehring and D'Amore [263] based on the following reactions

$$\text{Fischer-Tropsch:} \quad CO_2(g) + 4H_2(g) \leftrightarrow CH_4(g) + 2H_2O \qquad [13]$$

$$CO_2\text{-}H_2: \quad H_2 + \frac{1}{2}O_2 \leftrightarrow H_2O; \quad C + O_2 \leftrightarrow CO_2 \qquad [14]$$

$$NH_3: \quad \frac{1}{2}N_2 + \frac{3}{2}H_2 \leftrightarrow NH_3 \qquad [15]$$

$$CO_2\text{-}H_2S: \quad 3FeS_2 + 2H_2 + 4H_2O \leftrightarrow Fe_3O_4 + 6H_2S; \quad C + O_2 \leftrightarrow CO_2 \qquad [16]$$

and those reported by D'Amore and Truesdell [176] based on three equations for H_2S, H_2, CH_4, CO_2, and the steam fraction, x. All of these are extremely useful for well fluids, yet more difficult to use for fumarole fluids as in all cases the steam fraction need be known to obtain the subsurface temperature and it is not easy to determine. A problem with the Fischer–Tropsch reaction is that it does not reach equilibrium quickly except at relatively high temperatures. Giggenbach [243] devised some theoretical gas geothermometers that do not rely on knowledge of the steam fraction. His H_2-Ar geothermometer generally gives good results but his CO_2-Ar geothermometer gives different results according to the origin of CO_2 and his CH_4-CO_2 is based on the Fischer–Tropsch reaction but works well at relatively high temperatures. The CO geothermometer of Bertrami *et al.* [177] based on the reaction

$$3CO_2 + CH_4 \leftrightarrow 4CO + 2H_2O \qquad [17]$$

holds promise but has not been widely used due to the difficulty involved in the analytical determination of CO at the low levels required.

Several empirical gas geothermometers have been reported, that is, those based on CO_2, H_2S, H_2, CO_2/H_2, CO_2/H_2S, and H_2S/H_2 by Arnórsson and Gunnlaugsson [178] and CO_2/N_2 by Arnórsson [179] and modified by Arnórsson *et al.* [180]. The gas geothermometers reported based on reactions of CH_4, H_2, H_2S, and CO_2 by D'Amore and Panichi [181] and on reactions of CH_4, H_2, and CO_2 by Tonani [182] suffer from the uncertainty that P_{CO_2} is assumed to be known or can be obtained empirically. Of these gases H_2 is probably the most reliable for geothermometry. For the evaluation of empirical geothermometers it is essential to establish thermodynamic properties for comparison. Arnórsson and Gunnlaugsson [178] came to the conclusion that there was a relationship between temperature and CO_2 fugacity with respect to the mineral buffer zoisite + prehnite +calcite + quartz at zoisite activity 0.5 on which they based their geothermometer. Zhao and Ármannsson [183] studied data on mineral assemblages that might control H_2 and H_2S concentrations at various temperatures and came to the conclusion that the H_2 concentration is apparently controlled by the Fe-bearing minerals epidote and prehnite which are also active in controlling the H_2S concentration and thus the H_2S/H_2 ratio, and that the controlling buffers are magnetite + epidote + hematite +prehnite at $t < 200$ °C for H_2, pyrite + magnetite + epidote + prehnite for H_2S relatively in dilute solutions at $t < 220$ °C, but pyrrhotite + epidote +pyrite + prehnite at $t > 200$ °C for both. All this is in agreement with Giggenbach's [184] finding that pyrites + iron-containing aluminum silicates are expected to control the H_2S/H_2 ratio. Similar findings have been reported by Arnórsson et al. [180] and Karingithi et al. [185] who conclude that the redox conditions rather than the salinity control which assemblage is active.

For systems whose fluids contain higher hydrocarbons, Darling [70] has found that there is a clear tendency for an increase in the C_1/C_2 ratio with rise in temperature and proposed an empirical geothermometer based on the regression line obtained for samples from geothermal fields worldwide, that is,

$$t°C = 57.8 \log\left(\frac{CH_4}{C_2H_6}\right) \qquad [18]$$

Isotope geothermometers. Isotope geothermometers based on several isotope exchange reactions have been reported.

Exchange between the carbon isotopes ^{13}C and ^{12}C during the Fischer–Tropsch reaction [12] has been found useful at high temperatures. It has also been used for lower subsurface temperatures at which bacterial catalysis has been shown to promote equilibrium. The same exchange reaction has also been employed successfully for the reaction between CO_2 and HCO_3^- but has to be deployed with care as it is pH and temperature dependent.

Although it is a disadvantage that H and O are major constituents, some reactions involving those elements have been reported. Exchange between the isotopes ^2H and ^1H in the following compounds has been used: H_2–H_2O which equilibrates fast; CH_4–H_2 which is slower; and CH_4–H_2O which has not been fully established.

Exchange between the isotopes ^{18}O and ^{16}O in the following compounds has been used: SO_4–H_2O which involves an exchange reaction at a useful rate to show temperatures in exploitable geothermal systems and is very efficient; CO_2–H_2O which only works for exchanges in the liquid phase and water steam; H and O which is only applicable under certain conditions.

Exchange between the sulfur isotopes ^{34}S and ^{32}S has been used for the reaction between the compounds H_2S (HS^-) and SO_4^{2-} (HSO_4^{2-}) and has been found to be pH dependent and give a slow response similar to that of the CO_2–CH_4 described above. Similarly this exchange is useful for very hot fluids at great depths that may be precursors feeding natural geothermal systems.

7.04.10 Applications during Production

Changes in temperature and flow. Geothermometry is a powerful tool for monitoring the temperature of well fluids as sampling for chemical analysis can be effected at the wellhead without any changes in the flow of the well, but if temperature logging is to reveal the true reservoir temperature the flow needs to be stopped. Furthermore, geothermometer temperatures tend to respond quicker to temperature changes, for example, due to mixing with a cooler aquifer. Geothermometers respond at different rates, K/Mg temperature very fast, silica temperatures relatively fast, but Na/K temperature more slowly. The changes in quartz and Na/K temperature in well BG-10, Námafjall, North Iceland, following the flow of cold groundwater into the geothermal system during the Krafla volcanic eruption in 1977 are illustrated in **Figure 34**.

Stable isotope ratios and concentrations of conservative constituents will reveal mixing with different waters, for example, if there is an inflow of seawater into a dilute fluid geothermal system. In **Figure 35** it is shown how a small inflow of seawater into the Seltjarnarnes geothermal system, Southwest Iceland, was detected from the results of monitoring chloride concentrations [186].

In the Bakki geothermal system, South Iceland, changes in chloride concentrations were detected in one well, BA-01, and confirmed by changes in stable isotope ratios whereas similar changes were not observed in an adjacent well HJ-01 (**Figures 36** and **37**). Months later the temperature started dropping in well BA-01 but not in HJ-01. Thus, it was demonstrated that water from a cold aquifer with different characteristics was mixing with the fluid in B-01 but the HJ-01 was separate [186].

Measurements of enthalpy and flow. Dilution methods have become quite common for the determination of enthalpy and flow in boreholes over the years. One of their main advantages is that the wells need not be taken out of production during the determination. A known amount of tracer material is dosed into the well flow and a sample collected some distance downstream, the concentration of the dosing material determined, and the degree of dilution found. As with all such measurements another parameter, usually liquid flow, is determined and the total enthalpy and flow computed from the two results (for dilution and liquid flow). The requirements for materials are similar to those for tracers (see Section 7.04.7) except that the method of determination need not be as sensitive. In **Table 26** there is a list of materials that have been used for this purpose.

Production problems, general. The most common production problems due to the chemistry of geothermal fluids are deposition and corrosion. Pollution is usually dealt with as an environmental problem. Examples of studies of potential pollution are given in Section 7.04.7.

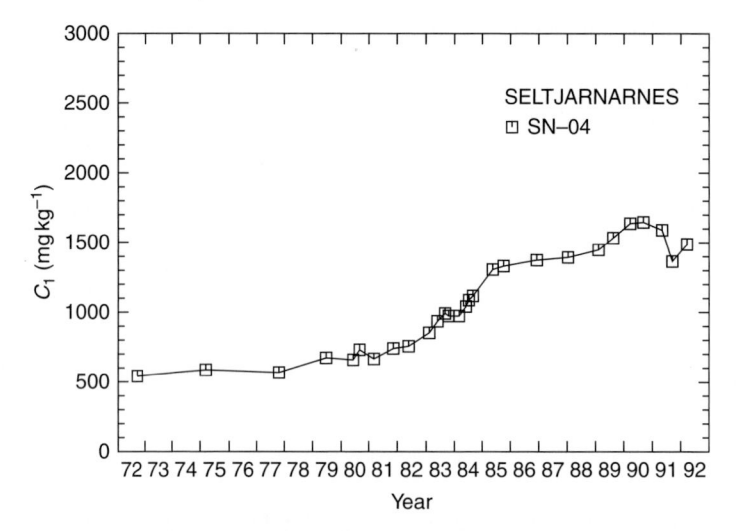

Figure 35 Changes in chloride concentrations with time in well SN-04, Seltjarnarnes, Southwest Iceland. From Kristmannsdóttir H and Ármannsson H (1996) Chemical monitoring of Icelandic geothermal fields during production. *Geothermics* 25: 349–364.

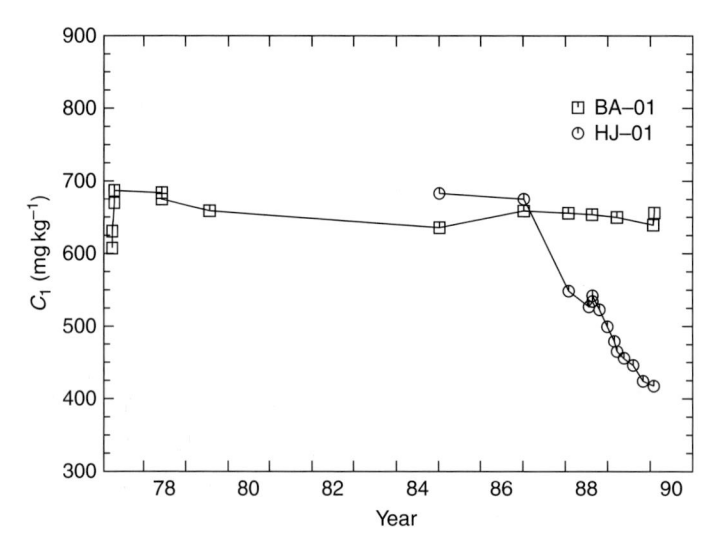

Figure 36 Changes in chloride concentrations with time in wells BA-01 and HJ-01, Bakki, South Iceland. From Kristmannsdóttir H and Ármannsson H (1996) Chemical monitoring of Icelandic geothermal fields during production. *Geothermics* 25: 349–364.

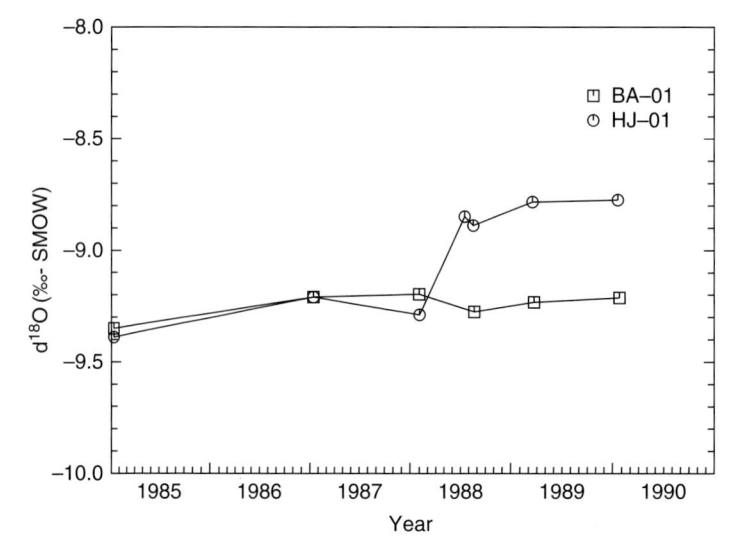

Figure 37 Changes in oxygen isotope ratios with time in wells BA-01 and HJ-01, Bakki, South Iceland. From Kristmannsdóttir H and Ármannsson H (1996) Chemical monitoring of Icelandic geothermal fields during production. *Geothermics* 25: 349–364.

Table 26 Information on some tracers used in dilution methods for enthalpy and flow determinations

Tracer	Analytical methods	Phase	Advantages	Disadvantages	References
NaCl (Cl⁻)	Ion chromatography (IC)	Liquid	Simple method, easy to apply in the field	High background values in many geothermal systems	[187]
MgCl$_2$/ MgSO$_4$ (Mg^{2+})	Atomic absorption spectrophotometry (AAS), Inductively coupled plasma (ICP), IC	Liquid	A selection of convenient methods, some applicable in the field	Mg–SO$_4$ complexes, Mg-silicate or carbonate depositor may interfere	[187,188,190]
KF (F⁻)	IC, selective electrode	Liquid	Convenient methods, applicable in the field	Relatively high background values, expensive	[189]
NaBr (Br⁻)	IC	Liquid	Convenient method, applicable in the field	High background values in some geothermal systems	[189,190]
Sodium benzoate (benzoate)	IC, high-performance liquid chromatography (HPLC)	Liquid	IC convenient, applicable in the field	HPLC not easily applicable in the field	[188,191]
Sodium fluorescein (fluorescein)	Fluorescence spectrophotometer	Liquid	Convenient method, applicable in the field	Material damaged at high temperature and by UV radiation	[188,248]
Isopropanol	Gas chromatograph (GC)	Liquid, vapor	Good, reliable method	Not easily applicable in the field. Destroyed at >240 °C	[190,192]
Ar	GC	Vapor	Good, reliable method	Not easily applicable in the field	[187]
N$_2$	GC	Vapor	Good, reliable method	Not easily applicable in the field. High background values possible	[190]
SF$_6$	GC with electron capture detector	Vapor	Extremely reliable and sensitive method	Not easily applicable in the field	[188,191]
C$_3$H$_8$	GC	Vapor	Good, reliable method	Not easily applicable in the field	[189]

Deposition. The most common deposits in geothermal utilization are due to silica, iron oxides, iron silicates, sulfides, calcite, and magnesium silicates. Deposits due to aluminum silicates, anhydrite, barite, apatite, borates, and sulfur are also known. Studies of deposits are twofold, that is, a theoretical thermodynamic study to find out whether deposition can take place and an experimental kinetic study to find out whether the deposition is fast enough to cause problems.

Silica deposits are usually not formed inside wells but may form in surface equipment and reinjection wells. The solubility of quartz controls the dissolution of silica, but due to different reaction kinetics the saturation temperature and pressure of amorphous silica control its deposition. Thus from **Figure 38** (Fournier, 1981) it can be found that the solubility of quartz at 270 °C is about 500 ppm, whereas for amorphous silica the same solubility is found at about 120 °C. A liquid saturated with quartz at 270 °C needs to be cooled to 120 °C before deposition sets in. This can be calculated; rate experiments may be performed to find out whether it is possible to operate at an even lower temperature.

If there is a significant concentration of iron in the fluid, deposition of iron silicates will set in at a higher temperature than the silica deposition, but at lower temperatures iron tends to be deposited in the form of oxides.

In saline geothermal fluids or in fluids disturbed by the effects of volcanic gas sulfide deposits are prone to form by reaction of metal(s) with H$_2$S. In saline solutions these tend to comprise PbS (galena), ZnS (wurtzite, sphalerite), CuS (covellite), Cu$_2$S (chalcocite), CuFeS$_2$ (chalcopyrite), and bornite (Cu$_5$FeS$_4$). In Mt. Amiata, Italy, SbS$_2$ (stibnite) is a major deposit. Where volcanic gas affects the system FeS$_2$ (pyrite) and FeS (pyrrhotite) are the most common sulfides.

Flashing causes CO$_2$ stripping and a pH increase, which may lead to calcite deposition according to

$$Ca^{2+} + 2HCO_3^- \leftrightarrow CaCO_3 + CO_2 + H_2O \qquad [19]$$

Calcite solubility is retrograde, that is, it decreases with increasing temperature. The extent of supersaturation can be calculated and the reaction is very fast so rate experiments need not be carried out. Several inhibitors have been used to stem calcite deposition. Examples of much used inhibitors are listed in **Table 27**. Arnórsson [242] has described the theoretical aspects of calcite deposition.

Prediction of calcite scaling in Krafla wells. During the early stages of production from the Krafla field calcite scaling was observed in some of the shallower wells and reaming with a drillrig was the chosen method for controlling the scaling. It was important to know the extent of formation, its rate, and the depth at which it was formed. The first step is to predict whether or not a deposit will form which is carried out by a thermodynamic calculation in which the supersaturation of calcite is found by comparing analyzed values with theoretical values. In **Figure 39** there is an example of a diagram showing supersaturation for well KJ-9 in Krafla. The diagram shows that at the reservoir temperature at the bottom of the well the sample is saturated, but as the sample boils and cools it becomes significantly supersaturated but with more cooling it becomes less so. Deposition is expected to start soon after the initial oiling, rises to a maximum and then diminishes.

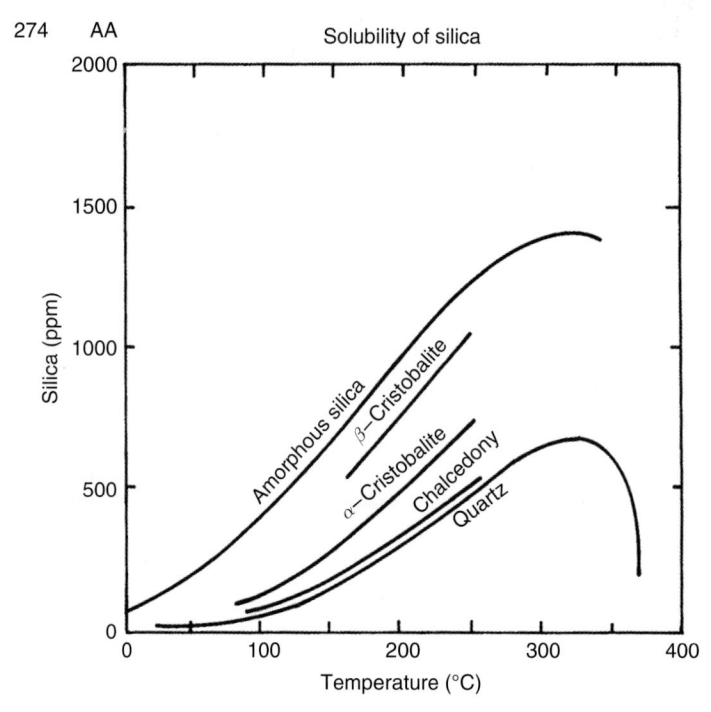

Figure 38 Solubilities of different silica minerals vs. temperature. From Fournier RO (1981) Application of water geochemistry to geothermal exploration and reservoir engineering. In: Rybach L and Muffler LJP (eds.) *Geothermal Systems: Principles and Case Histories*, pp. 109–143. New York: John Wiley.

Table 27 Some common inhibitors against calcite scaling in geothermal installations

Trade name	Composition	Concentration (%)	Price (USD kg^{-1})
Dequest 2006	Aminotri(methylene phosphonic acid) 38–42%	2–10	1.35
Nalco 95D0666	Polymaleic acid 30–60%; maleic acid 1–5%	1–5	4.95
Nalco 1340 HP	Polyacrylate	2–10	4.95
Drewsperse 747A	Polycarboxylic acid 40–55% (acrylic copolymer)	0.5–10	4–5

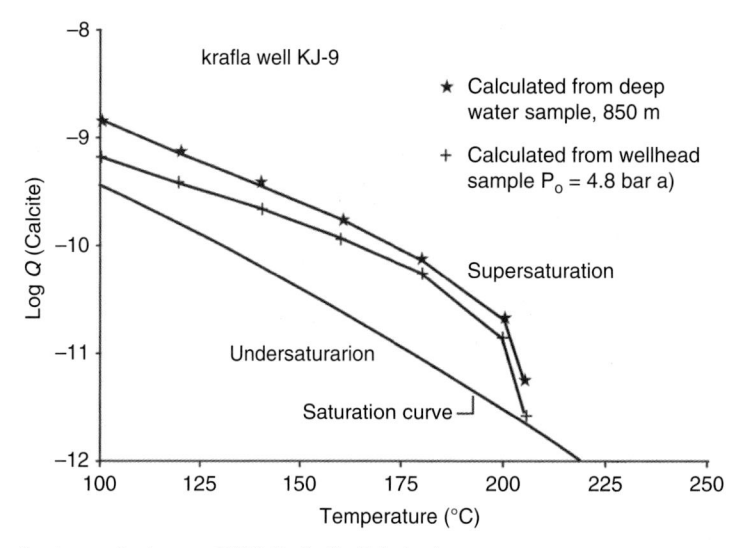

Figure 39 Calcite supersaturation in samples from well KJ-9, Krafla, North Iceland.

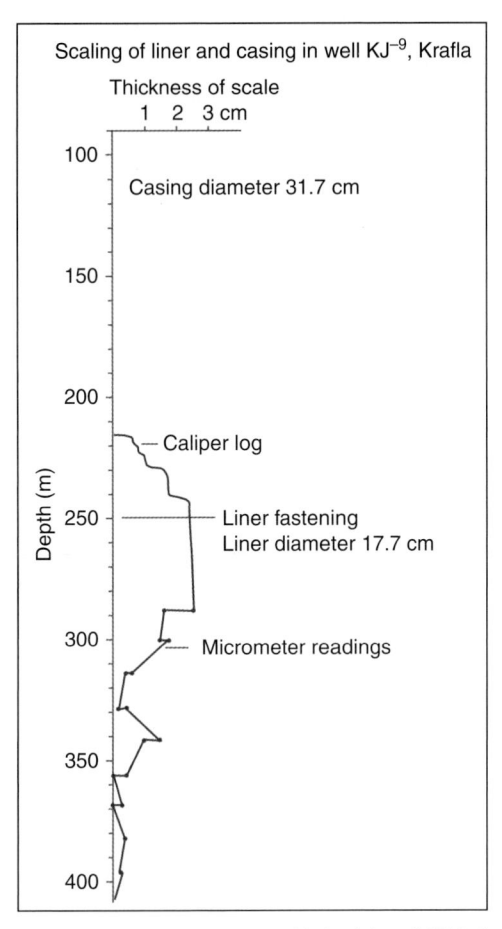

Figure 40 Results of caliper log of casing and measurement of scale in liner with depth in well KJ-9, Krafla.

A method of finding the extent of deposition is to collect a subsurface sample and compare the calcium concentration with that of a wellhead sample collected at a similar time and assume that the difference in concentration is due to calcite deposition. Information on flow from the well and the time of production can then be used to calculate the total mass of deposit formed in the well. This was done for well KJ-9 and a check could be carried out on this method because it was decided to deepen the well and the liners were removed from it. Thus, it was possible to measure the length and thickness of the scale inside the liner and combine with caliper logs from the casing to determine the volume of scale formed (**Figure 40**). Analysis of the scale gave 98.6% calcite and its density was 2500 kg m^{-3} and thus it was possible to calculate the mass of the deposit. The two results were compared with the results presented in **Table 28**.

Thus it was confirmed that the method of determination of calcium in downhole and wellhead samples assuming the difference to be due to calcite deposition was justified. It was also important to know how fast the deposition was taking place and this was observed by monitoring the flow of the wells and determining when a decrease in flow started. Generally when a decrease started it was very fast and the well soon became a very poor producer. The monitoring results for well KJ-9 (KJ-9, before deepening, KJ-9b after deepening are shown in **Figure 41**) show that the period of relatively undisturbed flow was similar between reamings and this helped very much in planning the use of the well, as well as for the time at which the drillrig should be brought in for reaming. As is to be expected, the wellhead pressure affects the scale formation because it will affect the depth at which the scale is formed. The higher the wellhead pressure, the shallower is the depth at which deposits form. The clogging of the well occurs when the opening through which the fluid flows has become extremely narrow and therefore it is possible to prolong the period of relatively undisturbed flow by varying the wellhead pressure although this means that a greater quantity of deposit forms. In 1984 a comparison was made of the

Table 28 Quantity of calcite formed in well KJ-9, Krafla, in 1977 according to determinations of volume of deposit and by calculation based on differences in calcium concentrations at wellhead and close to the bottom of the well

Method	Volume determined (m^3)	Mass determined (kg)
Caliper log and thickness measurements	1.1	2700
Chemical analysis		2400

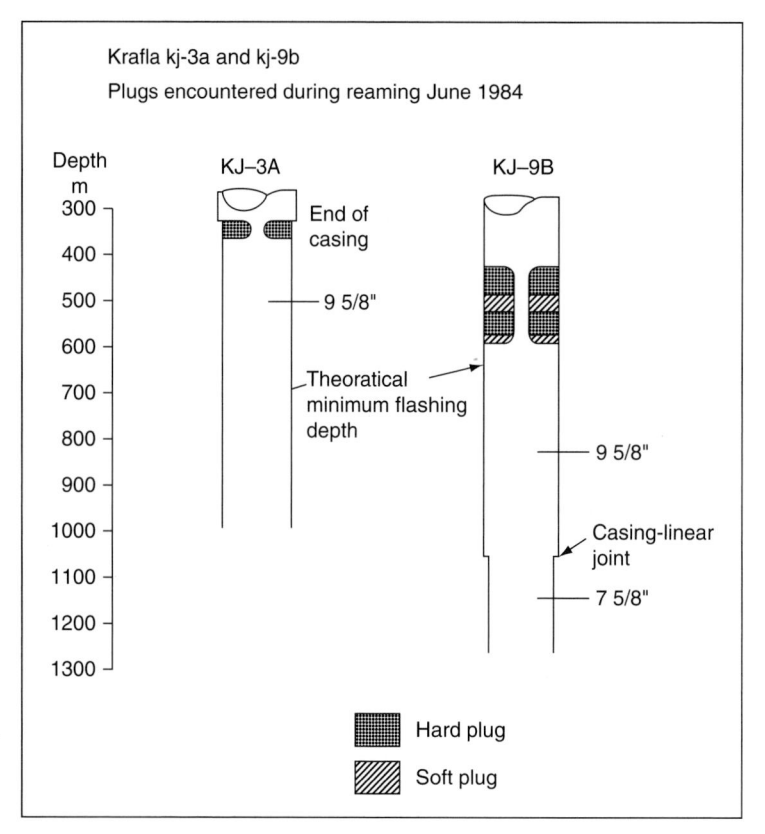

Figure 41 Depth of plugs reamed from wells KJ-3A and KJ-9B in 1984.

deposits in two wells, one of which, KJ-9, had been producing at a variable wellhead pressure but the other at the same wellhead pressure throughout. The resulting depth of deposit formation is shown in **Figure 41** [193].

Wangyal [194] used the program Hola [264] to calculate the flashing depth at different wellhead pressures for several wells in Iceland with the results shown in **Figure 42**. It is clear that by controlling the wellhead pressure the depth of deposit formation can be varied and if the producer can tolerate the reduced flow due to high pressure a smaller and cheaper drillrig may be deployed for reaming wells with deposits at a shallow depth.

Magnesium silicates are formed upon heating of silica containing groundwater or mixing of cold groundwater and geothermal water. They have been shown to consist mainly of poorly developed antigorite [195]. Their solubility decreases (deposition increases) with increased temperature and pH. The rate of deposition has been found to increase linearly with supersaturation but exponentially with temperature.

Corrosion. Corrosion is a term used for the chemical destruction of materials. Steel is the most important material used in geothermal installations and its corrosion is due to the following half-reactions.
Anodic half-reactions:

$$Fe \rightarrow Fe^{2+} + 2e^- \qquad [20]$$

$$Fe \rightarrow Fe^{3+} + 3e^- \qquad [21]$$

Cathodic half-reactions:

$$H_2O + \frac{1}{2}O_2 + 2e^- \rightarrow 2OH^- \qquad [22]$$

$$H_2O + 2e^- \rightarrow H_2 + 2OH^- \qquad [23]$$

$$2H_2CO_3 + 2e^- \rightarrow 2HCO_3^- + H_2 \qquad [24]$$

The most common corrosive species in geothermal fluids are O_2 at low temperatures; H^+ (pH) but low pH favors the first two cathodic half-reactions; Cl which gives

$$Fe^{2+} + Cl^- \leftrightarrow FeCl^+ \qquad [25]$$

thus favoring the first anodic half-reaction; CO_2 which controls pH and favors the last cathodic half-reaction. H_2S attacks Cu, Ni, Zn, and Pb. H_2S, CO_3^{2-}, and SiO_2 may form protective films on steel.

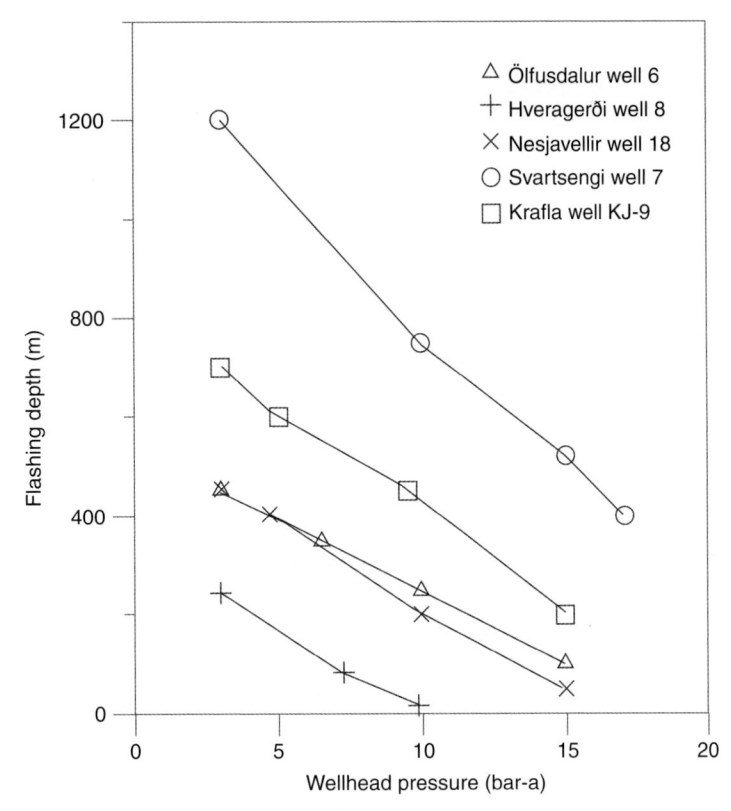

Figure 42 Flashing depth vs. wellhead pressure in some geothermal wells in Iceland. From Wangyal P (1992) Calcite deposition related to temperature and boiling in some Icelandic geothermal wells. *Geothermal Training Programme Report 1992–11*, United Nations University, 33pp.

The following materials have been used in geothermal installations and their advantages and disadvantages are recorded: Ti and Cr are very corrosion resistant but expensive; stainless steel is relatively resistant but is corroded in acid fluids. It is generally not as expensive as Ti and Cr; mild and low-alloy steels are corroded to a considerable degree but cheap; Cu, Ni, and alloys are susceptible to H_2S corrosion and should at least not be used in high-temperature fluids; Pb and Sb alloys are corroded to some extent and usually not recommended; and Al and Zn alloys are not considered suitable for geothermal fluids. Different parts of the geothermal installations are variably sensitive to corrosion, for example, the condenser lining and the turbine blade in a flash geothermal power plant tend to be most sensitive and thus the most resistant materials are used there, but the borehole itself gets away with much less resistant material. Prior to the installation of the equipment various materials are tested to find out how resistant materials are needed at each stage of the installation.

The occurrence of acid geothermal fluids. Truesdell *et al.* [196] and D'Amore *et al.* [197] came to the conclusion after the study of several areas (e.g., Tatun, Taiwan, Larderello, Italy, The Geysers, USA, and Krafla, Iceland) that the origin of acid fluids in geothermal systems was magmatic and their treatment should involve scrubbing the steam with alkaline water in accordance with the criteria laid down by Allegrini and Benvenuti [198] who first described such fluids, that is,

1. scrubbing occurs at the wellhead,
2. the injection water contains less Na^+ than the total content of the steam condensate to prevent sodium borate precipitation,
3. the injection does not saturate the steam, and
4. the liquid is entirely separated using an efficient separator after mixing.

Acid fluids have been observed in several fields worldwide since and some of the experiences and reactions will be described below.

Italy, Larderello. Steam scrubbing using NaOH has been practiced both downhole using a capillary and at the wellhead using corrosion-resistant wellheads, with stainless AISI 309 steel for cladding and Stellite 6 as an overlay. Such wellheads were described by Thórhallsson *et al.* [199]. The system in general was described by Bell [200].

USA, The Geysers, California. NaOH has been used similarly to the use in Larderello [201] and some success has been obtained in trials with dry steam scrubbing using calcite packed beds and amines which avoids the reduction in steam utilization efficiency experienced with the NaOH injection [202].

Mexico, Los Humeros. Acid fluids in wells in the Los Humeros field have been ascribed to reactions in vapor with halites and silicates which produce HCl. Not much argillic alteration typical of acid fluids has been found at depth where acidity is observed. Thus, it is suggested that the acidity was generated in a stage subsequent to the deposition of minerals but may be derived from a deep low liquid saturation reservoir favoring the formation of HCl gas which then is transported in vapor to the upper liquid-dominated reservoir forming hydrochloric acid [203]. No mitigation measures were suggested.

Costa Rica, Miravalles. Moya et al. [204] reported on five wells that produced water at pH 2.3–3.2. Although chloride is the main anion, the acid well fluids distinguish themselves by a higher sulfate concentration than fluids in the other wells. Thus it is apparently the sulfate that controls the acidity. To meet the supply requirements of the power plant two of these wells were subjected to treatment with an acid neutralization system using a deep injection of NaOH. This has been successful and shown to be economically beneficial although problems have been encountered such as loss of downhole dispersion head, rupture of capillary tubing, pump problems, and anhydrite scaling.

The Philippines, Mahanagdong. In the Philippines at least 80 MW of proven generation is currently unavailable in producing fields due to acid fluids and the potential of such generation nationwide could exceed 300 MW. Villa et al. [205] have described acid chloride-sulfate fluids in Mahanagdong with pH 2.26–5.90 from well MG-9D, Mahanagdong. As the fluid flows to the surface the pH drops from 4.2 to 3.4 starting at a depth of 800 m caused by the formation of acid sulfate water by dissociation of H_2SO_4. An increase of pH from 2.87 to 4.05 was attained by pumping a relatively concentrated NaOH solution through a 1" Incoloy 825 tubing at 20 m depth. At the same time a decline in the thinning rate of the pipeline from 1.05 to 0.21 mm day^{-1} was observed. For ideal corrosion control a pH of 4.5 needs to be attained.

Tiwi. Sugiaman et al. [206] have described the geochemical response to production from the Tiwi geothermal field. The pH of the acid fluids which are produced from some wells is 2.8–3.6. It is an acid sulfate fluid and somewhat cooler than other fluids. It is restricted to thin layers at depth between 500 and 750 m below sea level and is indicated by the occurrence of advanced argillic alteration. The fluids are thought to be formed through mixing of deeply circulated meteoric water with sulfur-rich gases from a magmatic heat source. Similar conditions are known in Karaha-Telaga Bodas, Indonesia [207], and other Philippine geothermal systems [208, 209]. In one well acidic entries were identified at 1550 and 1615 m measured depth from advanced argillic alteration. The production liner was removed and the corrosive zones isolated and since then it has produced benign brine. In another corrosive well, commercial production has been achieved by injection of 4 wt.% NaOH at a depth of 1070 m (below the deepest argillic alteration lens) through a 12.7 mm capillary tubing of Inconel 625. The injection sub includes spray nozzles, weight bars, a centralizer, and a subcheck valve. Two master valves were used to facilitate run-in and pull-out of the injection assembly without killing the well. The pH is controlled at 4.5–5.0. Overdosing with NaOH (pH > 6) is found to exacerbate silica scaling. Dissolved iron concentrations in the fluid have been reduced by 80% by the NaOH treatment and the well provides 7 MW$_e$ after the mitigation.

South Sambaloran. Angcoy et al. [210] have described a rather complicated process in which suspended solids in a vapor-dominated flow initially consisting of formation material erode layers of corrosion products formed while discharge was water dominated and relatively acid and cause thinning of pipes by erosion. Suggested mitigation measures include lining vulnerable portions with an abrasive-resistant layer and hot brine wellhead washing.

Indonesia, Lahendong, North Sulawesi. Two wells have been abandoned due to corrosion by acids. The problem has furthermore been encountered in a recently drilled well but decision on action is pending (Hari Koestano, personal communication).

Japan, Otake-Hatchobaru. Kiyota et al. [211] have reported on acid brine in the Otake-Hatchobaru field probably originating in brine from which steam is boiled. This acid brine has been used to mitigate silica deposition.

New Zealand, Rotokawa. Acid fluids are common in geothermal pools in New Zealand, but there are few references to problems due to such fluids in geothermal plants in the country. Bowyer et al. [212] reported acid fluids causing corrosion in the Rotokawa geothermal field. These are believed to have formed where hot fluids from a deep production reservoir leaked upward, boiled, and released CO_2 and H_2S into the steam phase causing the formation of SO_4^{2-} and hence acid. It is suggested that the two-phase zone has been resaturated and the corrosive fluids neutralized by shallow injection.

Krafla, Iceland. Since the beginning of the development of the Krafla field in 1974, the output and the chemical properties of steam and water from wells have been closely monitored.

Initially the wells were drilled in fields north of the power plant (Leirbotnar and Vítismór). It turned out that in these areas the reservoir is of dual character. The shallow part down to 1000–1400 m depth contains hot water (210–220 °C). The water in this upper zone contains little gas and has alkaline character. Silica and other dissolved ions are in close equilibrium with the rock minerals at measured temperatures.

In these shallow wells the CO_2 gas concentration increases toward the fissure Hveragil (**Figure 10**) that is considered the main upflow path for steam from the deep reservoir to the surface. In the shallow wells close to the Hveragil fissure, calcite precipitation causes well blocking while in wells just few hundred meters to the west, this problem is absent [89].

Initially deep wells were cased down to 600 m depth and the inflow was both from the shallow hot water aquifer and from aquifers at around 1800–2200 m depth. The temperature of the deep aquifers was 300–340 °C and the inflow water and steam and in some cases superheated dry steam.

A few months after the construction of the plant started, there was an eruption in the Leirhnjúkur volcano to the northwest of the power plant. At that time only three wells had been flow tested. Well KG-3 was a good producer with a low steam gas concentration. Shortly after the eruption there was a sudden increase of steam gas concentration in this well. The output of the well decreased rapidly and the well was unusable after a few months [265].

Well KG-4 was being drilled when the eruption started. Before well completion, high-pressure steam, from deep aquifers, flowed up the well and into the shallower aquifers of the upper zone. The well was completed in a hurry, but the wellhead was not designed for the high pressure and started to leak. The steam contained acid and the wellhead corroded rapidly and in the end the situation was uncontrollable and the well went out of control and formed a crater. The water, which flowed from the crater, had a pH of 1.86 [265].

Further drilling was postponed and the well design revised. The casing depth was increased to 800 m and the wellhead pressure class increased.

Some of the wells drilled subsequently in Leirbotnar and Vítismór (KJ-6, KJ-7, and KG-10) turned to be high in enthalpy and high in gas concentration. The effluent water had a black color caused by precipitation of iron sulfides and silicates that formed in the well when acid fluids, containing iron from the corroding liner, mixed with alkaline water from the upper aquifers. The output of these wells decreased rapidly and produced mostly from the upper zone and was unusable. They were reamed and found to be clogged with iron sulfide and silicate scales [154]. When flow was tested, after reaming they were rapidly clogged again.

The well design was again revised and the casing depth increased to block the inflow from the upper zone and avoid precipitation of iron compounds in the wells. Well KG-12 was drilled to 2222 m depth and cased to 985 m. Its flow was superheated dry steam containing hydrogen chloride (HCl), which was converted to hydrochloric acid upon condensation. Examination of the wellhead showed great damage by acid corrosion and the turbine blades suffered erosion by iron chloride dust formed during the corrosion. The corrosion was most rapid at sites with conductive cooling (vents and flanges) and where the flow speed was high (orifices and bends). To make the steam usable for the plant the wellhead was insulated to prevent condensation and the steam mixed with alkaline water from the nearby well KJ-9 [213].

Well KG-12 produced for a few years, but the enthalpy dropped gradually and water started to flow from the well. The steam flow decreased rapidly for the first 2 months but was after that relatively stable until 2004 when the wellhead pressure was too low for the well to be usable [214].

The CO_2 gas concentration in steam from the wells in Leirbotnar field decreased steadily after reaching a maximum soon after the eruptions started. A few wells have been drilled over the years to check whether the acid character of the deep zone was also decreasing (KG-25, KG-26, and KJ-29). The flow from the deep aquifers turned out to be acid as before, despite the decrease in CO_2 gas concentration of the steam.

It became evident that the drilling field would have to be relocated in order to supply the plant with sufficient good quality steam. Wells were drilled in the south slopes of the Krafla mountain (Suðurhlíðar) and in an area south of the power plant (Hvíthólaklif) where chemical analysis of steam from fumaroles had indicated less magmatic influence than in Leirbotnar and Vítismór [89].

The steam quality was better, but the productivity of the wells was insufficient. The plant was thus operated at half power for several years. The gas changes due to the magmatic activity were described in detail by Ármannsson et al. [89, 117].

Later (1997–2000) a new drill field in the west slopes of the Krafla mountain was explored (Vesturhlíðar). This field was productive and since 1999 the power plant has been operated at full power [266]. The concentration of CO_2 and H_2S gas in the well steam is relatively high, but acid steam was not observed.

Recently seven new wells have been drilled to obtain steam for further expansion of the Krafla power plant.

Well KJ-35 was located northwest of the plant and directionally drilled toward the Leirhnúkur volcano. It was a good producer, but the output declined steadily during flow test. The chemical analysis of the fluid collected at the wellhead did not show clear evidence of acid or iron precipitation in the well [267]. Logging of the well showed blocking at 1960 m depth and a plug consisting of iron sulfide and silicate similar to the scale that had blocked other acid wells in Krafla was reamed out of the well.

Well KJ-36 was located southeast of the Víti crater and directionally drilled to northwest under the crater. When flow tested the well was very powerful. The steam collected at the wellhead was acid and corrosive. The flow test was stopped after 6 days when a hole had formed in the wellhead pipe. The well was tested again for 32 days after fortification of the wellhead. The steam was still acid but turned from dry steam to saturated steam after a while. The corrosion rate was very rapid so the well was shut in and the acid aquifer blocked by cementing [215]. Now the well produces from aquifers at 1600–1700 m depth and the steam is used for 5 KJ-36 and drilled to the north. It has also hit acid aquifers and is being flow tested.

The location of the wells in Krafla is shown in **Figure 10** and those wells, that have hit acid aquifers, are shown with a red symbol. Generally wells which are deeper than 2000 m and west of the Hveragil fissure have hit acid aquifers; wells east of this fissure have not been contaminated.

Collection of representative samples from the deep acid aquifers has been difficult. The first wells were of dual character and alkaline water from the upper zone obscured the character of the deep zone steam. By mass balance calculations it was possible though to show that the inflow was of acid character [213].

Well KG-12 was drilled with a 985 m deep casing and a sample of the deep steam could be obtained [213]. Well KG-25 was drilled with a 1145 m deep casing, but the upper alkaline zone reached deeper there and alkaline water flowed into the well at a depth of 1455 m [216].

In well KJ-36 the deep acid aquifer was very powerful and initially the flow from shallower aquifers did not obscure the character significantly [215].

The composition of main constituents of water and steam in wells KG-12, KG-25, and KJ-36 is shown in **Table 29**. When comparing the steam gas concentration, the time of sampling should be considered, as the CO_2 concentration in steam has been decreasing through the years.

The Krafla field is located in the center of a caldera volcano with underlying magma chamber. The volcano erupted several times from 1975 to 1984. The magma chamber has been located by analysis of seismic data at 3–7 km depth under the geothermal field [123].

Figure 43 shows a hypothetical model of the Krafla geothermal system based on chemical, geological, and geophysical data.

On top of the magma chamber is a steam zone, which contains acid gases (HCl and SO_2) rising from the magma. The acid steam expels CO_2 and H_2S gas from the rock but is isolated from the upper zone by impermeable rock. The CO_2 and H_2S may originate in the magma, but reaction of the acid magmatic fluids with alkaline rock may also release these gases. The low permeability of the cap

Table 29 Chemical composition of steam and water from acid wells in Krafla

Well		KG-12	KG-25	KJ-36
Date		1980-06-08	1990-10-29	2008-01-19
Enthalpy	kJ kg^{-1}	2887	1786	2803
Flow	kg s^{-1}	6,3	44,9	16,9
Sampling pressure	Bar	5,9	16,5	4,35
Water (steam)	*kg s^{-1}*	(6,3)	21,5	(16,9)
pH		3,01	6,80	3,96
pH-Temp	°C	22,0	20,2	21,9
Cond	µS cm^{-1}	455		3250
TDS	mg kg^{-1}	229	682	1583
CO$_2$	mg kg^{-1}	19 100	81,8	8409
H$_2$S	mg kg^{-1}	1678	31,7	1356
SO$_4$	mg kg^{-1}	9,15	169,9	29
SiO$_2$	mg kg^{-1}		308	359
B	mg kg^{-1}			3,18
F	mg kg^{-1}	0,24	3,61	3,3
Na	mg kg^{-1}	0,17	157,9	220
Mg	mg kg^{-1}	0,04	0,053	2,21
Al	mg kg^{-1}			0,241
Cl	mg kg^{-1}	86,3	69,2	885,4
K	mg kg^{-1}	0,05	15,4	88,2
Ca	mg kg^{-1}	0,18	4,25	44,3
Mn	mg kg^{-1}			37,4
Fe	mg kg^{-1}	44	15	292
Steam	*kg s^{-1}*	6,3	23,4	16,9
CO$_2$	mg kg^{-1}	19 100	4927	8409
H$_2$S	mg kg^{-1}	1678	897	1356
H$_2$	mg kg^{-1}	46,8	8,4	27,9
N$_2$	mg kg^{-1}		34,3	81,7
CH$_4$	mg kg^{-1}		1,41	4,72
Ar	mg kg^{-1}			2,05

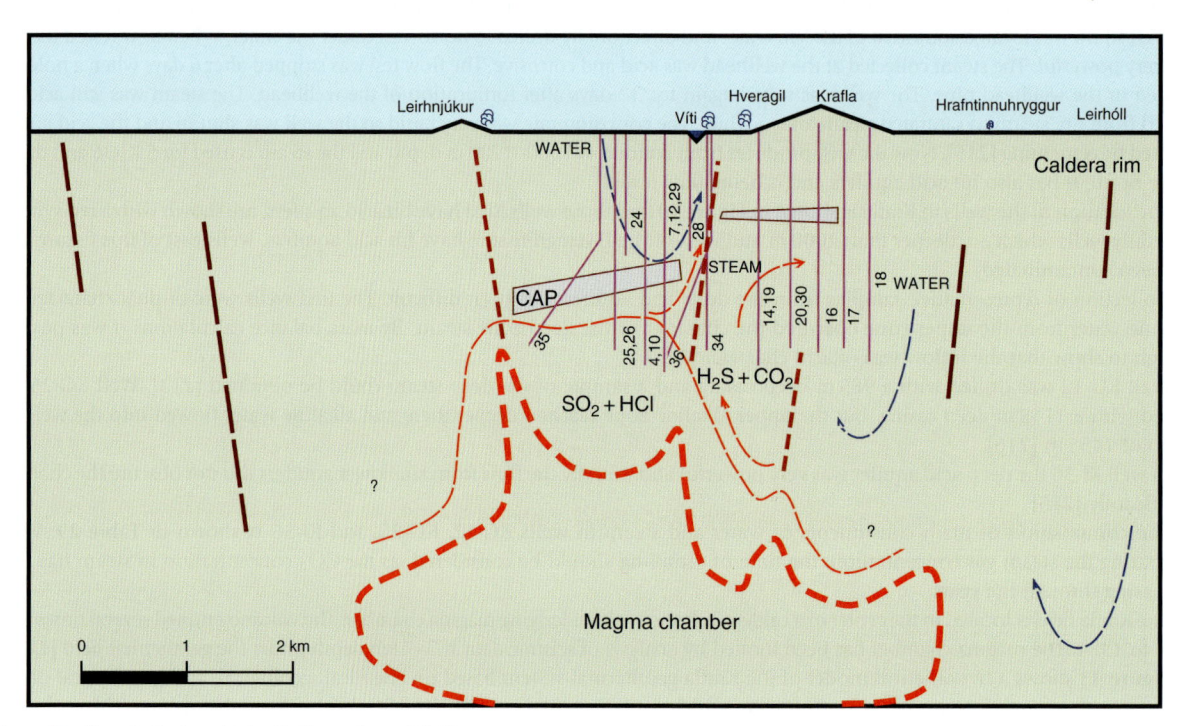

Figure 43 Hypothetical model for Krafla geothermal field.

rock may be caused by precipitation of minerals washed out of the rock by the underlying acid fluids. When the water is degassed at a shallower depth the minerals precipitate and seal the rock.

Two main upflow zones to surface are shown. The Hveragil fissure is considered to be a main path for steam and gas from the deep reservoir to the surface.

To the west of Hveragil fissure the wells hit the acid steam zone at 2000 m depth but to the east of the fissure the acid steam zone lies deeper. The 2000 m deep wells east of the Hveragil fissure hit CO_2- and H_2S-rich steam.

The fissure that connects the Leirhnúkur volcano with the magma chamber is another main upflow zone for gas and steam and is expected to contain acid magmatic gases.

Two types of acid fluids are observed, acid sulfate fluids and acid chloride fluids. Acid sulfate fluids are more common in relatively cool liquid-dominated systems whereas acid chloride fluids are more prevalent in hot vapor-dominated systems. NaOH scrubbing has proved successful for both types of fluids. The use of acid-resistant materials as sole mitigation has apparently not been deployed but in Miravalles Incalloy 825 has been used, in Larderello Stellite 6, and in Tiwi Inconel 625 in conjunction with NaOH scrubbing. Incalloy 825 is considered to have potential for alloy cracking [217] and so the other two may be preferable. The following solutions are being considered for the acid wells in Krafla:

- screening of water inflow and producing dry acid steam;
- operate well without liner with downhole mixing with alkaline water;
- use of acid-resistant material for liner, casing, and wellhead;
- injection of alkaline solution and neutralizing the acid inflow;
- injection of corrosion inhibitor; and
- injection of alkaline water into the acid aquifer to neutralize and cool it down.

Example of a study of scaling and corrosion, Assal, Djibouti. In 1989 and 1990, Virkir-Orkint [218] carried out a comprehensive scaling/corrosion study in Asal, Djibouti [218]. The objective was to find out whether there is a certain pattern of scaling with reference to temperature, pressure, and salinity and to quantify possible scaling and corrosion of selected materials.

A layout of the equipment used for the Djibouti study is shown in **Figure 44**. The 'Flow line' was used for enthalpy and flow measurements and for drawing fluid samples at the beginning and end of the test but remained closed for the rest of the time. Coupons were placed in the 'Separator line' and the 'Brine pipe' at various spots in the 'Aging tank' and the three pipes of the 'Inhibitor line'. Flow was determined by the method of James [219] and the flow in the 'Inhibitor line' pipes adjusted using orifices and valve adjustment. Two-phase fluid samples were separated using a mini Webre separator. Brine samples were partitioned into raw, filtered, untreated, acidified, precipitated, and extracted according to the constituent to be determined. Steam samples were collected into NaOH for the determination of acid gases by titration and the head space gas was determined by gas chromatography (see, e.g., [1]).

Na, K, Li, Ca, Mg, Sr, Fe, Zn, Cd, Hg, Cu, Ni, Pb, and Ag were determined by AAS; Al and Ba by ICP/AES; CO_2, H_2S, and Cl by titration; NH_3, SiO_2, B, Fe, and Mn by UV/Vis spectrophotometry; Cl, Br, F, and SO_4 by IC; Al by fluorimetry; and pH and

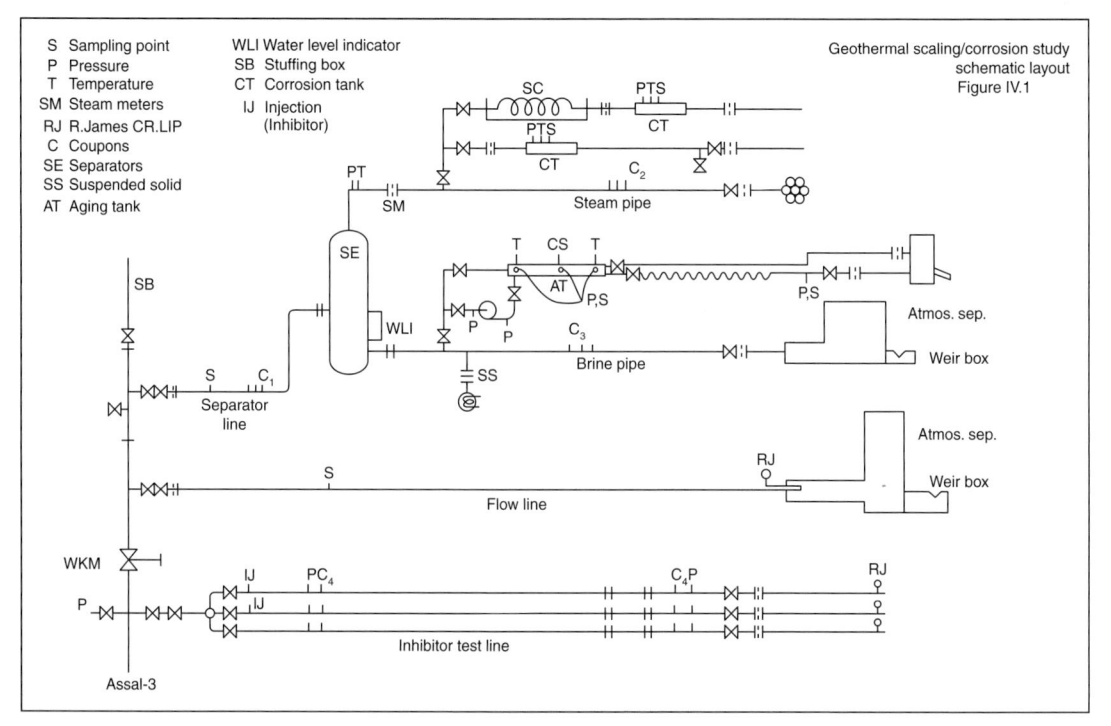

Figure 44 Layout of equipment used for the scaling/corrosion test on well Asal-3, Djibouti.

Table 30 Some chemicals in total fluid in well Asal-3, compared with seawater (35‰) [220]

Constituent (mg kg^{-1})	Asal-3	Seawater (35‰)
Enthalpy (kJ kg^{-1})	1133	
P_0 (bar)	20.4	
pH[a]	4.1	
SiO$_2$	460	6.4
Na	26 471	10 800
K	4451	392
Cl	70 979	19 800
Fe	32.3	0.003
Zn	37.0	0.005
Pb	2.6	
Cu	0.27	0.000 9
Ni	<0.1	

[a] Calculated using WATCH [143, 144].

conductivity by electrometry. A specific extraction technique was deployed for Zn, Cd, Cu, Ni, Pb, and Ag analysis [268,269] and a specific gold amalgamation technique for Hg analysis [4].

Metal coupons from three types of steel, that is, carbon steel 37 and stainless steels AISI 304 and 316 measuring 76 × 13 × 3.5 mm, as well as a few ORMAT coupons measuring 70 × 16 × 1 mm, were fixed on coupon holders.

The results of chemical analysis of fluids from well Asal-3 are reported in **Table 29** as total composition calculated from vapor and steam analyses and compared with the composition of seawater [220]. The Djibouti brine is evaporated and is about 3.5 times more saline than seawater but shows obvious alterations relative to seawater due to high temperature, that is, relatively high SiO$_2$, K, Ca, and Mn concentrations, but low Mg and SO$_4$ concentrations. The Ca, Mn, Al, and Fe concentrations are, however, considerably higher than would be expected from the evaporative effect alone. A large increase in Zn over seawater was observed along with a significant concentration of Pb and a moderate concentration of Cu.

Certain patterns can be discerned in distance from wellhead, deposition at different pressures, and possibly the environment of deposition. In **Table 30** the analysis of scales from different sampling locations is reported normalized to a sum of 100%.

The composition differs greatly according to the distance from the wellhead. Sulfides, mostly galena and sphalerite, are more prominent close to the wellhead but silicates and silica further away from the wellhead.

Chalcopyrite was also observed in the P_c line and significant concentrations of carbonate (0.5–2.2% as CO$_2$), characterized as siderite, were also found.

The distance from the wellhead does not tell the whole story. A sample from an orifice at the opening of the separator line in Asal-3 contained nearly exclusively galena. The thickness of the scale is also pressure dependent and an experiment on the separator line in Asal-3, Djibouti, shows a significant increase in scaling rate between 17.7 and 16.2 bar (**Figure 45**),

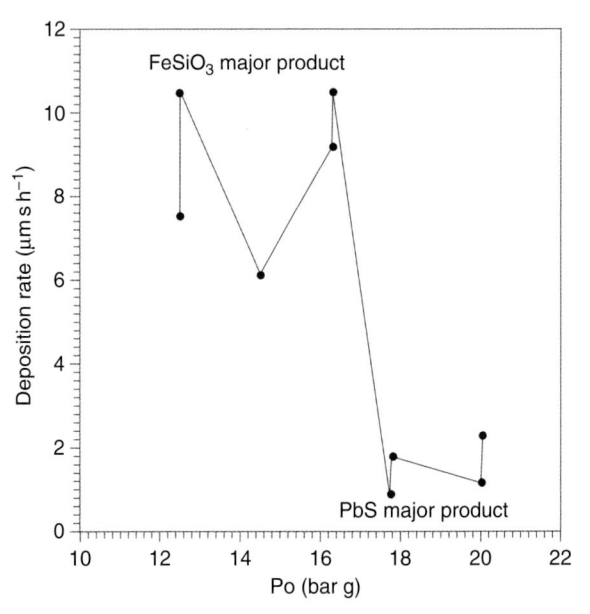

Figure 45 Asal-3, Djibouti. Thickness of scales on coupons at different pressures.

Table 31 Composition of scales from well Asal-3, Djibouti

Constituent (%)	WH	OR[a]	TP	SP[a]	BP	SS[a]	WB
P_0 (bar)	20.0	17.7	17.7	17.7	17.7	0	0
SiO_2	19.6	0	6.7	40.7	30.5	56.4	72.9
Al_2O_3	3.7	0	1.0	4.3	3.4	8.6	2.7
Fe_2O_3	22.5	0	6.7	31.8	25.8	14.8	2.7
MnO	2.3	0	0.9	5.8	3.7	0.7	0.2
MgO	1.6	0	0.1	0.7	1.1	0.2	0.2
CaO	0.6	0	0.6	1.6	1.4	8.4	12.8
Na_2O	4.4	0	0.3	1.4	1.7	8.1	0.8
K_2O	0.1	0	0	0.7	0.4	1.9	2.9
S	13.7	14.9	18.3	4.0	8.0	0.2	0.4
Cu	0.4	0	0	0.1	0	0.1	0.1
Pb	22.3	85.1	65.4	7.2	23.3	0.2	0.4
Zn	8.8	0	0	1.7	1.0	0.4	0.1

Table 32 Fe/Si mole ratio for some samples from well Asal-3, Djibouti, in which scales had formed at different temperatures

Temperature (°C)	Fe/Si mole ratio
215	0.70
209	0.60
200	0.45
100	0.07

the increase being concomitant with a large increase in iron silicate deposition (**Table 31**). The Fe/Si mole ratio of the scales (**Table 32**) varies similarly to that of deposits from Salton Sea which varied linearly from 0.1 at 100 °C to 1 at 220 °C [221], suggesting that iron silicates predominate at high temperatures but silica at lower ones. Characterization of the scales shows that at relatively high temperatures a compound with a composition close to minnesotaite is observed, but at lower temperatures silica and iron oxides exist as separate compounds. Silica absorption on iron oxides [222] may further contribute to the variation in the Fe:Si ratio. At lower temperatures (<150 °C) amorphous silica precipitation becomes prominent. Bench scale studies suggested that silica colloidal formation was not important at >100 °C but became fast at a lower temperature and a higher pH. A similar pattern of deposition has been observed at Reykjanes, Iceland by Hardardóttir and coworkers [245, 246].

Injection of air and chemical oxidizing agents to reduce sulfide concentrations has been suggested to reduce the extent of sulfide scaling but suffers from possible corrosion effects and/or formation of secondary precipitates [223]. In Asal two types of inhibitors from the Nadar Chemical Company, Italy, were tested for sulfide inhibition, a sequestration agent for heavy metals (Nadar 4093) and a sequestering and dispersing against calcium and magnesium salts and silica (Nadar 1008). Both inhibited metal sulfide formation. The former was deemed unsuitable due to iron silicate formation and the latter caused the formation of calcium chloride, avoided by acidification, but corrosion problems arose. Gallup [224] has used reducing agents, namely sodium formate, to control ferric silicate deposition and found that the formate also mitigates against acid corrosion.

Silica scale. At or close to atmospheric pressure the deposits were predominantly amorphous silica. As such deposition could be a serious problem if reinjection were to be attempted bench scale tests were carried out to find out the effect of changing the pH and lowering the temperature. As the ammonium molybdate spectrophotometric method commonly used for the determination of silica only detects monomeric silica it can be used to follow the polymerization stage which is the precursor to the deposition of amorphous silica. From **Figures 46** and **47** it can be seen that for the first hour or so there is little change in the initial sample (pH = 5.3), a very fast decrease in the sample whose pH was raised to 7.3, but that acidification to pH = 3.0 slows down the polymerization. Keeping the temperature high does not slow down the initial polymerization, but the higher the temperature, the higher the amorphous silica saturation temperature, and this is reflected in the results.

Thus the sulfide scales may be dealt with by inhibition, the iron silicate scales by pressure control or inhibition, but the amorphous silica deposits by pressure (temperature) control.

Corrosion tests were carried out both with the vapor phase after separation and with condensed vapor. Coupons made of the materials listed in **Table 33** were tested.

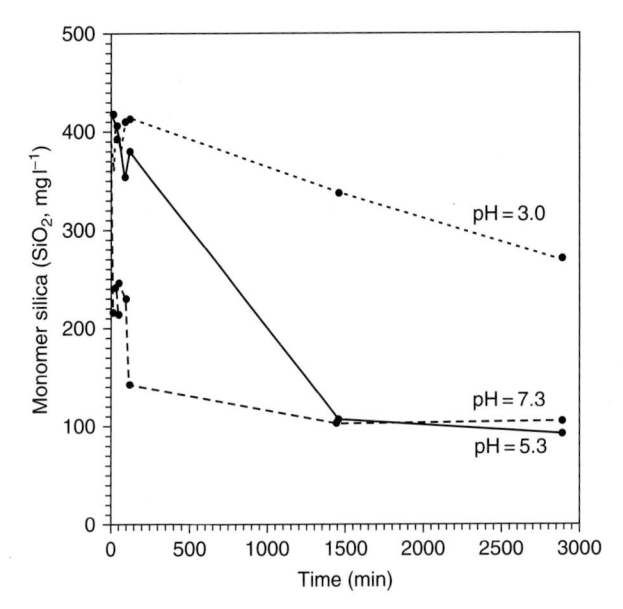

Figure 46 Monomer decrease of silica at different pH values in brine collected at 19.4 bar g pressure.

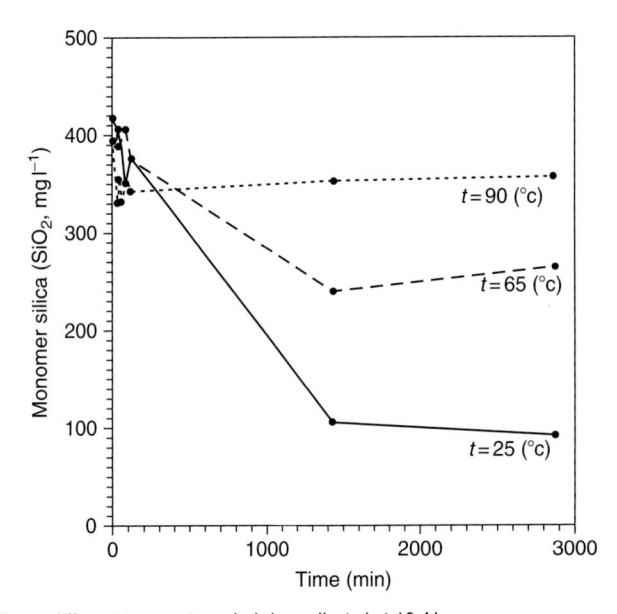

Figure 47 Monomer decrease of silica at different temperatures in brine collected at 19.4 bar g pressure.

Table 33 Materials tested in corrosion tests on steam from well Asal-3, Djibouti

Material	Typical use
Stainless steel (304,316,405,2205,904L, 254SMO)	Turbine blade, condenser lining
12CrMo stainless steel, welded and unwelded	Turbine blade
13%CrMo stainless steel	Turbine blade
17-4PH steel, welded and unwelded	Turbine blade
CrMoNiV steel	Turbine shaft
CrMoV steel	Turbine rotor
CrMoNi steel	
Carbon steel	Turbine casing
Mild steel	Pipe, casing
Ti alloy	Condenser lining

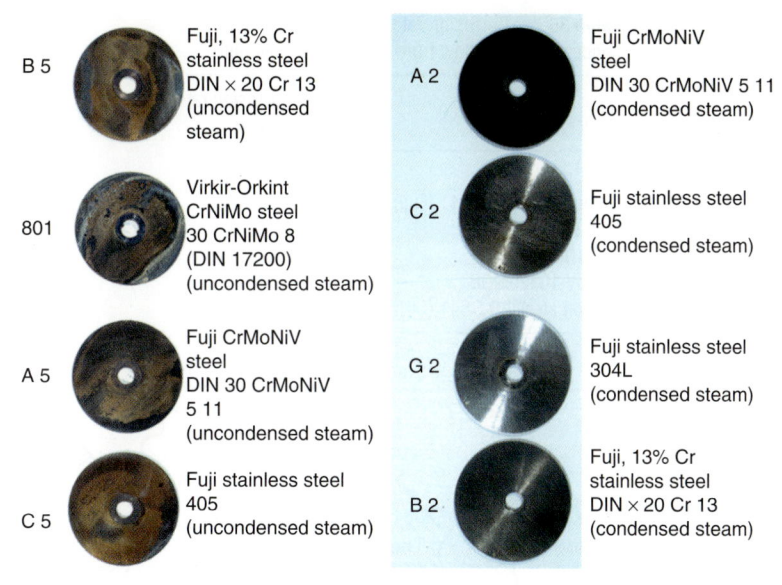

Figure 48 Some coupons after being placed in uncondensed (left) and condensed (right) steam flows.

Table 34 Weight change, visual observations, and results of chemical analysis of coupons placed in uncondensed steam flow

Material	Weight change (%)	Visual signs	Fe (%)	Al (%)	Si (%)	S (%)
CrMoV	+0.05	Many small pits	43.0	2.2	43.1	0.9
Ti alloy	+0.31	Uncorroded	22.2	9.5	34.5	0.8
CrNiMo	+0.22	Few small pits	13.3	1.3	81.1	0.7
Mild	+0.43	Small even corrosion	44.5	1.2	39.1	2.3
CrMoV	−0.06	Slight pitting	28.9	0.2	26.2	0.6
CrMoV-coated CHEMIFLAKE EV70	−0.44	Cracked coat, base metal corroded				

Table 35 Weight change, visual observations, and results of chemical analysis of coupons placed in condensed steam flow

Material	Weight change (%)	Visual signs	Fe (%)	Al (%)	Si (%)	S (%)
CrMoV	−4.61	Even corrosion	45.5	0.2	0.1	27.3
St. 405	+0.19	Uncorroded	88.0	0.5	1.5	4.5
Mild	−2.04	Small even corrosion	56.6	7.6	0.2	33.0
CrMoV welded	−2.79	Even with small pitting, pronounced in heat-affected zone	61.9	0.1	0.2	36.2

Three sets of coupons were inserted, one for the client, one for the contractor, and one for the vendor. The contractor dealt with the contractor and client's specimens; however, the third set was sent to the vendor. They were photographed, dried, weighed, and characterized. Examples of test coupons are seen in **Figure 48**. Results for those placed in uncondensed steam are presented in **Table 34** and those placed in condensed steam in **Table 35**.

These results suggest that there is more danger of corrosion in the condensed steam flow and the annual corrosion rate was estimated from the tests with the results in **Table 36**. Thus the stainless steel samples appear uncorroded, but CrMoV considerably, yet evenly corroded. The welded steel appeared unsatisfactory as there was some pitting, but the mild steel was less and evenly corroded. These results lead to a decision by the client and the vendor as to which materials to use for each part of the installation.

7.04.11 Case History. Exploration of a Geothermal Area. Theistareykir, NE Iceland

In this case history the main emphasis is on the geochemical part but other methods of investigation will be briefly reviewed to show how the combination leads to a model of the area.

Theistareykir is a high-temperature geothermal area in NE Iceland (**Figure 49**). For centuries it hosted the main sulfur mine in Iceland, providing the Danish king with raw material for gun powder. Early records tell of prospecting for sulfur; Bemmelen and

Table 36 Corrosion rate of various materials in condensed steam flow from well Assal-3, Djibouti

Steel type	Corrosion rate (mm yr^{-1})
DIN CrMoNiV 5 11	0.28
Carbon steel JIS SS41 (Fuji)	0.28
Mild steel (No. 37)	0.29
30 CrNiMo 8	0.22
CrMoV 10325MGB	0.34
Carbon steel JIS SS41 (MHI)	0.15

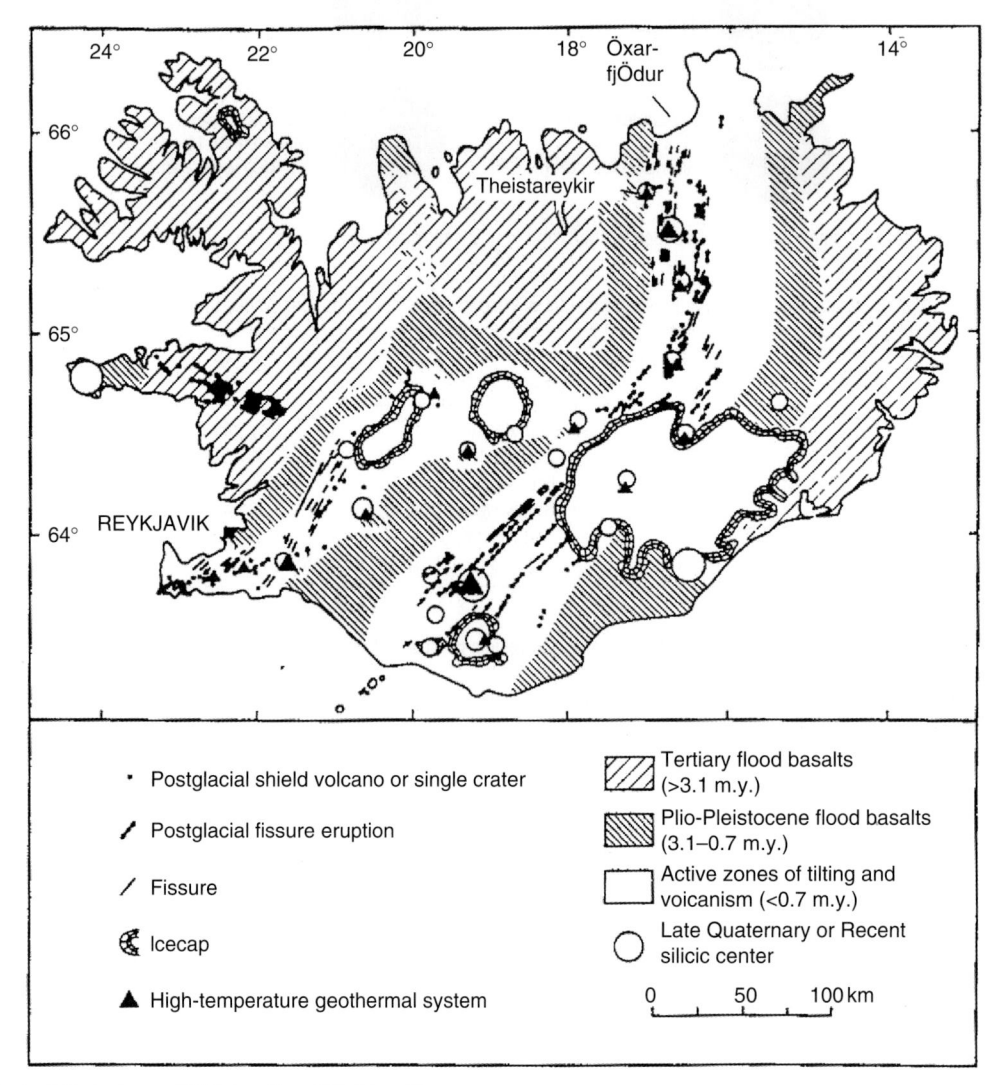

Figure 49 Iceland. Tectonic map [115]. Location of Theistareykir.

Rutten [225] mapped interglacial lava and palagonite, and Kjartansson [226] reported on exploration for clay. The first geothermal exploration was carried out in 1972–1974 [227], and a major geothermal assessment was made in 1981–1984 [55, 228–230]. The area was monitored intermittently from 1991 to 2000 [231], and Ármannsson [232] reviewed research in the area up to the year 2000.

Gautason *et al.* [233] suggested drill sites based on available knowledge. The first well was drilled in 2002, the second in 2003, the third in 2006, the fourth and fifth in 2007, one more drilled and another redrilled in 2008. Two more wells were drilled in 2011. The purpose of this chapter is to reflect on the results of drilling with reference to information gained from surface exploration.

Surface exploration. The main features in the geology of the area are an E–W trending heat source astride a N–S tectonic structure connected to an active central volcano. A N–S fissure swarm, 4–5 km wide, stretches from Lake Mývatn in the south and to the sea in

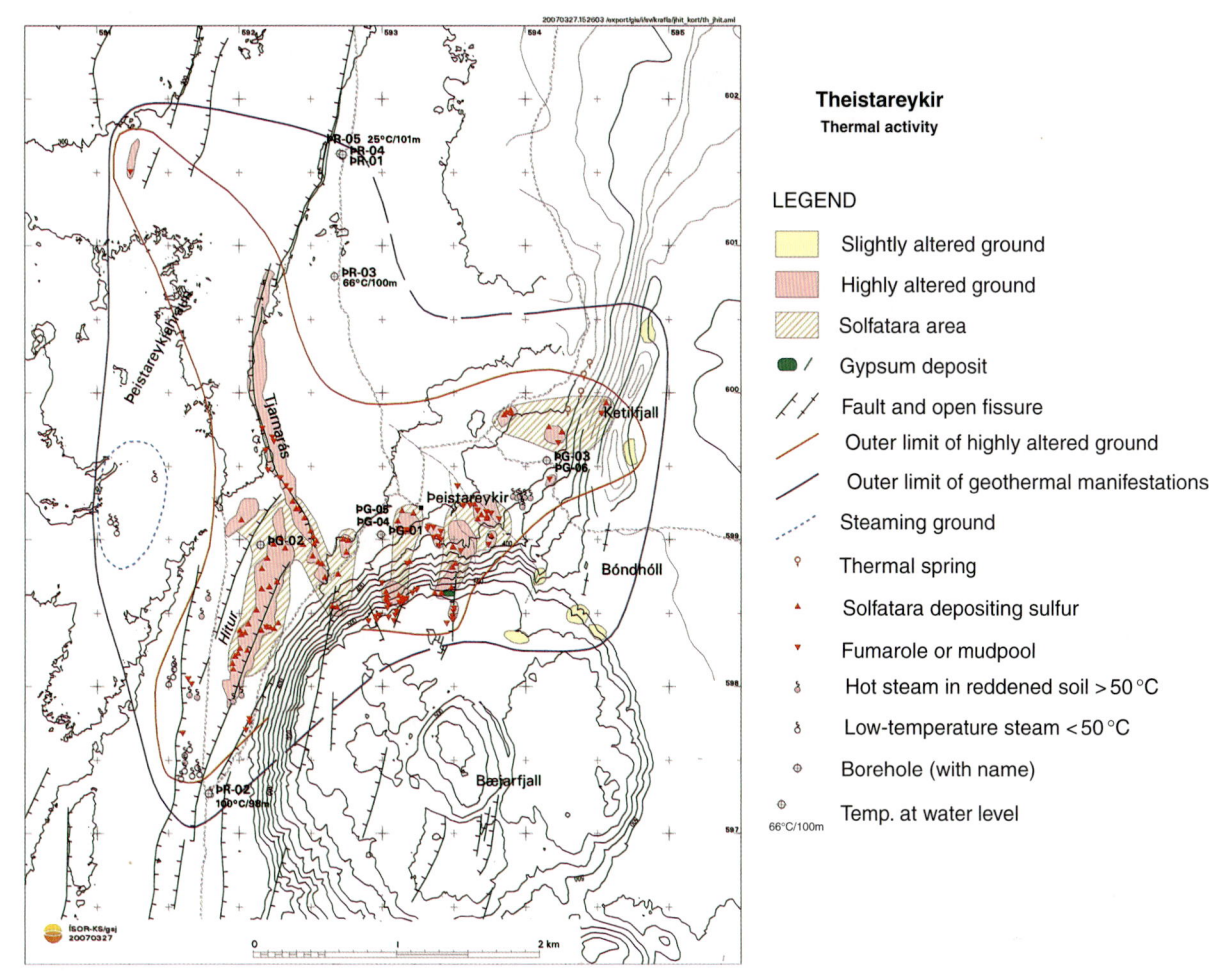

Figure 50 A geothermal map of the Theistareykir geothermal system.

Öxarfjörður in the north. The area is covered in lava, all of which except for one being erupted in the last stages of the Ice Age or shortly afterward. The youngest lava is about 2700 years old.

Surface manifestations have been estimated to cover about 11 km^2 [229] as is shown on the geothermal map (**Figure 50**) [234], but recent time-domain electromagnetic (TEM) and magneto-telluric (MT) soundings suggest that the extent of the actual geothermal area be up to 45 km^2 [235, 236] (**Figure 51**).

Ármannsson et al. [228] divided the active surface area into five subareas (**Figure 52**), three of which (A, C, and D) appeared promising for drilling. Gas geothermometers gave the temperature ranges shown in **Table 37**. Darling and Ármannsson [55] concluded from isotope values for fumarole steam that, in area D (Tjarnarás), the steam had been condensed to a fraction of 0.15–0.25 of the original steam at temperatures in the range 130–200 °C, and that gas geothermometer temperatures were probably too high. Their interpretation of isotope values for area C (Theistareykjagrundir) was that the steam was mostly secondary steam and that the geothermometer temperatures were probably too low.

They concluded, however, that the steam rising from area A (Ketilfjall) was undisturbed and that the geothermometer temperatures were close to true values. Ármannsson et al. [228] proposed a deep inflow to the area from the southeast with area C closest to the source. Thus area C was considered promising, even though the gas geothermometer values seemed rather low. A relatively large, cool, shallow flow was predicted through Bóndólsskarð (**Figure 52**), preventing primary steam from rising to the surface in area B. Areas C and D are more accessible than area A, and therefore the suggestion was that the first drill holes be situated in these two subareas. The dissolved solids content of the steam was very low, suggesting that the reservoir fluid was dilute. Low radon concentrations were interpreted to suggest good permeability especially in area D.

Monitoring and heat loss. The area was visited again in 1991 at the beginning of a monitoring program in which some unexploited high-temperature areas were to be monitored to establish the extent of natural changes in geothermal areas as opposed to changes due to production [231]. Changes in surface manifestations were mapped and steam samples collected from three fumaroles, one from each of areas A, C, and D. At that time considerable changes in surface manifestations were observed, mainly cooling in area D (**Figure 52**). There was information from local people that following earthquakes in 1958 the surface activity in the area had increased drastically but had been declining since. The gas geothermometer temperature for the fumarole from area D (G-6,

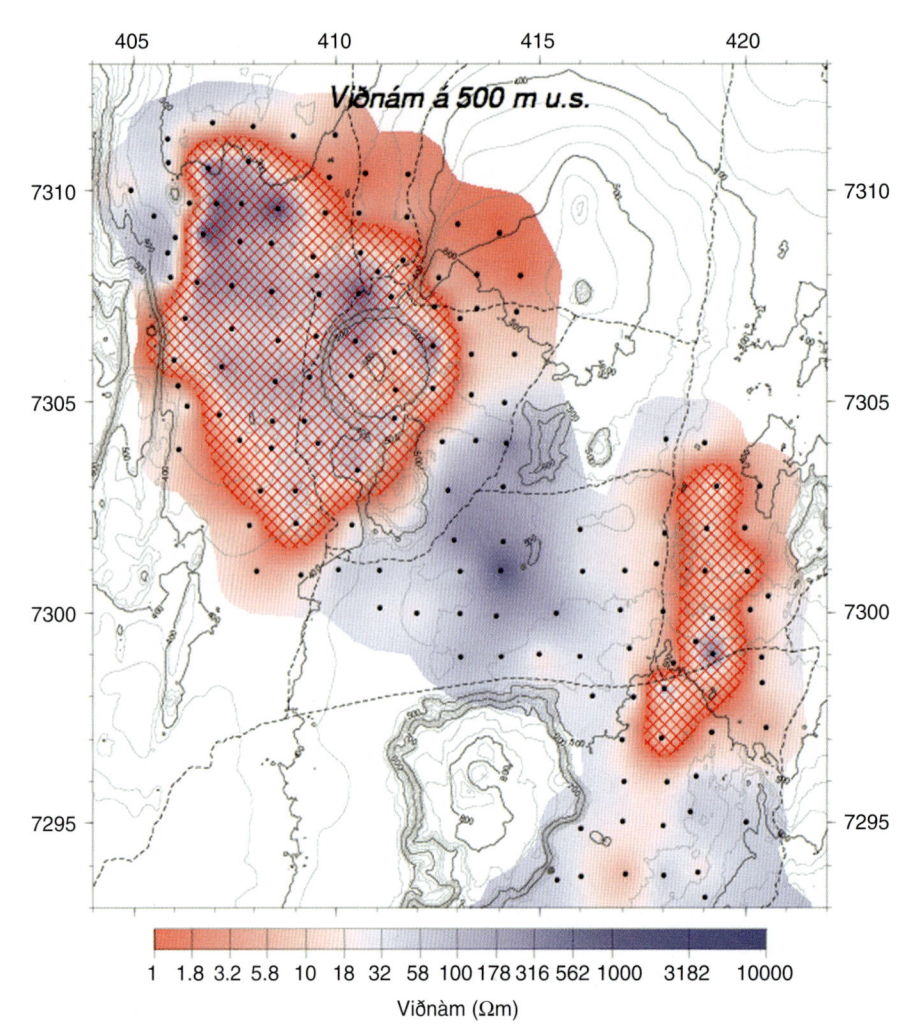

Figure 51 Resistivity at 500 m bsl at Theistareykir (top left) and Gjástykki (bottom right) [235]. High-resistivity cores are surrounded by low resistivity.

Figures 52 and 53) had decreased drastically, but little change or a slight increase was recorded for gas geothermometer temperatures for fumarole steam from areas A (G-3, **Figures 52** and **53**) and C (G-1, **Figures 52** and **53**; **Table 37**). It is possible that the secondary effects suggested by Darling and Ármannsson [55], condensation and formation of secondary steam, were less pronounced this time. The area has been visited a few more times, but it has remained relatively unchanged after 1991.

Using information from Hafstad ([237], personal communication) about the Lón estuary in Öxarfjörður, 20 km to the north of the Theistareykir area, Ármannsson [232] calculated the heat loss from the Theistareykir area (**Table 38**). This estuary is believed to receive solely subsurface water from the Theistareykir area. The values are minimum but they suggest a total output of 300 MW. Therefore, a powerful geothermal system with a temperature of about 280 °C recharged with dilute, probably relatively old, water from far south and with an isotope signature of $\delta D = -100‰$ and $\delta^{18}O = -12‰$ was predicted prior to drilling.

Drilling results. Prior to deep drilling, four shallow 'cold water' wells, ThR-1–ThR-4 (**Figure 52**), were drilled to obtain drilling fluid. Well ThR-2, which is 102 m deep, just reached the groundwater table, and the temperature of the water proved close to boiling. In ThR-3, the groundwater table is also close to 100 m depth. The temperature was 66 °C there, but 90 °C at 140 m depth. The groundwater table was at about 100 m depth in wells ThR-1 and ThR-4, the former is 128 m deep and the temperature of the water was 26–28 °C, but the latter is 150 m deep, with water temperature 26–35 °C [238]. Water from these two wells was used as drilling fluid for the deep geothermal wells.

Well ThG-1 was drilled in area C (Theistareykjagrundir; **Figure 52**) in autumn 2002 to a depth of 1953 m, with a casing 614 m deep. The major inflows are at 620–640 m depth and 1620–1640 m depth. Other inflows are observed at 710, 860–880, 1050, 1230–1240, and 1350 m depths and possibly at 1780–1800 and 1900–1910 m depths. An overpressured aquifer was observed at 212 m depth [239]. The well started discharging in late October 2002.

The results of chemical analysis suggest that in November 2002 the fluid was still contaminated by drilling fluid and thus the results from July 2003 (**Table 39**) are used for the purpose of interpretation. The measured enthalpy at the surface was 2180 kJ kg^{-1} and the total flow from the well 16–17 kg s^{-1}. The calculated steam fraction at a depth of 280 °C was 0.611.

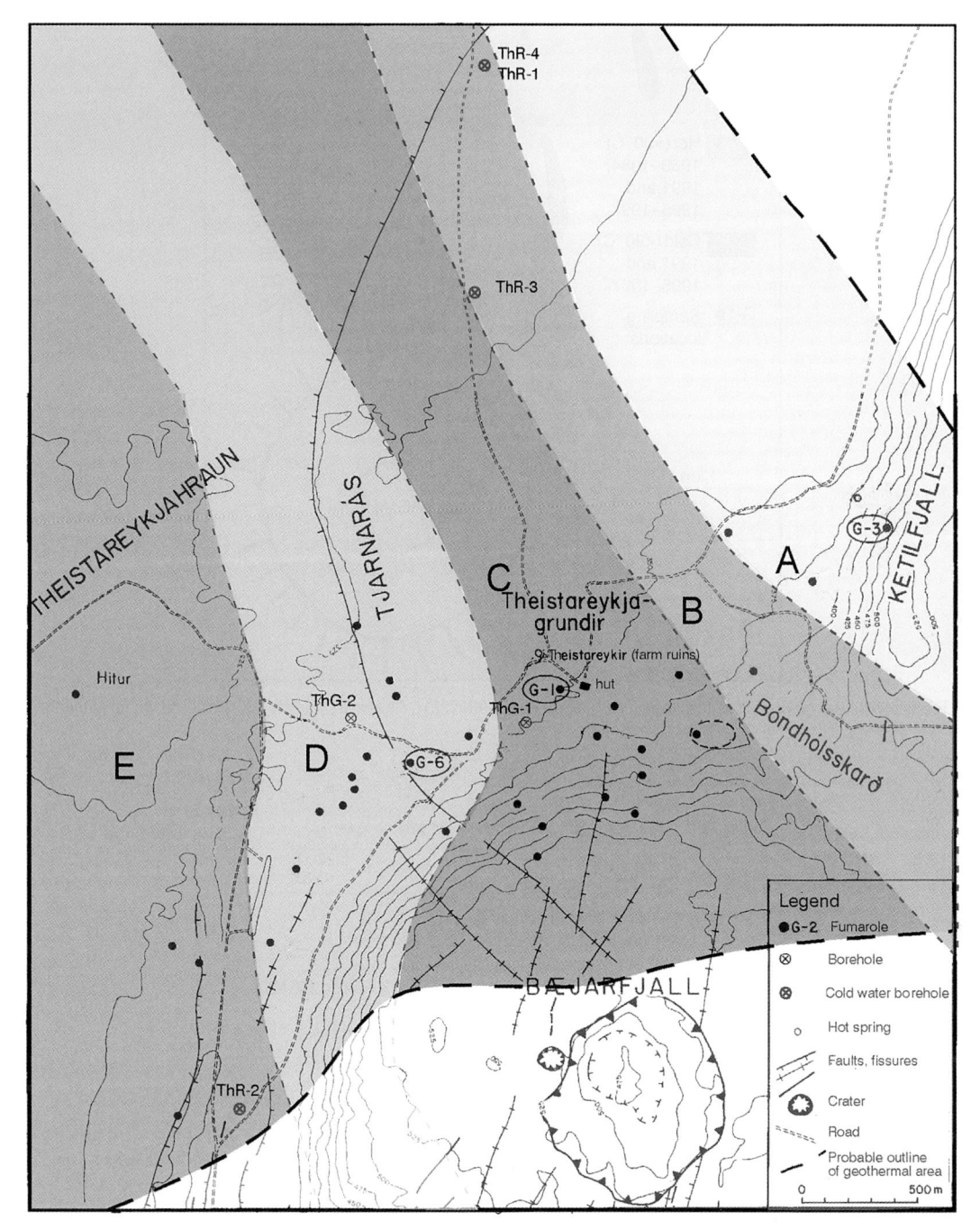

Figure 52 Theistareykir. Division into five subareas [228]. Geothermal and cold water boreholes in and north of the geothermal area are shown as well as three fumaroles sampled during monitoring 1991–2000.

Table 37 Gas geothermometer temperatures in A, C, and D (°C)

Subarea	1980s (°C)	Fumarole	1991 (°C)
A	272–315	G-3	289
C	232–271	G-1	284
D	274–309	G-6	263

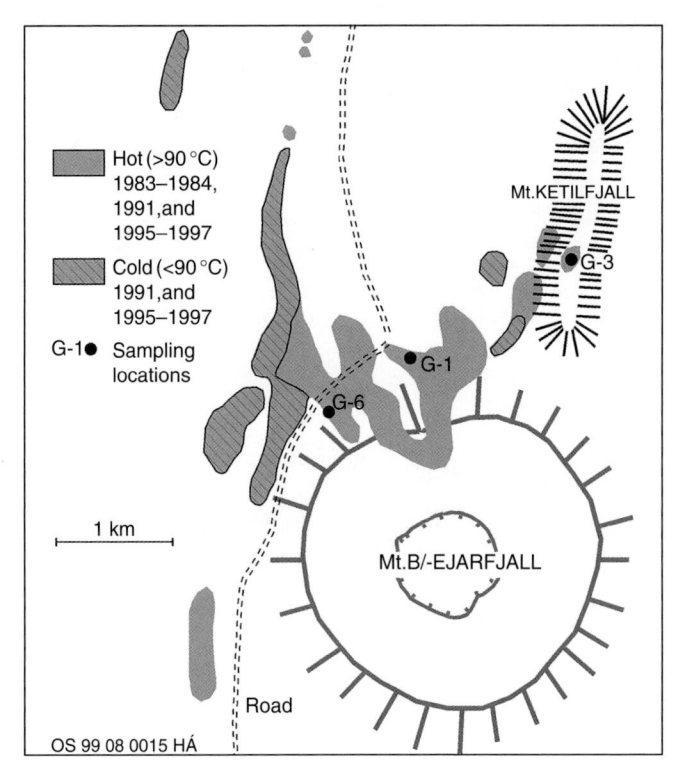

Figure 53 Theistareykir. Changes in surface manifestations 1983–1984 to 1991 [231]. Fumarole sampling locations used during monitoring are shown.

Table 38 Heat loss from the Theistareykir area

Inflow to Lón, Öxarfjörður	$20\,m^3\,s^{-1}$
Local groundwater ambient temperature	3.7 °C
Inflow to Lón, mean temperature	7.2 °C
Excess temperature	3.5 °C
Heat power of area	$3.5 \times 20 \times 42 \approx 300$ MW
Areal extent of Theistareykir	15 km²
Heat loss from area	$300/15 = 20$ MWkm^{-2} = W m^{-2}

The stable isotope composition for the total fluid was $\delta D = -108‰$ and $\delta^{18}O = -12.7‰$, or a little lower than predicted. Thus the fluid probably originated as precipitation far to the south of the area, probably as far south as Vatnajökull, and it may also be 100 years old or more.

Geothermometer temperatures were calculated in six ways with the results reported in **Table 40**. As is apparent, the results come in pairs, and there is a significant difference between the pairs. It had been suggested that, in this part of the area, some secondary steam was formed in fumaroles. Using the calibrations of Arnórsson et al. [180] for the CO_2, H_2S, and H_2 geothermometers, the same kind of pattern emerges from the results as for the fumaroles, that is, CO_2 and H_2S temperatures around 240 °C, but H_2 temperatures of about 300 °C or higher. As H_2 and Ar are relatively insoluble at these conditions they may not be affected by the secondary steam formation whereas CO_2 and H_2S will dissolve in the water phase and be released again at a lower temperature.

One model that explains these geothermometer temperatures assumes that the main inflows are at 620–640 and 1620–1640 m, that the upper inflow is essentially liquid phase at 280 °C, but the deeper one essentially vapor phase at 300 °C or higher. The logged temperatures of well ThG-1 are 270–280 °C at 6–700 m and 300–305 °C at 1600–1700 m. The temperature of the liquid phase at 280 °C is reflected in the results for the solute geothermometers, whereas the temperature of the steam phase is approximated by the H_2 and H_2/Ar temperatures. CO_2 and H_2S travel some way after being dissolved in the water phase and before the fluid flashes at a lower temperature.

Well ThG-2 was drilled from October to December 2003. After some circulation losses suggesting aquifers in the top layers, the well was cased to a depth of about 260 m. Shortly after drilling started again, a total loss of circulation was encountered and persisted. Logging revealed a well diameter in excess of 30″ over a 10 m interval. An attempt to seal off this interval by gradually

Table 39 Chemical composition of deep water and deep steam in fluid from well ThG-1, Theistareykir, at 280 °C

Constituent	Water phase	Steam phase
pH	7.96	
CO_2 (mg l^{-1})	37.53	1463
H_2S (mg l^{-1})	30.65	265
B (mg l^{-1})	1.29	
SiO_2 (mg l^{-1})	574.3	
Na (mg l^{-1})	89.44	
K (mg l^{-1})	18.36	
Mg (mg l^{-1})	0.003	
Ca (mg l^{-1})	0.38	
F (mg l^{-1})	0.79	
Cl (mg l^{-1})	80.81	
SO_4 (mg l^{-1})	7.06	
Al (mg l^{-1})	1.57	
Fe (mg l^{-1})	0.0055	
Mo (mg l^{-1})	0.0144	
Mn (mg l^{-1})	0.0014	
Zn (mg l^{-1})	0.0050	
As (mg l^{-1})	0.0057	
H_2 (mg l^{-1})		25.3
N_2 (mg l^{-1})	0.10	33.8

Table 40 Chemical geothermometer results for fluid from well ThG-1, Theistareykir

Type	Quartz[a]	Na/K[b]	CO_2[c]	H_2S[c]	H_2[c]	H_2/Ar[d]
t (°C)	276	279	244	237	295	302

[a] [240],
[b] [165],
[c] [180],
[d] [243].

pouring 120 m³ of gravel and sand into the well and cementing with 140–150 m³ of concrete failed to stop the circulation loss. Drilling was resumed, a total loss of circulation was encountered again at 327 m depth, but drilling was still continued with total loss to 617 m depth where it was cased again. The final depth was 1720 m, drilled again with a total loss of circulation (>50–55 l s^{-1}) from 657 m depth. It was finished with a slotted liner. Pumping tests suggested very high permeability.

Extremely strong flows are inferred from 260 m depth and considerably below this. There is a possibility that this constitutes a large cave or some such feature whose temperature has been estimated at a little over 200 °C, and that this large flow might cause cooling of the rock over some distance from the cave, possibly sufficient to cause partial condensation of steam rising to the surface in the vicinity. It is suggested that this may be the mechanism responsible for the condensation of steam in area D suggested by Darling and Ármannsson [55].

Using information from wells ThG-1 and ThG-2 a model of the flow in the system was constructed (**Figure 54**) showing the large relatively cool flow in area D, the intermediate aquifers at 600–800 m depth, and the deep hot aquifer at about 1600–1800 m depth.

Well ThG-3 was drilled in area A in 2006 to a depth of 2659 m and the maximum temperature recorded was 380 °C. Its flow oscillated with enthalpy varying from about 1600 to 2600 kJ kg^{-1} but has approached the higher value with time and eventually settled as a high-enthalpy well giving 10–12 kg s^{-1} of high-temperature steam. The total dissolved solids in the fluid are low and so is the gas concentration.

Wells ThG-4 and ThG-5 were both drilled directionally from the same well pad as well ThG-1. ThG-4 is to the SE beneath Mt. Bæjarfjall, but well ThG-5 is toward well ThG-2. Well ThG-4 is a high-enthalpy well with a steam flow of 30 kg s^{-1} of high-temperature steam, but well ThG-5 is a low-enthalpy well similar to well ThG-2 with a large liquid water flow. The concentration of dissolved solids and gas is low in these two wells and the results for the wells drilled after ThG-2 do not conflict with the model suggested in **Figure 55**.

Finally, well ThG-5 was redrilled under a sharper angle in 2008 (ThG-5b) and well ThG-6 was drilled directionally from the well pad of well ThG-3 to the west. These wells started discharging in early November. In late October the maximum temperature in

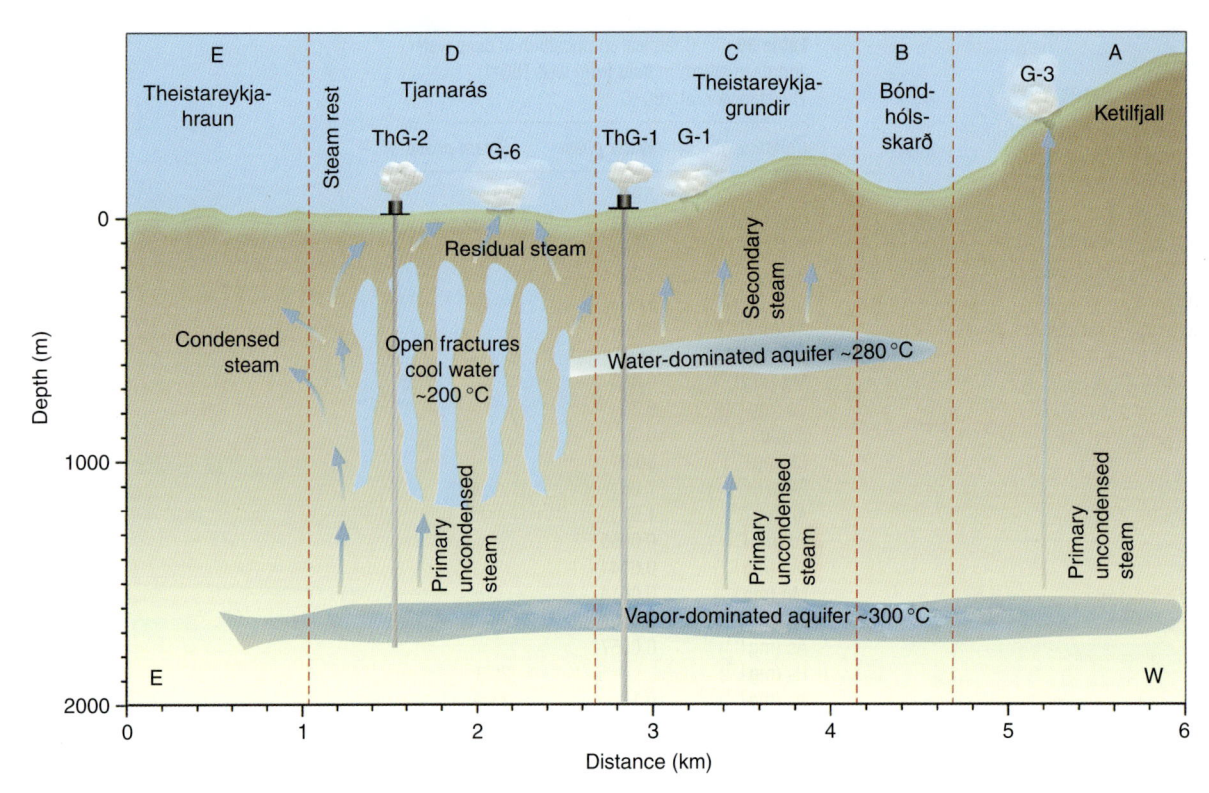

162 Geochemical Aspects of Geothermal Utilization

Figure 54 The most important aspects of fluid flow in the Theistareykir geothermal system based on surface exploration and results of drilling wells ThG-1 and ThG-2.

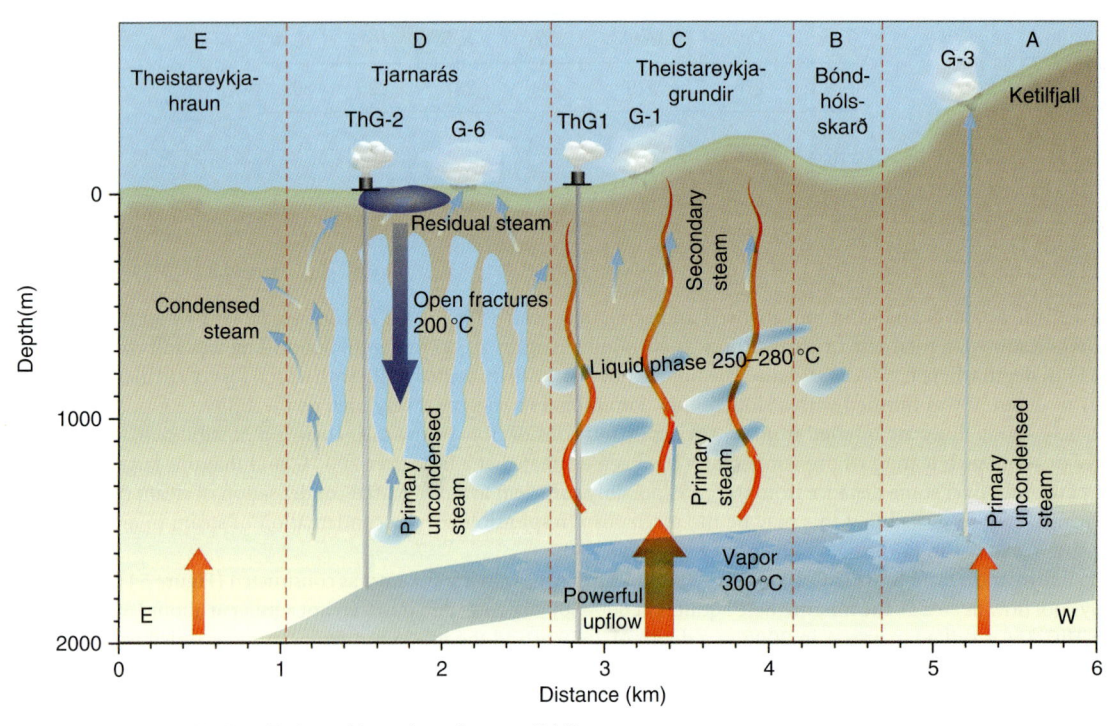

Figure 55 A conceptual model of the Theistareykir geothermal system [241].

ThG-5b was 300 °C but in ThG-6 312 °C. In early December the enthalpy of ThG-5b flow was 1485 kJ kg^{-1} and the amount of high-temperature steam 20.8 kg s^{-1}, but the enthalpy of the ThG-6 flow was 2663 kJ kg^{-1} and high-temperature steam 13.2 kg s^{-1}.

The strata observed in the wells show thick palagonite strata (tuff, breccias, and pillow lavas) in the top part. The number of intrusions increases with depth. At a depth of about 1150–1300 m a change occurs and lava layers with intermediate layers become prominent. The alteration pattern suggests a steadily increasing temperature with depth.

The results of temperature and pressure logging show wells ThG-2 and ThG-5 to be cooler than the others, presumably reflecting cooling from the surface of the fissure system shown in **Figure 55**.

A conceptual model (**Figure 55**) has been presented on the lines of **Figure 54** showing a strong upflow in area C, a weaker one in area A, and a possible one in area E but a possible downflow in area D. The possible potential of the system has been estimated using the so-called Monte Carlo method and the most probable values are 348 MW$_e$ (90% probability 191–622 MW$_e$) for 30 years, 209 MWe (90% probability 115–373 MWe) for 50 years, and 104 MWe (90% probability 57–187 MW$_e$) for 100 years [241].

Main findings. The results of surface exploration in the Theistareykir area suggested that it encompassed three distinct subareas (A, C, and D, **Figure 52**) suitable for drilling, drawing fluid from a single base reservoir with a temperature of at least 280 °C. The fluid originates far to the south of the area and is probably more than 100 years old. Results for stable isotopes in fumarole steam suggested that in area D, there was condensation of fumarole steam during its passage from the reservoir to the surface, but that in area C the fumarole steam was in some cases secondary steam.

During drilling of wells ThG-1 and ThG-2 large inflows of relatively shallow cool water, which can explain condensation and secondary steam formation in areas C and D, were encountered. Good permeability was predicted for area D from the results of surface exploration. Thus the preliminary results of drilling do not contradict those of surface exploration.

The results for wells ThG-1 to ThG-6 confirm these results and show area C to be powerful probably above the main upflow, although a smaller upflow is predicted for area A.

References

[1] Ármannsson H and Ólafsson M (2006) Collection of geothermal fluids for chemical analysis. *ÍSOR Report*, ÍSOR-2006/016, 17pp. Reykjavic, Iceland: ISOR.
[2] Chiodini G, Cioni R, Guidi M, *et al.* (1998) Soil CO$_2$ flux measurements in volcanic and geothermal areas. *Applied Geochemistry* 13: 543–552.
[3] Parkinson KJ (1981) An improved method for measuring soil respiration in the field. *Journal of Applied Ecology* 18: 221–228.
[4] Ólafsson J (1974) Determination of nanogram quantities of mercury in sea water. *Analytica Chimica Acta* 68: 207–211.
[5] Alvis-Isidro R, Urbino GA, and Pang Z (2002) Results of the 2001 IAEA inter-laboratory comparison. *IAEA Report*, 57pp. Vienna, Austria: IAEA.
[6] Friedman I (1953) Deuterium content of water and other substances. *Geochimica et Cosmochimica Acta* 4: 89–103.
[7] Coleman ML, Shepherd TJ, Durham JJ, *et al.* (1982) Reduction of water with zinc for hydrogen isotope analysis. *Analytical Chemistry* 54: 993–995.
[8] Horita J (1988) Hydrogen isotope analysis of natural waters using an H2-water equilibrium method: A special implication to brines. *Chemical Geology (Isotope Geoscience Section)* 72: 89–94.
[9] Donnelly T, Waldron S, Tait A, *et al.* (2001) Hydrogen isotope analysis of natural abundance and deuterium-enriched waters by reduction over chromium on-line to a dynamic dual inlet isotope-ratio mass spectrometer. *Rapid Communications in Mass Spectrometry* 15: 1297–1303.
[10] Schoeller DA, Colligan AS, Shriver T, *et al.* (2000) Use of an automated chromium reduction system for hydrogen isotope ratio analysis of physiological fluids applied to doubly labeled water analysis. *Journal of Mass Spectrometry* 35: 1128–1132.
[11] Epstein S and Mayeda T (1953) Variation of ^{18}O content of waters from natural sources. *Geochimica et Cosmochimica Acta* 4: 213–224.
[12] Yanagisawa F and Sakai H (1983) Thermal decomposition of barium sulphate vanadium pentoxide silica glass mixture for preparation of sulfur dioxide in sulfur isotope ratio measurements. *Analytical Chemistry* 55: 985–987.
[13] Nehring NI, Bowen PA, and Truesdell AH (1977) Techniques for the conversion to carbon dioxide of oxygen from dissolved sulphates in thermal waters. *Geothermics* 5: 63–66.
[14] Urbino GA and Pang Z (2004) 2003 Inter-laboratory comparison of geothermal water chemistry. *IAEA Report*, 42pp. Vienna, Austria: IAEA.
[15] White DE (1986) Subsurface waters of different origins. In: Ólafsson J and Ólafsson M (eds.) *Fifth International Symposium on Water-Rock Interaction. Extended Abstracts*, pp. 629–632. Reykjavík: International Association of Geochemistry and Cosmochemistry, National Energy Authority.
[16] Ellis AJ and Mahon WAJ (1977) *Chemistry and Geothermal Systems*, 392pp. New York: Academic Press.
[17] Franzson H, Zierenberg R, and Schiffman P (2008) Chemical transport in geothermal systems in Iceland: Evidence from hydrothermal alteration. *Journal of Volcanology and Geothermal Research* 173: 217–229.
[18] Kristmannsdóttir H (1978) Alteration of basaltic rocks by hydrothermal activity at 100–300°. In: Mortland M and Farmer VC (eds.) *International Clay Conference*, pp. 359–367. Amsterdam: Elsevier Scientific Publishing Company.
[19] Franzson H (2007) Temperature and salinity changes in three high temperature systems at Reykjanes peninsula, SW-Iceland. Evidence from fluid inclusion data. In: Bullen TD and Wang Y (eds.) *Water–Rock Interaction*, pp. 947–951. London: Taylor & Francis Group.
[20] Arnórsson S, Gunnarsson I, and Stefánsson A, *et al.* (2002) Major element chemistry of surface- and ground waters in basaltic terrain. N-Iceland. I: Primary mineral saturation. *Geochimica et Cosmochimica Acta* 66: 4015.
[21] Johnson JW, Oelkers EH, and Helgeson HC (1992) SUPCRT92 – A software package for calculating the standard molal thermodynamic properties of minerals, gases, aqueous species, and reactions from 1 bar to 5000 bar and 0 °C to 1000 °C. *Computational Geoscience* 18: 899–947.
[22] Arnórsson S (1995) Geothermal systems in Iceland: Structure and conceptual models–I. High-temperature areas. *Geothermics* 24: 561–602.
[23] Kristmannsdóttir H and Tómasson J (1978) Zeolite zones in geothermal areas in Iceland. In: Sand LB and Mumpton FA (eds.) *Natural Zeolites*, pp. 227–284. Oxford: Pergamon Press Ltd.
[24] Saemundsson K and Gunnlaugsson E (2002) *Icelandic Rocks and Minerals*, 233pp. Reykjavík: Mál og menning.
[25] Franzson H, Gunnlaugsson E, Árnason K, *et al.* (2010) The Hengill geothermal system, conceptual model and thermal evolution. In: Horne R (ed.) *Proceedings of the World Geothermal Congress 2010*, 9pp. Bali, Indonesia, 25–29 April 2010. Reykjavic, Iceland: IGA.
[26] Franzson H, Thordarson S, Björnsson G, *et al.* (2002) Reykjanes high-temperature field, SW-Iceland, geology and hydrothermal alteration of well RN-10. In: Kruger P and Raney Jr. HJ (eds.)*Proceedings of the 27th Workshop on Geothermal Reservoir Engineering*, 8pp. Stanford University, California, SGP-TR-171.
[27] Craig H (1961) Isotopic variation as in meteoric water. *Science* 153: 10702–10703.
[28] Ólafsson J (1991) The basis of life in Lake Mývatn (in Icelandic). In: Gardarsson A and Einarsson Á (eds.) *Náttúra Mývatns*, pp. 140–165. Reykjavík: Hid íslenska Náttúrufrædifélag.
[29] De Zeeuw E and Gíslason G (1988) The effect of volcanic activity on the groundwater system in the Námafjall geothermal area, NE Iceland. National Energy Authority OS-88042/JHD-07, 39pp.
[30] Ármannsson H and Ólafsson M (2002) Chemical studies of water from wells, springs and fissures in Búrfellshraun lava and vicinity (in Icelandic). National Energy Authority OS-2002/076, 35pp.
[31] Einarsson Á (1982) The palaeolimnology of Lake Mývatn, Northern Iceland: Plant and animal microfossils in the sediment. *Freshwater Biology* 12: 63–82.

[32] Sæmundsson K (1991) The geology of the Krafla system. In: Gardarsson A and Einarsson Á (eds.) *The Natural History of Mývatn* (in Icelandic), pp. 24–95. Reykjavík: Hid íslenska náttúrufrædifélag.
[33] Thórarinsson S (1951) Laxárgljúfur and Laxárhraun. A tephro-chronological study. *Geografiska Annaler Stockholm H* 1–2, 1–89.
[34] Thórarinsson S (1979) The postglacial history of the Mývatn area. *Oikos* 32: 17–28.
[35] Jónasson PM (ed.) (1979) Ecology of eutrophic, subarctic Lake Mývatn and the River Laxá. *Oikos* 32: 308pp.
[36] Líndal B (1959) Diatomite production from bottom deposits in Lake Mývatn (in Icelandic). *Tímarit Verkfrædingafélags Íslands* 44: 19–29.
[37] Einarsson Á, Stefánsdóttir G, Jóhannesson H, *et al.* (2004) The ecology of Lake Mývatn and the River Laxá: Variation in space and time. *Aquatic Ecology* 38: 317–348.
[38] Ólafsdóttir R and Gudmundsson HJ (2002) Holocene land degradation and climatic change in Northeastern Iceland. *The Holocene* 12: 159–167.
[39] Käyhkö J, Alho P, Hendriks JPM, and Rossi MJ (2002) Geomorphology of the Ódáðahraun Semi-desert, NE Iceland: A landsat TM-based land cover mapping. *Jökull* 51: 1–16.
[40] Árnason B (1976) Groundwater systems in Iceland traced by deuterium. *Vísindafélag Íslendinga* 42: 236pp.
[41] Gíslason GM (1994) River management in cold regions: A case study of the River Laxá, North Iceland. In: Calow P and Petts GE (eds.) *The Rivers Handbook. Hydrological and Ecological Principles*, vol. 2, pp. 464–483. Oxford: Blackwell Scientific Publications.
[42] Ólafsson J (1979) The chemistry of Lake Mývatn and River Laxá. *Oikos* 32: 82–112.
[43] Wetzel RG (2001) *Limnology. Lake and River Ecosystems*, 3rd edn. London: Academic Press.
[44] Thorbergsdóttir IM and Gíslason SR (2004) Internal loading of nutrients and certain metals in the shallow eutrophic Lake Mývatn, Iceland. *Aquatic Ecology* 38: 177–189.
[45] Sæmundsson K (1969) *Drilling at Námafjall* (in Icelandic), 55pp. Jarðhitadeild: National Energy Authority.
[46] Sæmundsson K, Arnórsson S, Ragnars K, *et al.* (1975) Krafla. A report on the results of exploratory drilling 1974 (in Icelandic). National Energy Authority OS JHD7506, 47pp.
[47] Ármannsson H (2003) The disposal of effluent from the Krafla and Bjarnarflag power plants (in Icelandic). National Energy Authority OS-2003/032, 32pp.
[48] VST – Virkir hf (1975) Kröfluveita. Pre-feasibility report on pipelines for the Krafla Power Station (in Icelandic). National Energy Authority, 48pp.
[49] Arnórsson S and Gunnlaugsson E (1976) The catchment of the stream Hlídardalslækur and effluent from the Krafla Power Station (in Icelandic). National Energy Authority OS JHD 7602,13pp.
[50] Ingimarsson J, Elíasson J, and Sigurdsson STh (1976) Discharge from the Krafla Power Plant. National Energy Authority OSSFS-7602, 30pp.
[51] Jóhannesson B (1977) On groundwater currents in a strip of land extending from Dyngjufjöll Mountains in the south to Öxarfjördur Bay in the north (in Icelandic). *Tímarit Verkfræðingafélags Íslands* 62: 33–38.
[52] Jóhannesson B (1980) On groundwater in the catchment area of Lake Mývatn (in Icelandic). *Tímarit Verkfræðingafélags Íslands* 65: 74–77.
[53] Thóroddsson ThF and Sigbjarnarson G (1983) The diatomite plant by Lake Mývatn. Groundwater studies (in Icelandic). National Energy Authority OS-83118/VOD-10, 41pp.
[54] Verkfræðistofan Vatnaskil (1999) Lake Mývatn. Groundwater model of Lake Mývatn catchment area (in Icelandic). *Report*, 82pp. Reykjavík: Verkfræðistofan Vatnaskil.
[55] Darling WG and Ármannsson H (1989) Stable isotopic aspects of fluid flow in the Krafla, Námafjall and Theistareykir geothermal systems in northeast Iceland. *Chemical Geology* 76: 197–213.
[56] Hjartarsson A, Sigurðsson Ó, Guðmundsson Á, *et al.* (2004) A computer simulation of the Námafjall geothermal system and forecast about its future state upon production of 90 MW electricity from Bjarnarflag (in Icelandic). ÍSOR-2004/009, 119pp.
[57] Kristmannsdóttir H, Hauksdóttir S, Axelsson G, *et al.* (1999) A tracer test in the Lake Mývatn area (in Icelandic). National Energy Authority OS-99028, 48pp.
[58] Kristmannsdóttir H, Axelsson G, Hauksdóttir S, *et al.* (2001) A tracer test with potassium iodide in Bjarnarflag 2000–2001 (in Icelandic). National Energy Authority OS-2001/042, 57pp.
[59] Elíasson ET, Ármannsson H, Sæmundsson K, *et al.* (1998) The disposal of hot effluent from the Krafla Power Station (in Icelandic). National Energy Authority ETE/HÁ/KS/KÁ/BS/Krafla, 002, 5pp.
[60] Ármannsson H, Axelsson G, and Ólafsson M (2009) Reinjection into well KG-26. Tracer test with KI KI 2005-2007. Description and results. Landsvirkjun LV-2009/099; ÍSOR-2009/050, 19pp.
[61] Gadalia A, Braiband G, Touzelet S, and Sanjun B (2010) Tracing tests using organic compounds in a very high temperature geothermal field, Krafla (Iceland). *Final Report*. BRGM/RP-57661-FR, 99pp.
[62] Kristmannsdóttir H and Ármannsson H (2004) Groundwater in the Lake Mývatn area, North Iceland: Chemistry, origin and interaction. *Aquatic Ecology* 38: 115–128.
[63] Jardboranir ríkisins (1951) *Chemical Analysis of Hot Springs and Hot Pools*. Jardboranir ríkisins, 88pp.
[64] Stefánsson U (1970) A few observations of the chemistry of Lake Mývatn in the summer of 1969 (in Icelandic). *Náttúrufræðingurinn* 40: 187–196.
[65] Ármannsson H, Kristmannsdóttir H, and Ólafsson M (1998) Krafla – Námafjall. The effect of volcanic activity on groundwater (in Icelandic). National Energy Authority OS-98066, 33pp.
[66] Ármannsson H, Kristmannsdóttir H, and Ólafsson M (2000a) Geothermal influence on groundwater in the Lake Mývatn area, North Iceland. In: Iglesias E, Blackwell D, Hunt T, *et al.* (eds.) *Proceedings of the World Geothermal Congress 2000*, pp. 515–520. International Geothermal Association, Pisa, Italy.
[67] Ármannsson H and Ólafsson M (2004) Monitoring the effect of disposal of effluent from the Krafla Power Plant and the Bjarnarflag Power Plant (in Icelandic). Landsvirkjun LV-2004/052, ÍSOR ÍSOR-2004/005, 14pp.
[68] The Ministry of the Environment (1999) Regulation No. 76/1999 on Protection against Water Pollution. In: *Law and Ministerial Gazette of Iceland*, Series B, 785–810, 2231–2253.
[69] Ármannsson H and Ólafsson M (2010) Monitoring the effect of disposal of effluent from the Krafla and Bjarnarflag Power Plants (in Icelandic). Landsvirkjun LV-2010/055, ÍSOR ÍSOR-2010/018, 17pp.
[70] Darling WG (1998) Hydrothermal hydrocarbon gases: 1. Genesis and geothermometry. *Applied Geochemistry* 13: 815–824.
[71] Darling WG (1998) Hydrothermal hydrocarbon gases: 2. Application in the East African Rift System. *Applied Geochemistry* 13: 825–840.
[72] Darling WG, Griesshaber E, Andrews JN, *et al.* (1995) The origin of hydrothermal and other geysers in the Kenya Rift Valley. *Geochimica et Cosmochimica Acta* 59: 2501–2512.
[73] VGK and VBL (1993) Nesjavellir Power Plant. Hydrogen sulfide abatement. *A Report to Reykjavík Heating Company* (in Icelandic), 112pp. VGK, VBL Engineering.
[74] Delgado H, Piedad-Sànchez N, Galvian L, *et al.* (1998) CO_2 flux measurements at Popocatépetl volcano: II. Magnitude of emissions and significance (abstract). *EOS Transactions of the American Geophysical Union* 79(45): 926.
[75] Favara R, Giammanco S, Inguaggiatio S, and Pecoraino G (2001) Preliminary estimate of CO_2 output from Pantelleria Island volcano (Sicily, Italy): Evidence of active mantle degassing. *Applied Geochemistry* 16: 883–894.
[76] Baubron J-C, Mathieu R, and Miele G (1991) Measurement of gas flows from soils in volcanic areas: The accumulation method (abstract). In: Tedesco D (ed.) *Proceedings of the International Conference on Active Volcanoes and Risk Mitigation*. Osservatorio, Vesuviano, 27 August–1 September 1991.
[77] Etiope G, Beneduce P, Calcara M, *et al.* (1999) Structural pattern and CO_2-CH_4 degassing of Ustica Island, Southern Tyrrhenian basin. *Journal of Volcanology and Geothermal Research*. 88: 291–304.
[78] Werner C and Brantley S (2003) CO_2 emissions from the Yellowstone volcanic system. *Geochemistry Geophysics Geosystems* 4(7): 1061.
[79] Sorey ML, Evans WC, Kennedy BM, *et al.* (1998) Carbon dioxide and helium emissions from a reservoir of magmatic gas beneath Mammoth Mountain, California. *Journal of Geophysical Research* 103(15): 303–315, 323.
[80] Evans WC, Sorey ML, Cook AC, *et al.* (2002) Tracing and quantifying magmatic carbon discharge in cold groundwaters: Lessons learned from Mammoth Mountain, USA. *Journal of Volcanology and Geothermal Research* 114: 291–312.
[81] Gerlach TM, Doukas MP, McGee KA, and Kessler R (2001) Soil efflux and total emission rates of magmatic CO_2 at the Horseshoe Lake tree kill, Mammoth Mountain, California, 1995–1999. *Chemical Geology* 177: 101–116.

[82] Wardell LJ and Kyle PR (1998) Volcanic carbon dioxide emission rates: White Island, New Zealand and Mt. Erebus, Antarctica (abstract). *EOS Transactions*, AGU 79(45) (Fall Meeting supplement): 927.
[83] Cruz JV, Couthinho RM, Carvalho MR, *et al.* (1999) Chemistry of waters from Furnas volcano, São Miguel, Azores: Fluxes of volcanic carbon dioxide and leached material. *Journal of Volcanology and Geothermal Research* 92: 151–167.
[84] Gerlach TM (1991) Etna's greenhouse pump. *Nature* 315: 352–353.
[85] Marty B and Tolstikhin IN (1998) CO_2 fluxes from mid-ocean ridges, arcs and plumes. *Chemical Geology* 145: 233–248.
[86] Fridriksson T, Kristjánsson BR, Ármannsson H, *et al.* (2006) CO_2 emissions and heat flow through soil, fumaroles, and steam heated mud pools at the Reykjanes geothermal area, SW Iceland. *Applied Geochemistry* 21: 1551–1569.
[87] Mörner NA and Etiope G (2002) Carbon degassing from the lithosphere. *Global and Planetary Change* 33: 185–203.
[88] Kerrick DM (2001) Present and past non-anthropogenic CO_2 degassing from the solid earth. *Reviews in Geophysics* 39: 564–585.
[89] Ármannsson H, Gíslason G, and Hauksson T (1982) Magmatic gases aid the mapping of the flow pattern in a geothermal system. *Geochimica et Cosmochimica Acta* 46: 167–177.
[90] Ármannsson H (2002) Green accounting applied to geothermal energy. Gaseous emissions compared with those from other energy sources (in Icelandic). In: Gunnarsdóttir MJ (ed.) *Samorka's Conference on Matters Relating to Distribution System Undertakings*, 9pp. Akureyri, 30–31 May 2002. Samorka, Reykjavic.
[91] Ármannsson H, Fridriksson Th, and Kristjánsson BR (2005) CO_2 emissions from geothermal power plants and natural geothermal activity in Iceland. *Geothermics* 34: 286–296.
[92] Bachu S, Gunter WD, and Perkins EH (1994) Aquifer disposal of CO_2: Hydrodynamic and mineral trapping. *Energy Conversion and Management* 35: 269–279.
[93] Benson SM and Cole DR (2008) CO_2 sequestration in deep sedimentary formations. *Elements* 4: 325–331.
[94] Holloway S (2001) Storage of fossil fuel-derived carbon dioxide beneath the surface of the earth. *Annual Review of Energy and the Environment* 26: 145–166.
[95] Metz B, Davidson O, de Coninck H, *et al.* (eds.) (2005) *IPCC Special Report on Carbon Dioxide Capture and Storage*. New York: Cambridge University Press.
[96] Oelkers EH and Cole DR (2008) Carbon dioxide sequestration. A solution to a global problem. *Elements* 4: 305–310.
[97] Kharaka YK, Cole DR, Hovorka SD, *et al.* (2006) Gas-water-rock interactions in Frio Formation following CO_2 injection: Implications for the storage of greenhouse gases in sedimentary basins. *Geology* 34: 577–580.
[98] Hawkins DG (2004) No exit: Thinking about leakage from geologic carbon storage sites. *Energy* 29: 1571–1578.
[99] Rochelle CA, Czernichowski-Lauriol I, and Milodowski AE (2004) The impact of chemical reactions on CO_2 storage in geological formations: A brief review. *Geological Society of London, Special Publications* 233: 87–106.
[100] Gíslason SR, Wolff-Boenisch D, Stefánsson A, *et al.* (2010) Mineral sequestration of carbon dioxide in basalt: A pre-injection overview of the CarbFix project. *International Journal of Greenhouse Gas Control* 4: 537–545.
[101] Gíslason SR and Arnórsson S (1990) Saturation state of natural waters in Iceland relative to primary and secondary minerals in basalts. In: Spencer RJ and Chou I.-M (eds.) *Fluid–Mineral Interactions: A Tribute to Hans Eugster*, pp. 373–393. Geochemical Society. Special Publication No. 2. San Antonio, Texas.
[102] Gíslason SR, Veblen DR, and Livi KJT (1993) Experimental meteoric water–basalt interactions: Characterization and interpretation of alteration products. *Geochimica et Cosmochimica Acta* 57: 1459–1471.
[103] Gíslason SR and Eugster HP (1987) Meteoric water–basalt interactions. II. A field study in N.E. Iceland. *Geochimica et Cosmochimica Acta* 51: 2841–2855.
[104] Gíslason SR and Eugster HP (1987) Meteoric water–basalt interactions. I. A laboratory study. *Geochimica et Cosmochimica Acta* 51: 2827–2840.
[105] Gysi AP and Stefánsson A (2008) Numerical modelling of CO_2–water–basalt interaction. *Mineralogical Magazine* 72: 55–59.
[106] Matter JM, Takahashi T, and Goldberg D (2007) Experimental evaluation of in situ CO_2-water-rock reactions during CO_2 injection in basaltic rocks. Implications for geological CO_2 sequestration. *Geochemistry, Geophysics, Geosystems* 8, doi: 10.1029/2006GC001427.
[107] Oelkers EH and Gíslason SR (2001) The mechanism, rates, and consequences of basaltic glass dissolution. I. An experimental study of the dissolution rates of basaltic glass as a function of aqueous Al, Si, and oxalic acid concentration at 258 °C and pH = 3 and 11. *Geochimica et Cosmochimica Acta* 65: 3671–3681.
[108] Kelemen P and Matter JM (2008) In situ carbonation of peridotite for CO_2 storage. *Proceedings of the National Academy of Sciences of the United States of America* 105: 17295–17300.
[109] McGrail BP, Schaef HT, Ho AM, *et al.* (2006) Potential for carbon dioxide sequestration in flood basalts. *Journal of Geophysical Research* 111: B12201.
[110] O'Connor WK, Rush GE, and Dahlin DC (2003) Laboratory studies on the carbonation potential of basalt: Applications to geological sequestration of CO_2 in the Columbia River Basalt Group. In: *AAPG Annual Meeting Expanded Abstracts*, Salt Lake City, Utah, USA, vol. 12, pp. 129–130. Tulsa, OK: AAPG.
[111] Oelkers EH, Gislason SR, and Matter J (2008) Mineral carbonation of CO_2. *Elements* 4: 331–335.
[112] Ólafsson M, Friðleifsson G.Ó, Eiríksson J, *et al.* (1993) On the origin of organic gas in Öxarfjörður, NE-Iceland. National Energy Authority Report OS-93015/JHD-05, 76pp.
[113] Schoell M (1980) The hydrogen and carbon isotopic composition of methane from natural gases of various origins. *Geochimica et Cosmochimica Acta* 44: 649–661.
[114] Jakobsson SP and Friðleifsson GÓ (1989) Asphalt in amygdales in Skyndidalur, Lón (in Icelandic with English abstract). *Náttúrufræðingurinn* 59: 169–188.
[115] Saemundsson K (1980) Outline of the geology of Iceland. *Jökull* 29: 7–28.
[116] Des Marais DJ, Stallard ML, Nehring NL, and Truesdell AH (1988) *Chemical Geology* 71: 159–167.
[117] Ármannsson H, Benjamínsson J, and Jeffrey A (1989) Gas changes in the Krafla geothermal system, Iceland. *Chemical Geology* 76: 175–196.
[118] Sano Y, Urabe A, Wakita H, *et al.* (1985) Chemical and isotopic compositions of gases in geothermal fluids in Iceland. *Geochemical Journal* 19: 135–148.
[119] Gunter BD and Musgrave BC (1971) New evidence on the origin of methane in hydrothermal gases. *Geochimica et Cosmochimica Acta* 35: 113–118.
[120] Arnórsson S and Gíslason SR (1994) CO_2 from magmatic sources in Iceland. *Mineralogical Magazine* 58A: 27–28.
[121] Óskarsson N (1996) Carbon dioxide from large volcanic eruptions. Short term effects (in Icelandic). In: Bragason A *et al.* (eds.) *Biological Society of Iceland. The Carbon Budget of Iceland Conference*, Program and Abstracts, p. 17. Reykjavík, Iceland, 22–23 November 1996.
[122] Ármannsson H, Fridriksson T, Wiese F, *et al.* (2007) CO_2 budget of the Krafla geothermal system, NE-Iceland. In: Bullen TD and Wang, Y (eds.) *Water–Rock Interaction*, pp. 189–192. London: Taylor & Francis Group.
[123] Einarsson P (1978) S-wave shadows in the Krafla caldera in NE Iceland, evidence for a magma chamber in the crust. *Bulletin of Volcanology* 43: 1–9.
[124] Björnsson A (1985) Dynamics of crustal rifting in NE Iceland. *Journal of Geophysical Research* 90(B12): 10151–10162.
[125] Mortensen AK, Gudmundsson Á, Steingrímsson B, *et al.* (2009) Overview of research of the geothermal system and a review of the conceptual model (in Icelandic). Landsvirkjun LV-2009, 111, 206pp + 2 maps.
[126] Ármannsson H, Guðmundsson Á, and Steingrímsson BS (1987) Exploration and development of the Krafla geothermal area. *Jökull* 37: 13–30.
[127] Ármannsson H (2001) Reaction of groundwater with rock from the Krafla area, N-E Iceland and volcanic gas. In: Cidu R (ed.) *Water-Rock Interaction*, pp. 779–782. The Netherlands: Balkema, Swets & Zeitlinger, Lisse.
[128] Sinclair AJ (1974) Selection of threshold in geochemical data using probability graphs. *Journal of Geochemical Exploration* 3: 129–149.
[129] Ingri N, Kakolowicz W, Sillén LG, and Warnqvist B (1967) High-speed computers as a supplement to graphical methods-V: Haltafall, a general program for calculating the composition of equilibrium mixtures. *Talanta* 14: 1261–1286.
[130] Eriksson G (1979) An algorithm for the computation of aqueous multi-component, multi-phase equilibria. *Analytica Chimica Acta* 112: 375–383.
[131] Morel F and Morgan J (1972) A numerical method for computing equilibria in aqueous chemical systems. *Environmental Science and Technology* 6: 58–67.
[132] Westall JC, Zachary JL, and Morel FFM (1976) *MINEQL, a Computer Program for the Calculation of Chemical Equilibrium Composition of Aqueous Systems*. Technical Note 18, R.M. Parsons Laboratory, Department of Civil and Environmental Engineering, Massachusetts Institute of Technology, Cambridge, MA.
[133] Truesdell AH and Jones BF (1974) WATEQ, a computer program for calculating chemical equilibria of natural waters. *U.S. Geological Survey Journal of Research* 2: 233–248.

[134] Kharaka YK, Gunter WD, Aggarwal PK, et al. (1988) SOLMINEQ88, a computer program for geochemical modelling of water-rock interactions. *U.S. Geological Survey Water Resources Investigations Report 88–4227*.
[135] Kharaka YK and Barnes I (1973) SOLMINEQ: Solution-mineral equilibrium computations. *U.S. Geological Survey Computer Contributions Report PB–215–899*.
[136] Wolery TJ (1979) Calculation of chemical equilibrium between aqueous solutions and minerals: The EQ3/6 software package. *Lawrence Livermore National Laboratory Report UCRL–52658*.
[137] Wolery TJ (1983) EQ3NR, a computer program for geochemical aqueous speciation-solubility calculations: User's guide and documentation. *Lawrence Livermore National laboratory Report UCRL–53414*.
[138] Wolery TJ (1992) EQ3/EQ6, a software package for geochemical modelling of aqueous systems, package overview and installation guide (version 7.0). *Lawrence Livermore National Laboratory Report UCRL-MA-110662 (1)*.
[139] Wolery TJ (1992) EQ3NR, a computer program for geochemical aqueous speciation-solubility calculations: Theoretical manual, user's guide and related documentation (version 7.0). *Lawrence Livermore National laboratory Report UCRL-MA-110662 (3)*.
[140] Reed MH (1977) *Calculations of Hydrothermal Metasomatism and Ore Deposition in Submarine Volcanic Rocks with Special Reference to the West Shasta District*. PhD Dissertation, University of California, Berkeley.
[141] Reed MH (1982) Calculation of multi-component chemical equilibria and reaction processes in systems involving minerals, gases and an aqueous phase. *Geochimica et Cosmochimica Acta* 46: 513–528.
[142] Reed MH, Spycher NF, and Palandri JL (2010) *SOLVEQ-XPT: A Program for Computing Aqueous-Mineral-Gas Equilibria*, 41pp. Eugene, OR: University of Oregon.
[143] Arnórsson S, Sigurðsson E, and Svavarsson H (1982) The chemistry of geothermal waters in Iceland. I. Calculation of aqueous speciation from 0 °C to 350 °C. *Geochimica et Cosmochimica Acta* 46: 1513–1532.
[144] Bjarnason JÖ (1994) *The Speciation Program WATCH, Version 2.1*, 7pp. Reykjavík: National Energy Authority.
[145] Helgeson HC, Brown TH, Nigrini A, and Jones TA (1970) Calculation of mass transfer in geochemical processes involving aqueous solutions. *Geochimica et Cosmochimica Acta* 34: 569–592.
[146] Reed MH, Spycher NF, and Palandri JL (2010) *CHIM-XPT: A Computer Program for Computing Reaction Processes in Aqueous-Mineral-Gas Systems and MINTAB Guide*, 73pp. Eugene, OR: University of Oregon.
[147] Gunnlaugsson E and Einarsson Á (1989) Magnesium silicate scaling in mixture of geothermal water and deaerated fresh water in a district heating system. *Geothermics* 18: 113–120.
[148] Kristmannsdóttir H, Ólafsson M, and Thórhallsson S (1989) Magnesium silicate scaling in district heating systems in Iceland. *Geothermics* 18: 191–198.
[149] Kristmannsdóttir H, Ildefonse Ph, Bertaux J, and Flank AM (1998) Crystal-chemistry of Mg-Si and Al-Si scales in geothermal waters, Iceland. In: Ármannsson H (ed.) *Geochemistry of the Earth's Surface*, pp. 519–522. Rotterdam: Balkema.
[150] Liping B (1991) Chemical modelling programs for predicting calcite scaling, applied to low temperature geothermal waters in Iceland United Nations Geothermal Training Programme, Reykjavík, *Iceland Report 3*, 1991, 45pp.
[151] Reed MH and Spycher NF (1984) Calculation of pH and mineral equilibria in hydrothermal water with application to geothermometry and studies of boiling and dilution. *Geochimica et Cosmochimica Acta* 48: 1479–1490.
[152] Kristmannsdóttir H, Axelsson G, Sæmundsson K, et al. (1998) The Rangæingar Heating Company. Monitoring of geothermal production 1997–1998 and the status of water provision (in Icelandic) National Energy Authority Report OS-98077, 89pp.
[153] Kristmannsdóttir H, Axelsson G, Sæmundsson K, et al. (2002) The Rangæingar Heating Company. Monitoring of geothermal production in the company's production areas in Laugaland in Holt and Kaldárholt 2001 (in Icelandic) National Energy Authority Report OS-2002/009, 20pp.
[154] Swanteson J and Kristmannsdóttir H (1978) The chemical composition of altered rock in Krafla (in Icelandic). Report OSJHD-7822. Reykjavík: National Energy Authority.
[155] Gerlach TM (1980) Evaluation of volcanic gas analyses from Surtsey volcano, Iceland 1964–1967. *Journal of Volcanology and Geothermal Research* 8: 191–198.
[156] Ármannsson H (1993) Námafjall geothermal system. Geo-chemical investigations (in Icelandic) National Energy Authority Report OS-93053/JHD-29 B, 30pp.
[157] Reed MH and Spycher NF (1989) *SOLTHERM: Data base of Equilibrium Constants for Aqueous-Mineral-Gas Equilibria*. Eugene, OR: Department of Geological Sciences, University of Oregon.
[158] Guðmundsson Á (1993) Alteration heat of the Námafjall geothermal system (in Icelandic). National Energy Authority Report OS-93065/JHD 31B, 21pp.
[159] Guðmundsson Á, Steingrímsson B, Sigursteinsson D, et al. (1983) Krafla, Well KJ-13. Redrilling in July and August 1983 (in Icelandic). National Energy Authority Report OS-83077/JHD 23B, 29pp.
[160] Kristmannsdóttir H, Guðmundsson Á, Kjartansdóttir M, and Friðleifsson GÓ (1976) Krafla. Well KG-8, drilling, inflows, pressure testing, permeability testing, lithology and alteration (in Icelandic) National Energy Authority Report OS JHD 7713.
[161] Torssander P (1986) Origin of volcanic sulfur in Iceland. A sulfur isotope study. Doctoral thesis, Stockholm: Department of Geology, University of Stockholm. No. 269, 164pp.
[162] Tole MP, Ármannsson H, Pang Z, and Arnórsson S (1993) Fluid/mineral equilibrium calculations for geothermal fluids and chemical geothermometry. *Geothermics* 22: 17–37.
[163] Fournier RO and Rowe JJ (1966) Estimation of underground temperatures from the silica content of water from hot springs and wet steam wells. *American Journal of Science* 264: 685–697.
[164] Arnórsson S (1975) Application of the silica geothermometer in low-temperature hydrothermal areas in Iceland. *American Journal of Science* 275: 763–784.
[165] Fournier RO (1977) Chemical geothermometers and mixing models for geothermal systems. *Geothermics* 5: 41–50.
[166] Truesdell AH and Fournier RO (1975) Calculation of deep reservoir temperatures from chemistry of boiling hot springs of mixed origin. In: *The 2nd United Nations Symposium on the Development and Use of Geothermal Resources*, Abstract Volume III, p. 25. San Francisco, 20–29 May 1975. Washington, DC: Government Printing Office.
[167] Arnórsson S (1985) The use of mixing models and chemical geothermometers for estimating underground temperatures in geothermal systems. *Journal of Volcanology and Geothermal Research* 23: 299–335.
[168] Fournier RO and Potter RW II (1982) An equation correlating the solubility of quartz in water from 25° to 900 °C at pressures up to 10,000 bars. *Geochimica et Cosmochimica Acta* 46: 1969–1974.
[169] Fournier RO and Potter RWII (1982) A revised and expanded silica (quartz) geothermometer. *Geothermal Resources Council Bulletin* 11(10): 3–12.
[170] Gíslason SR, Heaney PJ, Oelkers EH, and Schott J (1997) Kinetic and thermodynamic properties of moganite, a novel silica polymorph. *Geochimica et Cosmochimica Acta* 61: 1193–1204.
[171] Fournier RO (1981) Application of water geochemistry to geothermal exploration and reservoir engineering. In: Rybach L and Muffler LJP (eds.) *Geothermal Systems: Principles and Case Histories*, pp. 109–143. New York: John Wiley.
[172] Ragnarsdóttir KV and Walther JW (1983) Pressure sensitive 'silica geothermometer' determined from quartz solubility experiments at 250 °C. *Geochimica et Cosmochimica Acta* 47: 941–946.
[173] Fournier RO and Truesdell AH (1973) An empirical Na-K-Ca geothermometer for natural waters. *Geochimica et Cosmochimica Acta* 37: 515–525.
[174] Fournier RO and Potter RW II (1979) Magnesium correction to the Na-K-Ca chemical geothermometer. *Geochimica et Cosmochimica Acta* 43: 1543–1550.
[175] Giggenbach WF (1988) Geothermal solute equilibria. Derivation of Na-K-Mg-Ca-geoindicators. *Geochimica et Cosmochimica Acta* 52: 2749–2765.
[176] D'Amore F and Truesdell AH (1985) Calculation of geothermal reservoir temperatures and steam fraction from gas compositions. 1985 International Symposium on Geothermal Energy. *Geothermal Resources Council Transactions* 9: 305–310.
[177] Bertrami R, Cioni R, Corazza E, et al. (1985) Carbon monoxide in geothermal gases. Reservoir temperature calculations at Larderello (Italy). *Geothermal Resources Council Transactions* 9: 299–303.
[178] Arnórsson S and Gunnlaugsson E (1985) New gas geothermometers for geothermal exploration – Calibration and application. *Geochimica et Cosmochimica Acta* 49: 1307–1325.

[179] Arnórsson S (1987) Gas chemistry of the Krísuvík geothermal field, Iceland, with special reference to evaluation of steam condensation in upflow zones. *Jökull* 37: 32–47.
[180] Arnórsson S, Fridriksson T, and Gunnarsson I (1998) Gas chemistry of the Krafla geothermal field, Iceland. In: Arehart GB and Hulston JR (eds.) *Water-Rock Interaction*, pp. 613–616. Rotterdam: Balkema.
[181] D'Amore F and Panichi C (1980) Evaluation of deep temperature of hydrothermal systems by a new gas geothermometer. *Geochimica et Cosmochimica Acta* 44: 549–556.
[182] Tonani F (1980) Some remarks on the application of geochemical techniques in geothermal exploration. In: Strub AS and Ungemach P (eds.) *Proceedings of the 2nd International Seminar on the Results of E.C. Geothermal Energy Research*, Strasbourg, France, pp. 428–443. Strasbourg: EC.
[183] Zhao P and Ármannsson H (1996) Gas geothermometry in selected Icelandic geothermal fields with comparative examples from Kenya. *Geothermics* 25: 307–347.
[184] Giggenbach WF (1980) Geothermal gas equilibria. *Geochimica et Cosmochimica Acta* 44: 2021–2032.
[185] Karingithi CW, Arnórsson S, and Grönvold K (2010) Processes controlling aquifer fluid compositions in the Olkaria geothermal system, Kenya. *Journal of Volcanology and Geothermal Research* 196: 57–76.
[186] Kristmannsdóttir H and Ármannsson H (1996) Chemical monitoring of Icelandic geothermal fields during production. *Geothermics* 25: 349–364.
[187] Björnsson S and Benediktsson S (1968) An account of enthalpy and flow measurements in steam boreholes (in Icelandic). National Energy Authority, 15pp.
[188] Macambac RV, Salazar ATN, Villa RR, *et al.* (1998) Field-wide application of chemical tracers for mass flow measurements in Philippine geothermal fields. In: *Proceedings of the 19th Annual PNOC EDC Geothermal Conference*, Makati City, Philippines, pp.153–159. Manila, Philippines.
[189] Hirtz P and Lovikin J (1995) Tracer dilution measurements for two-phase geothermal production: Comparative testing and operating experience. In: Barbier E, Frye G, Iglesias E, and Pálmason G (eds.) *World Geothermal Congress*, pp. 1881–1886. Florence, Italy. Auckland, New Zealand: IGA.
[190] Agamata-Lu CS (1998) Chemical tracer applications at the Broadlands-Ohaaki and Wairakei geothermal fields. In: *Proceedings of the 19th Annual PNOC EDC Geothermal Conference*, Makati City, Philippines, pp.137–151. Manila, Philippines.
[191] Magadadaro MC (1998) Sodium benzoate analysis for on-line brine flow measurements. In: *Proceedings of the 19th Annual PNOC EDC Geothermal Conference*, Makati City, Philippines, pp. 169–176. Manila, Philippines.
[192] Adams MC (1995) Vapor, liquid and two-phase tracers for geothermal systems. In: Barbier E, Frye G, Iglesias E, and Pálmason G (eds.) *World Geothermal Congress*, pp. 1875–1880. Florence, Italy. Auckland, New Zealand: IGA.
[193] Ármannsson H (1989) Predicting calcite deposition in Krafla boreholes. *Geothermics* 18: 25–32.
[194] Wangyal P (1992) Calcite deposition related to temperature and boiling in some Icelandic geothermal wells. *Geothermal Training Programme Report 1992-11*, United Nations University, 33pp.
[195] Gunnarsson I, Arnórsson S, and Jakobsson S (2005) Precipitation of poorly crystalline antigorite under hydrothermal conditions. *Geochimica et Cosmochimica Acta* 69: 2813–2828.
[196] Truesdell AH, Haizlip JR, Ármannsson H, and D'Amore F (1989) Origin and transport of chloride in superheated geothermal steam. *Geothermics* 18: 295–304.
[197] D'Amore F, Truesdell AH, and Haizlip JR (1990) Production of HCl by mineral reaction in high temperature geothermal systems. In: Tsang CF (ed.) *Proceedings of the 15th Workshop on Geothermal Reservoir Engineering*, pp. 23–25. Stanford University, Stanford, CA.
[198] Allegrini G and Benvenuti G (1970) Corrosion characteristics and geothermal power plant protection. U.N. symposium on the development and utilization of geothermal resources. *Geothermics* 2(Part 1): 865–881.
[199] Thórhallsson S, Pálsson B, Fridleifsson GÓ, *et al.* (2008) Description of ENEL corrosion resistant wellheads. *IDDP Drilling Technology Report*, 6pp.
[200] Bell D (1989) Description of an operational desuperheating and chloride scrub system. *Geothermal Resources Council Transactions* 13: 303–307.
[201] Hirtz P, Buck C, and Kunzman R (1991) Current techniques in acid-chloride corrosion control and monitoring at the Geysers. In: Degens G and Neuman SP (eds.) *Proceedings of the 16th Workshop on Geothermal Reservoir Engineering*, pp. 83–95. Stanford University, Stanford, CA.
[202] Hirtz PN, Broaddus ML, and Gallup DL (2002) Dry steam scrubbing for impurity removal from superheated geothermal steam. *Geothermal Resources Council Transactions* 26: 751–754.
[203] Izquierdo G, Arellano VM, Aragón A, *et al.* (2000) Fluid acidity and hydrothermal alteration at the Los Humeros geothermal reservoir Puebla, Mexico. In: Iglesias E *et al.* (eds.) *Proceedings of the World Geothermal Congress 2000*, pp. 1301–1305. Kyushu-Tohoku, Japan. Pisa, Italy: IGA.
[204] Moya P, Nietzen F, and Sanchez E (2005) Development of the neutralization system for production wells at the Miravalles geothermal field. In: *Proceedings of the World Geothermal Congress 2005*, 10pp. Antalya, Turkey. Reykjavic, Iceland: IGA.
[205] Villa RR, Siega FL, Martinez-Oliver MM, *et al.* (2000) A demonstration of the feasibility of acid well utilization: The Philippines' well MG-9D experience. In: Zaide-Delfin, MC (ed.) *Proceedings of the 20th Annual PNOC EDC Geothermal Conference*, pp. 25–32. Philippines.
[206] Sugiaman F, Sunio E, Molling P, and Stimac J (2004) Geochemical response to production of the Tiwi geothermal field, Philippines. *Geothermics* 33: 57–86.
[207] Moore JN, Christenson B, Browne PRL, and Lutz SJ (2002) The mineralogic consequences and behaviour of descending acid-sulfate waters: An example from the Karaha-Telaga Boda geothermal system, Indonesia. In: Kruger P and Raney Jr HJ (eds.): *Proceedings of the 27th Workshop on Geothermal Reservoir Engineering*, pp. 257–265. Stanford University, Stanford, CA.
[208] Reyes AG (1990) Petrology of Philippine geothermal systems and the application of alteration mineralogy to their assessment. *Journal of Volcanology and Geothermal Research* 43: 279–309.
[209] Reyes AG (1991) Mineralogy, distribution and origin of acid alteration in Philippine geothermal systems. In: Matsuhisa Y, Masahiro A, and Hedenquist J (eds.) *High temperature Acid Fluids and Associated Alteration and Mineralization*, Geological Survey of Japan Report, vol. 277, pp. 59–65. Tsukuba, Japan: Geological Survey of Japan.
[210] Angcoy EC, Abarquez AL, Andrino RP, *et al.* (2008) Mechanisms of erosion-corrosion in well 311D, South Sambaloran, Leyte geothermal production field. In: *Proceedings of the 29th Annual PNOC EDC Geothermal Conference*, pp. 159–164. Markati City, Philippines.
[211] Kiyota Y, Matsuda K, and Shimada K (1996) Characterization of acid water in the Otake-Hatchobaru geothermal field. In: *Proceedings of the 17th Annual PNOC EDC Geothermal Conference*, pp. 131–135. Makati City, Philippines.
[212] Bowyer D, Bignall G, and Hunt T (2008) Formation and neutralization of corrosive fluids in the shallow injection aquifer, Rotokawa geothermal field, New Zealand. Tauhara North No. 2 Trust, GNS, Mighty River Power. wwww.geothermal.org/Powerpoint08/Tuesday/Geochemistryl/BowyerTue08.ppt (accessed December 2010).
[213] Hauksson T (1979) Well KG-12 (in Icelandic). National Energy Authority Well Letter No. 11, 5pp.
[214] Hauksson T and Benjamínsson J (2005) Krafla and Bjarnarflag. Borehole production and the chemical composition of water and steam in boreholes and production equipment in 2004 (in Icelandic). *Landsvirkjun Report*, Krafla Power Station, 78pp.
[215] Hauksson T and Gudmundsson A (2008) Krafla. Acid wells. *Landsvirkjun Report*, 17pp.
[216] Ármannsson H and Gíslason G (1992) The occurrence of acidic fluids in the Leirbotnar field, Krafla, Iceland. In: Kharaka YK and Maest AS (eds.) *Water-Rock Interaction*, pp. 1257–1260. Rotterdam: Balkema.
[217] Sanchez Rivera E, Sequeira HG, and Vallejos Ruiz O (2000) Commercial production of acid wells at the Miravalles geothermal field, Costa Rica. In: *Proceedings of the World Geothermal Congress 2000*, pp. 1629–1633. Kyushu-Tohoku, Japan.
[218] Virkir-Orkint (1990) Djibouti. Geothermal scaling and corrosion study. *Final Report*. Electricité de Djibouti, Virkir-Orkint, Reykjavík, 270pp.
[219] James R (1962) Steam-water critical flow through pipes. *Proceedings of the Institution of Mechanical Engineers, London* 176: 741–745.
[220] Turekian KK (1969) The oceans, streams and atmosphere. In: Wedepohl KH (ed.) *Handbook of Geochemistry*, vol. 1, ch. 10, pp. 297–323. Berlin: Springer-Verlag.
[221] Gallup DL (1989) Iron silicate formation and inhibition at the Salton Sea geothermal field. *Geothermics* 18: 97–103.
[222] Swedlund PJ and Webster JG (1999) Adsorption and polymerisation of silicic acid on ferrihydrite, and its effect on arsenic adsorption. *Water Resources* 33: 3413–3422.
[223] Jost (1980) US Patent 4,224,151.
[224] Gallup DL (1993) The use of reducing agents for control of ferric silicate scale deposition. *Geothermics* 22: 39–48.

[225] Bemmelen RW and Rutten MG (1955) *Table mountains of Northern Iceland*, 217pp + 52 plates and maps. Leiden: E.J. Brill.
[226] Kjartansson H (1972) Clay formations in Dalasýsla and Thingeyjarsýsla districts (in Icelandic). National Energy Authority JKD, 83pp.
[227] Grönvold K and Karlsdóttir R (1975) Theistareykir. An interim report on the surface exploration of the geothermal area (in Icelandic). National Energy Authority JHD-7501, 37pp.
[228] Ármannsson H, Gíslason G, and Torfason H (1986) Surface exploration of the Theistareykir high-temperature geothermal area, Iceland, with special reference to the application of geochemical methods. *Applied Geochemistry* 1: 47–64.
[229] Gíslason G, Johnsen GV, Ármannsson H, *et al.* (1984) Theistareykir. Surface exploration of the high-temperature geothermal area (in Icelandic). National Energy Authority OS-84089/JHD-16, 134pp + 3 maps.
[230] Layugan DB (1981) Geo-electrical soundings and its application in the Theistareykir high-temperature area United Nations University. *Geothermal Training Programme Report 1981–5*, 101pp.
[231] Ármannsson H, Kristmannsdóttir H, Torfason H, and Ólafsson M (2000b) Natural changes in unexploited high-temperature geothermal areas in Iceland. In: Iglesias E, Blackwell D, Hunt T, *et al.* (eds.) *Proceedings of the World Geothermal Congress 2000*, Kyushu-Tohuku, Japan, pp. 521–526. International Geothermal Association, Pisa, Italy.
[232] Ármannsson H (2001) Theistareykir. A review of research, exploration and its cost (In Icelandic). National Energy Authority OS-2001/035, 24pp.
[233] Gautason B, Ármannsson H, Árnason K, *et al.* (2000) Thoughts on the next steps in the exploration of the Theistareykir geothermal area (in Icelandic). National Energy Authority BG-HÁ-KÁ-KS-ÓGF-STh-2000/04, 11pp.
[234] Sæmundsson K (2007) The geology of Theistareykir (in Icelandic). Iceland GeoSurvey Report, ÍSOR-07270, 23pp.
[235] Karlsdóttir R, Eysteinsson H, Magnússon ITh, *et al.* (2006) TEM soundings at Theistareykir and Gjástykki 2004–2006 (in Icelandic). Iceland GeoSurvey Report ÍSOR-2006/028, 88pp.
[236] Yu G, He LF, He ZX, *et al.* (2008) *Iceland Theistareykir 2-D MT survey. Data acquisition report*. KMS Technologies – KJT Enterprises Inc. and VGK-Hönnun.
[237] Hafstad TH (1989) Öxarfjördur. Groundwater investigations 1987–1988. A contribution to a special project on fish farming (in Icelandic). National Energy Authority OS-89039/VOD-08 B, 25pp.
[238] Hafstad TH (2000) Theistareykir: The drilling of a fresh water well (in Icelandic). National Energy Authority ThH-00/14, 6pp.
[239] Gudmundsson Á, Gautason B, Thordarson S, *et al.* (2002) Exploration drilling at Theistareykir. Well Th.G-1. 3rd stage: Drilling of production part to 1953 m depth (in Icelandic). National Energy Authority OS-2002/079, 59pp.
[240] Arnórsson S, Gunnlaugsson E, and Svavarsson H (1983) The chemistry of geothermal waters in Iceland III. Chemical geothermometry in geothermal investigations. *Geochimica et Cosmochimica Acta* 47: 567–577.
[241] Guðmundsson Á, Gautason B, Axelsson G, *et al.* (2008) A conceptual model of the geothermal system at Theistareykir and a volumetric estimate of the geothermal potential (in Icelandic). Iceland GeoSurvey, VGK-Hönnun and Vatnaskil Engineering Office, *Report*, 57pp.
[242] Arnórsson S (1989) Deposition of calcium carbonate minerals from geothermal waters – Theoretical considerations. *Geothermics* 18: 33–40.
[243] Giggenbach WF (1991a) Chemical techniques in geothermal exploration. In: D'Amore F (coordinator) *Applications of Geochemistry in Geothermal Reservoir Development*, pp. 119–142. Rome: UNITAR/UNDP Publication.
[244] Giggenbach WF (1991b) Isotopic shifts in waters from geothermal and volcanic systems along convergent plate boundaries and their origin. *Earth and Planetary Science Letters* 113: 495–510.
[245] Hardardóttir V, Ármannsson H, and Thórhallsson S (2005) Characterization of sulfide-rich scales in brines at Reykjanes. In: Horne R and Okenden E (eds.) *Proceedings of the World Geothermal Congress 2005*, 8pp. Antalya, Turkey, 24–29 April 2005. Reykjavic, Iceland: IGA.
[246] Hardardóttir V, Brown KL, Fridriksson Th, *et al.* (2009) Metals in deep liquid of the Reykjanes geothermal system, southwest Iceland: Implications for the composition of seafloor black smoker fluids. *Geology* 37: 1103–1106.
[247] Seward TM and Kerrick DM (1996) Hydrothermal CO_2 emission from the Taupo Volcanic Zone, New Zealand. *Earth Planetary Science Letters* 139: 105–113.
[248] Khalilabad MR, Axelsson G, and Gíslason SR (2008) Aquifer characterization with tracer test technique; permanent CO_2 sequestration into basalt. SW Iceland. *Mineralogical Magazine* 72: 121–125.
[249] Reed MH and Spycher NF (1989) *SOLVEQ: A Computer Program for Computing Aqueous-Mineral-Gas Equilibria. A Manual*, 37pp. Eugene, OR: Department of Geological Sciences, University of Oregon.
[250] Browne PRL (1984) *Lectures on Geology and Petrology*. UNU Geothermal Training Programme, Iceland. Report 1984-2, 92 pp.
[251] Browne PRL and Ellis AJ (1970) The Ohaaki-Broadlands hydrothermal area, New Zealand: Mineralogy and related geochemistry. *American Journal of Science* 269: 97–131.
[252] Rist S (1979a) Water level fluctuations and ice cover of Lake Mývatn. *Oikos*, 32: 67–81.
[253] Xu T, Apps JA, Pruess K, and Yamamoto H (2007) Numerical modelling of injection and mineral trapping of CO_2 with H_2S and SO_2 in a sandstone formation. *Chemical Geology* 242: 319–346.
[254] Rist S (1979b) The hydrology of River Laxá. *Oikos* 32: 271–280.
[255] Sigbjarnarson G, Tómasson H, Eliasson J, and Arnórsson S (1974) A report on the risk of pollution from a power plant situated either at Krafla or Hverarónd (in Icelandic). OS JHD 7427, OS ROD 7421, 16pp. Reykjavik, Iceland: Orkustofnun.
[256] Sveinbjörnsdóttir ÁE, Johnsen SJ, and Arnórssen S (1995) The use of stable isotopes of oxygen and hydrogen in geothermal studies in Iceland. In: Barbier E, Frye G, Iglesias E, and Pálmason G (eds.) *Proceedings of the World Geothermal Congress*, pp. 1043–1048. Florence, Italy. Auckland, New Zealand: International Geothermal Association.
[257] International Geothermal Association (2002) Geothermal power generating plant CO2 emission survey. *A Report, International Geothermal Association*, Pisa, Italy, 7pp.
[258] Sheppard D and Mroczek E (2004) Greenhouse gas emissions from the exploitation geothermal systems. *IGA Quarterly* 55: 11–13.
[259] Parkhurst DL, Thorstenson DC, and Plummer LN (1980) Phreeqe – A computer program for geochemical calculations. *US Geological Survey Water-Resources Investigations Report 80–96*.
[260] Böðvarsson G (1960) Exploration and exploitation of natural heat in Iceland. *Bulletin Volcanology Series 2* 23: 241–250.
[261] Haas JL, Jr. (1976) Physical properties of the coexisting phases and thermochemical properties of the H2O component in boiling NaCl solutions. *USGS Bulletin* 1421-A: 73 pp.
[262] Pačes T (1975) A systematic deviation from the Na-K-Ca geothermometer below 75 °C and above 10-4 atm PCO2. *Geochimica et Cosmochimica Acta* 29: 541–544.
[263] Nehring N and D'Amore F (1984) Gas chemistry and thermometry of the Cerro Prieto, Mexico, geothermal field. *Geothermics* 13: 75–89.
[264] Björnsson G and Böðvarsson G (1987) A multi-feedzone wellbore simulator. *Geothermal Resources Council Transaction* 11: 503–507.
[265] Gíslason G and Arnórsson S (1976) Interim report on changes in flow and chemical composition in Boreholes 3 and 4 in Krafla. Report OS-JHD-7640, 13pp. (in Icelandic). Reykjavik, Iceland: Orkustofnun.
[266] Gudmundsson A (2001) An expansion of the Krafla power plant from 30 to 60 MWe geothermal consideration. *GRC-Transactions* 25: 741–746.
[267] Giroud N, Ármannsson H, and Ólafsson M (2008) Well KJ-35 in Krafla. Chemical composition of liquid and steam in Autumn 2007. ÍSOR 08055, 10pp. Reykjavik, Iceland: Exposition ÍSOR.
[268] Ármannsson H (1979) Dithizone extraction and flame atomic absorption spectrometry for the determination of cadmium, zinc, lead, copper, nickel, cobalt and silver in sea water and biological tissues. *Analytica Chimica Acta* 110: 21–28.
[269] Ármannsson H and Ovenden PJ (1980) The use of dithizone extraction and atomic absorption spectrometry for the determination of silver and bismuth in rocks and sediments and a demountable hollow cathode lamp for the determination of bismuth and indium. *Journal of Environmental Analytical Chemistry* 8: 127–136.
[270] Gunnarsson G (2001) The cleaning of residual gas from geothermal plants (in Icelandic). In: Samorka GMJ (eds.) *Orkuþing (Energy Symposium)*. pp. 281–285. Abstracts. Reykjavik, Iceland, 11–13 October.

7.05 Direct Heat Utilization of Geothermal Energy

JW Lund, Geo-Heat Center, Oregon Institute of Technology, Klamath Falls, OR, USA

© 2012 Elsevier Ltd. All rights reserved.

7.05.1	Introduction	169
7.05.2	Current Utilization	169
7.05.3	Global Distribution of Geothermal Heat Utilization	170
7.05.4	Development of Direct Heat Utilization Projects	170
7.05.4.1	Spas and Pools	170
7.05.4.2	Space and District Heating	171
7.05.4.3	Greenhouses	174
7.05.4.4	Aquaculture	174
7.05.4.5	Industrial and Agricultural Drying	174
7.05.5	Selecting the Equipment	175
7.05.5.1	Downhole Pumps	176
7.05.5.2	Piping	177
7.05.5.3	Heat Exchangers	178
7.05.6	Environmental Considerations	179
7.05.7	Case Histories	180
7.05.7.1	Tomato Drying in Greece	180
7.05.7.2	District Heating in Reykjavik, Iceland	180
7.05.7.3	Greenhouse Heating in Hungary	181
7.05.7.4	Timber Drying in New Zealand	181
7.05.7.5	Onion Dehydration in the United States	182
7.05.7.6	Combined Heat and Power in Austria	182
7.05.7.7	Individual Building Heating in the United States	184
7.05.7.8	Aquaculture Pond Heating in the United States	184
References		185
Further Reading		186
Relevant Websites		186

7.05.1 Introduction

The direct heat utilizations of geothermal energy are traditional and well established worldwide. The people of Japan have lived in harmony with the earth's heat for centuries, utilizing it mainly for bathing and cooking food. In the Americas, the indigenous people have been awed by geothermal phenomena considering them sacred sites and a place of refuge. Nowadays there are many large-scale uses of geothermal energy. Well-known examples are district heating in Iceland, greenhouse heating in Hungary, process heat with steam in New Zealand, mineral extraction in Italy, and individual residential space heating in the United States. Direct heat applications of geothermal energy are also called nonelectric uses to distinguish them from electric power generation.

The technology of direct uses is generally well established. The various applications include: (1) space heating, including district heating systems; (2) greenhouse and covered ground heating; (3) aquaculture pond and raceway heating; (4) agricultural drying; (5) industrial applications; (6) bathing, swimming pools, and spa heating; and (7) snow melting and space cooling. Many of these earlier applications have been documented for over 25 countries in *Stories from a Heated Earth – Our Geothermal Heritage* [1]. More recent applications have been described in countries' reports for the World Geothermal Congress 2010 [2].

The Lindal diagram [3, 4], named after Baldur Lindal, the Icelandic engineer who first proposed it, indicates the temperature range suitable for various direct-use activities (**Figure** 1). His diagram indicates the specific temperature most suitable for the application. This diagram has recently been updated by the Geothermal Education Office to reflect the temperature range suitable for various applications rather than a single temperature (**Figure** 2). Typically, the greenhouse and aquaculture uses require the lowest temperatures, with geothermal fluid values from 25 to 90 °C. Space heating requires resource temperatures in the range of 50–100 °C. Industrial applications and refrigeration normally require temperatures over 100 °C. Swimming and spa pools require temperatures in the range of 30–50 °C, which often involves direct heat utilizations of geothermal energy.

7.05.2 Current Utilization

Today, 78 countries have reported some form of direct utilization of geothermal energy with a total installed capacity of 15 358 MWt and an annual energy use of 223 667 TJ (62 135 GWh; excluding geothermal heat pumps) [2]. The growth over the past 15 years is

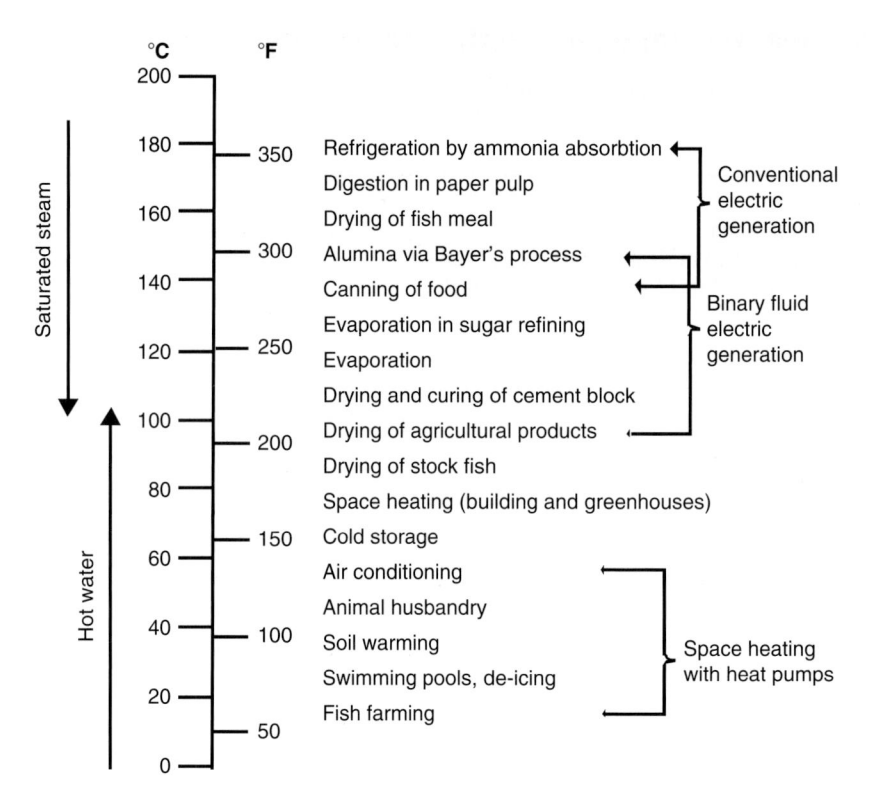

Figure 1 The Lindal diagram.

shown in **Figure 3**. Installed capacity has increased during this period by 2.26 times or 5.57% annually, and the annual energy use has increased 2.29 times or 5.67% annually.

The various applications of direct use for the period 1995–2010 are presented in **Tables 1** and **2** for installed capacity, annual energy use, and capacity factor. The capacity factor reflects the equivalent full-load operating hours in a year (annual energy use/ (installed capacity $\times$ 8760 h yr^{-1})). The higher the number, the more efficient the use of the geothermal resource (**Table 3**).

7.05.3 Global Distribution of Geothermal Heat Utilization

The leading users of geothermal energy for direct utilization of the heat are given in **Tables 1** and **2**.

In terms of the contribution of geothermal direct heat utilization to the national energy budget, two countries stand out: Iceland and Turkey. In Iceland, geothermal meets 89% of the country's space heating needs, which is important since heating is required almost all year-round and saves about US$100 million in imported oil [5]. Turkey has increased its installed capacity over the past 5 years from 1495 to 2084 MWt, most for district heating systems [6]. A summary of some of the significant geothermal direct-use contributions to various countries is given in **Table** 4.

7.05.4 Development of Direct Heat Utilization Projects

Before proceeding with a direct heat utilization project, several questions need to be investigated and answered by the potential developer: (1) What are the estimated (or known) temperature and flow rate of the resource? (2) What is the chemistry of the resource? (3) What potential markets do they have for the energy, and what would be the expected income? (4) Do they have the experience, or are you willing to hire experienced people to run the project? (5) Do they have financing and is the estimated net income enough to justify the investment? (6) Do they own or can you lease the property and the resource, and are there limitations on its use? **Figures 1** and **2** can help answering some of these questions – at least to establish the potential uses depending upon the temperature of the resource. The following sections describe in more detail some of the potential uses based on temperature and possible limitations.

7.05.4.1 Spas and Pools

People have used geothermal and mineral water for bathing and their health for many thousands of years. Balneology, the practice of using natural mineral water for the treatment and cure of disease, also has a long history. A spa originates at a location mainly due to the

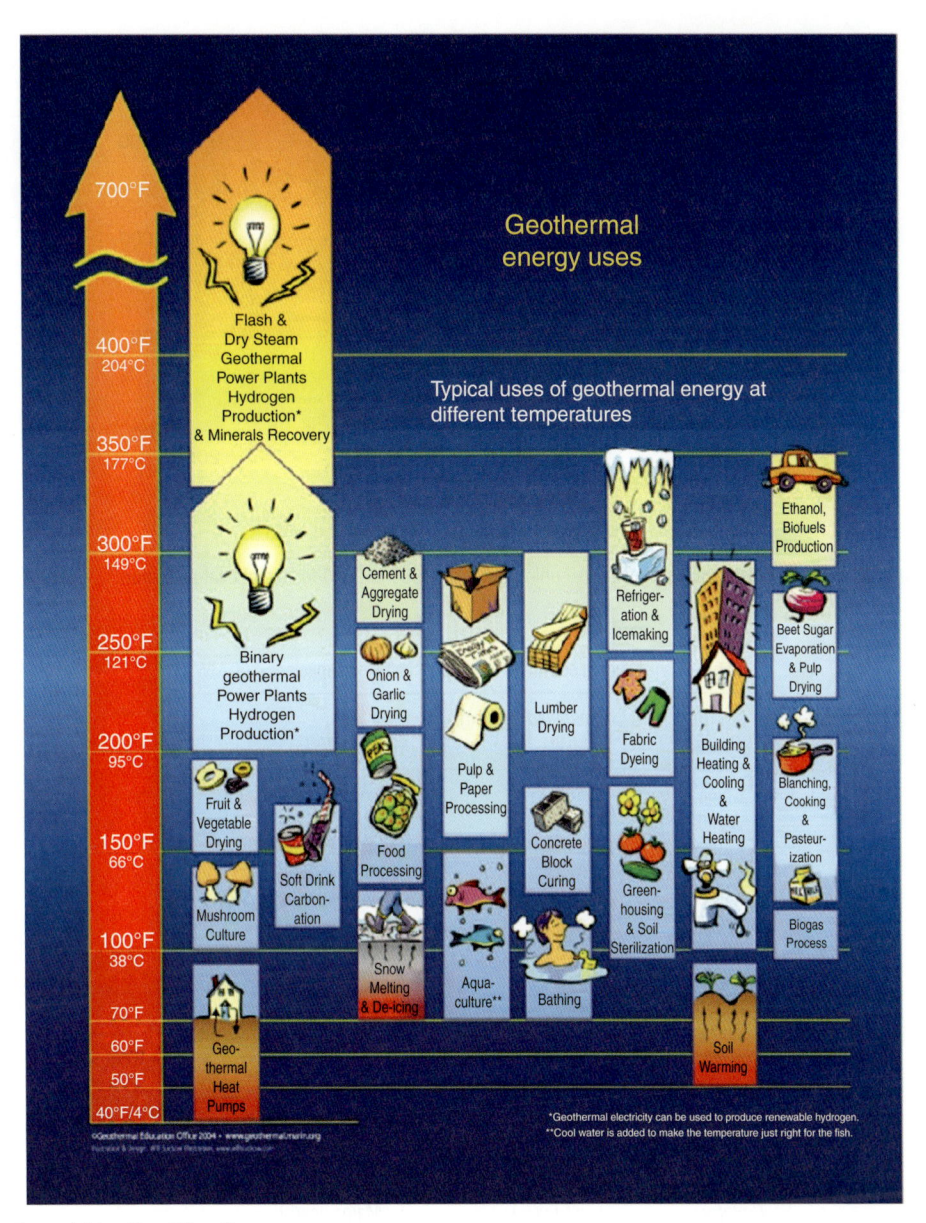

Figure 2 The Geothermal Education Office diagram.

water from a spring or well. The water, with certain mineral constituents and often warm, gives the spa certain unique characteristics that will attract customers. Associated with most spas is the use of muds (peoloids), which either are found at the site or are imported from special locations. The use of geothermal and mineral water for drinking and bathing, and the use of muds are thought to give certain health benefits to the user. Spas and pools for swimming, bathing, and soaking can use some of the lower temperature resources (generally <60 °C) – a minimum of 30 °C for pools and 45 °C for spas and soaking pools (hot tubs). Swimming pools have desirable temperature at 27 °C; however, this will vary from culture to culture by as much as 5 °C. Spas and soaking pools (hot tubs) generally are kept at 40 °C, but this can also vary by as much as 5 °C. If the geothermal water is higher in temperature, then some sort of mixing or cooling by aeration or in a holding pond is required to lower the temperature, or it can first be used for space heating and then cascaded into the pool. If the geothermal water is used directly in the pool, then a flow-through process is necessary to replace the 'used' water on a regular basis. In many cases, the pool water must be treated with chlorine; thus, it is more economical to use a closed loop for the treated water and have the geothermal water provide heat through a heat exchanger. To conserve heat, a pool may be covered by a temporary plastic cover or in a permanent building, preventing as much as 50% of the heat loss [7].

7.05.4.2 Space and District Heating

District heating involves the distribution of heat (hot water or steam) from a central location, through a network of pipes to individual houses or blocks of buildings. The distinction between a district heating system and a space heating is that space

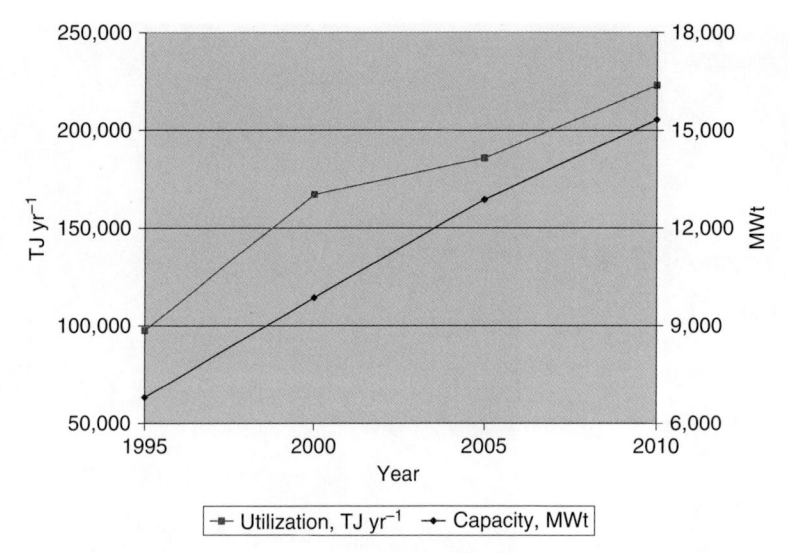

Figure 3 The growth rate of the installed capacity and annual utilization from 1995 to 2010 for direct heat utilization.

Table 1 Leading countries in terms of installed capacity (>300 MWt)

Country	Installed capacity (MWt)	Major use(s)
China	3688	Bathing, district heating
Japan	2086	Bathing
Turkey	2046	District heating, bathing
Iceland	1822	District heating
Italy	636	Space heating, bathing
Hungary	615	Bathing, greenhouses
USA	612	Space heating, aquaculture
New Zealand	386	Industrial
Brazil	360	Bathing
Russia	307	Greenhouses, space heating

Table 2 Leading countries in terms of annual energy use (>3000 TJ yr^{-1})

Country	Annual energy (TJ yr^{-1})	Major use(s)
China	46 313	Bathing, district heating
Turkey	36 349	Bathing, district heating
Japan	25 630	Bathing, space heating
Iceland	24 341	District heating
New Zealand	9 513	Industrial
Hungary	9 249	Bathing, greenhouses
USA	9 152	Bathing, space heating
Italy	8 980	Space heating, aquaculture
Brazil	6 622	Bathing
Mexico	4 023	Bathing
Slovakia	3 054	Bathing, space heating
Argentina	3 048	Bathing

heating usually involves one geothermal well per structure. District heating system has one or more wells serving a number of buildings through a central control station and an extensive piping network. An important consideration in district heating projects is the thermal load density, or the heat demand divided by the ground area of the district. A high heat density, generally >1.2 GJ h^{-1} ha^{-1}, or a favorability ratio of >2.5 GJ ha^{-1} yr^{-1} is recommended. Often fossil fuel peaking is used to meet the coldest period, rather than drilling additional wells or pumping more fluids, as geothermal can usually meet 50% of the

Table 3 Summary of the various applications for direct use worldwide for the period 1995–2010

	2010	2005	2000	1995
	Capacity (MWt)			
Space heating	5 394	4 366	3 263	2 579
Greenhouse heating	1 544	1 404	1 246	1 085
Aquaculture pond heating	653	616	605	1 097
Agricultural drying	125	157	74	67
Industrial uses	533	484	474	544
Bathing and swimming	6 701	5 401	3 957	1 085
Cooling/snow melting	368	371	114	115
Others	42	86	137	238
Total	15 360	12 885	9 870	6 810
	Utilization (TJ yr^{-1})			
Space heating	63 025	55 256	42 926	38 230
Greenhouse heating	23 264	20 661	17 864	15 742
Aquaculture pond heating	11 521	10 976	11 733	13 493
Agricultural drying	1 635	2 013	1 038	1 124
Industrial uses	11 746	10 868	10 220	10 120
Bathing and swimming	109 410	83 018	79 546	15 742
Cooling/snow melting	2 126	2 032	1 063	1 124
Others	955	1 045	3 034	2 249
Total	223 682	185 869	167 424	97 824
	Capacity factor			
Space heating	0.37	0.40	0.42	0.47
Greenhouse heating	0.48	0.47	0.45	0.46
Aquaculture pond heating	0.56	0.57	0.61	0.39
Agricultural drying	0.41	0.41	0.44	0.53
Industrial uses	0.70	0.71	0.68	0.59
Bathing and swimming	0.52	0.49	0.64	0.46
Cooling/snow melting	0.18	0.18	0.30	0.31
Others	0.72	0.39	0.70	0.30
Average	0.46	0.46	0.54	0.46

District heating is approximately 85% of the space heating values.

Table 4 National geothermal direct-use contribution

Iceland	Provides 89% of the country's space heating needs through 30 urban district heating systems and 200 rural systems
Turkey	Space heating has increased by 40% in the past 5 years, supplying 201 000 equivalent residences, and 30% of the country will be heated with geothermal energy in the future
Tunisia	Greenhouse heating has increased from 100 to 194 ha over the past 5 years
Japan	Over 2000 hot spring resorts (onsens), over 5000 public bath houses, and over 15 000 hotels, visited by 15 million guests per year
France	Geothermal district heating supplies heat to 150 000 dwellings, mainly in the Paris and Aquitaine basins
Hungary	Geothermal energy is used for a variety of applications, including heating greenhouses and animal farms, heating of spas and sports centers, for secondary oil recovery, and for district heating
China	Almost equal amount of geothermal energy is utilized for fish farming, heating greenhouses, agricultural crop drying, industrial process heat, district heating, and bathing and swimming. The country is the largest user of geothermal energy in the world, accounting for 20% of the annual energy used

load 80–90% of the time, thus improving the efficiency and economics of the system [8] as shown in **Figure 4**. Geothermal district heating systems are capital intensive: the principal liabilities are initial investment costs for production and injection wells, downhole and circulation pumps, heat exchangers, pipelines and distribution network, flow meters, valves and control equipment, and building retrofit. The distribution network may be the largest single capital expense, at approximately 35–75% of the entire project cost. Operating expenses, however, are in comparison lower and consist of pumping power, system maintenance, control, and management. The typical savings to consumers range from approximately 30% to 50% per year of the cost of natural gas [9].

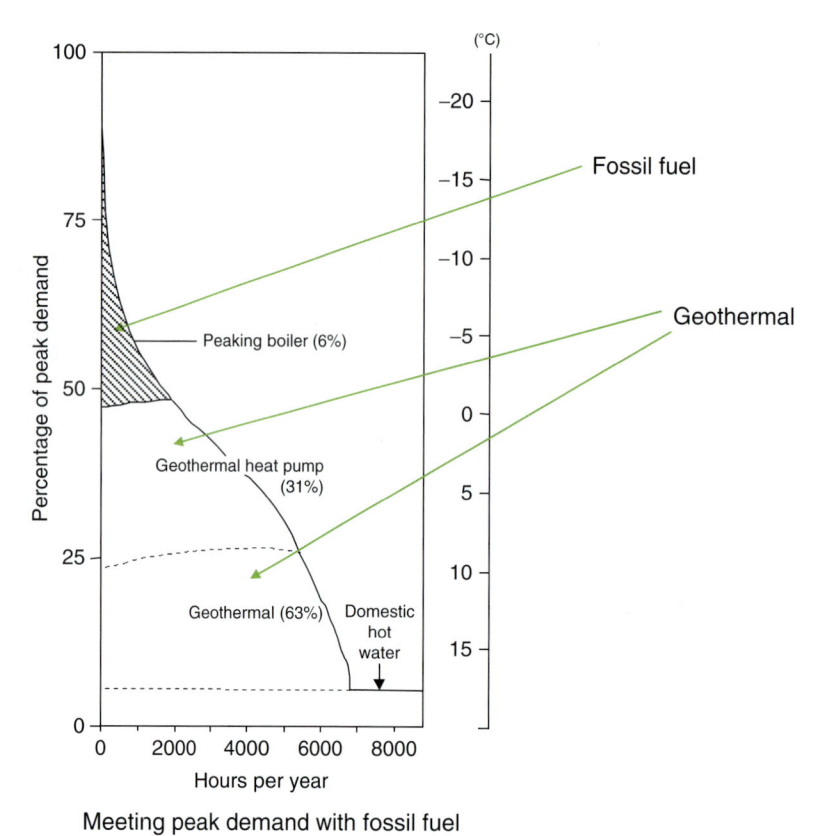

Figure 4 Peaking a geothermal system with fossil fuel.

7.05.4.3 Greenhouses

A variety of commercial crops can be raised in greenhouses, making geothermal resources in cold climates particularly attractive. Crops include vegetables, flowers (potted and cut), houseplants, and tree seedlings. Greenhouse heating can be accomplished by several methods: finned pipe, unit heater and fan coil units delivering heat through plastic tubes in the ceiling or under benches, radiant floor systems, bare tubing, or a combination of these methods. The use of geothermal energy for heating can reduce operating costs and allow operation in colder climates where commercial greenhouses would not normally be economical. It is also important, for certain crops as shown in **Figure 5**, to keep temperatures constant to optimize growth – a task ideally suited for geothermal energy. Economics of a geothermal greenhouse operation depends on many variables, such as type of crop, climate, resource temperature, type of structure, and market. Peak heating requirements in a temperate climate zone are around $1.0 \, MJ \, m^{-2}$, and a 2.0 ha facility would require $20 \, GJ \, yr^{-1}$ (5.5 MWt) of installed capacity. With a load factor of 0.50, the annual energy consumption would be around $90 \, TJ \, yr^{-1}$ (25 million $kWh \, yr^{-1}$).

7.05.4.4 Aquaculture

Aquaculture involves the raising of freshwater or marine organisms in a controlled environment to enhance production rates. The principal species raised are aquatic animals such as catfish, bass, tilapia, sturgeon, shrimp, tropical fish, and even alligators. The application temperature in fish farming depends on the species involved, ranging from 13 to 30 °C, and the geothermal water can be used in raceways, ponds, and tanks. The benefit of a controlled rearing temperature in aquaculture operations can increase growth rates by 50–100%, and thus increase the number of harvest per year (**Figure 6**). A typical outdoor pond in a temperature climate zone would require $2.5 \, MJ \, h^{-1} \, m^{-2}$, and a 2.0 ha facility would require an installed capacity of $50 \, GJ \, yr^{-1}$ (14 MWt) peak. With a load factor of 0.60, the annual heating requirement would be $260 \, TJ \, yr^{-1}$ (73 million $kWh \, yr^{-1}$). Water quality and disease control are important in fish farming and, thus, need to be considered when using geothermal fluids directly in the ponds.

7.05.4.5 Industrial and Agricultural Drying

Industrial and agricultural drying applications mostly need higher temperature as compared to space heating, greenhouses, and aquaculture projects, which is generally >100 °C. Examples of industrial operations that use geothermal energy are heap leaching operations to extract precious metals in the United States (110 °C), dehydration of vegetables in the United States (104 °C),

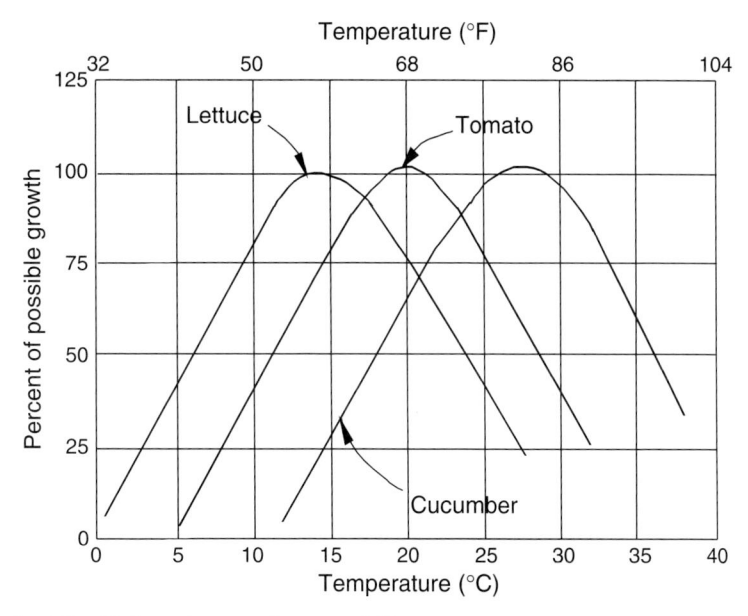

Figure 5 Temperature–growth relationship for various greenhouse vegetables.

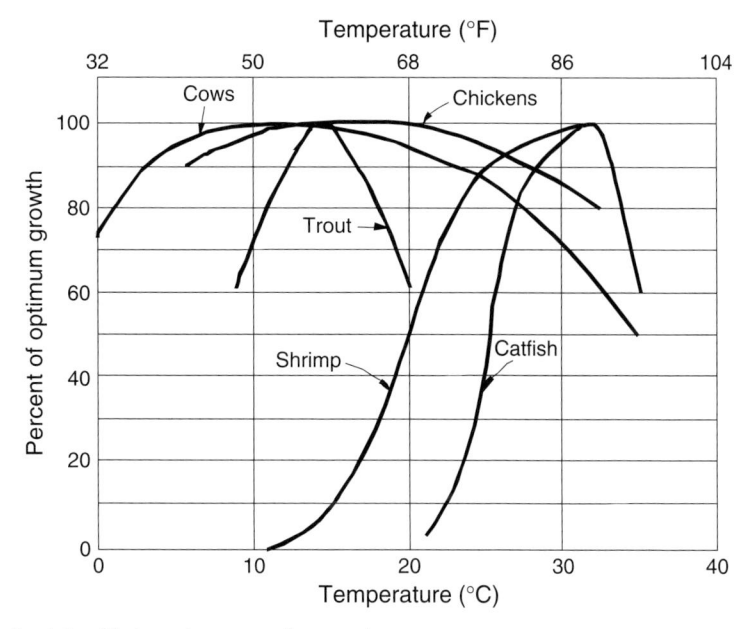

Figure 6 Temperature–growth relationship for various aquaculture species.

diatomaceous earth drying in Iceland (180 °C), and pulp and paper processing in New Zealand (205 °C). Drying and dehydration may be the two most important process uses of geothermal energy. A variety of vegetable and fruit products can be considered for dehydration at geothermal temperatures, such as onions, garlic, carrots, pears, apples, and dates. Industrial processes also make more efficient use of the geothermal resources as they tend to have high load factors in the range of 0.4–0.7. High load factors reduce the cost per unit of energy used as indicated in **Figure 7** (Rafferty, 2003).

7.05.5 Selecting the Equipment

It is often necessary to isolate the geothermal fluid from the user side to prevent corrosion and scaling. Care must be taken to prevent oxygen from entering the system (geothermal water is normally oxygen free), and dissolved gases and minerals such as boron, arsenic, and hydrogen sulfide must be removed or isolated as they are harmful to plants and animals. Hydrogen sulfide will also attack copper

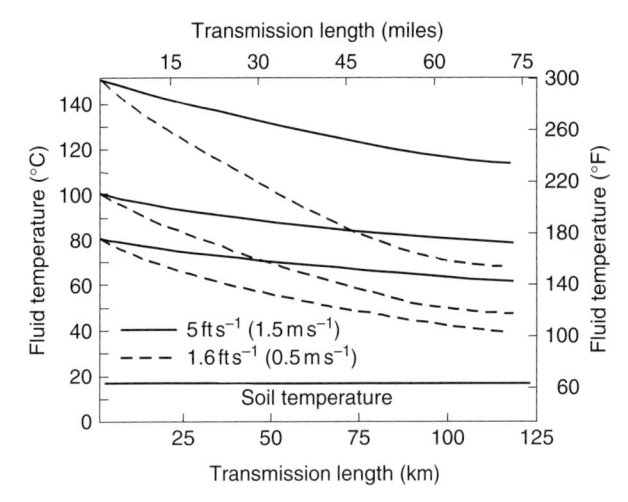

Figure 10 Temperature drop in hot water transmission line.

range of 0.1–1.0 °C km^{-1}, and in uninsulated lines, the loss is in the range of 2–5 °C km^{-1} (in the approximate range of flow of 5–15 l s^{-1} for a 15 cm-diameter pipe) [14] (**Figure 10**). For example, less than 2 °C loss is experienced in the new aboveground 29 km-long and 80 and 90 cm-diameter line (with 10 cm of rock wool insulation) from Nesjavellir to Reykjavik in Iceland. The flow rate is around 560 l s^{-1} and takes 7 h to cover the distance.

7.05.5.3 Heat Exchangers

Geothermal water, due to its high temperature, may contain a variety of dissolved chemicals that can be corrosive to various metals used in the heating system. Thus, it is usually advisable to isolate the geothermal water from the secondary heating system flowing through the various equipment components. To transfer the heat from the geothermal water to a secondary system (water or antifreeze fluid), a heat exchanger is used. The heat exchanger can be of the shell-and-tube type or a plate-and-frame type. The shell-and-tube types are not normally used in geothermal systems due to their large size compared to the plate-and-frame types and the difficulty of cleaning the tubes. The plate-and-frame types are the most common type of heat exchangers used in geothermal systems due to the superior thermal performance (i.e., low temperature loss between the geothermal and secondary fluid, called the approach temperature, which can be as low as 1–2 °C), the wide availability of corrosion-resistant alloys, ease of maintenance (they can easily be taken apart and the individual plates cleaned or replaced as necessary), the expandability (plates can easily be subtracted or added to the frame as needed), and the compact design [15] (**Figure 11**).

Downhole heat exchangers (DHEs) are the third type of heat exchangers used in geothermal systems, which eliminate the problem of disposal of geothermal fluid, since only heat is taken from the well. However, their use is limited to small heating loads (usually <1 MWt) such as heating of individual homes. The exchanger consists of a system of pipes suspended in a well through which secondary water is pumped or allowed to circulate by natural convection (**Figure 12**). These have been used successfully in Klamath Falls, Oregon, and Rotorua, New Zealand [16].

Two primary temperature differences govern the feasibility, flow requirements, and design of a heat exchanger: (1) the difference (ΔT) between the entering geothermal fluid temperature and the process temperature; and (2) the difference (ΔT) between the entering and leaving geothermal fluid temperature, which determines the flow rate. The temperature of the entering geothermal fluid must be sufficiently above the process (secondary fluid or air) temperature to be reasonable to size the heat exchanger

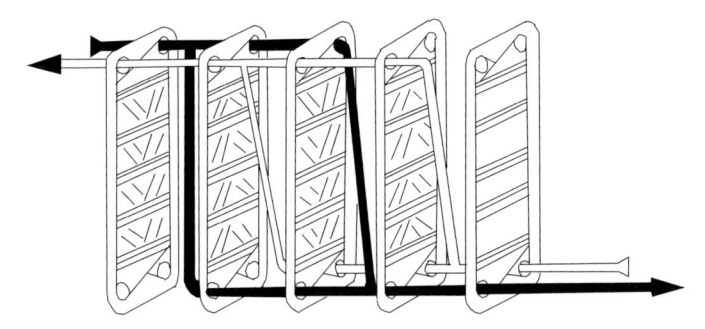

Figure 11 Plate heat exchanger.

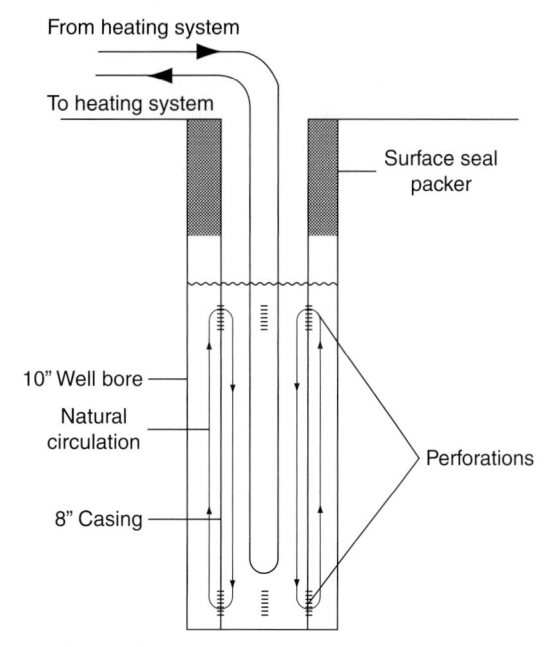

Figure 12 Typical downhole heat exchanger in Klamath Falls, Oregon.

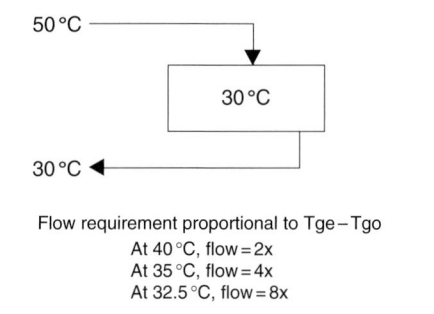

Flow requirement proportional to Tge – Tgo
At 40 °C, flow = 2x
At 35 °C, flow = 4x
At 32.5 °C, flow = 8x

Figure 13 Flow rate criteria. Tge, geothermal entering temperature; Tgo, geothermal exiting temperature.

(generally 5–10 °C greater). The greater the ΔT for the geothermal fluid, the lower the cost of the heat exchangers, and the lower the required flow rate as illustrated in **Figure 13** [17].

7.05.6 Environmental Considerations

Geothermal energy is considered a renewable and 'green' energy resource; however, there are several environmental impacts that must be considered and are usually mitigated. These are emission of harmful gases, noise pollution, water use and quality, land use, and impact on natural phenomena, wildlife, and vegetation [18].

Emissions: These are usually associated with steam power plant cooling towers that produce water vapor emission (steam), not smoke. The potential gases that can be released, depending upon the reservoir type, are carbon dioxide, sulfur dioxide, nitrous oxides, and hydrogen sulfide along with particulate matter. However, direct-use projects normally do not produce any pollutants, since the fluid is usually below boiling, and the water is injected back into the ground after use without exposing it to the atmosphere.

Noise: The majority of the noise produced at a direct-use site is during the well drilling operation, which can shutdown at night.

Water use: In arid areas or where surface water or groundwater has already been appropriated, this can limit the size and disposal system for a direct-use project. In most direct-use projects, only heat is extracted from the water, and the reject water is then returned to the aquifer, thus mitigating the water use problem.

Land use: Geothermal projects are designed to 'blend-in' with the surrounding landscape, and can be located near recreational areas with minimum land and visual impacts. Subsidence and induced seismicity are two land use issues that must be considered when withdrawing fluids from the ground. These are usually mitigated by injecting the spent fluid back into the same reservoir. In addition, utilizing geothermal resources eliminates the mining, processing, and transporting required for electricity generation from fossil fuel and nuclear resources.

Impact on natural phenomena, wildlife, and vegetation: Projects are usually prevented from being located near geysers, fumaroles, and hot springs, as the extraction of fluids might impact these thermal manifestations. Most projects are located in areas with no natural surface discharges. Designers and operators are especially sensitive about preserving manifestations considered sacred to indigenous people. Direct-use projects are usually small and, thus, have no significant impact on natural features.

In summary, the use of geothermal energy for direct-use is reliable, is renewable, has minimum to no air emission, has minimum environmental impacts, is combustion free, and is a domestic fuel source.

7.05.7 Case Histories

7.05.7.1 Tomato Drying in Greece

A small tunnel dryer has been constructed in northern Greece for dehydration of tomatoes [19]. The drying tunnel is a 14 m long × 1 m wide × 2 m high construction of polyurethane aluminum panels (**Figure 14**). Geothermal water at temperature 59 °C and flow rate 25 m^3 h^{-1} is fed into a finned-tube coil air/water heat exchanger for heating the drying air with a capacity of 1.26 MJ producing air temperature of 55 °C. The drying racks have 25 trays each holding about 7 kg of raw tomatoes. One rack is introduced into the head of the tunnel every 45 min. It then takes about 30 h for the rack to reach the end of the tunnel, reducing the moisture content from about 150% to 10% by dry weight; thus, 100 kg of raw product produces about 9.5 kg of dried product. The final product is then placed in oil and bottled for shipment. The long drying time appears to preserve the color and aroma of the tomatoes as compared to sun drying. Only three persons operate the plant. Up to 5.5 t has been produced in a year.

7.05.7.2 District Heating in Reykjavik, Iceland

The Reykjavik district heating began in 1930 when some official buildings and about 70 private houses received hot water from geothermal wells that were close to the old thermal springs in the city. In 1943, production of hot water from the Reykir field, 18 km from the city, started. Today, Reykjavik Energy utilizes low-temperature areas within and in the vicinity of Reykjavik as well as the high-temperature field at Nesjavellir, about 27 km away (**Figure 15**). A total of 91 wells provide water to the system, and the number used depends upon demand. The water is transported through 3846 km of pipelines delivering 79.7 million m^3 of water annually. Geothermal water is supplied to the downtown system from 89 to 125 °C, and then distributed to individual buildings at 75 °C. Large storage tanks are situated on a hill above the town to provide water for peaking, and an oil-fired booster station is provided to

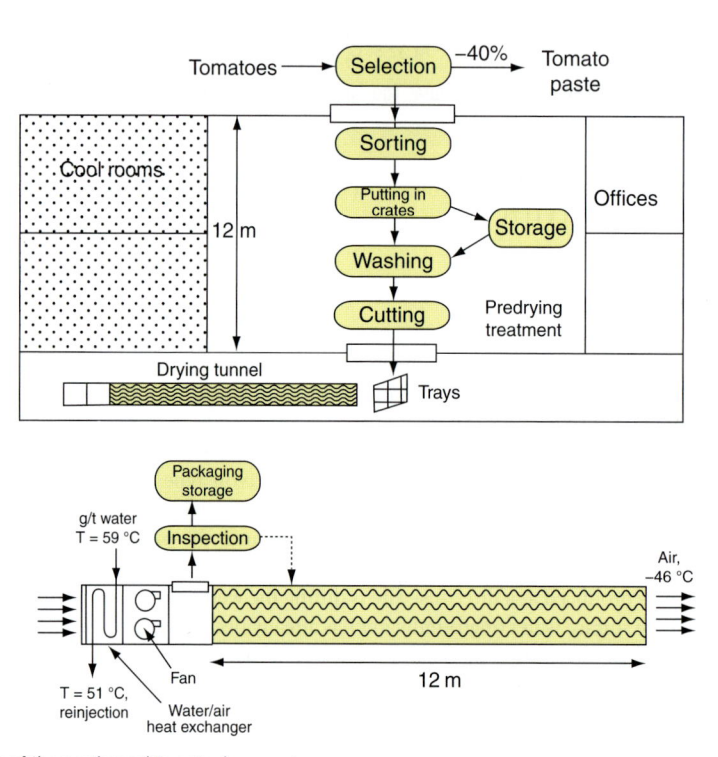

Figure 14 Schematic diagram of the geothermal tomato dryer system.

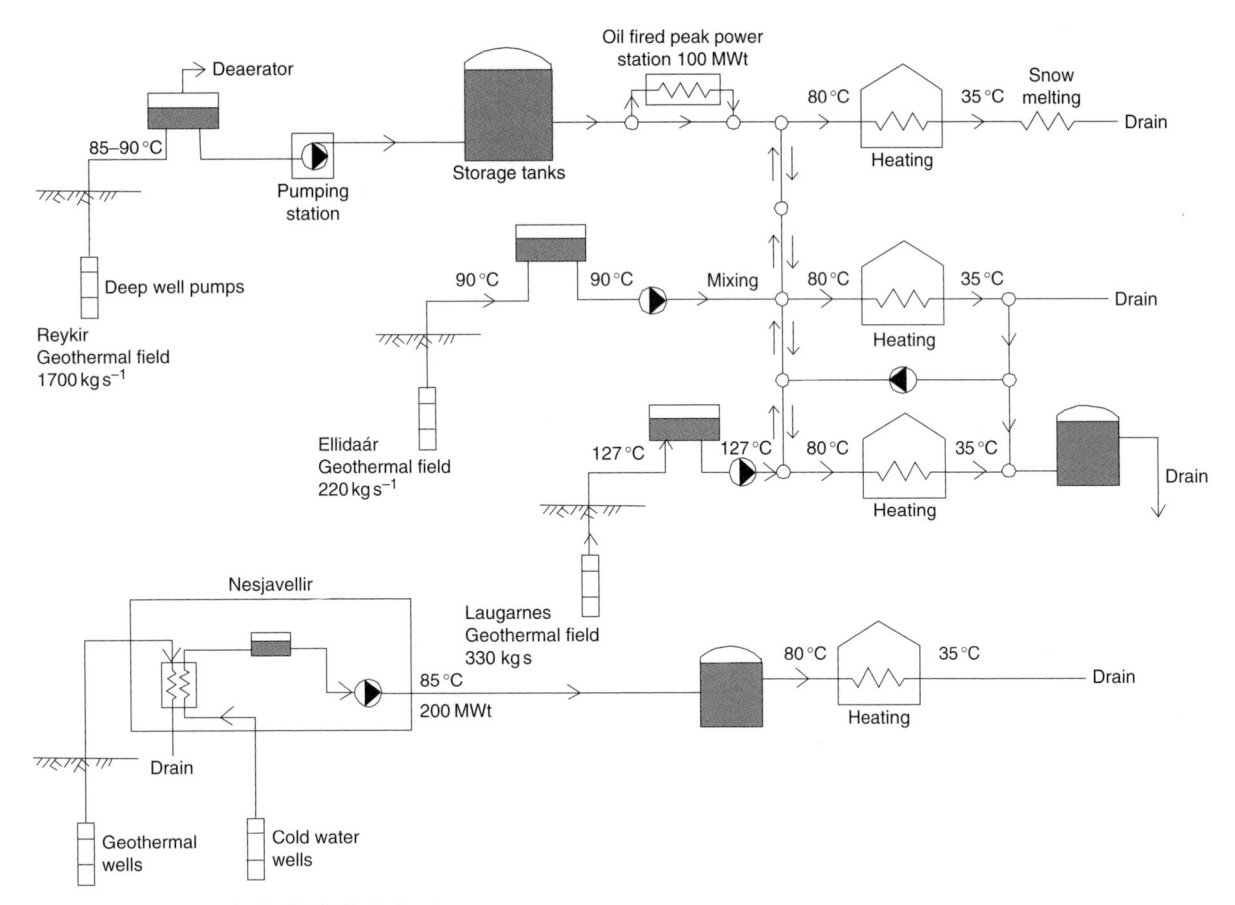

Figure 15 Schematic of the Reykjavik district heating system.

supply additional heat to the water in the coldest days. The system is adequate to −26 °C. Today, almost 200 000 people are served in buildings totaling 58 million m³. The installed capacity of the system is 1264 MWt with the peak load (2006) of 924 MWt [5].

7.05.7.3 Greenhouse Heating in Hungary

Agricultural use of geothermal energy is an important industry in Hungary. More than 67 ha of greenhouses and more than 232 ha of plastic tents are supplied with geothermal heat from 193 wells [20]. Vegetables, such as peppers, tomatoes, and cucumbers, are grown in about 25% of the greenhouses and 95% of the plastic tents. The remaining greenhouses are used for nursery stock, ornamental plants, and cut flowers. The most common greenhouse in use is one constructed of galvanized steel and glass mounted on 25 cm-high concrete strip foundations. The floor space is 3.2 × 6.4 m modules with an eave height of 2.7 m. The plastic tents are usually constructed of bent-to-shape plastic or galvanized steel pipes with a spacing of 1.5 m, which are anchored either directly in the ground or on concrete strip foundations. The width varies from 4.5 to 7.5 m, with the latter being the most common. The height is around 2 m and they can be up to 100 m long. A typical greenhouse and plastic tent geothermal heating system is illustrated in **Figure 16** [21, 22]. Water is produced by deep-well pumps and discharged into a degassing tank. The water then flows by gravity to a collection tank and then circulated by pumps to the greenhouse heating system. The greenhouse supply temperature is 80 °C and the exit temperature is 40 °C. The wastewater is then combined with geothermal water at 82 °C to produce 60 °C fluid for cascading to plastic tents. The final effluent, at 25 °C, is then stored for future use, such as irrigation. Ice and snow on the roof or in the downspouts can also be melted using the geothermal wastewater.

7.05.7.4 Timber Drying in New Zealand

The two main reasons for drying timber are to set the sap and to prevent warping. The sap usually sets at 57–60 °C and warping is prevented by establishing uniform moisture content through the thickness of wood, which is best achieved in a kiln. The drying rate varies with the species of wood and decreases (time increases) with thickness. With the rapid decline in the availability of native timber species in New Zealand, the large plantation-grown radiata pine was utilized. However, this species of pine has a very high moisture content – up to 130% by weight. Thus, kiln drying was necessary to be able to supply a completely predictable and uniform product. A drying kiln associated with the Tasman Pulp and Paper Plant at Kawerau operated by Fletcher Challenge Forest

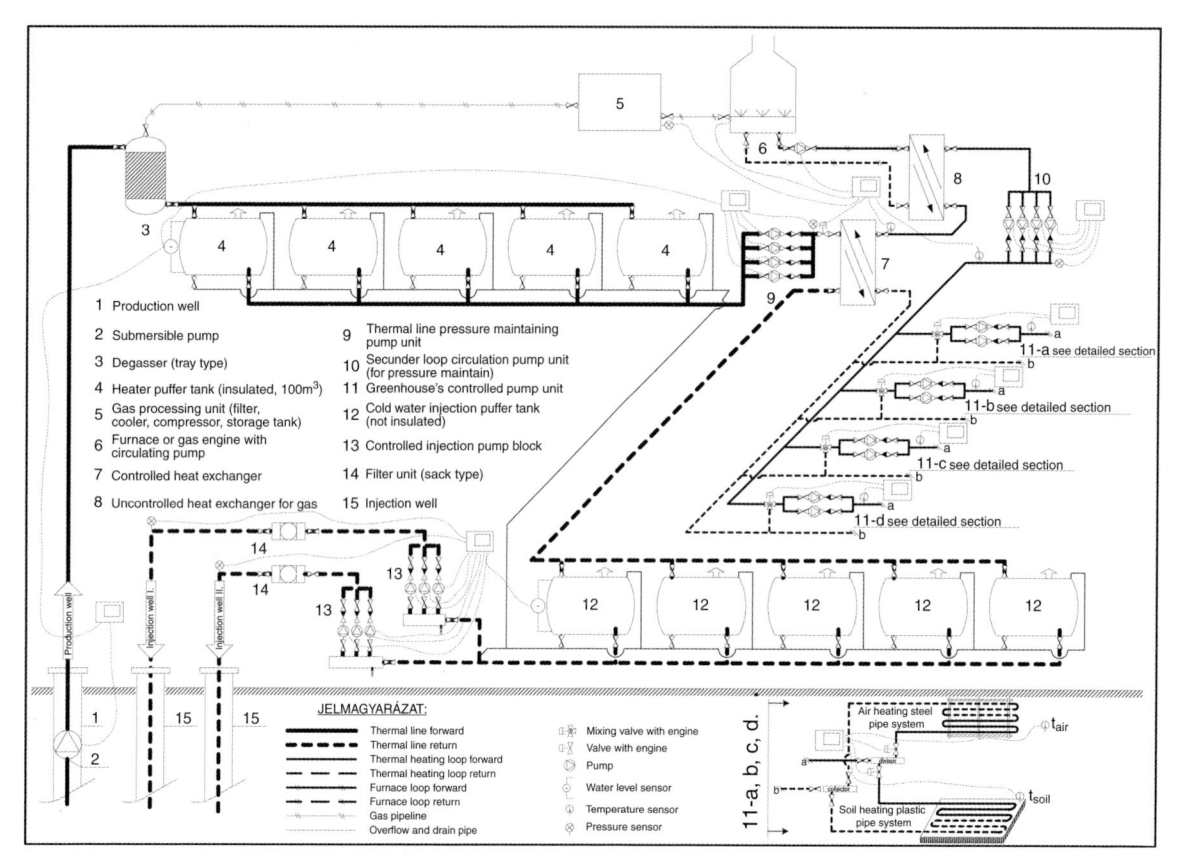

Figure 16 Schematic of greenhouse heating system in Hungary with greenhouses and plastic tents.

was selected for drying the radiata pine (**Figure 17**). This kiln uses 10 bar geothermal steam at an inlet temperature of 180 °C, which produces 150 °C temperature in the kiln. Radiata pine in batches of 80–100 m³ is moved into the kiln on three rail-mounted trucks. In the kiln, the moisture content is reduced from 150% to 10% in 20 h. Two-meter-diameter fans produce 9 m s⁻¹ air across pipe heat exchangers. The entire process creates a uniform moisture content throughout each piece of lumber. Prior to using geothermal energy, the lumber was dried at 70 °C for 4 days – a much more costly operation. Kiln drying costs about US$20 per m³, of which the cost of geothermal energy is about 5–10% [23].

7.05.7.5 Onion Dehydration in the United States

All onions for processing are grown from specific varieties best suited for dehydration. Specific strains of Creole Onion, Southport Globe Onion, and Hybrid Southport Globe were developed by the dehydration industry. They are white in color and possess a higher solid content, which yields a more flavorful and pungent onion. Onion dehydration involves the use of a continuous operation, belt conveyor using fairly low-temperature hot air from 40 to 100 °C. Typical processing plants will handle 4500 kg of raw product per hour (single line), reducing the moisture content from around 83% to 4% (680–820 kg of finished product). These plants can produce 2.3 million kg of dry product per year using from 51 to 68 kJ per dry kg produced. Two geothermal onion dehydration plants have operated in the United States located in Nevada – Integrated Ingredients near Empire (presently shutdown due to economic reasons) and Geothermal Food Processors at Brady's Hot Spring. The single-line dryer at these plants is divided into four stages, starting at 100 °C in the A stage down to 50 °C in the D stage. A total of 27.2 GJ h⁻¹ of geothermal energy is used. Geothermal fluid at temperature 104 °C and flow rate 3.4 m³ min⁻¹ is supplied from wells. Finned air/water heat exchangers are used in each compartment, using the geothermal water to supply the heated air to the onions from below (**Figure 18**). The energy requirement for the operation of the dryer varies due to difference in outside temperature, dryer loading, and requirement for the final moisture content of the product [24].

7.05.7.6 Combined Heat and Power in Austria

Altheim is a town in the Upper Austrian 'Inn-region' with a population of 5000. A geothermal district heating system supplied by 106 °C geothermal fluid flowing from an aquifer about 2300 m deep at 85 l s⁻¹ was established in 1989. Presently, about 650 consumers are connected to the heat supply, with a thermal power load of 10 MWt. About 40% of the inhabitants of Altheim are connected to the heat supply. The supply network has a length of about 14.5 km. The biggest single consumers are municipal facilities with about 1.0 MWt of thermal power utilized. The rest of the buildings are one- and two-family houses. In 1994, a second

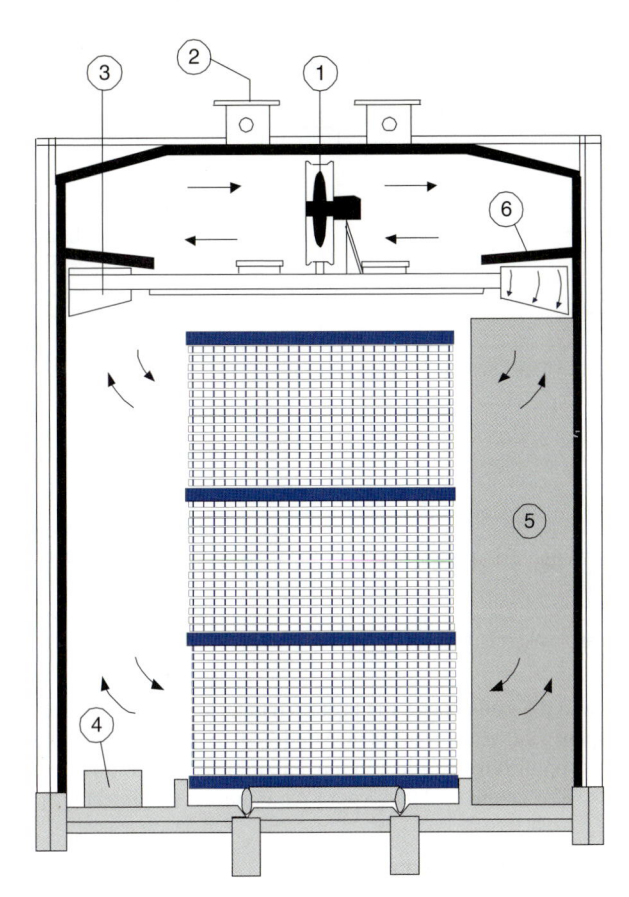

1. Adjustable pitch aluminum fan
2. Aluminum ventilator
3. Aluminum side air baffle
4. Water trough for humidification
5. Adjustable aluminum vertical end air baffle
6. Bi-metallic estruded aluminum finned heat Exchanger tubes

Figure 17 Cross section of timber drying kiln at Kawerau, New Zealand.

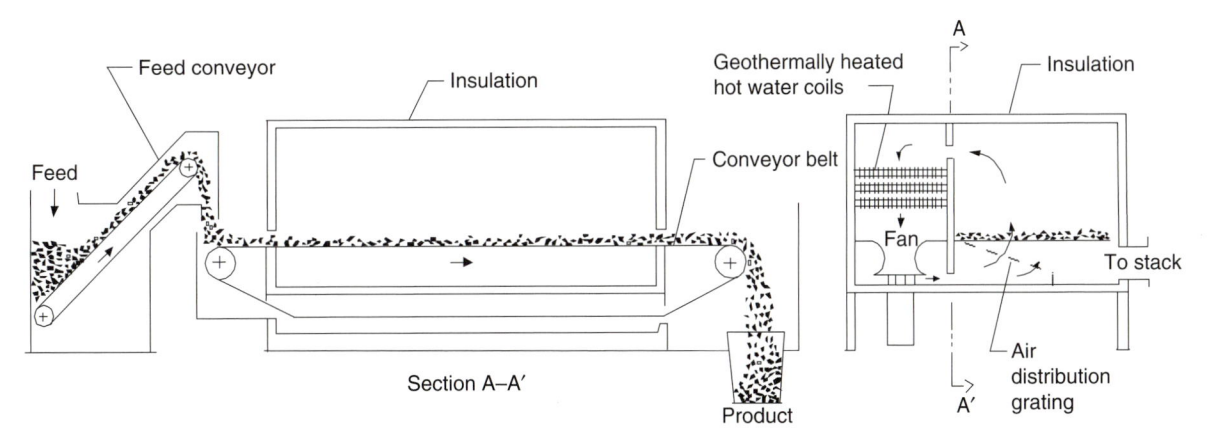

Figure 18 Cross sections of a typical food dehydrator.

well was drilled to provide energy for a binary power plant. This well came is at 93 °C, thus it was used as the injection well for the system. A 1.0 MWe Turboden (Brescia, Italy) binary power plant was installed in 2000. The plant has been operated at a peak of 564 kWe, occurring in the summer when space heating is not needed, and at a low of 360 kWe in the winter. Heated water is supplied to the homes and municipal buildings (about 8 MWt) through a heat exchanger at 90 °C and is returned at 60 °C to the heat exchanger. The power plant receives 106 °C water at a heat exchanger at about half the supply of 85–100 l s^{-1} (the other half

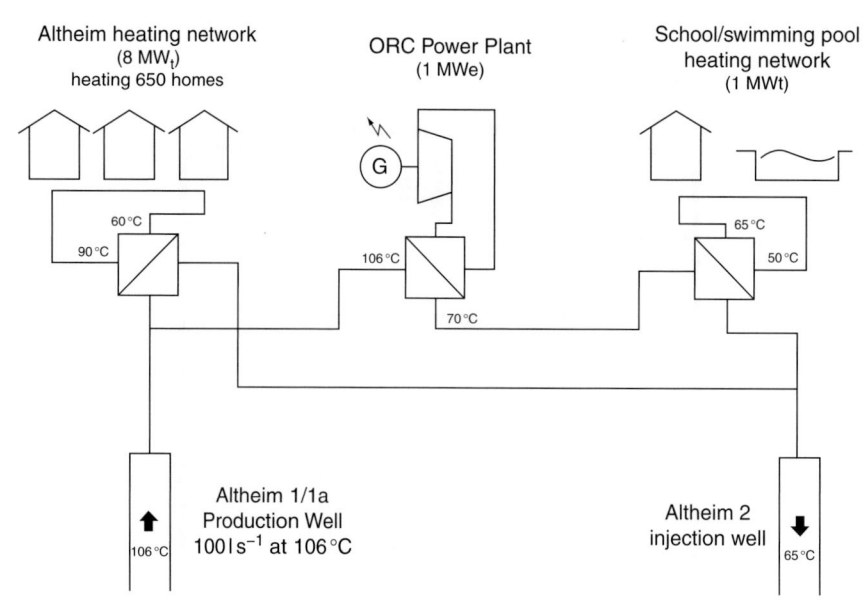

Figure 19 Combined heat and power plant in Altheim, Austria.

goes to the district heating system) and the water leaves the heat exchanger at 70 °C to be delivered to the school and swimming pool heat exchanger. The collected spent geothermal water is then delivered to the injection well at 65 °C (**Figure 19**). About 63% of the gross electric power production is supplied to the grid and the remaining is used to power various pumps in the system. Heat is supplied to customers between US$0.027 5 and US$0.044 5 per kWh (summer to winter) [25].

7.05.7.7 Individual Building Heating in the United States

In Klamath Falls, Oregon, approximately 600 buildings (individual homes and schools) are heated with geothermal energy using a DHE. The DHE eliminates the problem of disposal of geothermal fluid, since only heat is taken from the well. The DHE consists of a system of pipes or tubes suspended in a well through which 'clean' secondary water (city water) is pumped or allowed to circulate by natural convection. These systems offer substantial economic savings over surface heat exchangers where a single-well system is adequate (typically less than 0.8 MWt, with well depths up to about 150 m, and may be economical under certain conditions at well depths to 450 m). The wells in Klamath Falls are 25–30 cm in diameter, drilled 6 m or more into 'live water' (fractured volcanics) after which a 20 cm-diameter casing is installed. The casing is perforated at the bottom of the well in the live water area and just below the lowest static water level. These perforations and the open annulus area between the casing and the well sides generate a vertical convection cell to circulate the hotter water over the entire length of the well. Space heating is provided by a 4–5 cm-diameter black iron pipe with a return U at the bottom and domestic hot water by a 2–2.5 cm-diameter pipe with a similar U at the bottom (see **Figure 12**). The in-house heating system consists of a circulation pump (if needed), city water feed-in with a pressure reducing and pressure relief valve, and an air expansion tank. The space heating loop is a closed system providing heat to baseboard radiators, a forced air system, or in-floor heating. The domestic hot water loop is open ended [26].

7.05.7.8 Aquaculture Pond Heating in the United States

Giant freshwater prawns (*Macrobrachium rosenbergii*) were raised experimentally on the Oregon Institute of Technology (OIT) campus in Klamath Falls, Oregon. The optimum growth temperature is from 27 to 28 °C, but they can exist in waters with temperatures between 13 and 35 °C [27]. For best results the ponds should be between 0.1 and 0.2 ha, about 15–30 m wide, 64 m long, and 1.2 m deep, thus making them relatively easy for four people to seine harvest the crop. The wastewater from the OIT system was used to supply temperatures between 55 and 65 °C to the ponds. The initial ponds constructed were about 0.2 ha each (30.5 × 64 m) (**Figure 20**). The geothermal water was supplied through a 5 cm-diameter header of black iron pipe (however, plastic pipe can also be used) to 3.75 cm-diameter diffuser pipes with 4 mm-diameter holes at 0.65 m separation on the bottom of the ponds. These diffuser pipes provide water of uniform temperature throughout the ponds. The temperature of the water in the ponds was controlled by a solenoid valve on the header pipe. The flow of geothermal water varied from about 10 l s^{-1} at –3 °C to almost zero in the summer. The stocking density of the ponds was about 14 prawns per m^2; thus, a 0.2 ha pond could be stocked with approximately 31 500 post-larval species. Growth rates were about 2 cm per month, about double the normal rates for unheated ponds in warmer climates. Another prawn, tilapia, and tropical fish farm near Klamath Falls is currently successful and does not use the diffuser pipes. It, instead, allows approximately 90 °C water to flow into one end and then empty at the other end – allowing the animals to find their own comfort temperature zone [28, 29].

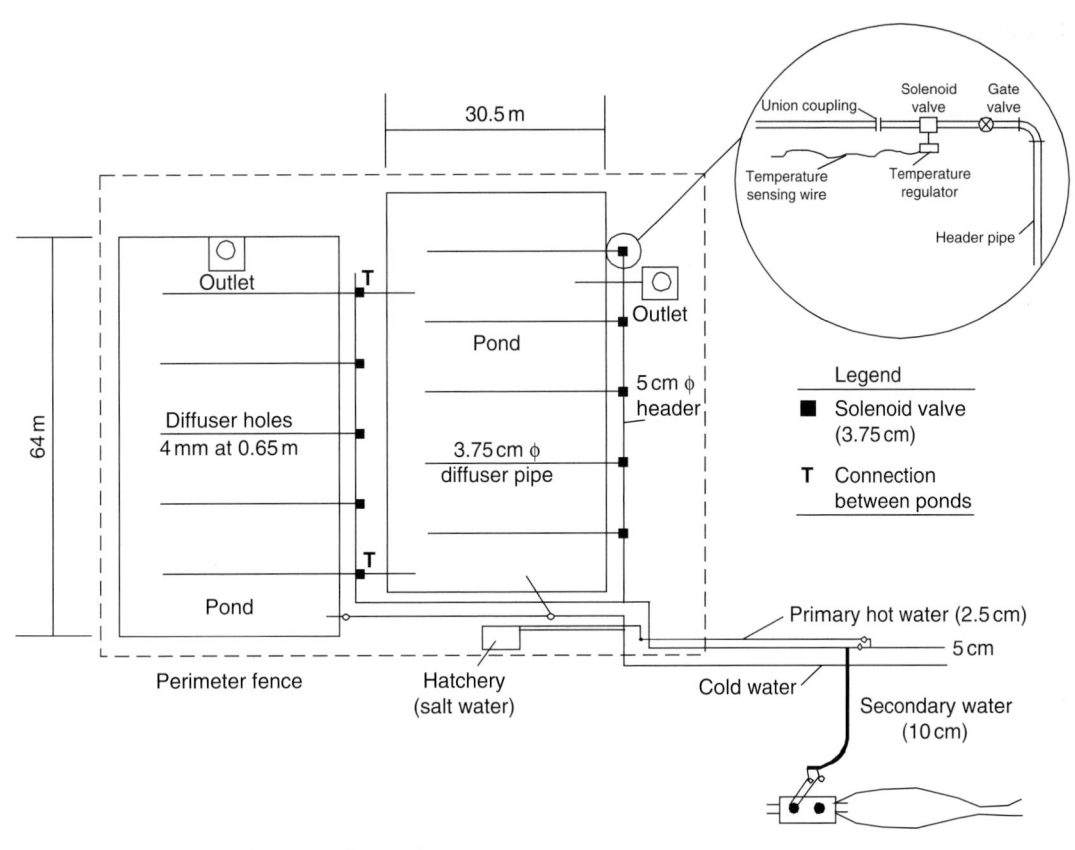

Figure 20 Oregon Institute of Technology aquaculture project.

References

[1] Cataldi R, Hodgson S, and Lund J (eds.) (1999) *Stories from a Heated Earth – Our Geothermal Heritage*, 569pp. Davis, CA: Geothermal Resources Council.
[2] Lund JW, Freeston DH, and Boyd TL (2010) Direct utilization of geothermal energy 2010 worldwide review. *Proceeding of the World Geothermal Congress 2010*. Bali, Indonesia, paper no. 0007.
[3] Gudmundsson JS and Lund JW (1985) Direct uses of earth heat. *International Journal of Energy Research* 9: 345–375.
[4] Gudmundsson JS, Freeston DH, and Lienau PJ (1985) The Lindal diagram. *Geothermal Resources Council Transactions* 9(1): 15–19.
[5] Ragnarsson A (2010) Geothermal development in Iceland 2005–2009. *Proceedings of the World Geothermal Congress 2010*. Bali, Indonesia, paper no. 0124.
[6] Mertoglu O, Simsek S, Dagistan H, et al. (2010) Geothermal country update report for Turkey (2005–2010). *Proceedings of the World Geothermal Congress 2010*. Bali, Indonesia, paper no. 0119.
[7] Lund JW (2000) Balneological use of thermal waters. *Geo-Heat Center Quarterly Bulletin* 21(3).
[8] Bloomquist RG, Nimmons JT, and Rafferty K (1987) *District Heating Development Guide*, vol. 1. Olympia: Washington State Energy Office.
[9] Lienau PJ (1998) Introduction. In: Lund JW (ed.) *Geothermal Direct-Use Engineering and Design Guidebook*, ch. 1, pp. 1–25. Klamath Falls, OR: Geo-Heat Center.
[10] Lund JW (1998) Geothermal direct-use equipment overview. *Geo-Heat Center Quarterly Bulletin* 19(1): 1–6.
[11] Culver G and Rafferty KD (1998) Well pumps. *Geo-Heat Center Quarterly Bulletin* 19(1): 7–13.
[12] Rafferty K and Keiffer S (2002) Thermal expansion in enclosed lineshaft pump columns. *Geo-Heat Center Quarterly Bulletin* 23(2): 11–15.
[13] Rafferty K (1998) Piping. *Geo-Heat Center Quarterly Bulletin* 19(1): 14–19.
[14] Ryan G (1981) Equipment used in direct heat projects. *Geothermal Resources Council Transactions* 5: 483–486.
[15] Rafferty K (1998) Heat exchangers. *Geo-Heat Center Quarterly Bulletin* 19(1): 20–26.
[16] Geo-Heat Center (1999) Downhole heat exchangers. *Geo-Heat Center Quarterly Bulletin* 20(3): 28.
[17] Rafferty K (2004) Direct-use temperature requirements: A few rules of thumb. *Geo-Heat Center Quarterly Bulletin* 25(2).
[18] Kagel A, Bates D, and Gawell K (2005) *A Guide to Geothermal Energy and the Environment*, 75pp. Washington, DC: Geothermal Energy Association.
[19] Andritsos N, Dalampakis P, and Kolios N (2003) Use of geothermal energy for tomato drying. *Geo-Heat Center Quarterly Bulletin* 24(1): 9–12.
[20] Toth A (2010) Hungary country update 2005–2009. *Proceedings of the World Geothermal Congress 2010*. Bali, Indonesia, paper no. 0125.
[21] Karai J, Kocsis J, Liebe P, et al. (1990) Present status of geothermal energy: Use in agriculture of Hungary. *Geothermal Resources Council Bulletin* 19(1): 3–14.
[22] Lund JW (1990) Geothermal agriculture in Hungary. *Geo-Heat Center Quarterly Bulletin* 12(3): 27–32.
[23] Scott JW and Lund JW (1998) Timber drying at Kawerau. *Geo-Heat Center Quarterly Bulletin* 19(3): 19–20.
[24] Lund JW and Lienau PJ (1994) Onion dehydration. *Geo-Heat Center Quarterly Bulletin* 15(4): 15–21.
[25] Pernecker G and Uhlig S (2002) Low-enthalpy power generation with ORC-turbogenerator – The Altheim project, upper Austria. *Geo-Heat Center Quarterly Bulletin* 23(1): 26–30.
[26] Culver G and Lund JW (1999) Downhole heat exchangers. *Geo-Heat Center Quarterly Bulletin* 20(3): 1–11.
[27] Smith KC (1981) A Layman's guide to geothermal aquaculture. *Geo-Heat Center, Technical Paper 63* (tp63), Klamath Falls, OR, 14pp.
[28] Clutter T (2002) Out of Africa – aquaculturist Ron Barnes uses geothermal water in southern Oregon to rear tropical fish from African Rift lake. *Geo-Heat Center Quarterly Bulletin* 23(3): 6–8.
[29] Geo-Heat Center (2003) Gone fishing' aquaculture project Klamath falls, Oregon. *Geo-Heat Center Quarterly Bulletin* 24(2): 7–9.

Further Reading

[1] Cataldi R, Hodgson SF, and Lund JW (eds.) (1999) *Stories from a Heat Earth – Our Geothermal Heritage*, 569pp. Davis, CA: International Geothermal Association and Geothermal Resources Council. Available from the Geothermal Resources Council – wwww.geothermal.org.

[2] Lund JW, Lienau PJ, and Lunis BC (eds.) (1998) *Geothermal Direct-Use Engineering and Design Guidebook*, 454pp. Klamath Falls, OR: Geo-Heat Center, Oregon Institute of Technology. Can be purchased from http://geoheat.oit.edu.

[3] Lund JW (1996) Lectures on direct utilization of geothermal energy. *United National University, Geothermal Training Program, Report 1*, 123pp. Reykjavik, Iceland: Orkustofnun. Available from www.os.is/id/620.

Relevant Websites

http://geoheat.oit.edu – Technical paper and *Quarterly Bulletin* articles from the Geo-Heat Center, Oregon Institute of Technology, Klamath Falls, OR.
http://www.geothermal.org –Technical papers from the proceedings of the Geothermal Resources Council annual meetings, Davis, CA.
http://www.geothermal-energy.org – Technical papers from the World Geothermal Congresses, International Geothermal Association.

7.06 Shallow Systems: Geothermal Heat Pumps

L Rybach, GEOWATT AG, Zurich, Switzerland

© 2012 Elsevier Ltd. All rights reserved.

7.06.1	Introduction	187
7.06.2	The Resource	187
7.06.3	Geothermal Heat Pumps	190
7.06.3.1	Common Types	190
7.06.3.2	Further Types: Energy Piles, Geothermal Baskets	191
7.06.3.3	The Core Piece: The HP	192
7.06.4	Heating and Cooling with GHPs	193
7.06.5	Site Investigations for Dimensioning	195
7.06.5.1	Conventional Thermal Response Test	195
7.06.5.2	Determination via Local Heat Flow Value	196
7.06.5.3	Enhanced Thermal Response Test	196
7.06.6	Engineering Design	197
7.06.7	Installation of GHPs	199
7.06.7.1	Borehole Heat Exchangers	200
7.06.7.2	Groundwater-Based GHPs	201
7.06.8	Operation and Maintenance (O&M)	202
7.06.9	Capital and O&M Costs, Comparison with Conventional Heating Systems	202
7.06.10	Production Sustainability	203
7.06.11	Licensing, Environmental Issues	203
References		205
Relevant Websites		205

7.06.1 Introduction

A new chapter in geothermal direct use opened with the advent of geothermal heat pumps (GHPs). This technology enables space heating, cooling, and domestic warm water production with the same installation. The GHP application is now in the focus of private, public, and municipal interest [1].

GHPs are one of the fastest growing applications of renewable energy in the world and definitely the fastest growing segment in geothermal technology in an increasing number of countries. Recent statistical data [2] indicate rapid growth (see **Figures 1** and **2**).

GHPs represent a rather new but already well-established technology, utilizing the immense renewable storage capacity of the ground. GHPs use the relatively constant temperature of the ground to provide space heating, cooling, and domestic hot water for homes, schools, factories, and public and commercial buildings. The applicational size can vary from single-family homes with 1–2 borehole heat exchangers (BHEs) to large-scale complexes with hundreds of BHEs. The decentralized systems can be tailor-made, taking into account the local conditions. It is essential to employ proper installation design that takes into account meteorological conditions, ground property, and technical supply conditions. By these means, reliable long-term operation can be secured. Of the local conditions, the thermal conductivity of ground materials and the groundwater properties are of key importance.

7.06.2 The Resource

Shallow geothermal resources (the heat content of rocks in the top few 100 m of the continental crust) represent a major and ubiquitous energy source. The Earth as planet can afford to give off heat by a thermal power of 40 million MW, without cooling down. Without utilization, the terrestrial heat flow is lost to the atmosphere. In this case, the isotherms run parallel to the Earth's surface (i.e., horizontal in flat terrain) and the heat flow lines are perpendicular to them. If, instead, the heat flow can be captured, for example, by a heat extraction device such as a BHE (see later), the isotherms are deformed and the heat flow lines can be diverted toward heat sinks (**Figure 3**).

Shallow Systems: Geothermal Heat Pumps

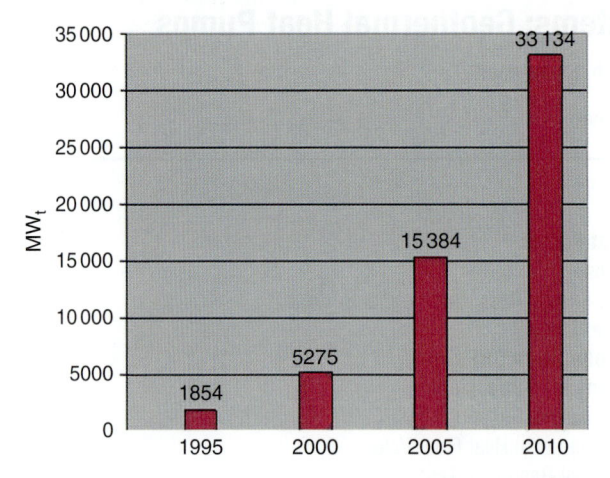

Figure 1 Worldwide installed capacity (MW$_t$) of geothermal heat pumps. Data from Lund JW, Freeston DH, and Boyd TL (2010) Direct utilization of geothermal energy 2010 worldwide review. *Proceedings of the World Geothermal Congress 2010.* Bali, Indonesia (CD-ROM) [2].

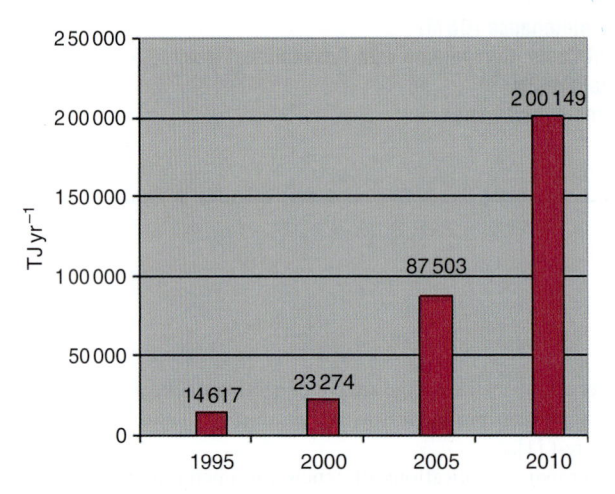

Figure 2 Worldwide use (TJ yr^{-1}) for heating by geothermal heat pumps. Data from Lund JW, Freeston DH, and Boyd TL (2010) Direct utilization of geothermal energy 2010 worldwide review. *Proceedings of the World Geothermal Congress 2010.* Bali, Indonesia (CD-ROM) [2].

The terrestrial heat flow is lost to the atmosphere

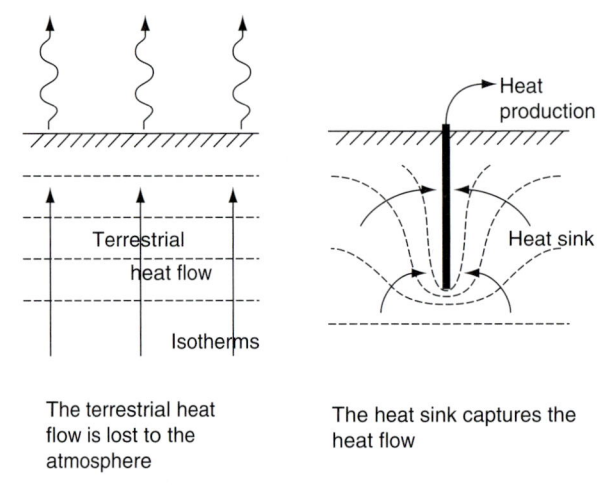

The heat sink captures the heat flow

Figure 3 Principle of geothermal heat extraction and production. Reproduced from Rybach L (2008) The international status, development, and future prospects of geothermal energy. *Proceedings of Renewable Energy 2008.* Busan, S. Korea (CD-ROM) [3].

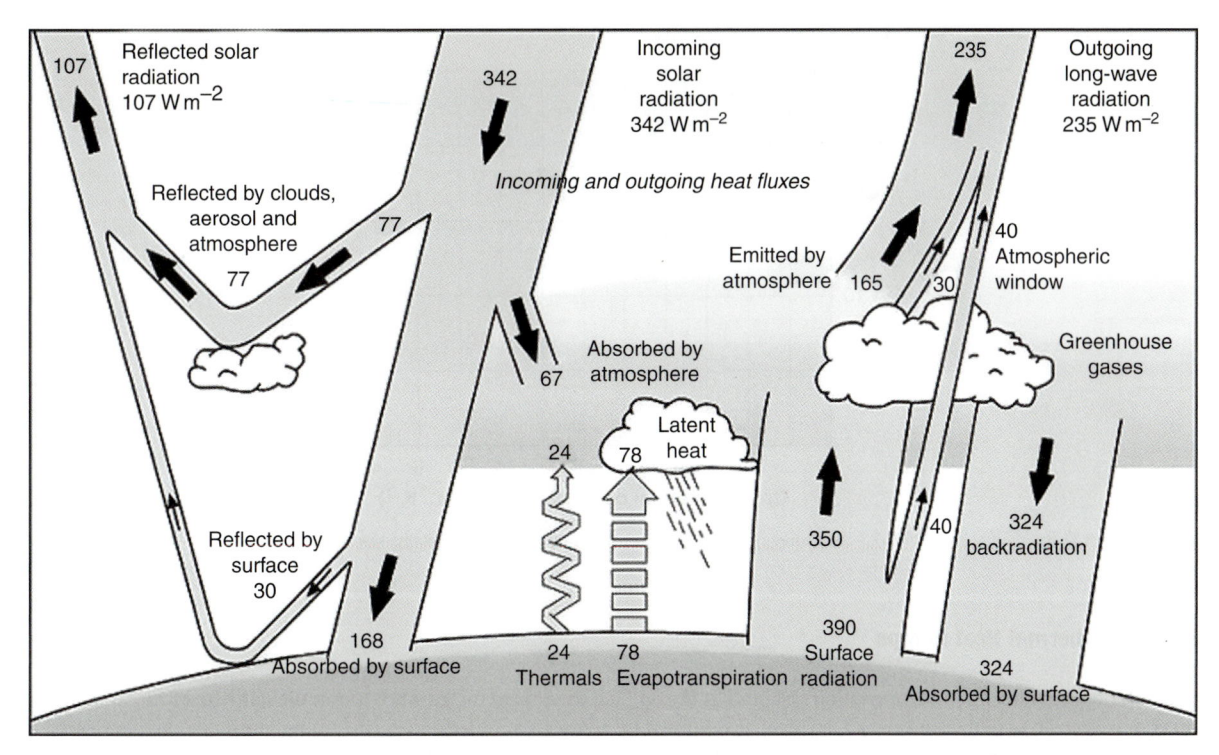

Figure 4 Incoming and outgoing solar radiation at the Earth's surface. Reproduced with modification from Kiehl JT and Trenberth KE (1997) Earth's annual global mean energy budget. *Bulletin of the American Meteorological Society* 78: 197–208 [4].

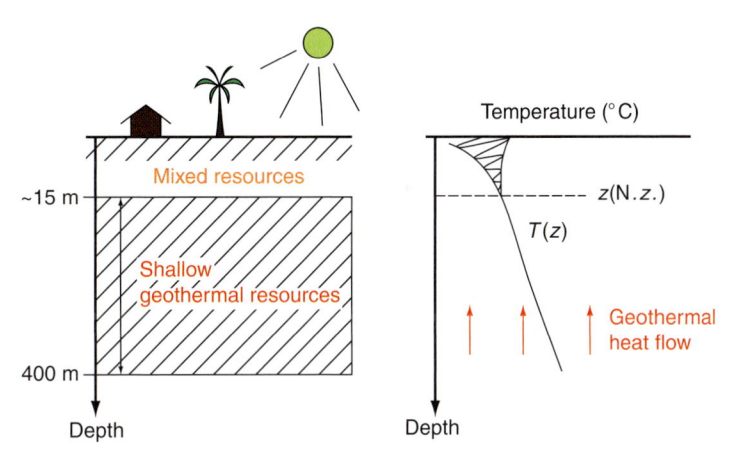

Figure 5 The depth domain of shallow geothermal resources (left) and the general temperature–depth function. In the topmost 10–20 m, the annual surface temperature variations are noticeable. z(N.Z.) denotes the depth of the neutral zone. For details, see text.

Occasionally, it is claimed that the shallow geothermal resource consists of stored solar energy. This is completely wrong – the thermal conditions at the Earth's surface are balanced: the solar heat energy irradiated is reradiated completely back to the atmosphere (otherwise the Earth's surface would be heated up and life would be impossible). **Figure 4** shows the numerical values of solar incoming and outgoing heat fluxes.

By definition, geothermal energy is the energy in the form of heat beneath the surface of the solid Earth. The domain of shallow geothermal energy is customarily considered to comprise the topmost 400 m of the Earth's continental crust. Temperature changes at the earth's surface propagate down to a certain depth; at any location, there is a depth at which the amplitude of annual variations decreases to become negligible. This depth is termed the 'depth of neutral zone', z(N.Z.); **Figure 5** shows the situation. The depth z(N.Z.) depends on the amplitude of annual temperature variations and on the local ground thermal conductivity λ. For example, in moderate climate, the depth z(N.Z.) is approximately $10\lambda^{1/2}$; **Figure 6** depicts the dependence of z(N.Z.) on λ.

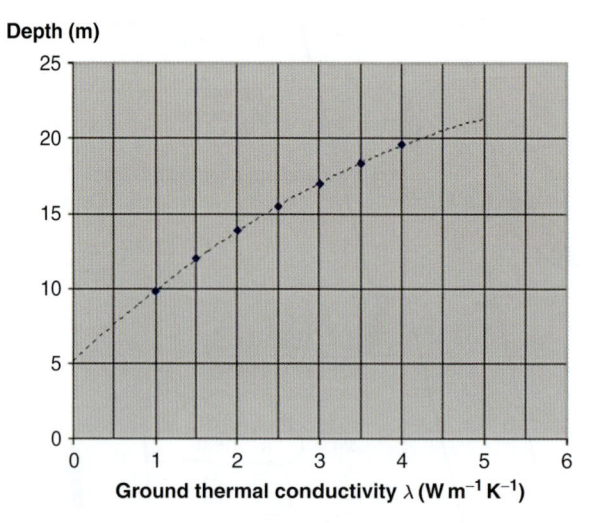

Figure 6 Depth of the neutral zone, z (N.Z.), as a function of ground thermal conductivity. For details, see text.

7.06.3 Geothermal Heat Pumps

A GHP is a decentral heating and/or cooling system that moves heat to or from the ground. It uses the Earth as a heat source (in the winter) or a heat sink (in the summer). GHPs are also known by a variety of other names, including ground-source, geoexchange, earth-coupled, earth energy, or water-source heat pumps (HPs). They can be designed and installed in sizes from a few thermal kW to several MW capacity (the latter in modular assemblage).

7.06.3.1 Common Types

There exist mainly two types of GHPs: closed and open (**Figure 7**). In ground-coupled systems, a 'closed loop' of plastic (polyethylene (PE 100)) pipe is placed in the ground, either horizontally at 1–2 m depth or vertically in a borehole down to 50–300 m depth. A water–antifreeze solution is circulated through the pipe. Thus heat is collected from the ground in the winter and optionally heat is rejected to the ground in the summer. An 'open-loop' system uses groundwater or lake water directly as a heat source in a heat exchanger and then discharges it into another well, a stream, or lake, or even on the ground. The installation of horizontal coils requires relatively large surface area and extensive earthworks (digging the ground down to the level of coil layout); the prerequisite for extracting the heat of groundwater is the presence of a shallow water table. For these reasons, the most widespread technology of shallow heat extraction is by BHEs. Heat extraction is established by closed-circuit fluid circulation (a few $m^3\,h^{-1}$ of pure water or with an antifreeze additive) through the BHE and the evaporator side of the HP.

Three basic components make up a GHP system: (1) the heat extraction/storage part in the ground; (2) the central HP; and (3) the heat distributor/collector in the building (e.g., floor panel). These three circuits are shown in **Figure 8**. The key component is the

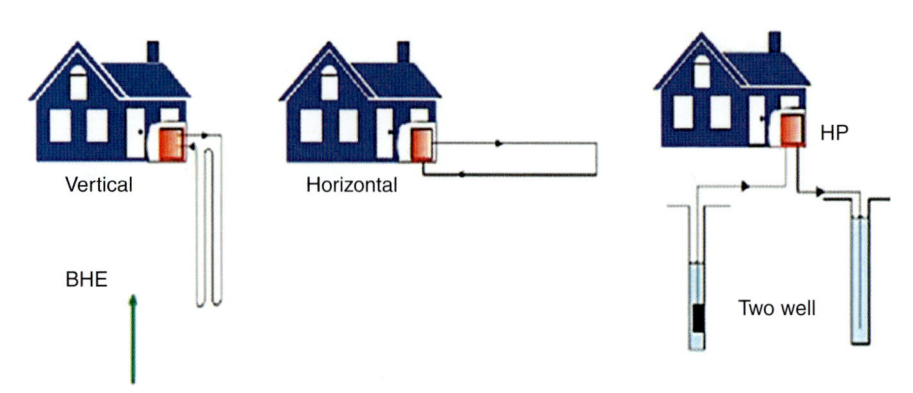

Figure 7 Closed-loop (vertical and horizontal) and open-loop (groundwater) heat pump systems. The green arrow indicates the most common system, with borehole heat exchangers (BHEs). The heat pump (HP) is shown in red. Reproduced with modification from Lund J, Sanner B, Rybach L, *et al.* (2003) Ground source heat pumps – A world review. *Renewable Energy World* July–August: 218–227 [5].

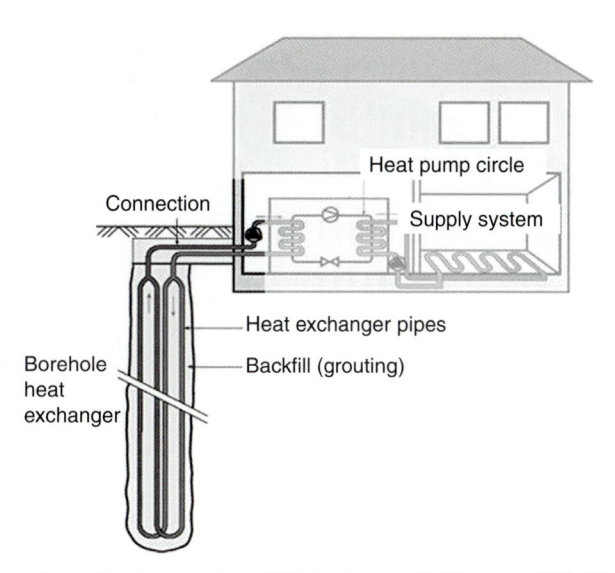

Figure 8 The three main circuits of a geothermal heat pump system: (1) the heat source (in this case, a BHE); (2) the heat pump; (3) the heating/cooling circle (in this case, floor panel heating).

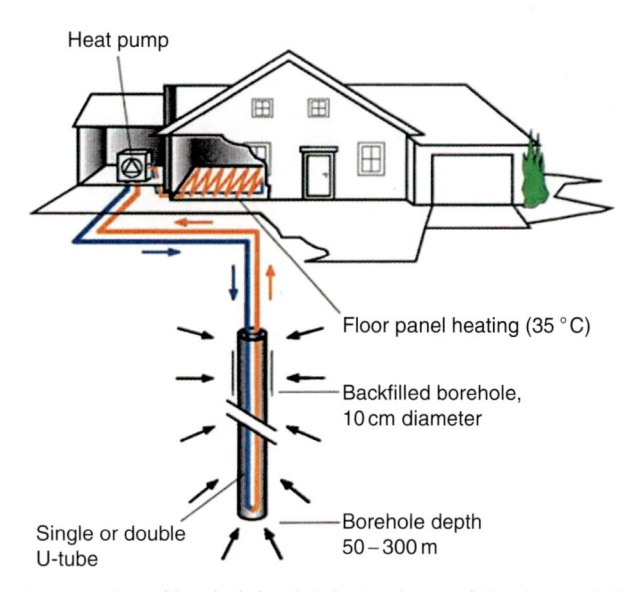

Figure 9 Sketch of a geothermal heat pump system with a single borehole heat exchanger. Colored arrows indicate circulation in the U-tube heat exchanger and black arrows heat extraction from the ground (heating mode in winter). In summer, the arrows are reversed; heat is extracted from the building and stored in the ground.

HP. In essence, HPs are nothing more than refrigeration units that can be reversed. In the heating mode, the efficiency is described by the coefficient of performance (COP), which is the heat output divided by the electrical energy input for the HP. Typically, this value lies between 3 and 4 [6]. Except for larger singular applications where gas-driven HPs are used, most HPs use electricity for their compressors. Therefore, GHPs are electricity consumers. The source of electricity varies from country to country; it would be elegant if the electricity to operate the GHPs would originate from renewable sources like solar, wind, or even geothermal. The principal components of a BHE-based GHP system are depicted in **Figure 9**.

7.06.3.2 Further Types: Energy Piles, Geothermal Baskets

'Energy piles' are foundation piles equipped with heat exchanger piping. The piles are installed in ground with poor load-bearing properties. The energy piles use the ground beneath buildings as heat source or sink, according to the season. The systems need careful design, taking into account especially the spacing between the piles, the ground thermal properties, and possible static influence of temperature changes in the piles. **Figure 10** shows installation and system sketch of energy piles.

Figure 10 Energy pile system sketch (left). 1: energy piles; 2: connections; 3: distributor; 4: general connection; 5: central unit. Installation of heat exchanger pipes in a foundation pile (right).

Figure 11 Geothermal basket example and placement sketch: a basket with 0.5 m diameter and 2 m length (total pipe length 55 m, left); implantation in 1.5–3.5 m deep holes (right).

'Geothermal baskets' are spirally wound polyethylene pipes to be installed in shallow pits, usually backfilled with the excavated material. They provide a relatively new alternative for conventional BHEs in cases of low heating demand and where normal (deeper) BHEs cannot be licensed. They can also be applied to compensate for overly short-dimensioned BHEs. **Figure 11** shows an example and a system sketch.

All systems need an electrical HP by which the low BHE output temperature (rarely above 10 °C) can be raised to the required level (35–50 °C, depending upon the heating system like underfloor panels). The smaller the increase of temperature needed, the higher the HP performance efficiency.

7.06.3.3 The Core Piece: The HP

The ground provides an immense reservoir of heat, inexhaustible on human timescales. Although the temperature level in shallow geothermal resources is only 10–20 °C, this level can be raised by an HP: this device converts the low-temperature heat of the ground to heat at higher temperature that can then be used for space heating, warming domestic water, and so on.

Figure 12 shows the principal HP components and processes: (3) evaporator: heat uptake from the ground or groundwater by a working fluid that evaporates; (1) compressor: compression of this gas, thereby increasing its temperature; (2) condenser: heat transfer to the heating circuit by condensation of the compressed medium; (4) expansion valve: expansion of the condensed working fluid to lower pressure. The four components are connected to a closed circuit. The working fluid usually is an organic compound with a low boiling temperature (e.g., tetrafluoroethane (R134a), –26 °C). In most cases, the compressor is driven by electric power. As previously mentioned, the ratio heat delivered/electricity consumed is the COP. The smaller the temperature difference between heat uptake and delivery, the higher the COP (cf. **Figure 18**).

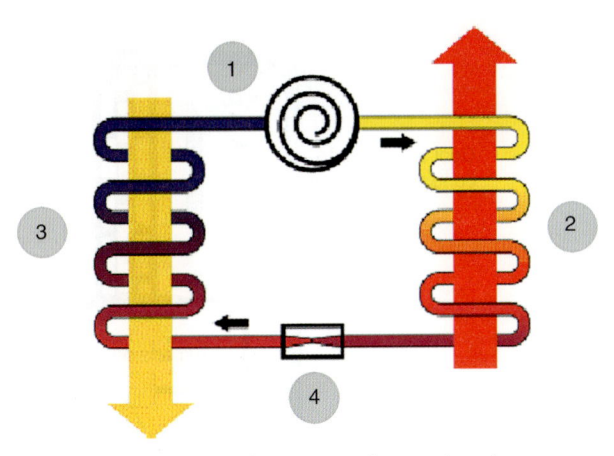

Figure 12 Heat pump components. 1: compressor; 2: condenser; 3: evaporator; 4: expansion valve.

7.06.4 Heating and Cooling with GHPs

As mentioned above, GHP systems can provide space cooling also. In moderate climates, in summer, the ground below about 15 m depth is significantly colder than outside air. Thus, a large geothermal store with favorable heat capacity is available where the heat can be exchanged (extracted from the building and deposited in summer, extracted from the ground store and supplied to the building in winter). The thermal capacity of the system depends – excluding the volume – on the thermal and hydrogeologic characteristics of the installation site; these must be carefully considered in system dimensioning. In summer, most of the time, the HP can be bypassed and the heat carrier fluid circulated through the ground by the BHEs and through the heating/cooling distribution (e.g., floor panels). By these means, the heat is collected from the building and deposited in the ground for extraction in the next winter ('free cooling').

When free cooling alone cannot satisfy the cooling needs, HPs can be reversed for cooling since they can operate in normal (heating) and reverse (cooling) mode. Both operations need electricity for the compressor. **Figures 13** and **14** show the normal

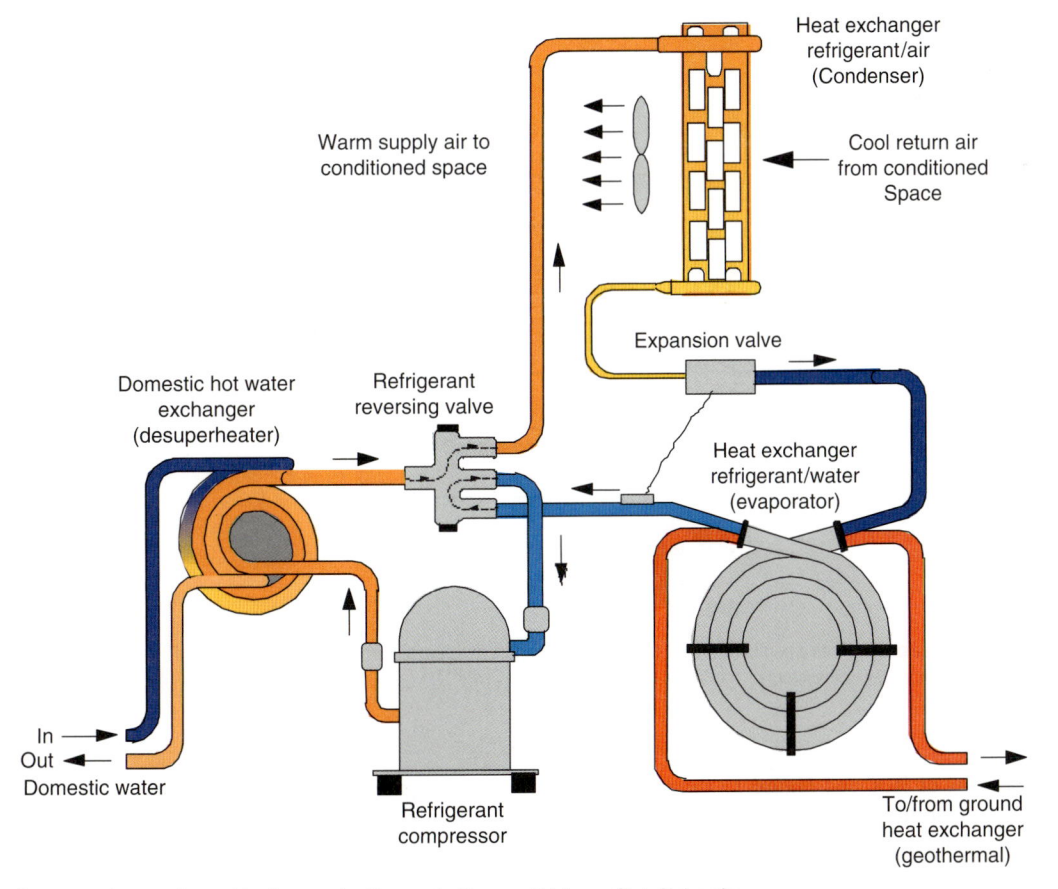

Figure 13 Heat pump in a geothermal heat pump, heating mode. Source: Oklahoma State University.

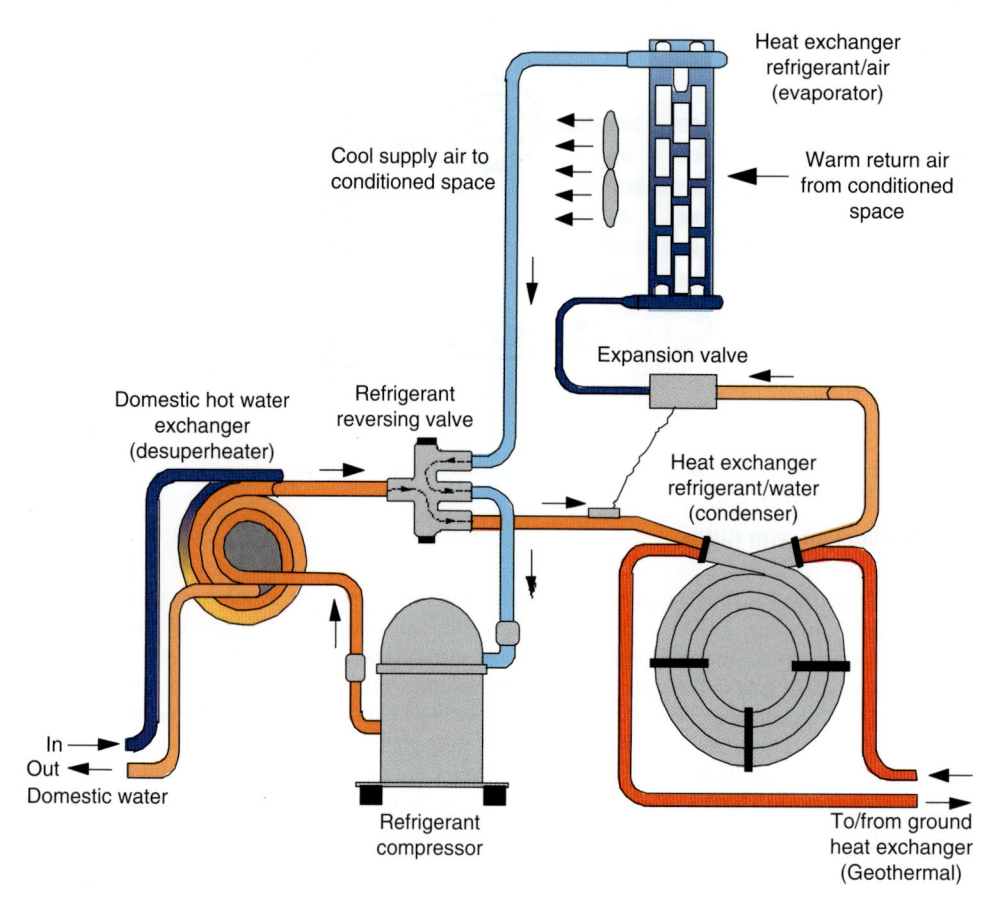

Figure 14 Heat pump in a geothermal heat pump, cooling mode. Source: Oklahoma State University.

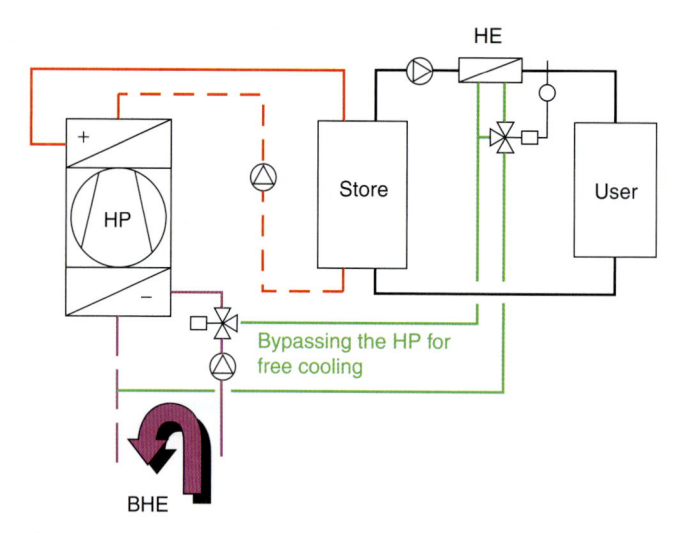

Figure 15 Scheme of free cooling with a geothermal heat pump. BHE, borehole heat exchanger; HE, heat exchanger; HP, heat pump. User: the buildings heat/cold supply (hydronic or fan coil system).

and reverse modes of HPs, and **Figure 15** the scheme of free cooling. **Figure 15** also shows the three main components of GHPs: (1) the heat source (in this case a BHE); (2) the HP; (3) the building's heating/cooling system. Small pumps, circulating the heat carrier through the HP's evaporator and the BHE and another circulating the heated/cooled medium to the user, are not shown.

7.06.5 Site Investigations for Dimensioning

The energetic performance of GHP systems strongly depends on the local ground conditions. The key property dominating the performance is the ground thermal conductivity. Reliable values are needed for the design of large-scale systems. These can be determined *in situ*. Site investigations, by specific equipment and procedures (wireless temperature logger, repeated measurements, numerical model simulations), provide the vertical thermal conductivity profile along with the temperature profile. These are especially needed for systems intended for space heating and cooling.

The key factor dominating the performance is the heat exchange between BHE and the surrounding ground; it depends directly upon the ground thermal conductivity λ at the site in question. λ is thus a key parameter in designing BHE-coupled GHP systems; the specific heat extraction rate (W per meter BHE length) is directly proportional to λ (see **Table 1**). This must be considered especially in the design of BHE groups, that is, optimization of the BHE group by determining the BHE number, spacing, and depth.

Ground thermal conductivity λ must be determined *in situ* at the BHE/HP system site; sizing of the system needs to be implemented immediately after receiving the λ information. This is usually performed in a special test BHE installed at the beginning of drill site preparation. Laboratory determination of λ on rock samples from BHE drill holes is also possible, for example, on cuttings (see Reference 8), but it is time consuming.

7.06.5.1 Conventional Thermal Response Test

Thermal response test (TRT) is the customary method to determine ground thermal conductivity *in situ*. A standard TRT circulates a heated fluid in a test BHE and yields average values of thermal conductivity, thermal borehole resistance, and ground temperature over the BHE, by using a linear heat source model (for details see, e.g., Reference 9).

In the TRT, a defined heat load is put into the test BHE and the resulting changes of the circulated fluid are measured (see, e.g., Reference 10). **Figure 16** shows the TRT scheme and **Table 2** presents thermal borehole resistance values; the resistance r_b governs

Table 1 BHE performance (single BHE, depth ~150 m) in different rock types

Rock type	Thermal conductivity ($W\,m^{-1}\,K^{-1}$)	Specific extraction rate (W per m)	Energy yield ($kWh\,m^{-1}\,yr^{-1}$)
Hard rock	3.0	Max. 70	100–120
Unconsolidated rock, saturated	2.0	45–50	90
Unconsolidated rock, dry	1.5	Max. 25	50

BHE, borehole heat exchanger.
Reproduced from Rybach L (2001) Design and performance of borehole heat exchanger/heat pump systems. *Proceedings of the European Summer School on Geothermal Energy Applications.* Oradea, Romania (CD-ROM) [7].

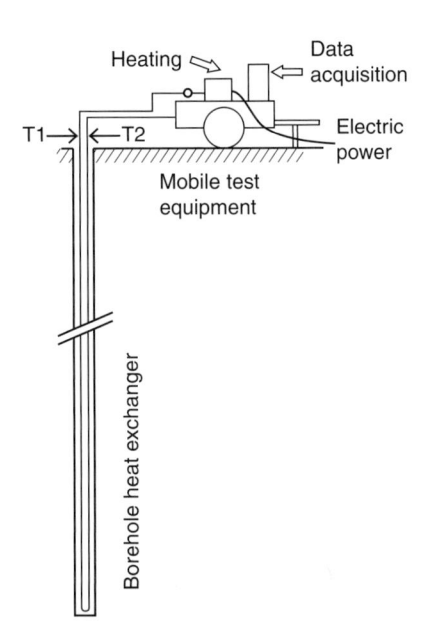

Figure 16 Schematic of a thermal response test. T1, fluid input temperature; T2, fluid output temperature. Reproduced from Lund J, Sanner B, Rybach L, *et al.* (2003) Ground source heat pumps – A world review. *Renewable Energy World* July–August: 218–227 [5].

Table 2 Borehole thermal resistance with different grouting materials and polyethylene U-pipes

Type of BHE	λ_{grout} (W m^{-1} K^{-1})	r_b (K m W^{-1})
Single-U	0.8	0.196
	1.6	0.112
Double-U	0.8	0.134
	1.6	0.075

BHE, borehole heat exchanger.
Reproduced from Lund J, Sanner B, Rybach L, et al. (2003) Ground source heat pumps – A world review. *Renewable Energy World* July–August: 218–227 [5].

the temperature losses between the undisturbed ground and the fluid inside the BHE pipes. The plastic pipes in the BHE are cemented to the surrounding ground by a special grouting material; the higher its thermal conductivity λ_{grout}, the lower r_b will be.

For efficient design of large BHE arrays, more specific input data are needed (especially about the vertical variation of ground thermal properties) than average values. New, innovative approaches enable determination of the vertical profile of ground thermal conductivity λ at a give site.

7.06.5.2 Determination via Local Heat Flow Value

This method requires a high-resolution measurement of the vertical temperature profile. For this purpose, the small and wireless borehole probe NIMO-T® is used. This probe (235 mm long, 23 mm diameter, 99.8 g) sinks through its own weight to the bottom of a BHE U-tube and records pressure (=depth) and temperature at preselected time intervals during descent. After completion of the logging, the probe is flushed back to the surface by a small pump where the probe is connected to a laptop computer for data retrieval. The measurement run for a 300 m deep BHE takes less than 60 min. The instrument has a temperature resolution of ±0.003 °C. Further details like construction, calibration, field deployment, and data evaluation are given in Reference 11.

In data processing, the λ profile of the logged BHE is calculated, with a regional heat flow value at hand, from the temperature gradient along the BHE to be derived from the measured temperature log. From the measured temperature profile, the local geothermal gradient is then calculated layerwise (first derivative; (∇T_i is the temperature gradient of depth section i)

$$\nabla T_i = \frac{T_u - T_1}{z_u - z_1} \quad [1]$$

where T_u is the temperature measured at the top ($z = z_u$) and T_1 at the bottom ($z = z_1$) of interval i. Finally, with the local terrestrial heat flow value q_{loc} (obtainable from regional heat flow maps; in Switzerland, e.g., from Reference 12), the thermal conductivity of each individual depth section can be calculated:

$$\lambda_i = \frac{q_{loc}}{\nabla T_i} \quad [2]$$

Figure 17 shows an example of λ determination based on a local heat flow value. On the left side, the temperature profile is displayed (black line) along with the profile of the temperature gradient. The latter is given by a green line (original data with a constant Δz of 1.1 m) and by a light brown line (smoothed; sliding average over $\Delta z = 13$ m). The right side of **Figure 17** displays the thermal conductivity profile as calculated by eqn [2]. For comparison, the results of laboratory measurements of thermal conductivity are also given (black vertical bars). The agreement is remarkably good; thus the method of calculating the thermal conductivity profile from the temperature profile measured by the wireless probe yields highly reliable, *in situ* thermal conductivities.

7.06.5.3 Enhanced Thermal Response Test

A conventional TRT yields only average values of the local ground thermal conductivity λ, over the BHE length. For a more reliable dimensioning especially of large multiple BHE arrays, the vertical variation of λ is needed. Besides, if a BHE system shall provide direct cooling ('free cooling') it can be important in forming the energy concept to know not only the mean temperature of the ground but also the temperature–depth profile. The enhanced thermal response test (e-TRT) is designed to yield both ground characteristics: $\lambda(z)$ and $T(z)$.

The new concept is based on repeated temperature measurement over the entire length of the BHE using the wireless temperature probe NIMO-T® mentioned above. The temperature in the BHE is measured (1) before the response test and (2) after approximately

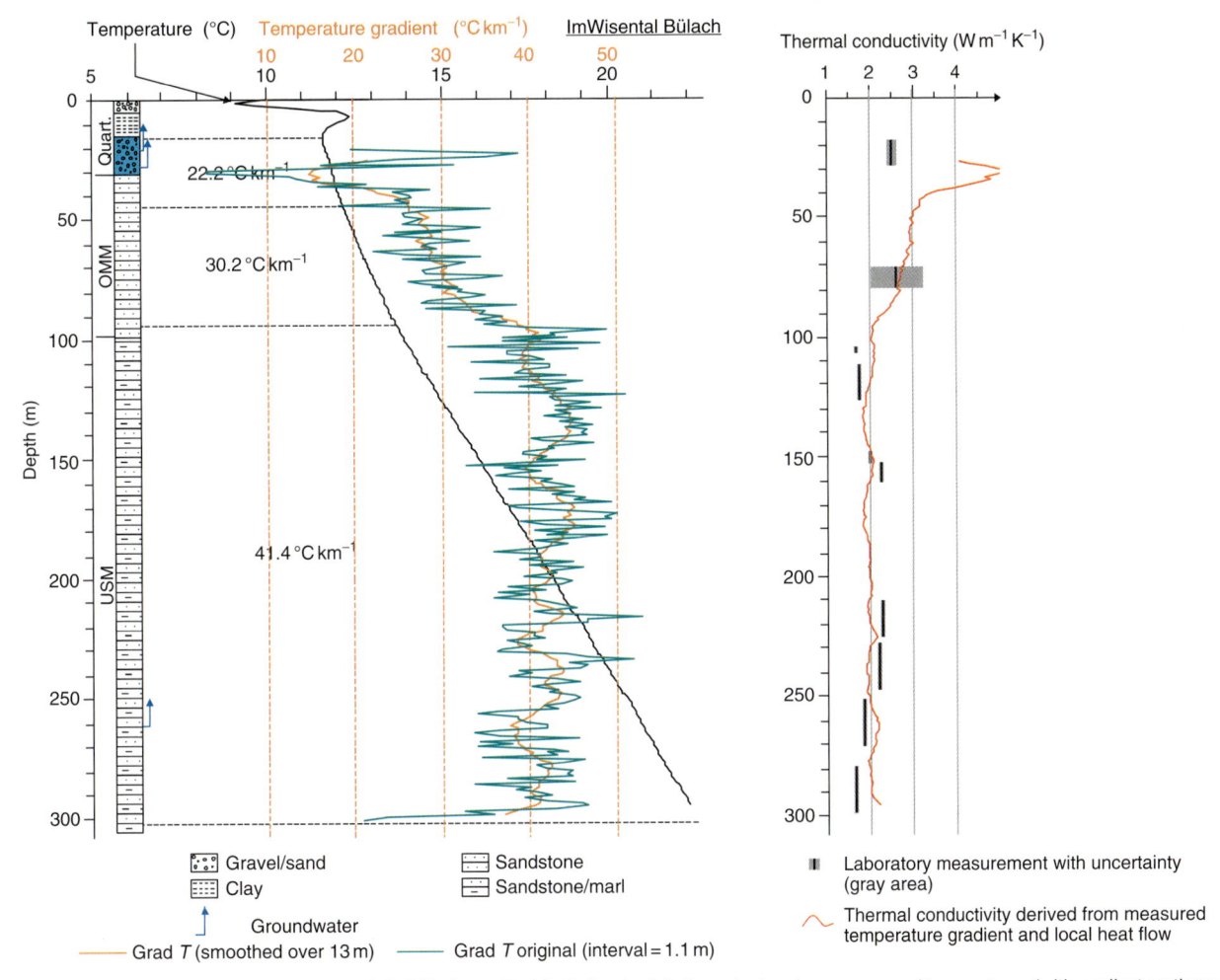

Figure 17 Borehole heat exchanger borehole in Bülach near Zurich, Switzerland. Left: geologic column, measured temperatures (with gradient sections; black line), gradient calculated with the original measurement spacing of $\Delta z = 1.1$ m (blue line) and smoothed over $\Delta z = 13$ m (brown line). Right: calculated thermal conductivity profile (brown line) with laboratory results (black bars). Reproduced from Rohner E, Rybach L, and Schaerli U (2005) A new, small, wireless instrument to determine ground thermal conductivity *in-situ* for borehole heat exchanger design. *Proceedings of the World Geothermal Congress 2005* (CD-ROM) [11].

one and/or two more days, when the temperature field in the ground recovers and approaches its undisturbed state. The temporal behavior of the three temperature–depth profiles reproduces the vertical variation of the ground thermal conductivity in the vicinity of the BHE. The measured temperature data are evaluated by numerical simulation, using a detailed finite element mesh, which maps the BHE and ground geometry as detailed as possible (for details see Reference 13). This procedure allows for calculation of the vertical variation of ground thermal properties and groundwater flow and thus provides a reliable assessment of the BHE performance.

Figure 18 shows an example of a thermal conductivity profile which was derived from an e-TRT measurement. This example shows a sudden increase of thermal conductivity at approximately 110 m depth. This discontinuity corresponds exactly to the transition from unconsolidated rock to solid rock.

7.06.6 Engineering Design

The design of GHP systems aims at the appropriate sizing of the system components by taking into account a number of influencing factors. In sizing, the demand characteristics of the object to be supplied must be considered (size/extension, heating alone, heating and domestic water, combined heating/cooling) as well as the local site conditions (climate, ground properties).

The proper design of GHP systems is a complex and demanding task, especially for large installations with several 10s or 100s of BHEs. Correspondingly, more sophisticated approaches and methods are needed and are also available. Common in all design endeavors is that – starting with the heating and/or cooling needs of the objects in question – the number, depth, and spacing of

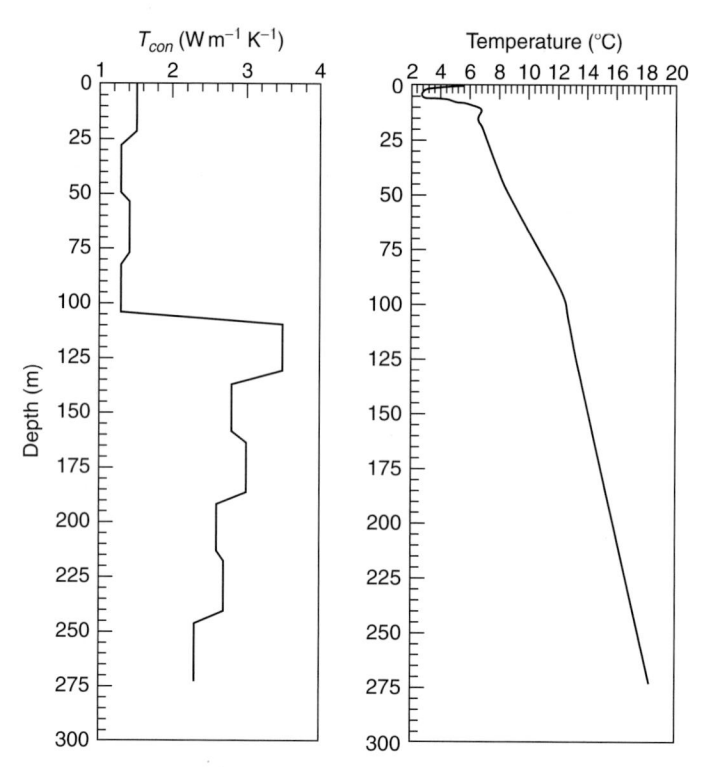

Figure 18 Thermal conductivity profile (left side; T_{con}, thermal conductivity) and temperature–depth profile (right side), derived from an enhanced thermal response test measurement in a 270 m deep Test-BHE in Andermatt, Switzerland. Reproduced from Megel T, Rohner E, Wagner R, and Rybach L (2010) The use of the underground as a geothermal store for different heating and cooling needs. *Proceedings of the World Geothermal Congress 2010.* Nusa Dua, Bali, Indonesia (CD-ROM) [14].

BHEs are determined. Depth and number of the BHEs depend on the utilization purpose (heating alone, combined heating/cooling, heating and domestic hot water), the object size, and also on the local conditions. The BHE/HP design must take into account all these factors.

Generally, a simpler dimensioning procedure is sufficient for smaller objects. The limit is usually set to 30 kW capacity. Here we start with small installations (simple GHP system for a single-family dwelling, for heating only).

The first step is to evaluate the demand. This consists of several ingredients like the energy need in MWh per year and the capacity in kW. In many countries, there are norms that describe how the necessary sizing input data are to be evaluated, using peak heat load, heating degree days (HDD), and so on (e.g., for Switzerland the norms SIA 382/2 and 380/1, for Germany DIN 4701). The BHE construction characteristics (diameter, tube type and configuration, circulating fluid, backfill) must also be fixed beforehand. Also the user-side characteristics (HP type, capacity, performance coefficient, evaporator ΔT) need to be fixed.

The local conditions are of great importance. Ground temperatures (mainly determined by the site elevation for a given climatic zone) and ground properties like the presence or absence of overburden and bedrock groundwater are more or less dominant influencing factors.

A key property is the thermal conductivity of the ground surrounding the BHE. The higher the rock thermal conductivity λ (W m^{-1} K^{-1}), the higher the specific heat extraction rate (W m^{-1}) and the energy yield (kWh m^{-1} yr^{-1}) per unit BHE length (see **Table 1**).

Figure 19 displays the influencing factors (demand, site, HP characteristics) and demonstrates the method of sizing for a small object (note the ranges of validity): first the top left diagram is entered with the demand characteristics power (kW) and total energy (MWh yr^{-1}); from the point so defined a vertical line is drawn down until the site elevation (m.a.s.l.) is met. From there the line continues horizontally to the HP performance coefficient (COP); then the line goes vertically up until the local (average) ground thermal conductivity λ (W m^{-1} K^{-1}). Finally, a horizontal line exits to the necessary BHE length (for one or two BHEs). An HP COP of 4 means that 25% electrical energy is needed for the system and 75% heat is coming from the ground.

Larger objects (>30 kW capacity, which need several BHEs) require a more sophisticated sizing approach. Specific computer software is needed for this purpose. Of these sizing software packages, the EED (Earth Energy Designer; see, e.g., Reference 15) is widely used. EED calculates the BHE fluid exit temperatures over many years of BHE operation, for predefined monthly heating/cooling loads and a given borehole depth/spacing ratio. The reliability of EED for regular BHE patterns (=rectangular equidistant grid) has been confirmed by measurements [16].

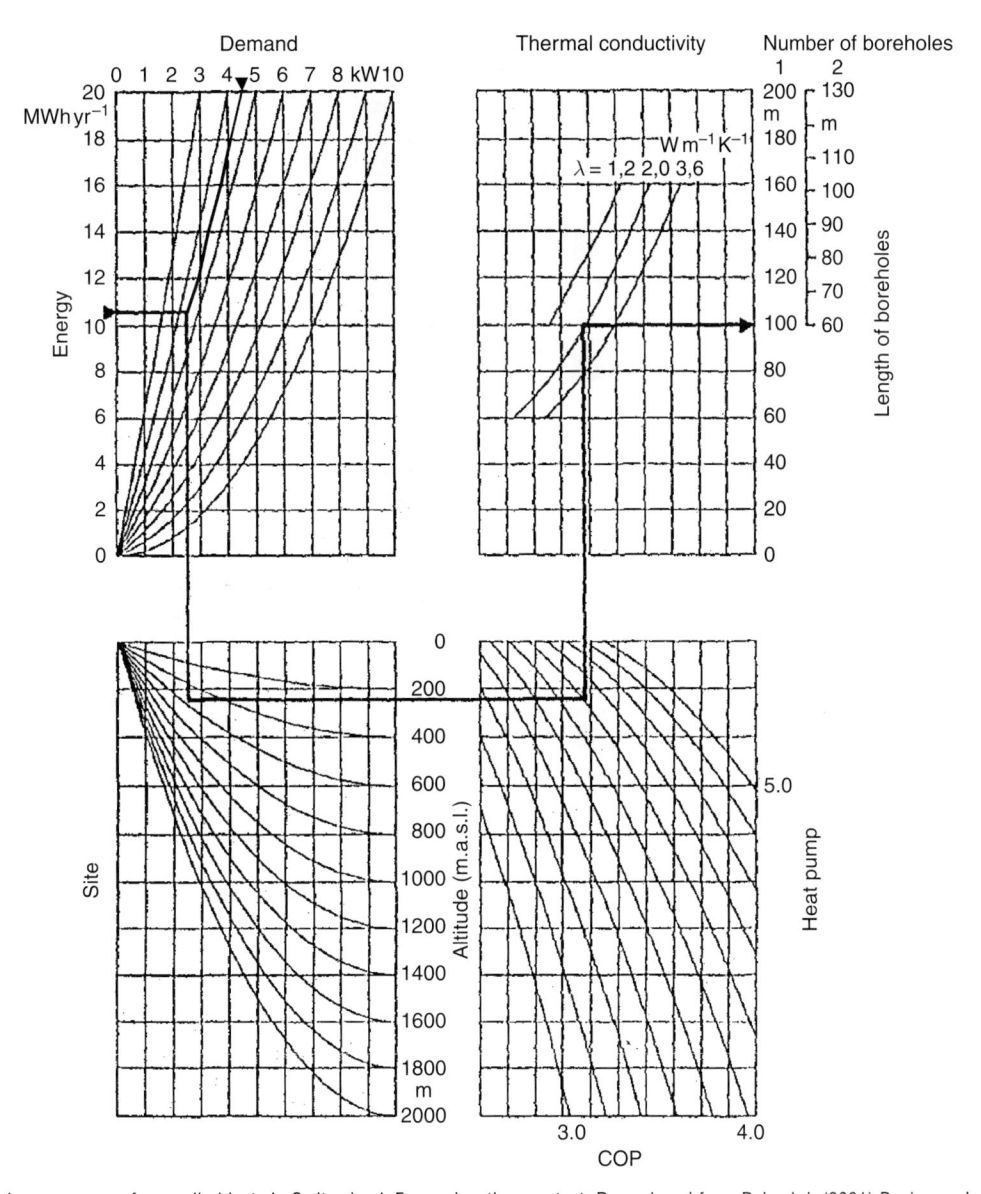

Figure 19 Sizing nomogram for small objects in Switzerland. For explanation see text. Reproduced from Rybach L (2001) Design and performance of borehole heat exchanger/heat pump systems. *Proceedings of the European Summer School on Geothermal Energy Applications.* Oradea, Romania (CD-ROM) [7].

The sizing software EED has, however, its limitations. Varying ground thermal properties cannot be considered, and irregular BHE configurations (which are often dictated by ground property boundaries) cannot be handled. Also, the influence of moving groundwater cannot be taken into account. More flexible software like the package FRACTure [17] has lately been used successfully to eliminate these shortcomings [18].

Figure 20 shows the general procedure in dimensioning. From the monthly heating/cooling needs of a given object, the number, depth, and spacing of the BHEs are determined and the corresponding heating and cooling energies (free cooling as well as cooling with the HP) are calculated; these must match the demand. The diagram also shows the electricity demand.

7.06.7 Installation of GHPs

In planning and installation of GHP systems, the three main circuits (heat source, HP, heating/cooling unit) must be considered and optimized. While HPs and heating/cooling units (hydronic or fan coil systems) can readily be purchased 'off the shelf', the installation (=drilling and completion) of GHP boreholes is a demanding task.

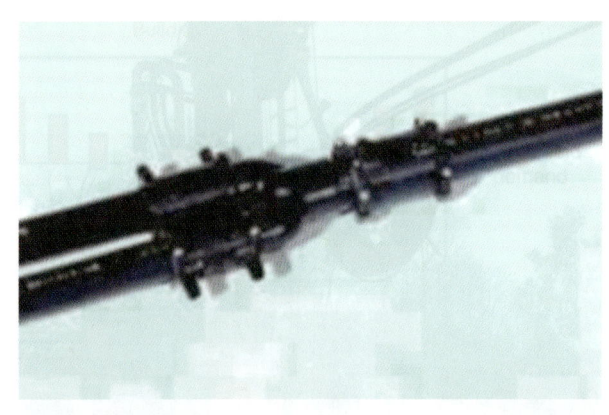

Figure 22 'Y part' to join the U-tube at BHE wellhead.

Figure 23 Distributors (green) assemble the incoming and outgoing BHE connections.

7.06.8 Operation and Maintenance (O&M)

One of the most attractive benefits of GHPs is the low level of maintenance. The HPs are closed, packaged, usually modular units that are located indoors. Unlike with air-source HPs where the most critical period for the compressor is the start-up after defrost, HPs in GHP do not have a defrost cycle. The simple system requires fewer components: the fewer the components, the lower the maintenance. In general terms, GHP installations have a long service life and need very little maintenance.

7.06.9 Capital and O&M Costs, Comparison with Conventional Heating Systems

Installation of GHPs needs considerable upfront investment, due to the earth works (usually drilling and completion) and components (HP, connections, and distributors). On the other hand, running costs are generally low (mainly only electricity for HPs and circulation pumps).

The economics of GHP systems can best be considered in comparison with other conventional and fossil-fired systems. For the comparison, a common single-family house with 150 m² living space, a heating system with 7.5 kW$_t$ capacity (heating needs), and an annual energy requirement of 65 GJ for a season of 2400 heating hours per year is considered, in comparison with gas and oil heaters [22]. **Table 4** shows the comparison.

Of course the future price development of oil, gas, and electricity is unknown; usually it is assumed that electricity prices will increase significantly slower than oil and gas prices. In the above comparisons, the issues of CO_2 emission (i.e., a CO_2 taxation) are not considered. A CO_2 tax for space heating has already been introduced in several European countries. It can be expected that this trend will continue and thus the GHP systems will have increasing advantages. In addition, the above comparison is made only for heating. The great advantage of GHP systems is that the same equipment can be used for cooling in summer, which is a real benefit in times of global warming.

Table 4 Cost comparison of (1) BHE-based GHP heater, (2) gas condensing heater, and (3) oil heater

	GHP/BHE	Gas heater	GHP/BHE	Oil heater
Investment cost	18 000 €	8800 €	18 000 €	12 500 €
Higher GHP investment		9200 €		5500 €
O&M cost/year	680 €	1720 €	680 €	2000 €
GHP savings/year		1040 €		1320 €
Amortization period				
Without investment payment		9 years		Just < 5 years
At 6% interest		13 years		Just >5 years

BHE, borehole heat exchanger; GHP, geothermal heat pump; O&M, operation and maintenance.
Data from Auer J (2010) Geothermal energy – Construction industry a beneficiary of climate change and energy scarcity. *Deutsche Bank Research*. ISSN Print 1612-314X [22].

7.06.10 Production Sustainability

For GHPs, the issue of sustainability concerns the various heat sources [23]. In the horizontal systems (cf. **Figure 7**), the heat exchanger pipes are buried at shallow depth; the longevity of their smooth operation is guaranteed by the constant heat supply from the atmosphere by solar radiation. In the case of combined heating/cooling by GHPs, the heat balance (in/out) is given by the system design itself: replacement of heat extracted in winter by heat storage in summer. In the case of groundwater-coupled GHPs, the resupply of fluid is secured by the hydrologic cycle (infiltration of precipitation) and the heat comes either 'from above' (atmosphere) and/or 'from below' (geothermal heat flow); the relative proportions depend on aquifer depth. This leads to a more or less constant aquifer temperature all year without any significant seasonal variation. Any deficit created by heat/fluid extraction is replenished by the (lateral) groundwater flow. Theoretical and experimental studies have been performed to establish a solid base for the long-term reliability of GHP production characteristics [24–27]. Experience shows that properly designed GHP systems operate fully satisfactorily over decades.

7.06.11 Licensing, Environmental Issues

Installation of a GHP usually requires a permit from a licensing agency. These authorities cover also the aspects of groundwater protection. In groundwater protection zones – as delimited in special maps – no GHP types can be established; the systems with shallow horizontal pipe loops make no exception here. The basic concerns of groundwater protection authorities are

1. the risk of leakage of circulated fluid (usually with some antifreeze) from BHE or horizontal pipes and
2. the risk of establishing vertical hydraulic connections between separate aquifer layers through improper backfill of drillings.

The first priority in groundwater use is for drinking water. Domestic hot water is also produced from this supply. Much household water comes from extended, shallow gravel aquifers, mainly located at the bottom of valleys. Incidentally, such gravel layers (now usually mapped as groundwater protection zones) have low thermal conductivity, which makes heat extraction from the ground for energetic use inefficient. For example, the heat extraction rate for BHEs depends directly on the ground thermal conductivity (see, e.g., Reference 25). Therefore, it is technically unfeasible to establish vertical (BHE) or horizontal pipes in such formations and so a conflict between energy source and groundwater protection aspects does not exist. For the placement of a GHP installation, the local groundwater situation must therefore be considered.

Ideally, maps exist with exclusion or limitation zones. For example, in Switzerland, there are special maps demarcating such zones. Switzerland consists of 23 cantons; several cantonal water protection authorities have established maps for demarcation of various zones. In Canton Zurich, a special map for GHP/BHE licensing applications with BHE is placed on the Internet under http://www.erdsonden.zh.ch/internet/bd/awel/gs/gw/de/Bw_Gw/Erdsonden.html

The scale can be enlarged by browsing, from 1:500 000 through 1:200 000, 1:100 000, 1:50 000 down to 1:25 000. **Figure 24** shows a detail of a map at a scale of 1:25 000. The maps show

- topography, roads, rivers, etc.,
- groundwater protection zones, groundwater captures,
- zones in which BHEs are permissible,
- zones in which BHEs are permissible only with specific restrictions,
- zones in which BHE installation needs further clarification,
- zones in which BHEs are not permitted, and

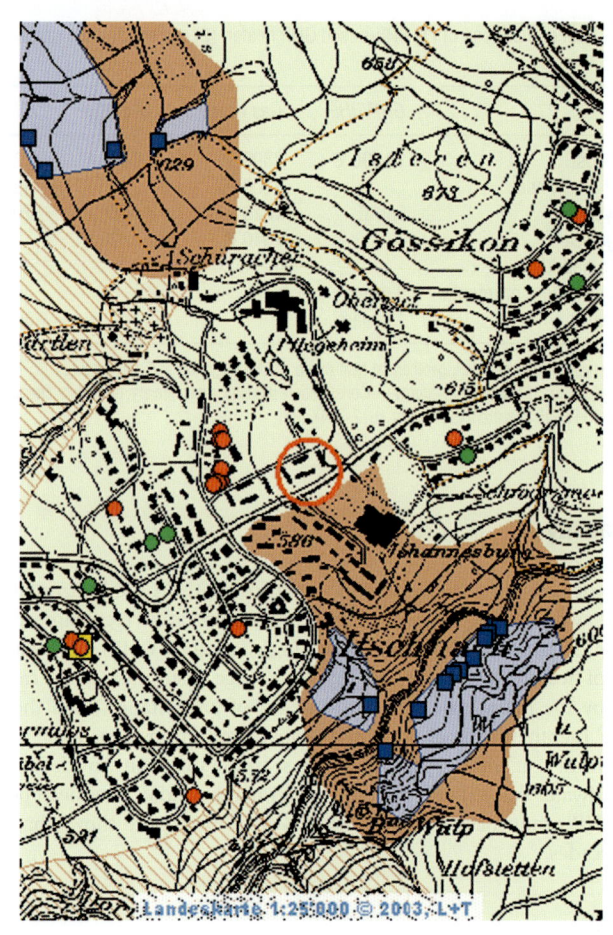

Figure 24 Details of the BHE map of Canton Zurich. Blue and brown: groundwater protection zones; blue squares: groundwater captures; existing BHEs with (green) and without (red) geologic profiles.

- existing BHE installations, with/without geologic profile.

Most maps are being continuously updated. The cantonal authorities also distribute the necessary application forms in order to get the necessary installation permits.

Besides the groundwater protection aspects, there have been no problems so far with the siting or the density of BHE installations. Of course, when the distance between individual neighboring drillings becomes small, conflicts with adjacent owners ('neighbor rights') could emerge. Therefore, the issue of BHE spacing must be considered carefully. At the same time, the thermal conditions and processes in the influenced ground like the long-term behavior or the resource renewal must be understood and, if necessary, managed. More details are given in Reference 28.

The licensing authorities also need application forms; in some countries, these can be completed through the web. In Switzerland, various qualification and tests' records (e.g., for drilling and pipe tightness) are also required. These and other design and completion requirements are assembled in the engineering norm SIA 384/6 [29], a first comprehensive norm for BHE-coupled GHP systems.

GHPs have significant environmental benefits compared to conventional (mainly fossil fuel-based) heating/cooling systems, since combustion processes are involved. GHPs thus have great CO_2 emission reduction potential when replacing fossil sources of energy. Further development – depending on future growth rates – could reduce CO_2 emissions even more significantly.

The HP, a basic GHP system component, needs auxiliary power to accomplish the temperature increase needed in the system. In most cases, HPs use electric power. With proper system design, seasonal performance coefficients in the heating mode of 4.0 (heating energy supplied by the GHP system/electricity input for HP and circulation pumps) can be reached. This means that GHP systems need 75% less fuel than fossil-fired systems.

This represents the 'saving' of fossil fuels and the corresponding CO_2 emission. But one should not fall into the trap of thinking that it would also mean CO_2 emission reduction as it only avoids additional emission. It must be emphasized that new GHP installations do not provide any emission reduction – unless they replace at the same time old, fossil-fueled systems. Therefore, true CO_2 emission reduction results only when GHP systems are installed during renovations.

When GHPs are used for space cooling in the 'free cooling mode', there are even more fossil fuel savings; because the HP is bypassed, there is no need for electricity during this time. But again here real CO_2 emission reduction can only be achieved when an 'old' air-conditioning system fed by 'dirty' electricity gets replaced. In any case, the source and CO_2 emission characteristics of the electricity consumed by the HP need to be carefully considered. More details are given in Reference 30.

References

[1] Banks D (2008) *An Introduction to Thermogeology – Ground Source Heating and Cooling*, p. 349. Oxford: Blackwell Publishing.
[2] Lund JW, Freeston DH, and Boyd TL (2010) Direct utilization of geothermal energy 2010 worldwide review. *Proceedings of the World Geothermal Congress 2010*. Bali, Indonesia (CD-ROM).
[3] Rybach L (2008) The international status, development, and future prospects of geothermal energy. *Proceedings of Renewable Energy 2008*. Busan, S. Korea (CD-ROM).
[4] Kiehl JT and Trenberth KE (1997) Earth's annual global mean energy budget. *Bulletin of the American Meteorological Society* 78: 197–208.
[5] Lund J, Sanner B, Rybach L, *et al.* (2003) Ground source heat pumps – A world review. *Renewable Energy World* July–August: 218–227.
[6] Rybach L (2005) The advance of geothermal heat pumps world-wide. *IEA Heat Pump Center Newsletter* 23: 13–18.
[7] Rybach L (2001) Design and performance of borehole heat exchanger/heat pump systems. *Proceedings of the European Summer School on Geothermal Energy Applications*. Oradea, Romania (CD-ROM).
[8] Schärli U and Rybach L (2002) Bestimmung thermischer Parameter für die Dimensionierung von Erdwärmesonden: Vergleich Erfahrungswerte – Labormessungen – Response Test. In: Eugster WJ and Laoui L (eds.) *Proceedings of the Workshop on Geothermische Response Tests/Tests de Réponse Géothermique, Geothermische Vereinigung e.V.*, Geeste, Germany, pp. 76–88. ISBN 3-932570-43-X.
[9] Gehlin S and Spitler J (2002) Thermal response test – State of the art. *2001 Report IEA ECES Annex 13*.
[10] Eugster WL and Laloui L (eds.) (2002) *Proceedings of the Workshop on Geothermische Response Tests/Tests de Réponse Géothermique, Geothermische Vereinigung e.V.*, Geeste, Germany, pp. 76–88. ISBN 3-932570-43-X.
[11] Rohner E, Rybach L, and Schaerli U (2005) A new, small, wireless instrument to determine ground thermal conductivity in-situ for borehole heat exchanger design. *Proceedings of the World Geothermal Congress 2005*, Antalya, Turkey (CD-ROM).
[12] Medici F and Rybach L (1995) Geothermal map of Switzerland 1:500'000 (heat flow density). *Beiträge zur Geologie der Schweiz, Serie Geophysik Nr.* 30, 36pp. Zurich, Switzerland.
[13] Wagner R and Rohner E (2008) Improvements of thermal response tests for geothermal heat pumps. *Proceedings of the 9th IEA Heat Pump Conference*, Zurich, Switzerland (CD-ROM).
[14] Megel T, Rohner E, Wagner R, and Rybach L (2010) The use of the underground as a geothermal store for different heating and cooling needs. *Proceedings of the World Geothermal Congress 2010*. Nusa Dua, Bali, Indonesia (CD-ROM).
[15] Sanner B and Hellström G (1996) 'Earth Energy Designer', eine Software zur Berechnung von Erdwärmesondenanlagen. In: *Tagungsband 4. Geothermische Fachtagung Konstanz*, pp. 326–333. Neubrandenburg, Germany: GtV.
[16] Sanner B and Gonka T (1996) Oberflächennahe Erdwärmenutzung im Laborgebäude UEG, Wetzlar. *Oberhessische naturwissenschaftliche Zeitschrift* 58: 115–126.
[17] Kohl T and Hopkirk R (1995) 'FRACTure' – A simulation code for forced fluid transport in fractured, porous rock. *Geothermics* 24: 333–343.
[18] Maraini S (2000) Vergleich von Software zur Dimensionierung von Erdwärmesonden-Anlagen. Diploma Thesis, Department of Earth Sciences, ETH Zurich, 128pp.
[19] Rybach L, Brunner M, and Gorhan H (2000) Swiss geothermal update 1995–2000. *Proceedings of the World Geothermal Congress 2000*, pp. 413–425. Kyushu-Tohoku, Japan.
[20] Allan M and Philippacopoulos A (2000) Performance characteristics and modelling of cementitious grouts for geothermal heat pumps. *Proceedings of the World Geothermal Congress 2000*, Kyushu-Tohoku Japan. pp. 335–336.
[21] Xu SH and Rybach L (2010) Innovative groundwater heat pump system for space heating and cooling in USA and China. *Proceedings of the World Geothermal Congress 2010*. Nusa Dua, Bali, Indonesia (CD-ROM).
[22] Auer J (2010) Geothermal energy – Construction industry a beneficiary of climate change and energy scarcity. *Deutsche Bank Research*. ISSN Print 1612-314X.
[23] Rybach L and Mongillo M (2006) Geothermal sustainability – A review with identified research needs. *Geothermal Resources Council Transactions* 30: 1083–1090.
[24] Rybach L, Eugster WJ, Hopkirk RJ, and Kaelin B (1992) Borehole heat exchangers: Long-term operational characteristics of a decentral geothermal heating system. *Geothermics* 22: 861–869.
[25] Rybach L and Eugster W (1998) Reliable long term performance of BHE systems and market penetration – The Swiss success story. In: Stiles L (ed.) *Proceedings of the 2nd Stockton International Geothermal Conference*, Pomona, NJ, USA. pp. 41–57.
[26] Eugster WJ and Rybach L (2000) Sustainable production from borehole heat exchange systems. *Proceedings of the World Geothermal Congress 2000*, pp. 825–830. Kyushu-Tohoku, Japan.
[27] Signorelli S, Kohl T, and Rybach L (2005) Sustainability of production from borehole heat exchanger fields. *Proceedings of the 29th Workshop on Geothermal Reservoir Engineering*, Palo Alto, CA, USA, pp. 358–361. Stanford University.
[28] Rybach L (2004) Use and management of shallow geothermal resources in Switzerland. In: Popovski K and Kepinska B (eds.) *Proceedings of the International Geothermal Days 'Poland 2004'*, Krakow, Poland. pp. 128–136.
[29] SIA (2010) Erdwärmesonden. Norm no. 384/6, Schweizerischer Ingenieur- und Architektenverein, ref. no. 546384/6:2010, Zurich, p. 76.
[30] Rybach L (2009) CO_2 emission mitigation by geothermal development – Especially with geothermal heat pumps. *Geothermal Resources Council Transactions* 43: 597–600.

Relevant Websites

GHPs are rapidly growing in numbers, size, and complexity. There is now astonishing growth in countries like Portugal and Spain, in which no GHPs existed just a few years ago. Instead of showing 'typical' examples, here a list of websites is given through which the latest developments, design types, status statistics, etc., can be found:

http://www.egec.org/ – European Geothermal Resources Council.
http://www.ehpa.org/ – European Heat Pump Association (EHPA).
http://www.geothermalheatpumpconsortium.org/ – Geothermal Heat Pump Consortium (GHPC).
http://www.heatpumpcentre.org/ – International Energy Agency Heat Pump Centre.
http://www.igshpa.okstate.edu/ – International Ground Source Heat Pump Association (IGSPHA).

In addition, there are active national associations in many countries.

7.07 Geothermal Power Plants

R DiPippo, University of Massachusetts Dartmouth, Dartmouth, MA, USA

© 2012 Elsevier Ltd. All rights reserved.

7.07.1	Introduction	208
7.07.2	Scope of the Section	208
7.07.3	Steam Plants	209
7.07.3.1	Direct, Dry-Steam Plants	209
7.07.3.1.1	General description	209
7.07.3.1.2	Systems analysis	211
7.07.3.2	Flash-Steam Plants	216
7.07.3.2.1	General description	217
7.07.3.2.2	System analysis	217
7.07.4	Binary Plants	222
7.07.4.1	Basic Organic Rankine Cycle Plants	222
7.07.4.1.1	General system analysis	224
7.07.4.1.2	Preheater and evaporator analysis	225
7.07.4.2	Advanced Binary Cycle Plants	226
7.07.4.2.1	Binary cycle with recuperator	226
7.07.4.2.2	Dual-pressure binary cycle	227
7.07.4.2.3	Dual-fluid binary cycle	228
7.07.4.2.4	Kalina binary cycles	228
7.07.5	Advanced Geothermal Plants	228
7.07.5.1	Hybrid Plants	229
7.07.5.1.1	Fossil–geothermal hybrid plants	229
7.07.5.1.2	Solar–geothermal plants	230
7.07.5.2	Combined Cycle Plants	231
7.07.5.2.1	Combined single- and double-flash plants	231
7.07.5.2.2	Flash–binary combined cycle plants	231
7.07.5.3	Enhanced Geothermal Systems	233
7.07.6	Plant Performance Assessment	235
7.07.6.1	Utilization Efficiency	235
7.07.6.2	Thermal Efficiency	235
7.07.6.3	Specific Geofluid Consumption	235
7.07.6.4	Typical Efficiencies for Geothermal Plants	236
References		236
Further Reading		236

Glossary

Binary plant Power plant using two or more working fluids. In the case of geothermal plants, one fluid is the geothermal fluid and the other(s) is(are) a low-boiling point organic fluid.

Double-flash plant Geothermal steam power plant in which the geofluid is subjected to two pressure-drop processes (flashes) in which steam is generated for use in a turbine.

Dry-steam power plant Geothermal power plant using dry or slightly superheated steam obtained directly from a well.

Enhanced geothermal systems (EGS) Technology that creates a permeable hot reservoir through drilling and stimulation, allowing the continuous circulation of geofluid from the reservoir to an energy conversion system and back to the reservoir.

Exergy Thermodynamically maximum available work output from a given set of fluid conditions relative to its surroundings.

Heat balance diagram Schematic flow diagram of the processes involved in a power plant, showing temperature, pressure, mass flow, and enthalpy at each important point.

Kalina binary cycle Power plant based on a binary cycle but involving a mixture of water and ammonia as working fluid together with various recuperative heat exchangers.

Single-flash plant Geothermal steam power plant in which the geofluid is subjected to a single pressure-drop process (flash) in which steam is generated for use in a turbine.

Specific geofluid consumption Amount of geofluid needed to produce a certain amount of net power from the plant.

> **Thermal efficiency** For a cycle, the ratio of the net power output to the rate of heat input.
>
> **Utilization efficiency** Ratio of net power output to the rate of exergy input for a power plant.

7.07.1 Introduction

The generation of electrical power from geothermal resources is among the most environmentally benign and most reliable means of electrical production. Geothermal power plants have been in continuous operation since 1904, except for a brief period near the end of World War II. Vast amounts of experience have accumulated over the past century that now allow nearly every sort of geothermal resource to be exploited for power generation.

In 1904, the Larderello field in the Tuscany region of Italy became the first place to generate electrical power from geothermal energy. Five small light bulbs were illuminated in the boric acid factory of Prince Piero Ginori Conti when a ¾-hp reciprocating steam engine was hooked up to a steam pipeline coming from the shallow wells in the field. The next year, the system was upgraded to a 40-hp engine and a 20-kW dynamo. By 1913, the technology had advanced to such an extent that construction began on the first commercial-sized power plant. In 1914, a 250 kW turbo-alternator was put into operation and provided electricity to the nearby towns of Volterra and Pomarance.

Italy remained the only country with geothermal power plants until 1958 when New Zealand commissioned its first geothermal unit at Wairakei. Two years later, the first unit in the United States came online at The Geysers field in northern California. Altogether, there have been 27 countries that have operated geothermal power plants. At this time, 24 countries have active geothermal power plants providing clean, economic, and renewable generation.

7.07.2 Scope of the Section

This section will present the most common systems used for geothermal power generation. Simple line diagrams and descriptions of major components will be provided. Working equations will be included to allow simple calculations of power output and efficiency. Much of the material draws upon the writer's earlier works, in particular Reference 1.

Plants designed to utilize dry-steam resources such as are found at Larderello and The Geysers are described in Section 7.07.3.1. All the plants in Italy are fed from a huge dry-steam reservoir that has had its boundaries extended many times through step-out wells and very deep wells. However, reservoirs of this type are not widespread, and these two examples represent the only significant dry-steam reservoirs so far discovered.

Far more common are liquid-dominated reservoirs filled with liquid and sometimes vapor that produce a mixture of hot water and steam at the wellhead. The Wairakei plant was the first to exploit such a reservoir on a commercial scale. Plants of this type are described in Section 7.07.3.2.

Both dry-steam and liquid-dominated reservoirs are called hydrothermal systems owing to the presence of high-temperature water from geothermally heated fractured rocks. The distribution of hydrothermal resources as a function of geofluid temperature shows the vast majority occur at the low end of the temperature spectrum, with only a few very high-temperature systems. Thus, in order to exploit geothermal systems more fully, it became necessary to devise energy conversion systems that could be used effectively on low-temperature reservoirs.

This need was fulfilled with the development of binary power cycles based on the familiar Rankine cycle used in conventional power stations. However, instead of using water–steam as the working fluid in the cycle, geothermal binary plants use organic fluids having low boiling temperatures. This allows them to receive heat from low- to moderate-temperature geofluids and still evaporate. The vapor so formed is then admitted to specially designed turbines to generate power. The working fluid is then condensed and pumped back to the evaporator in a closed-loop system. Binary plants are described in Section 7.07.4.

As technology advanced and experience with geothermal plants grew, several innovative arrangements emerged as logical extensions of these basic plant types. Some of these are described in Section 7.07.5. This section includes a description of a promising new technology that may one day open up vast areas to geothermal development, namely, enhanced geothermal systems (EGS).

Section 7.07.6 defines and explains several performance measures that may be used to assess the efficiency of geothermal power plants, and gives typical values for various types of geothermal energy conversion systems.

It is useful to see the flow of processes followed in a geothermal power plant regardless of the type of energy conversion system used at any particular geothermal resource. The power generation process can be described generally as following the sequence of steps shown in **Figure 1**.

Production of the geofluid from the reservoir can be either natural, artesian flow, or pumped flow. The gathering system consists of a network of pipes from the wellheads to the powerhouse. The preparation of the geofluid may involve scrubbing to remove

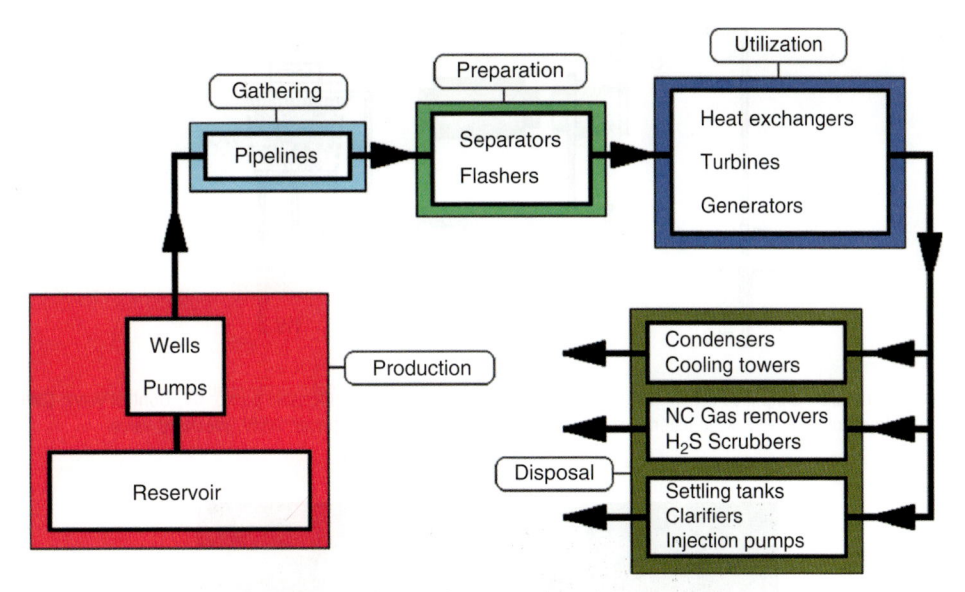

Figure 1 General sequence of processes for a geothermal power plant.

particulate matter entrained in the geofluid during its passage through the reservoir formation, removal of moisture from steam, removal of entrained noncondensable gases, separation of steam from liquid, and/or the generation of low-pressure steam through flashing of separated liquid. The utilization takes place in turbine–generator units that are similar to what is found in conventional power stations. Finally, there is disposal of noncondensable gases that accompany the geofluid, solid matter that may precipitate from the fluid, and waste heat that is dispersed to the surroundings, and the return to the reservoir of whatever geofluids remain after the utilization process via reinjection wells.

7.07.3 Steam Plants

Geothermal steam plants use steam obtained from the natural geofluid in the reservoir, either directly as in the case of a dry-steam resource or indirectly through a flashing process as in the case of a liquid-dominated resource. These two cases are discussed separately in this section.

7.07.3.1 Direct, Dry-Steam Plants

7.07.3.1.1 General description

The simplest geothermal steam plants are those at dry-steam reservoirs such as The Geysers in northern California and Larderello and its associated fields in Tuscany. In basic form, the steam obtained at the wellhead is passed through a piping system to the powerhouse where it drives a turbine–generator unit. The spent steam is condensed using cooling water derived from the steam condensate itself by means of a water-cooling tower. This is depicted schematically in **Figure 2**.

It is often convenient and economical to locate several wells on a single pad to minimize the amount of land and the number of access roads needed to develop a field. An arrangement of four steam production wells at The Geysers is shown in **Figure 3**. The wells are drilled directionally to intercept a large reservoir volume and to minimize the interference between them.

The steam gathering system can appear to be a bewildering, complex arrangement of piping, as seen in **Figure 4**. However, by interconnecting the pipes coming from various wells, the plant operators can have flexibility in selecting which wells are used to feed the plant at various times.

The turbine–generator set is not much different from a low-pressure turbine in any conventional power station. **Figure 5** shows a 55 MW unit at the Northern California Power Agency (NCPA) plant at the Geysers. There are two such units in a single powerhouse; a separate powerhouse replicates this arrangement, giving NCPA a total of 220 MW.

The cooling water needed to effect the condensation of the steam leaving the turbine is obtained from water-cooling towers, such as the one shown in **Figure 6**. The condensate from the condenser is piped to the top of the cooling tower and allowed to fall through an air stream drawn into the tower by large fans situated at the top. The cool air induces the warm condensate to partially

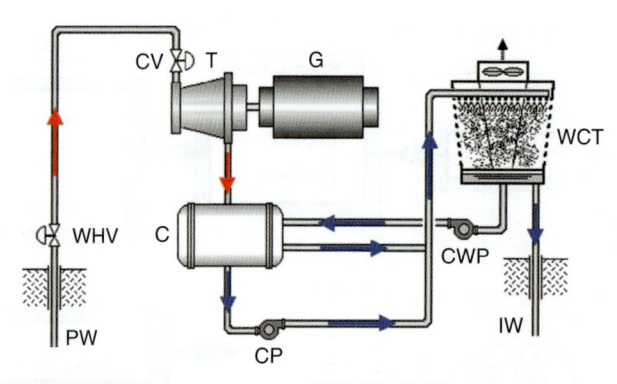

Figure 2 Dry-steam power plant – simplified schematic flow diagram. C, Condenser; CP, Condensate pump; CV, Control valve; CWP, Cooling water pump; G, Generator; IW, Injection well; PW, Production well; T, Turbine; WCT, Water-cooling tower; WHV, Wellhead valve.

Figure 3 Several wellheads and steam pipelines at The Geysers. Note the axial separators to remove particulate matter. Photo courtesy of Calpine Corporation [1].

Figure 4 Steam pipelines at the Valle Secolo power plant at Larderello. Photo: Google Earth.

evaporate, causing a temperature drop. The cooled water is returned to the condenser where it flows through tubes providing the heat sink to condense the spent turbine steam. In this way, the power plant can operate without a separate source of fresh cooling water or even make-up water, as there is more than enough condensate to supply sufficient cooling water, leaving an excess that is usually reinjected.

Figure 5 A double-flow 55 MW turbine–generator set at an NCPA power plant at The Geysers.

Figure 6 Cooling tower at The Geysers units 3 and 4. These two 27 MW power units were installed in 1967–68, but have since been decommissioned and dismantled in favor of more modern and efficient units.

7.07.3.1.2 *Systems analysis*

These power plants are designed using the basic principles of thermodynamics, fluid mechanics, and heat transfer. Although there are hundreds of components in a dry-steam geothermal power plant, we will describe only the major ones, which include moisture removers, turbines, generators, condensers, cooling towers, and pumps. As each of these selected components will be found in flash-steam plants (see Section 7.07.3.2) and some will be found in binary plants (see Section 7.07.4), most of the descriptions given in this section will be generally applicable.

7.07.3.1.2(i) *Moisture removers*

The purpose is to trap any moisture droplets that may have formed during the transport of the steam through the gathering-system piping. Steam traps are generally placed at intervals along the piping, but the moisture remover is the final place where droplets can be removed before the steam enters the turbine hall. **Figure 7** is a schematic of a typical vertical moisture remover. There are no

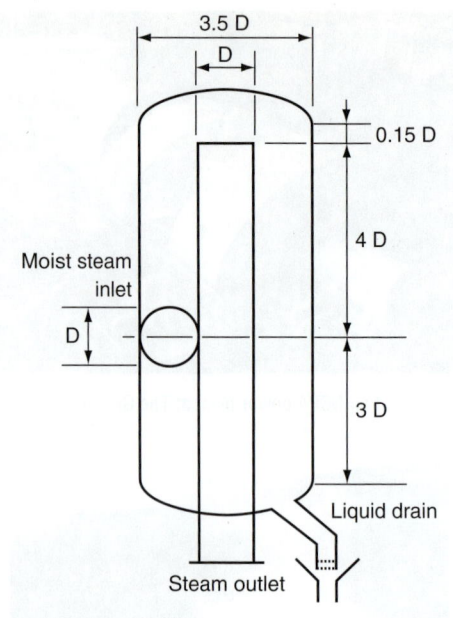

Figure 7 Optimal design dimensions for a moisture remover [1].

moving parts, and the droplets are simply forced to the wall of the vessel by centrifugal action, while the steam travels to the top and leaves via the central standpipe. There are other designs that employ baffles and other screens, but the one shown is the simplest and has been shown to be very effective when designed properly. The dimensions in **Figure 7** are chosen to lead to optimal performance. These are useful for removing relatively small water droplets from mainly steam flows and are situated just outside the powerhouse as the steam is about to enter the turbine hall.

Lazalde–Crabtree analyzed moisture separators for optimal performance and gave the dimensions shown in the figure and the guidelines shown in **Table 1**.

7.07.3.1.2(ii) Turbines

A typical turbine for a dry-steam plant consists of 5–9 stages of impulse–reaction blades, arranged in either a single- or a double-flow design and having a nominal power rating ranging from 20 to 60 MW. A cross section of a design used at The Geysers field is shown in **Figure 8**. This turbine has six stages consisting of a set of nozzles and blades arranged in a double-flow

Table 1 Maximum and recommended ranges for steam velocities

Parameter	Moisture remover ($m\,s^{-1}$ ($ft\,s^{-1}$))
Maximum steam velocity at two-phase inlet pipe	60 (195)
Recommended steam velocity at two-phase inlet pipe	35–50 (115–160)
Maximum upward annular steam velocity	6.0 (20)
Recommended upward annular steam velocity	1.2–4.0 (4–13)

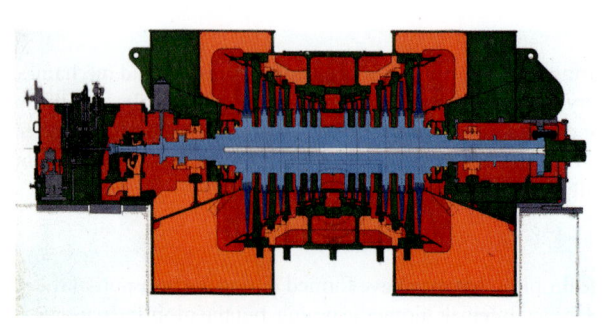

Figure 8 Double-flow turbine cross section – typical of many units at the Geysers.

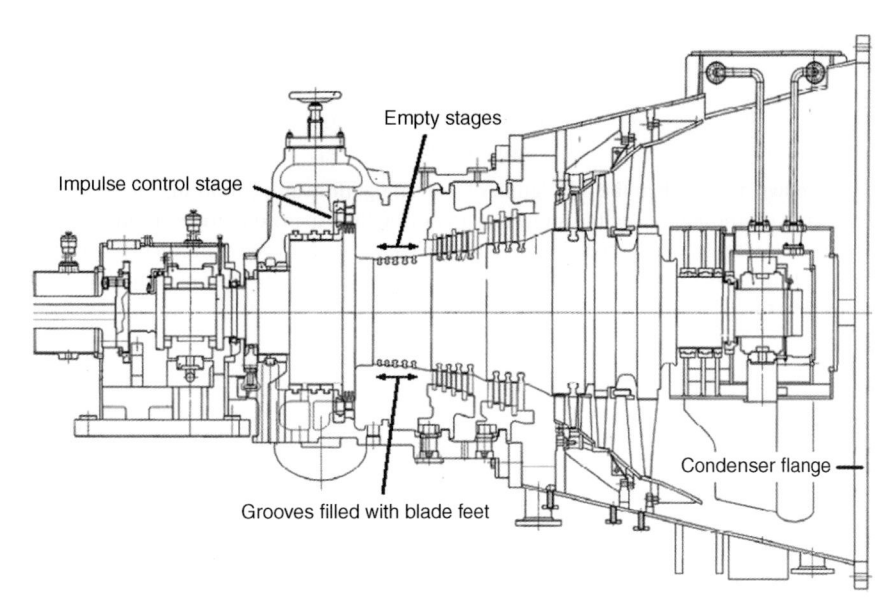

Figure 9 Cross section of an axial-flow turbine for use in dry-steam plants [1].

pattern. This design has a downward exhaust from the casing that directs the spent steam to the condenser. The rating of this turbine would be 55–60 MW.

There is a trend toward more flexible designs that allow the turbine steam path to be modified *in situ* should the steam pressure decline over the course of the plant lifetime. A design of this sort is shown in **Figure 9**. The power rating can be adjusted by the addition or removal of stages at the high-pressure end (left side) of the rotor. This design has an axial-flow exhaust that allows the condenser to be placed on the same level as the turbine, instead of in an excavated cellar. This reduces installation costs and speeds up the time for installation. At Larderello, units of this type are replacing older units that have outlived their usefulness.

The power generated by a steam turbine can be calculated in terms of the mass flow rate of the steam, and the inlet and outlet properties of the steam. If we let the inlet be denoted by 1 and the outlet by 2, then the power can be written as

$$\dot{W}_T = \dot{m}_S(h_1 - h_2) \qquad [1]$$

where $\dot{m}_S$ is the steam mass flow rate (assumed constant), and h_1 and h_2 are the inlet and outlet steam enthalpy, respectively. Both enthalpy values depend on the temperature and pressure of the steam as well as on the state of the steam, that is, saturated, superheated, or two-phase (a mixture of steam and water). Generally, the inlet conditions are well known, but only the outlet pressure is known. Furthermore, all geothermal steam turbines discharge wet steam with some fraction of liquid water mixed in with the steam.

The steam turbine process is depicted in **Figure 10**, a temperature–entropy state diagram, as the line from 1 to 2. The state 2s is the ideal outlet state that would be achieved if the turbine were perfect thermodynamically, that is, if it operated isentropically. The

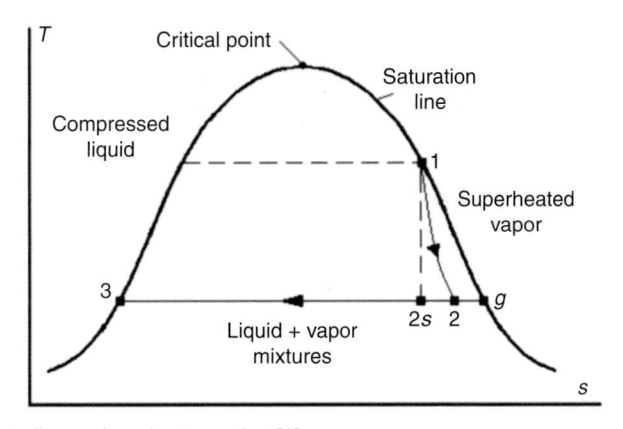

Figure 10 Temperature–entropy state diagram for a dry-steam plant [1].

enthalpy of that state can be calculated from the inlet conditions and the outlet pressure, using the properties of steam obtained from tables or from software. Then the actual outlet state can be found from the definition of the turbine isentropic efficiency, namely,

$$\eta_T = \frac{\text{actual output}}{\text{ideal output}} = \frac{h_1 - h_2}{h_1 - h_{2s}} \quad [2]$$

If the turbine efficiency is known *a priori*, then the calculation of h_2 is straightforward. Unfortunately, this is not usually the case, as the turbine efficiency depends on the amount of moisture present during the expansion process from 1 to 2. A method for dealing with this was proposed by Baumann, who postulated that a turbine loses 1% in efficiency for each 1% of average moisture during expansion, relative to a purely dry expansion. Thus, with reference to the state points labeled in **Figure 10**, it can be derived that the enthalpy of the exhaust steam can be written as

$$h_2 = \frac{h_1 - A\left[1 - \dfrac{h_3}{h_g - h_3}\right]}{1 + \dfrac{A}{h_g - h_3}} \quad [3]$$

where the term A is defined as

$$A = 0.5\eta_{T,\text{dry}}(h_1 - h_{2s}) \quad [4]$$

One may use an appropriate value for the dry turbine efficiency; for this method, 85% is typically used, which allows the last equation to be written as

$$A = 0.425\,(h_1 - h_{2s}) \quad [5]$$

7.07.3.1.2(iii) Generators

The generator for a dry-steam plant is of a generic design that can be used at any geothermal steam plant. Typical specifications might be three-phase, synchronous, direct-connected to the turbine (no gear box), air- or hydrogen-cooled, and with a power factor of 0.90. **Figure 11** shows a cut-away schematic of the generator used at the Hatchobaru plant in Japan.

7.07.3.1.2(iv) Condensers

In the first geothermal plants at Larderello and The Geysers, direct-contact, barometric condensers were used. The cooling water was obtained from the steam condensate that was cooled in either natural-draft or mechanically induced-draft cooling towers. **Figure 12** shows a flow diagram for a 'Cycle 3' plant at Larderello.

Shell-and-tube condensers are used at most geothermal steam plants nowadays. **Figure 13** shows the heat balance diagram for the Sonoma (originally SMUDGEO No.1) plant at The Geysers.

With reference to **Figure 10**, the amount of cooling water needed for a direct-contact condenser can be determined from the equation

$$\dot{m}_{CW} = \dot{m}_S \left[\frac{h_2 - h_3}{\bar{c}\,(T_3 - T_{CW})}\right] \quad [6]$$

where $\bar{c}$ is the average specific heat of the cooling water and T_{CW} is the temperature of the cooling water as it enters the condenser.

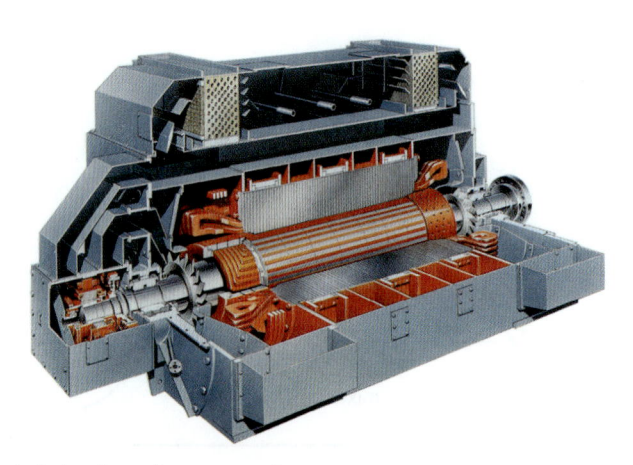

Figure 11 Cut-away schematic of a typical geothermal power generator.

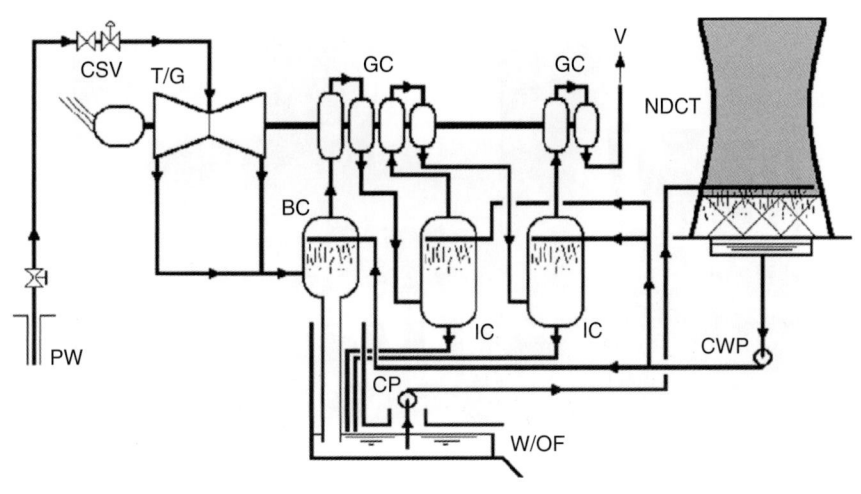

Figure 12 Flow diagram for Larderello Cycle 3 plant showing direct-contact barometric condenser with a natural-draft cooling tower [1]. BC, Barometric condenser; CP, Condensate pump; CSV, Control/stop valves; CWP, Cooling water pump; GC, Gas compressor; IC, Inter-condenser; NDCT, Natural-draft cooling tower; PW, Production well; T/G, Turbine/Generator; V, Vent; W/OF, Water overflow.

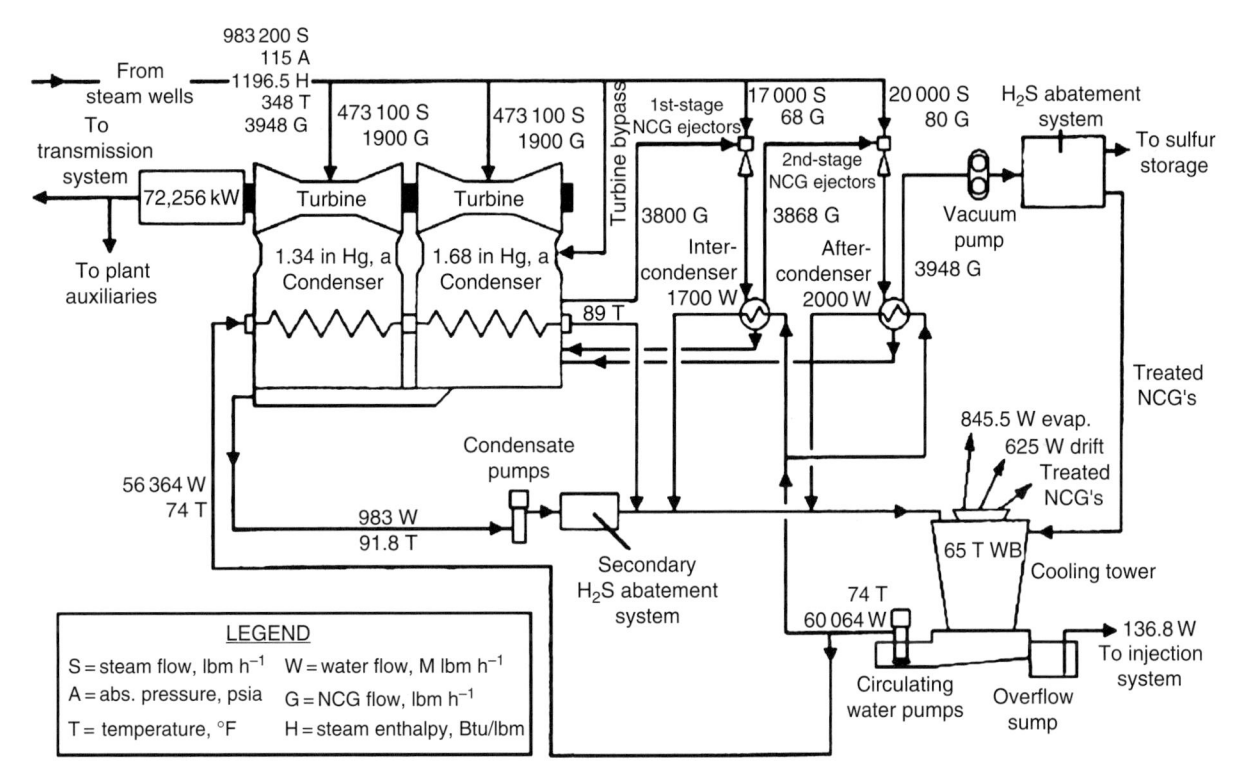

Figure 13 Heat balance diagram for the Sonoma plant at The Geysers showing shell-and-tube condensers with induced-draft cooling towers [1].

For a shell-and-tube condenser, the equation becomes

$$\dot{m}_{CW} = \dot{m}_S \left[\frac{h_2 - h_3}{\bar{c}\,\Delta T} \right] \Delta T \qquad [7]$$

where ΔT is the increase in water temperature as it passes through the condenser.

Equations [6] and [7] ignore any subcooling of the condensate before it leaves the condenser, as well as noncondensable gas removal, which will change the mass balance slightly.

7.07.3.1.2(v) Cooling towers

Nearly all geothermal steam plants use mechanically-induced-draft water-cooling towers, either crossflow or counterflow, to produce the cooling water needed to condense the spent steam from the turbine; see **Figure 6**. There are natural-draft cooling

Figure 14 Natural-draft water-cooling towers at Larderello 2 and 3 power stations.

towers only in some of the units at Larderello, at Matsukawa in Japan, and at Ohaaki in New Zealand. **Figure 14** shows the natural-draft towers at Larderello 2 and 3 power stations.

7.07.3.1.2(vi) Pumps

In order to move the steam condensate from the hot well of the condenser to the top of the cooling tower, it is necessary to pump the liquid by means of condensate pumps. Furthermore, in most cases, water-circulating pumps are needed to convey the cooled water from the cold well of the cooling tower back to the condenser. The latter pumps may be eliminated if sufficient gravity head is available. Both are generally of the centrifugal type, multi-stage, and driven by an electrical motor.

The power needed to drive a liquid pump can be calculated in terms of the mass flow rate of the liquid and the inlet and outlet state properties. If we let the inlet be denoted by 3 and the outlet by 4, then the power requirement can be written as

$$\dot{W}_P = \dot{m}_L(h_4 - h_3) \qquad [8]$$

where $\dot{m}_L$ is the liquid mass flow rate (assumed constant) and h_3 and h_4 are the inlet and outlet liquid enthalpy, respectively. Both enthalpy values depend on the temperature and pressure of the liquid. Similar to the case of the turbine, the inlet conditions are well known but only the outlet pressure is known. Furthermore, it is usually acceptable to take the pump efficiency as fixed, say 75% or 80%, or some other appropriate value. Thus the outlet enthalpy can be found from the pump efficiency definition as follows:

$$h_4 = h_3 + \frac{h_{4s} - h_3}{\eta_P} \qquad [9]$$

where h_{4s} is the ideal pump outlet enthalpy (isentropic process) and η_P is defined as

$$\eta_P = \frac{\text{ideal power input}}{\text{actual power input}} = \frac{h_{4s} - h_3}{h_4 - h_3} \qquad [10]$$

As liquids may be considered incompressible to a first approximation, the change in enthalpy for the ideal isentropic process may be approximated as follows:

$$h_{4s} - h_3 \approx v_3(P_4 - P_3) \approx (P_4 - P_3)/\rho_3 \qquad [11]$$

where v_3 and ρ_3 denote the specific volume and density, respectively, of the liquid entering the pump.

The next section deals with flash-steam plants, and many of the components described above will also apply to those plants.

7.07.3.2 Flash-Steam Plants

The vast majority of geothermal resources are liquid-dominated in nature. Wells produce a mixture of hot water and steam. As turbines are designed for steam-only, if liquid is allowed to enter the turbine severe damage will ensue to the nozzles and blades. Furthermore, the fraction of liquid that accompanies the steam is significant, ranging typically from 70% to 85% by mass. Thus, before the geofluid can be used in the turbine, the liquid must be removed as thoroughly as possible. The problem is similar to but more challenging than the moisture removal process described for dry-steam plants in Section 7.07.3.1.2. As will be shown, the rest of the plant is very similar to that used for dry-steam plants.

7.07.3.2.1 General description

There are two types of flash-steam plants commonly in use around the world: single-flash and double-flash plants. These are shown in simplified schematic flow diagrams in **Figures 15** and **16**, respectively. Both are similar to dry-steam plants but with the addition of a cyclone separator, CS, for single-flash plants, and both a separator and a flash vessel, F, for double-flash plants.

7.07.3.2.1(i) Single-flash plants

Single-flash plants are the simplest and most conservative design that can be installed at moderate- to high-temperature liquid-dominated reservoirs. They are the least expensive to build and operate, and are less prone to chemical precipitation problems stemming from silica scaling in the separated brine, but they produce roughly 15–25% less power output than a double-flash plant. They often are selected as the first units at a new field. Later on, additional units of the double-flash type may be installed if they are deemed feasible based on some years of operating experience with the single-flash units.

7.07.3.2.1(ii) Double-flash plants

Double-flash units require a fairly precise balance of high- and low-pressure steam to keep the dual-pressure turbine operating in a balanced and efficient manner. It is not uncommon for the characteristics of the geofluid to change over time, as typically reservoirs become more steam-dominated resulting in a deficiency of liquid for flashing into low-pressure steam. This can cause problems and has even led to the switch from double- to single-flash operation after a period of operation at some fields, albeit with a loss of efficiency.

7.07.3.2.2 System analysis

Flash-steam plants, like dry-steam plants, are designed on the basis of thermodynamics, fluid mechanics, and heat transfer. Although these plants comprise hundreds of components, many of them are identical in function to those described for dry-steam

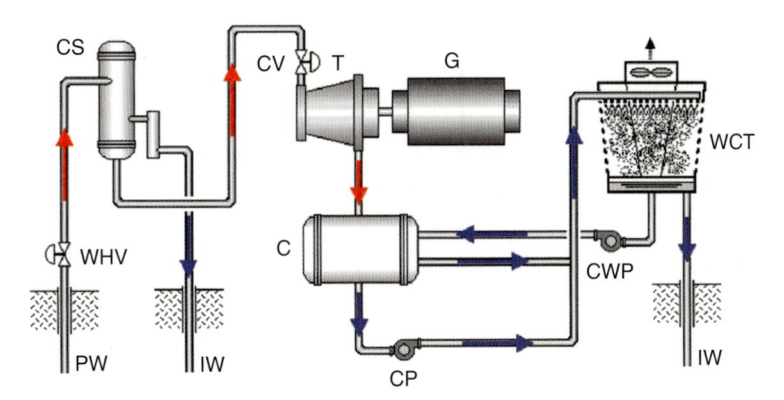

Figure 15 Single-flash power plant – simplified schematic flow diagram. C, Condenser; CP, Condensate pump; CS, Cyclone separator; CV, Control valve; CWP, Cooling water pump; G, Generator; IW, Injection well; PW, Production well; T, Turbine; WCT, Water-cooling tower; WHV, Wellhead valve.

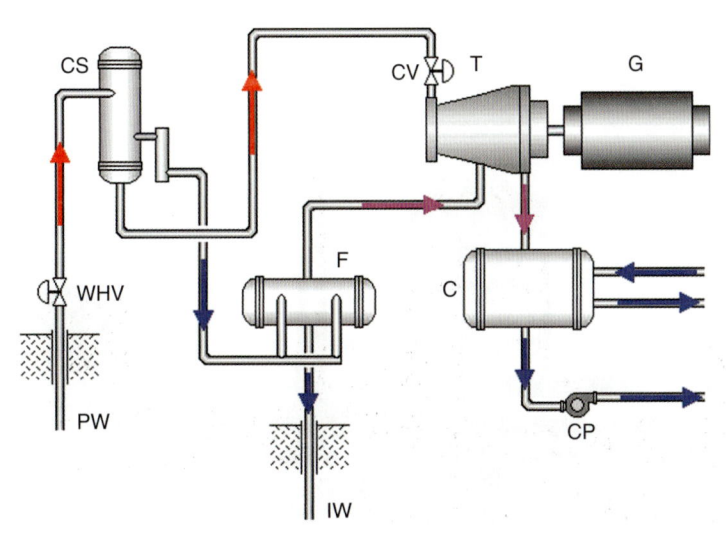

Figure 16 Double-flash power plant – simplified schematic flow diagram Note: water-cooling tower omitted for clarity. C, Condenser; CP, Condensate pump; CS, Cyclone Separator; CV, Control valve; F, Flash vessel; G, Generator; IW, Injection well; PW, Production well; WHV, Wellhead valve.

plants. Thus, only the major ones that differ from those already described will be covered here. These include primary steam separators, flash vessels (double-flash only), and dual-admission turbines (double-flash only).

7.07.3.2.2(i) Single-flash plants – Primary steam separators

Most single-flash plants employ vertical cyclone separators; a few plants mainly in Iceland use horizontal separators. **Figure 17** shows a vertical cycle separator with optimal dimensioning. The liquid outlet usually discharges to an external water-holding tank. This removes the liquid rapidly from the vessel, thereby minimizing the possible entrainment of liquid droplets by the rising steam. Although seldom used nowadays, the steam leaving from the bottom outlet pipe may be sent through a ball check valve as a precaution against liquid slugs entering the steam piping system. A complete wellhead arrangement is shown in **Figure 18**.

Lazalde–Crabtree analyzed vertical cyclone separators for optimal performance and gave the dimensions shown in the figure and the guidelines shown in **Table 2**.

Figure 19 shows an alternative separator design, namely, a horizontal vessel. Two-phase geofluid is directed downward at one end of the vessel where it encounters a series of baffles that generally directs the liquid to the bottom while the vapor rises to fill the upper section. At the opposite end, there is an enclosed volume with a perforated sheet that allows the vapor to freely pass upward to a pair of discharge ports. The liquid is drained through two bottom outlets.

Regardless of the design, the amount of steam generated from the total well flow can be calculated from

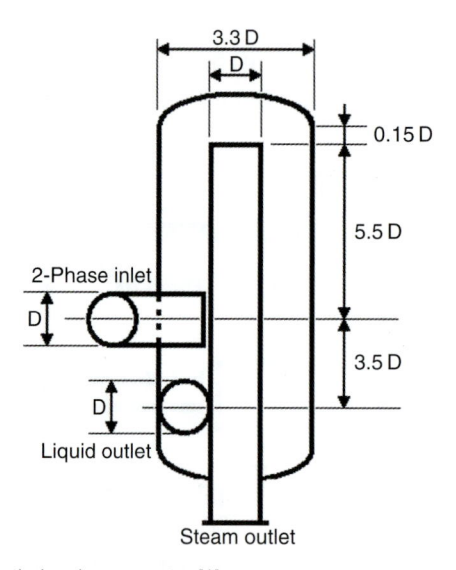

Figure 17 Optimal design dimensions for a vertical cyclone separator [1].

Figure 18 Wellhead equipment at well AH-06 at Ahuachapan, El Salvador. The ball check valve is on the left, and the water-holding tank is just to the right of the bottom of the separator. Photograph by DiPippo [1].

Table 2 Maximum and recommended ranges for steam velocities

Parameter	Cyclone separator ($m\,s^{-1}$ ($ft\,s^{-1}$))
Maximum steam velocity at two-phase inlet pipe	45 (150)
Recommended steam velocity at two-phase inlet pipe	25–40 (80–130)
Maximum upward annular steam velocity	4.5 (14.5)
Recommended upward annular steam velocity	2.5–4.0 (8–13)

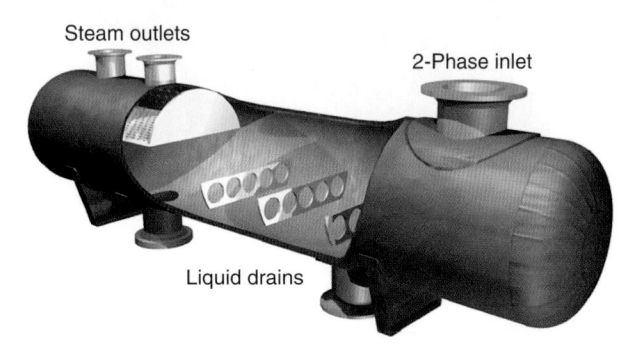

Figure 19 Cut-away schematic of a horizontal separator.

$$\dot{m}_S = \dot{m}_T \left[\frac{h_1 - h_3}{h_2 - h_3} \right] \quad [12]$$

where h_1 is the enthalpy of the geofluid in the reservoir or at the wellhead (assumed equal), h_2 is the enthalpy of the saturated steam leaving the separator, and h_3 is the enthalpy of the liquid leaving the separator. The reservoir enthalpy may usually be taken as that of saturated liquid at the reservoir temperature, whereas the other two enthalpies are taken as the saturation values at the separator pressure. The fraction of steam relative to the total mass flow generally ranges from about 15% to 30%.

The analysis of rest of the plant is the same as for dry-steam plants.

7.07.3.2.2(ii) Double-flash plants – Flash vessels

Double-flash plants are so called because the geofluid is subjected to an additional flash (i.e., a pressure reduction) besides that which occurs as the geofluid travels from the reservoir to the separator. The liquid removed from the separator is at the same pressure as that inside the separator (and equal to the primary steam pressure). Thus, by throttling that liquid to a lower pressure, additional steam, albeit at a pressure lower than the primary steam, can be produced.

Both vertical and horizontal cylindrical vessels are used for the flashing process. In most plants, the combination of vertical separators and a horizontal flasher is used, but at several Icelandic plants the opposite is true. **Figures 20 and 21** show a cut-away schematic and an actual installation of a flash vessel at unit 1 of the Hatchobaru plant in Japan. **Figure 22** shows the orientation of the vertical separators and the horizontal flash vessel at Hatchobaru unit 2.

The processes for generating the high- and low-pressure steam for a double-flash plant are shown in the temperature–entropy state diagram in **Figure 23**. The process labeled 1–2 is the flashing process that takes place from the reservoir to the entrance of the separator; it is modeled as a constant-enthalpy or isenthalpic process. The process labeled 3–6 is the isenthalpic flashing process that occurs across the pressure-letdown valve between the liquid outlet from the separator and the inlet to the flasher.

With reference to **Figure 23**, the two flash processes generate a fractional amount of steam given by the quality, x, of the two-phase mixture at states 2 and 6.

$$x_2 = \frac{h_2 - h_3}{h_4 - h_3} \quad [13]$$

$$x_6 = \frac{h_3 - h_7}{h_8 - h_7} \quad [14]$$

The mass flow rates of the high-pressure steam, the high-pressure separated liquid, and the low-pressure steam are found from the following equations, respectively:

$$\dot{m}_{HPS} = x_2 \dot{m}_T = \dot{m}_4 = \dot{m}_5 \quad [15]$$

$$\dot{m}_{HPL} = (1 - x_2) \dot{m}_T = \dot{m}_3 = \dot{m}_6 \quad [16]$$

$$\dot{m}_{LPS} = (1 - x_2) x_6 \dot{m}_T = \dot{m}_8 \quad [17]$$

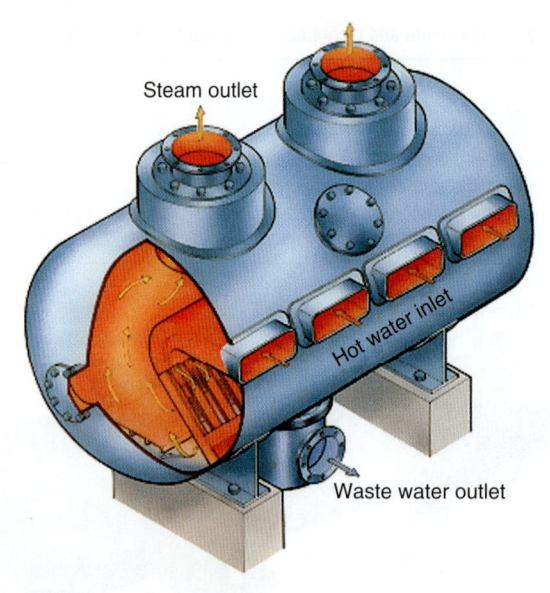

Figure 20 Cut-away schematic of a horizontal flash vessel.

Figure 21 Flash vessel at Hatchobaru Unit 1 on the Japanese island of Kyushu.

The steam mass flows will be used to calculate the power generated from the two stages of turbine expansion, which will be described in the next section.

7.07.3.2.2(iii) Double-flash plants – Dual-admission turbines

A cross section of a dual-admission, dual-pressure turbine is shown in **Figure 24**. In this design, there are two high-pressure (HP) stages and three low-pressure (LP) stages arranged in a horizontally opposed configuration. After passing through the HP stages, the HP steam mixes with the LP steam (from the flash vessel) in the mixing plenum, and the augmented steam flow completes the journey through the LP stages.

The analysis of the HP stages follows the same methodology described in the subsection 7.07.3.1.2(ii) 'Turbines', namely,

$$w_{HPT} = h_4 - h_5 \qquad [18]$$

$$\eta_{HPT} = \frac{h_4 - h_5}{h_4 - h_{5s}} \qquad [19]$$

$$\dot{W}_{HPT} = \dot{m}_{HPS} w_{HPT} = x_2 \dot{m}_T w_{HPT} \qquad [20]$$

Figure 22 Separators and flash vessel at Hatchobaru Unit 2.

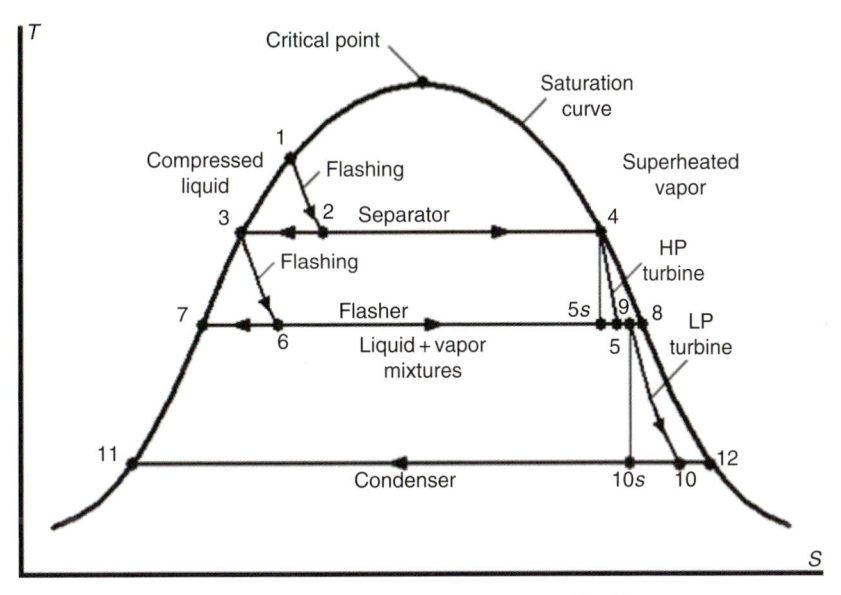

Figure 23 Temperature–entropy diagram for a double-flash plant having a dual-pressure turbine [1].

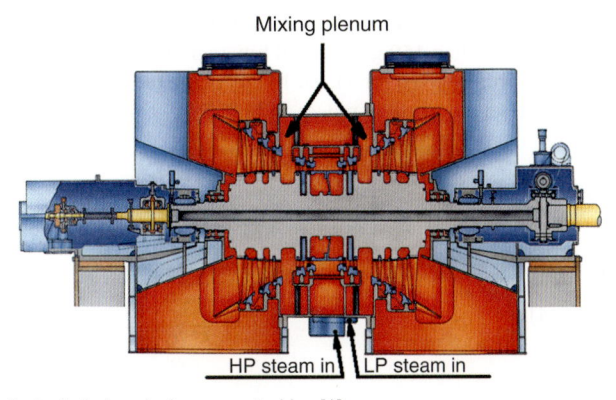

Figure 24 Cut-away schematic of a dual-admission, dual-pressure turbine [1].

where the notation shown in **Figure 23** has been used.

State 5, the actual outlet state from the HP section of the turbine, must be found using the Baumann rule, that is,

$$h_5 = \frac{h_4 - A\left[1 - \dfrac{h_6}{h_7 - h_6}\right]}{1 + \dfrac{A}{h_7 - h_6}} \qquad [21]$$

where the factor A is defined as

$$A = 0.425(h_4 - h_{5s}) \qquad [22]$$

The mixing point is analyzed using the First Law of thermodynamics and conservation of mass to find the enthalpy of the mixed state 9:

$$h_9 = \frac{x_2 h_5 + (1 - x_2) x_6 h_8}{x_2 + (1 - x_2) x_6} \qquad [23]$$

The LP turbine may now be analyzed as follows:

$$\dot{W}_{LPT} = \dot{m}_9 (h_9 - h_{10}) = (\dot{m}_5 + \dot{m}_8)(h_9 - h_{10}) \qquad [24]$$

$$h_{10} = \frac{h_9 - A\left[x_9 - \dfrac{h_{11}}{h_{12} - h_{11}}\right]}{1 + \dfrac{A}{h_{12} - h_{11}}} \qquad [25]$$

$$A = 0.425(h_9 - h_{10s}) \qquad [26]$$

Note that the term x_9 appears in eqn [25] because the steam quality at the inlet to the LP section is not 1, but x_9. Also, the dry turbine efficiency has been taken as 85%.

The total power generated is the sum of the power from each turbine:

$$\dot{W}_T = \dot{W}_{HPT} + \dot{W}_{LPT} \qquad [27]$$

7.07.4 Binary Plants

Binary geothermal power plants are used when the temperature of the geofluid is too low to justify flashing to obtain steam for use in steam turbines, or if flashing the geofluid, either in the well or during the processing of the fluid in surface equipment, would result in chemical precipitation of solid matter that could cause operating difficulties. Binary cycles are also increasingly being installed as bottoming plants at existing geothermal flash plants to extract more power from the same well flow.

There is evidence that the first geothermal plant of the binary type was installed at Kiabukwa in the Democratic Republic of the Congo in 1952 [2]; see **Figure 25**. The plant was rated at 200 kW and used hot water from a geothermal spring in the Upemba graben at a temperature of 91 °C and a flow rate of 40 l s^{-1}. Beyond this, little else is known about this plant owing to a lack of reports in the literature.

A 680 kW binary plant was put into operation in 1967 at Paratunka on the Kamchatka peninsula in the then Soviet Union; it has since been retired from service. The first commercial-sized binary plant was the 13 400 kW Magmamax plant installed in 1979 at East Mesa in the Imperial Valley of southern California in the United States; see **Figure 26**. Like its two predecessor binary plants, the Magmamax plant has also been dismantled.

However, although all three of these pioneering binary plants are no longer in existence, they set the stage for further development and have been followed by more than 150 geothermal binary power units across the world.

In the sections that follow, descriptions will be given for a basic binary plant and several advanced designs. As with geothermal steam plants, working equations will be presented to allow power and efficiency calculations.

7.07.4.1 Basic Organic Rankine Cycle Plants

A Rankine cycle in its simplest form consists of four processes carried out in a closed loop; see **Figure 27**:

(1) pumping process (1–2);
(2) heating–evaporating process (2–3–4);
(3) turbine expansion power process (4–5); and
(4) condensing process (5–1).

Figure 25 Geothermal binary plant at Kiabukwa, Democratic Republic of the Congo (best available copy) [2].

Figure 26 Original Magmamax binary plant at East Mesa, California, US. Photograph by DiPippo [1].

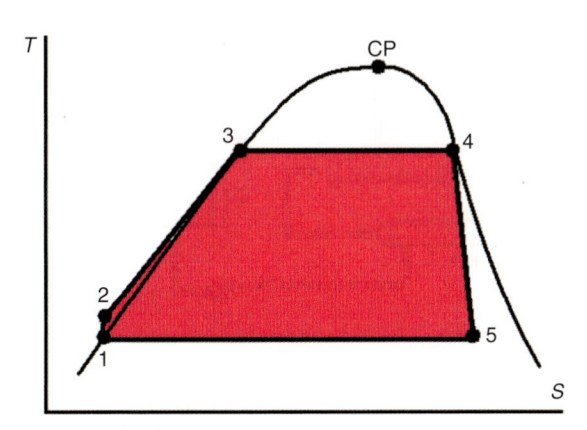

Figure 27 Temperature–entropy process diagram for a basic binary cycle using a working fluid with normal condensing properties. CP denotes the critical point.

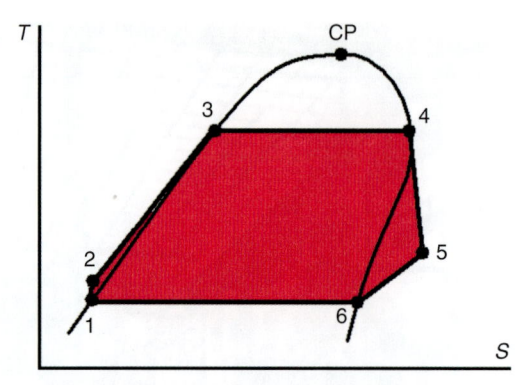

Figure 28 Temperature–entropy process diagram for a basic binary cycle using a working fluid with retrograde condensing properties.

This is the same cycle used in the earliest steam engines. Modern conventional steam power stations add superheat beyond state 4, reheat after the initial turbine expansion, and several stages of feedwater heating, all resulting in significantly higher efficiency as compared to a basic cycle.

Geothermal binary cycles operate on the simple cycle for most cases. A slight amount of superheating may be possible but is not always desirable. A heat recuperator may sometimes be inserted in the basic cycle as a type of feedwater heater, particularly if the cycle working fluid exhibits retrograde condensation; see **Figure 28**. The heat recuperator will always result in improved cycle efficiency. In later sections, more complex binary cycles will be discussed.

7.07.4.1.1 *General system analysis*

Binary plants are among the most environmentally benign power generating plants imaginable. The schematic flow diagram in **Figure 29** depicts how the cycle is conducted. The geofluid after being pumped from the reservoir is used solely for its heat energy. It passes through a series of heat exchangers, and is then reinjected back into the reservoir. The geofluid never comes into contact with the surface environment. The heat extracted from the geofluid is used to preheat and then evaporate a low-boiling-point working fluid, typically a hydrocarbon or other organic fluid. The working fluid circulates within a closed cycle generating an amount of net power equal to the difference between the power produced by the turbine and the power needed to run the well pump, the working-fluid condensate pump, and the cooling-water circulating pump, and the power to drive the cooling-tower fans.

The only significant environmental impact is that of the discharge of waste heat from the Rankine cycle through either a water-cooling tower (**Figure 29**) or an air-cooled condenser (**Figure 30**). In the former case, there is a need for significant amounts of make-up water for the cooling tower, unlike the situation with geothermal steam plants. This aspect is critical in areas where water is in short supply. The alternative air-cooled systems are used widely under such circumstances. Unfortunately, air-cooled power plants are more expensive to build, cover more land, tend to be noisier, experience major variations in net power output over the course of a year as ambient conditions change, and are less efficient than water-cooled systems. However, in many situations they are the only choice.

Because binary plants use pumps, turbines, and condensers as in geothermal steam plants, those components may be analyzed using the equations presented earlier. The heat exchangers comprising the preheater (PH) and the evaporator (E) deserve to be analyzed here as they are key elements in the performance of binary plants.

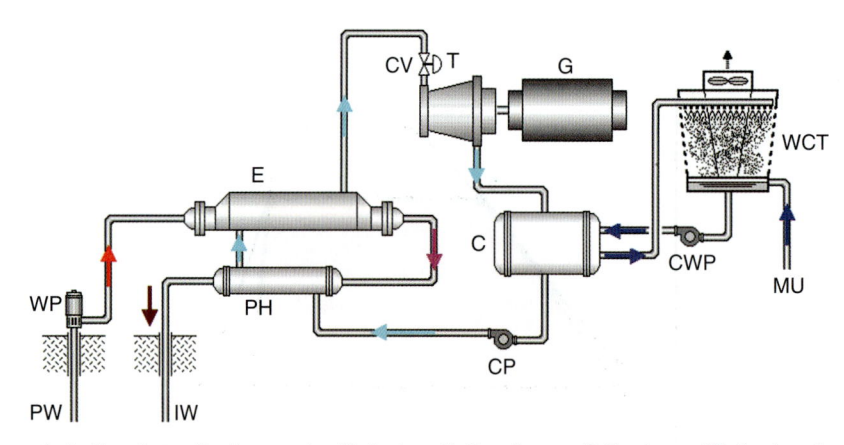

Figure 29 Binary power plant with water-cooling tower – simplified schematic flow diagram. C, Condenser; CP, Condensate pump; CV, Control valve; CWP, Cooling water pump; E, Evaporator; G, Generator; IW, Injection well; MU, Make-up water; PH, Preheater; PW, Production well; T, Turbine; WCT, Water-cooling tower; WP Well pump.

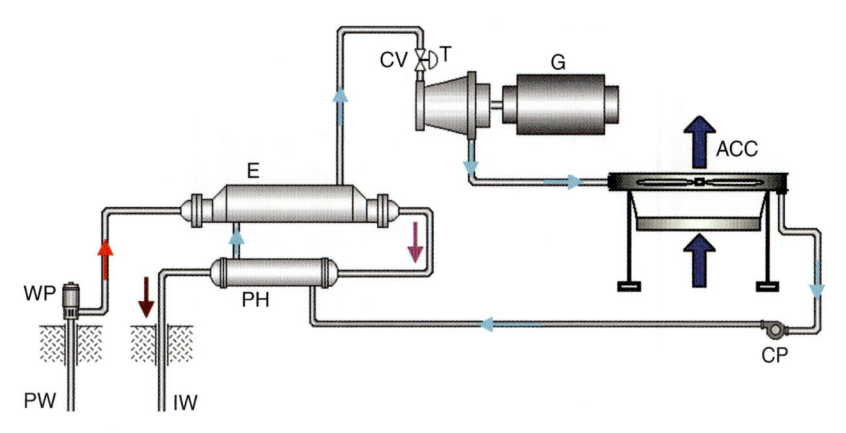

Figure 30 Binary power plant with air-cooled condenser – simplified schematic flow diagram. ACC, Air-cooled condenser; CP, Condensate pump; CV, Control valve; E, Evaporator; G, Generator; IW, Injection well; PH, Preheater; PW, Production well; T, Turbine; WP, Well pump.

7.07.4.1.2 Preheater and evaporator analysis

The preheater and the evaporator may be analyzed using the principles of thermodynamics, heat transfer, and mass conservation; see **Figure 31**. If one neglects the heat transfer between the vessels and the surroundings (i.e., adiabatic walls or perfect insulation), then the heat lost by the brine equals the heat gained by the working fluid in both vessels. Taking the entire configuration as the thermodynamic system, the governing equation is

$$\dot{m}_B(h_a - h_c) = \dot{m}_{WF}(h_1 - h_4) \tag{28}$$

If the brine can be characterized as an incompressible fluid with a constant specific heat, then the required brine flow rate for a given set of cycle design parameters can be found from

$$\dot{m}_B = \dot{m}_{WF}\frac{h_1 - h_4}{\bar{c}_B(T_a - T_c)} \tag{29}$$

The temperature–heat transfer or T–q diagram is a very useful tool for the analysis and design of the individual heat exchangers; see **Figure 32**. The full length of the horizontal axis represents the total amount of heat transferred from the brine to the working fluid. The pinch point is that place in the heat exchanger where the temperature difference between the brine and the working fluid is the smallest; the value of that difference is the pinch point temperature difference, ΔT_{pp}, and is shown in the figure at the interface between the preheater and the evaporator. The pinch point usually occurs there, but it is theoretically possible for it to occur at the cold end of the heat exchanger, but never at the hot end.

The conditions of pressure, temperature, and enthalpy at state points 4, 5, and 1 should be known from the cycle specifications: state 4 is a compressed liquid, the outlet from the feedpump; state 5 is a saturated liquid at the evaporator pressure; and state 1 is a saturated vapor and is the same as the turbine inlet condition, neglecting any pressure loss in the connecting piping. The two heat exchangers may be analyzed separately as follows:

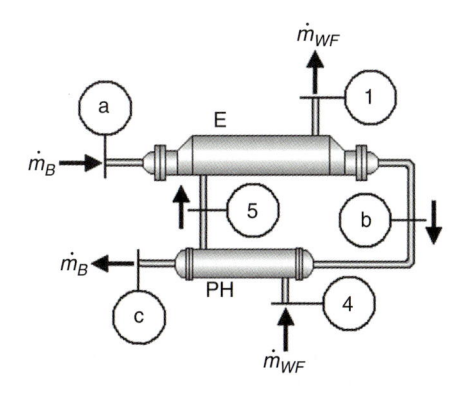

$$\text{Preheater:} \quad \dot{m}_B \bar{c}_B(T_b - T_c) = \dot{m}_{WF}(h_5 - h_4) \tag{30}$$

$$\text{Evaporator:} \quad \dot{m}_B \bar{c}_B(T_a - T_b) = \dot{m}_{WF}(h_1 - h_5) \tag{31}$$

Figure 31 Preheater and evaporator. E, Evaporator; $\dot{m}_B$, Mass flow rate of brine; $\dot{m}_{WF}$, Mass flow rate of working fluid; PH, Preheater.

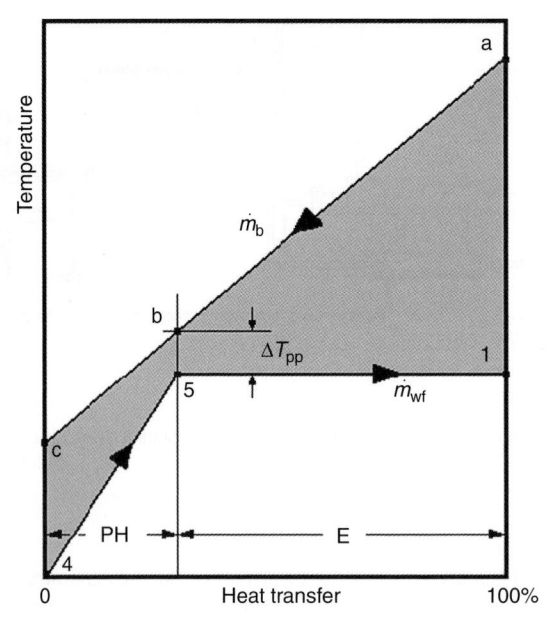

Figure 32 Temperature–heat transfer diagram for preheater and evaporator [1].

As the brine inlet temperature T_a is always known and the pinch point temperature difference is generally known from manufacturer's specifications, T_b can be found from the known value for T_5.

The heat transfer surface area inside the evaporator, A_E, can be calculated using the basic heat transfer relationship:

$$\dot{Q}_E = \bar{U} A_E \, \text{LMTD}|_E \qquad [32]$$

where $\bar{U}$ is the overall heat transfer coefficient and LMTD is the log mean temperature difference, which for the evaporator is found from

$$\text{LMTD}|_E = \frac{(T_a - T_1) - (T_b - T_5)}{\ln\left[\dfrac{T_a - T_1}{T_b - T_5}\right]} \qquad [33]$$

and the evaporation heat transfer rate is given by

$$\dot{Q}_E = \dot{m}_B \bar{c}_B (T_a - T_b) = \dot{m}_{WF}(h_1 - h_5) \qquad [34]$$

A similar set of equations can be derived for the preheater:

$$\dot{Q}_{PH} = \bar{U} A_{PH} \, \text{LMTD}|_{PH} \qquad [35]$$

$$\text{LMTD}|_{PH} = \frac{(T_b - T_5) - (T_c - T_4)}{\ln\left[\dfrac{T_b - T_5}{T_c - T_4}\right]} \qquad [36]$$

$$\dot{Q}_{PH} = \dot{m}_B \bar{c}_B (T_b - T_c) = \dot{m}_{WF}(h_5 - h_4). \qquad [37]$$

The overall heat transfer coefficient $\bar{U}$ should be determined by experiment with the appropriate fluids to be used in the plant. For preliminary calculations, values of $\bar{U}$ may be found in engineering handbooks or heat transfer textbooks. Correction factors must be used with the eqns [32–37] according to the configuration used inside each heat exchanger; see any standard heat transfer text, for example, Reference 3.

7.07.4.2 Advanced Binary Cycle Plants

7.07.4.2.1 Binary cycle with recuperator

One of the ways to improve the thermal efficiency of a binary plant is to add a heat recuperator to the cycle, if thermodynamically allowable. Such a plant is shown in **Figure 33**.

In order to use a recuperator, the temperature of the working fluid leaving the turbine (T) must be higher than that of the working fluid leaving the condensate pump (CP). Furthermore, unless that temperature difference is sufficiently large, it may not be practical to incorporate a recuperator owing to the increased cost of the plant relative to the improvement in performance. The recuperator reduces the amount of heat that must be supplied by the brine while maintaining the same net power. Thus, the brine

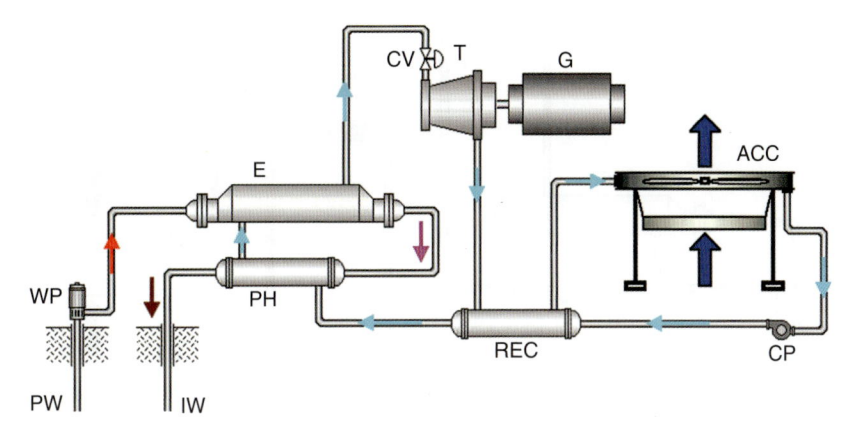

Figure 33 Binary power plant with a heat recuperator (REC). ACC, Air-cooled condenser; CP, Condensate pump; CV, Control valve; E, Evaporator; G, Generator; IW, Injection well; PH, Preheater; PW, Production well; REC, Recuperator; T, Turbine; WP, Well pump.

will be returned to the reservoir, assuming it is reinjected, at a higher temperature. This should make it less likely that chemical precipitation will occur anywhere in the reinjection system and reduce the potential for reservoir cooling.

7.07.4.2.2 Dual-pressure binary cycle

Another way to improve plant performance is to use a dual-pressure cycle. The working fluid is divided into two streams and evaporated at two different pressure levels. This allows a closer match between the brine cooling curve and the working fluid heating–evaporating line. **Figure 34** depicts a dual-pressure binary cycle plant.

The brine (shown in red) passes sequentially through the high-pressure evaporator (HPE) and the low-pressure evaporator (LPE), is divided and passes in parallel through the high-pressure preheater (HPPH) and the low-pressure preheater (LPPH), and finally is reinjected. The working fluid (shown in green) returns as a liquid from the air-cooled condenser (ACC) via the condensate pump (CP) and enters the LPPH. A portion of the working fluid continues on to the LPE and then to the low-pressure section of the turbine (LPT). However, the remainder of the working fluid is pumped to a higher pressure by the booster pump (BP) and then passes through the HPPH and the HPE, and then to the high-pressure section of the turbine (HPT). The low-pressure working fluid mixes with the partly expanded high-pressure stream, and the two streams expand through the low-pressure stages of the turbine before entering the ACC. By suitable selection of brine and working fluid flow rates, the heat transfer can be made more efficient than in a single-pressure system.

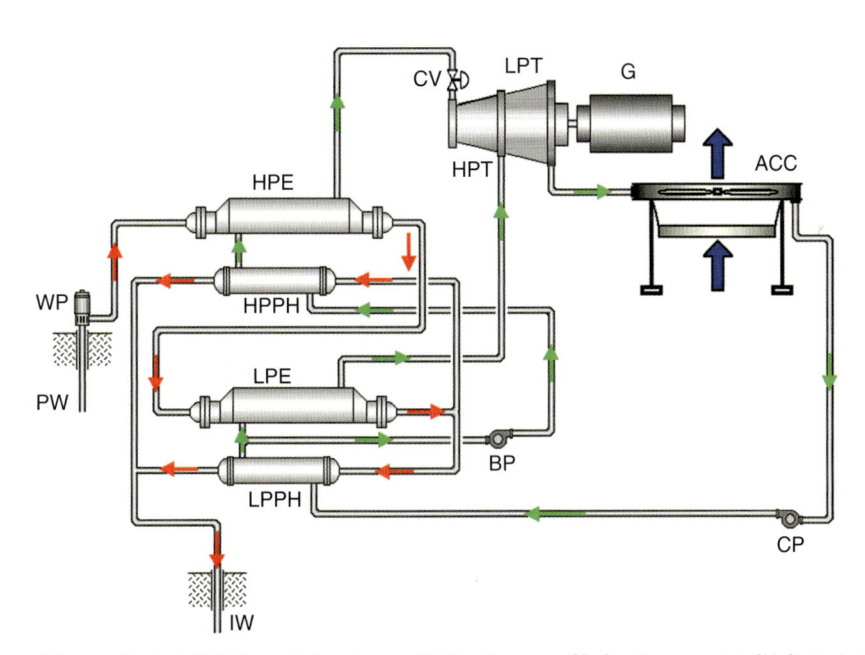

Figure 34 Dual-pressure binary cycle plant. ACC, Air-cooled condenser; BP, Booster pump; CP, Condensate pump; CV, Control valve; G, Generator; HPE, High-pressure evaporator; HPPH, High-pressure preheater; HPT, High-pressure turbine; IW, Injection well; LPE, Low-pressure evaporator; LPPH, Low-pressure preheater; LPT, Low-pressure turbine; PW, Production well; WP, Well pump.

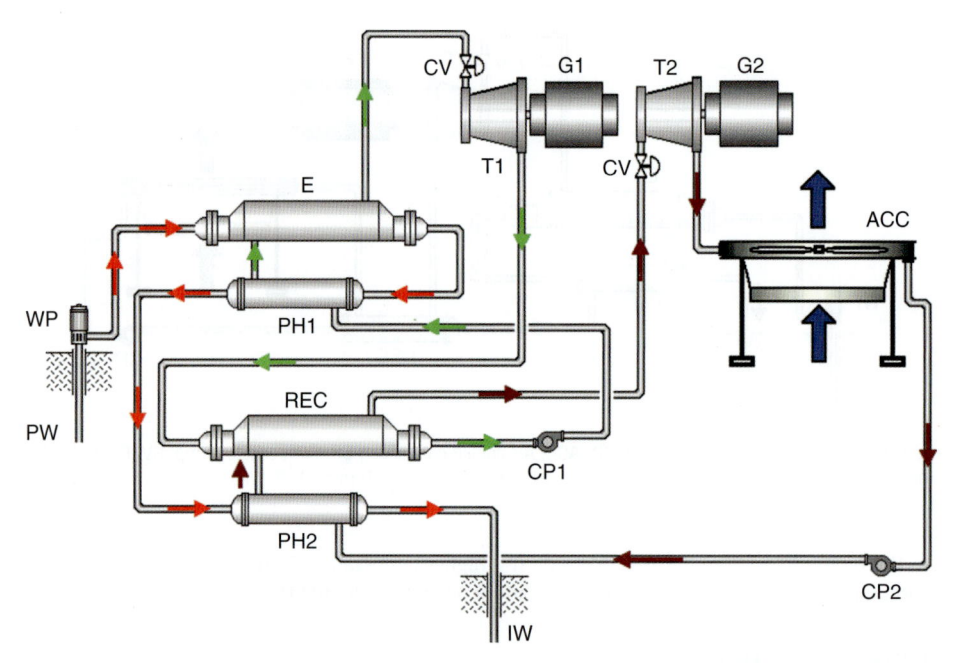

Figure 35 Dual-fluid binary cycle power plant. ACC, Air-cooled condenser; CP, Condensate pump; CV, Control valve; E, Evaporator; G, Generator; IW, Injection well; PH, Preheater; PW, Production well; REC, Recuperator; T, Turbine; WP, Well pump.

7.07.4.2.3 Dual-fluid binary cycle

By combining two different working fluids in an integrated binary cycle, as shown in **Figure 35**, it may be possible to achieve some gains in efficiency over a simple binary cycle. The green arrows follow one working fluid, whereas the brown ones follow the second one. The brine is used as the heating medium for the evaporator and preheater for working fluid 1 and for the preheater for working fluid 2; the heat needed to vaporize working fluid 2 comes from the condensation of working fluid 1 in the recuperator REC.

Interestingly, the first commercial binary plant, the Magmamax plant in the United States, used a cycle similar to this, where isobutane and propane were the two working fluids.

7.07.4.2.4 Kalina binary cycles

The last of the advanced binary cycles that will be covered are the Kalina cycles. There are many variations of the Kalina cycle, but the basic notion is that the working fluid is a mixture of water and ammonia. The composition may be fixed throughout the cycle, or it may be designed to vary depending on the component. In the latter case, the turbine would use an ammonia-rich mixture to capitalize on ammonia's inherent advantages over water during expansion. In either case, the evaporation and condensation processes occur at variable temperature allowing a better match between the brine cooling line and the working fluid heating–evaporating line at the hot end, and between the cooling water heating line and the working fluid condensing line at the cold end.

A Kalina cycle with variable composition is shown in **Figure 36**. The brine (red arrows) is used only to provide the final heating in the evaporator. The water–ammonia mixture (brown arrows) is separated (S) into a vapor stream rich in ammonia (green arrows) and a liquid stream rich in water (blue arrows). The two streams recombine just before entering the heat recuperator (REC), returning the mixture to the basic composition.

Although the Kalina cycles are capable of higher efficiencies than basic binary cycles, a binary cycle with a two-component mixed working fluid and a heat recuperator can reach comparable or higher efficiency, particularly if supercritical pressure is used. The choice between options depends on the cost effectiveness of one cycle over the other.

7.07.5 Advanced Geothermal Plants

Given that geothermal power plants have over a century of operating experience at a wide range of resources, the technology of energy conversion has advanced to the point where highly efficient designs can be built to exploit resources having a wide variety of thermodynamic and chemical characteristics. Even very aggressive brines such as the ones found at the Salton Sea in California's Imperial Valley can now be used for power generation in a reliable manner. Power plants can be built for geopressured resources and for ones at low temperature. Innovative plants that combine several different types of cycle have been designed and built, and are in operation at many sites around the world. Plants using a combination of energy sources such as fossil, solar, and geothermal have been designed; one has been operating for many years and a few have reached the feasibility stage.

In this section, some of the hybrid systems and combined cycle plants will be discussed.

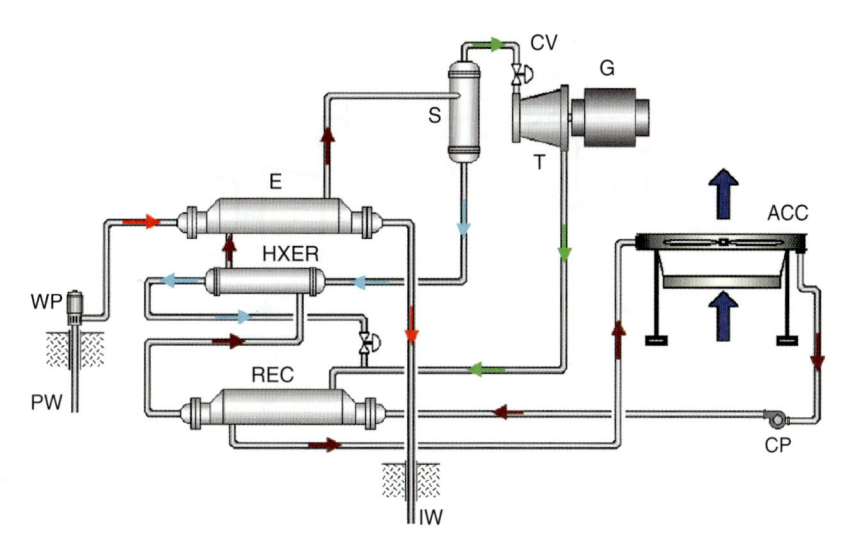

Figure 36 Kalina cycle with variable-composition working fluid mixture. ACC, Air-cooled condenser; CP, Condensate pump; CV, Control valve; E, Evaporator; G, Generator; HXER, Heat exchanger; IW, Injection well; PW, Production well; REC, Recuperator; S, Separator; T, Turbine; WP, Well pump.

7.07.5.1 Hybrid Plants

In an attempt to create synergy, plants with two (or more) energy sources have been designed. In some, the primary energy source is geothermal with the other source acting as a supplement, and for others the opposite is true. Two categories will be included in this section: fossil–geothermal and solar–geothermal plants.

7.07.5.1.1 Fossil–geothermal hybrid plants

Fossil energy sources that can be combined with geothermal include coal, natural gas, and biomass. As coal is used exclusively in large central power stations using sophisticated Rankine cycles that include one or two stages of reheating and multiple stages of feedwater heating, geothermal plays a supplementary role when combined with such a coal-fired plant. Assuming that the geothermal resource is collocated with the coal plant, geothermal energy can be used to replace one or two of the low-temperature feedwater heaters, allowing more low-pressure steam to flow through the last stages of the turbine and thereby produce more power. Rather low-grade geothermal resources can be used in this way to create the desired synergy, as such resources could only be used in very low efficiency binary cycles by themselves. A geothermal-preheat system is shown in a simplified schematic flow diagram in **Figure 37**. An alternative approach uses the fossil fuel (in this case most likely natural gas) to provide superheating of the geothermal steam. A simplified schematic of a fossil-superheat plant is shown in **Figure 38**. Finally, these two concepts can be combined in a compound hybrid plant, as shown in **Figure 39**. The latter two systems can be extended for use in double-flash cases at considerable complication but will achieve higher synergy and utilization efficiencies.

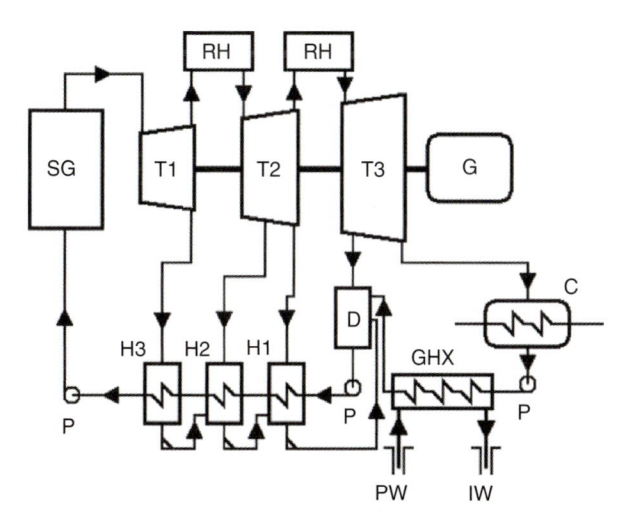

Figure 37 Geothermal preheat fossil–geothermal hybrid power plant. C, Condenser; D, Deaerator; G, Generator; GHX, Geothermal heat exchanger; H, Feedwater heater; IW, Injection well; P, Pump; PW, Production well; RH, Reheater; SG, Steam generator; T, Turbine

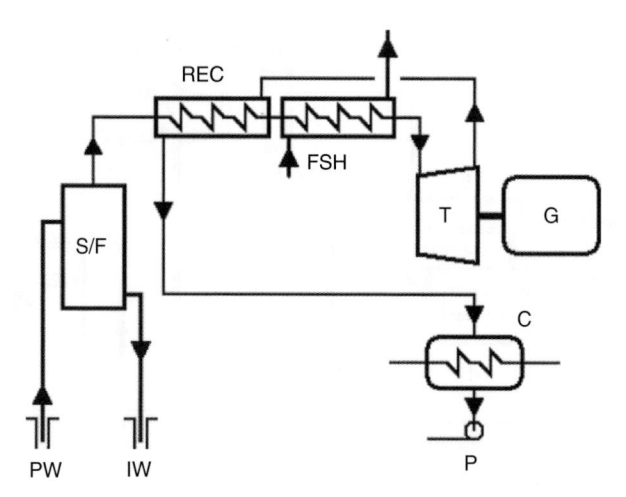

Figure 38 Fossil-superheat fossil–geothermal hybrid power plant. C, Condenser; FSH, Fossil-fired superheater; G, Generator; IW, Injection well; P, Pump; PW, Production well; REC, Recuperator; S/F, Separator/Flash vessel; T, Turbine.

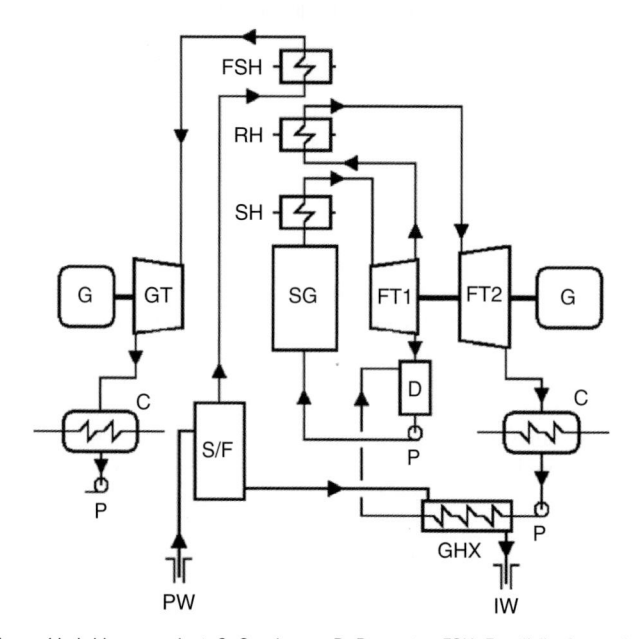

Figure 39 Compound fossil–geothermal hybrid power plant. C, Condenser; D, Deaerator; FSH, Fossil-fired superheater; FT1, FT2, Fossil-fired turbines; G, Generator; GHX, Geothermal heat exchanger; GT, Geothermal turbine; IW, Injection well; P, Pump; PW, Production well; RH, Reheater; S/F, Separator/Flash vessel; SG, Steam generator; SH, Superheater.

7.07.5.1.2 Solar–geothermal plants

The challenge in designing solar–geothermal power plants lies in the intermittent nature of solar energy versus the continuous nature of geothermal energy. If sufficient storage time were available for the thermal energy from the sun, then the two energy sources could be made completely compatible.

Two possible hybrid systems are presented here although there are many variations that can be devised. Solar energy can be used to supplement both geothermal binary and flash-steam plants, mainly through superheating and/or preheating processes. **Figure 40** shows a basic binary plant in which a solar array of parabolic collectors is used to superheat the binary working fluid prior to admission to the turbine. Unless the solar energy is available continuously as through thermal storage, the turbine inlet conditions will change when the sun sets or is obscured, and the performance will suffer.

A more complex arrangement is shown in **Figure 41** – a flash-binary plant with solar brine heating. Here a moderate-temperature geothermal brine is first heated with solar energy to a sufficiently high temperature to permit flashing and steam separation. Turbine T1 is a topping, back-pressure steam turbine that generates power to augment the binary cycle power coming from turbine T2. The T1 exhaust is condensed against the binary cycle working fluid in the condenser/preheater (C/PH) before being reinjected. The hot-separated brine is used in the final heating process for the binary working fluid, and then is recombined with the steam condensate prior to reinjection. When used with an air-cooled condenser as shown, this operation provides 100% reinjection of the geothermal fluid.

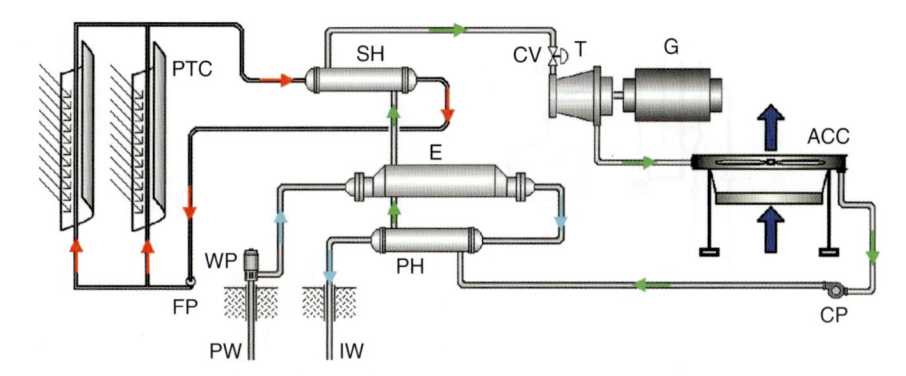

Figure 40 Solar–geothermal binary plant with solar superheating. ACC, Air-cooled condenser; CP, Condensate pump; CV, Control valve; E, Evaporator; FP, Feed pump; G, Generator; IW, Injection well; PH, Preheater; PTC, Parabolic trough collector; PW, Production well; SH, Superheater; T, Turbine; WP, Well pump.

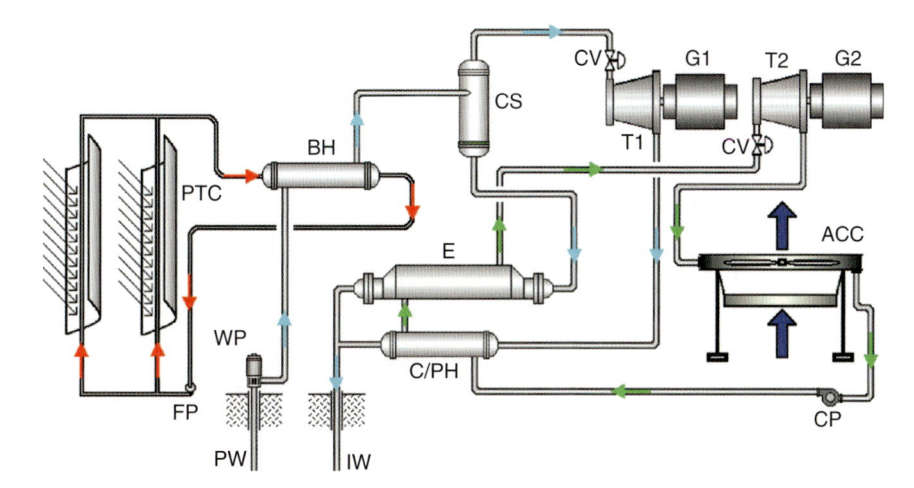

Figure 41 Solar–geothermal flash–binary plant with solar brine heating. ACC, Air-cooled condenser; BH, Brine heater; C/PH, Condenser/Preheater; CP, Condensate pump; CS, Cyclone separator; CV, Control valve; E, Evaporator; FP, Feed pump; G, Generator; IW, Injection well; PTC, Parabolic trough collector; T, Turbine; WP, Well pump.

7.07.5.2 Combined Cycle Plants

This section describes some power plants that combine different basic cycles into an integrated system that better utilizes the geothermal resource than do the individual units. They often are developed after one or two units have been in operation for sufficient time to allow a more thorough understanding of the resource and the reservoir under real operating conditions.

7.07.5.2.1 Combined single- and double-flash plants

Single-flash plants are often the first type of plant installed at liquid-dominated, moderate- to high-temperature resources. The hot brine separated from the two-phase fluid carries a significant fraction of the available energy from the wellhead fluid. By combining an additional unit, a combined single- and double-flash system may be created. **Figure 42** shows such an arrangement in simplified schematic form. The separated brine is collected and flashed to generate low-pressure steam for use in the new unit. Additional power is thus produced without the need for new production wells.

Depending on the reservoir conditions and the temperature of the wellhead fluid, it may be possible to carry out an additional flash process. Then, two additional streams of steam can be produced to generate even more power, as shown in **Figure 43**. A dual-pressure steam turbine is used in unit 3. With this arrangement, low-pressure wells that would not be usable in the single-flash units can be hooked to the third unit, further enhancing the utilization of the resource.

7.07.5.2.2 Flash–binary combined cycle plants

Instead of adding another flash plant to form a combined system, a binary plant can be added. This has the advantage of maintaining the chemical concentrations of any dissolved substances in the brine at the same level as in the original system, as contrasted with adding flash processes, which increases the concentration of impurities as the brine undergoes the flash processes and thereby increases the likelihood of chemical precipitation. To avoid this, the brine temperature needs to be kept higher than is the case for the combined flash–binary option.

232 Geothermal Power Plants

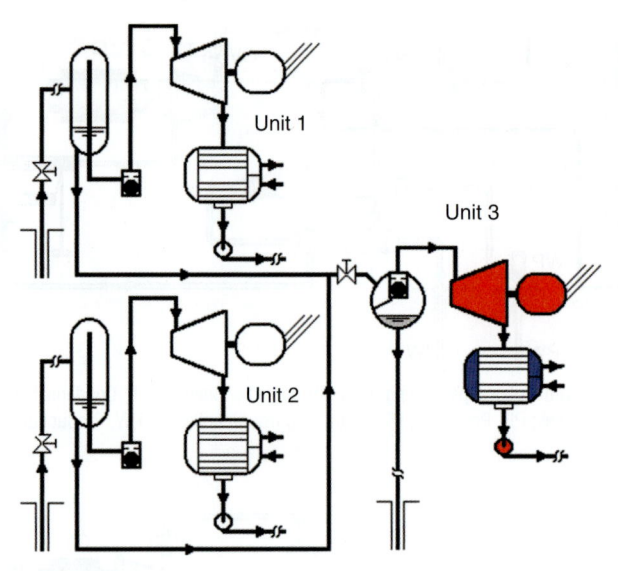

Figure 42 Two single-flash units integrated with a double-flash unit.

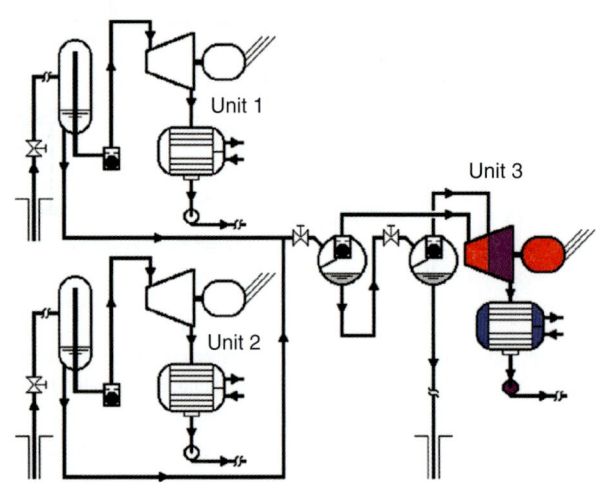

Figure 43 Two single-flash units integrated with a third unit after two additional flash processes.

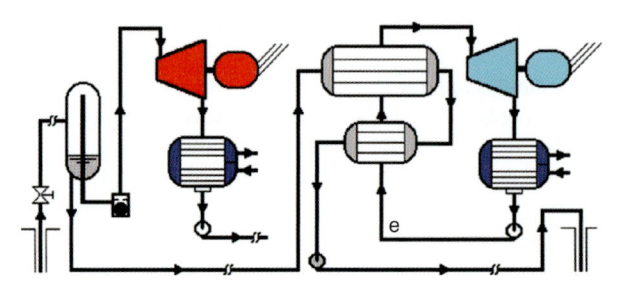

Figure 44 Combined single-flash/binary plant.

The simplest design is shown in **Figure 44** in which the brine is merely diverted from the reinjection manifold through the heat exchangers of the new binary unit. Up to 100% of the available brine may be used in this way. As reservoirs tend to become more vapor-dominated over time, it is wise to allow for some diminution in liquid flow and design the binary unit for something less than the full amount of brine available when the new unit is placed into service.

Whereas the system shown in **Figure 44** is usually constructed in two stages with the binary unit installed a few years after the start of the flash unit, a truly integrated flash–binary plant that can be designed and constructed as one package is shown in **Figure 45**.

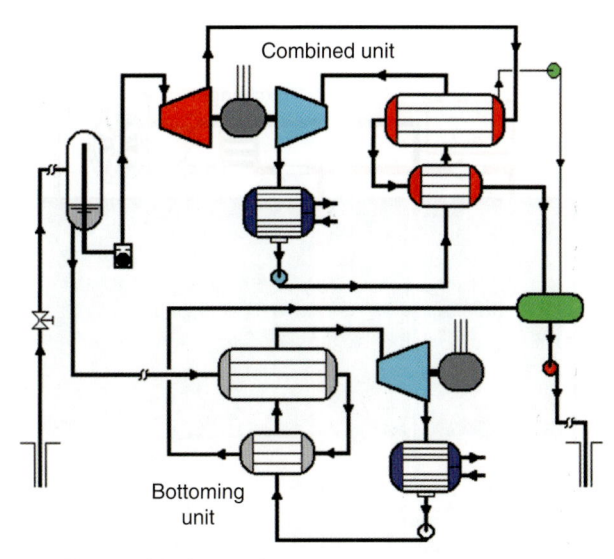

Figure 45 Integrated steam–binary plant with bottoming binary cycle.

The steam from the separator drives a back-pressure turbine (red); the exhaust steam is then used to heat and vaporize the working fluid for the binary side of the combined plant that drives the turbine (light blue) also connected to the same generator (gray) as is the steam turbine. The optional bottoming binary plant receives heat from the liquid leaving the separator. An additional feature shown in **Figure 45** is the recombination of the noncondensable gases with the spent geoliquid in a vessel (green) prior to reinjection. When operated in this manner, gaseous emissions from the entire plant are essentially zero.

7.07.5.3 Enhanced Geothermal Systems

The future of geothermal power lies in expanding the geographical coverage beyond local 'hot spots' that characterize nearly all of the current operating plants to areas having average temperature gradients and average heat fluxes. The methodology that must be developed to achieve this is called 'enhanced geothermal systems' or EGS. The bulk of this section is devoted to this interesting topic.

Another possibility for expanding geothermal power is in the direction of low-temperature resources. As the high-temperature reservoirs are the most favorable ones in terms of thermodynamic potential, they have been preferentially developed. But they are of very limited geographic frequency. The vast majority of naturally occurring resources are at the low end of the temperature spectrum. The difficulty with exploiting these lies in the very low efficiency of energy conversion and the high specific cost to build a plant of commercial size. There are a number of new companies attempting to apply binary technology to resources in the temperature range from 100 °C or less to 120 °C by using systems that can also be used for any low-temperature heat recovery applications.

The effort to create geothermal reservoirs in formations that fail to qualify as commercial-grade natural hydrothermal systems began in the 1970s at the Los Alamos National Laboratory (LANL) in New Mexico, United States. At that time, the technology was known as 'hot dry rock (HDR)'. Later, Japan, England, France, Switzerland, Australia, and Germany have tackled this formidable challenge with varying degrees of success [4–6].

The basic concept of EGS is that the permeability of hot rocks can be enhanced through the application of high pressure on the formation delivered by liquids pumped down deep wells. Knowledge of the stress field in the formation is critical to devising an appropriate stimulation process. Once the formation has been fractured over a sufficiently large volume of rock, say $10 \, km^3$, additional wells are drilled into the fractured rock to intercept many of the newly created fractures. Thus, paths are formed between and among the wells that allow fluid to be injected from the surface into one well and captured at the wellheads of other wells. Between the wells, the fluid passes through the induced or enhanced fractures in the hot rock, extracting heat and thereby raising its temperature to levels suitable for power production. Once the hot fluid reaches the surface, a fairly simple geothermal power plant, typically a binary cycle, can be deployed to generate electricity. The cooled fluid is then reinjected to be reheated. This concept is illustrated in **Figure 46**.

One of the most successful EGS projects is at Soultz-sous-Forêts in the Upper Rhine graben in France, close to the border with Germany. Three wells have been drilled to depths of about 5000 m, as illustrated in **Figure 47**. A combined heat and power plant has been constructed and is in operation; see **Figure 48**. The produced geofluid enters the plant as a pressurized liquid at 175 °C and a mass flow rate of $35 \, l \, s^{-1}$ (~$31.2 \, kg \, s^{-1}$), and is returned to the reservoir at 70 °C. The power cycle uses isobutane as the working fluid.

Germany placed into service in June 2009 a combined heat and power EGS plant at Unterhaching in Bavaria. This plant has a rating of 3.36 MWe and uses a Kalina-type binary cycle. It also produces 31 MWth of heat. Besides this plant, Germany plans to install another EGS heat (4 MWth) and power (5 MWe) plant at Sauerlach in 2011. The drilling began in October 2007. Several other deep geothermal projects are in the planning or early drilling stages in Germany. All of these projects involve wells drilled to depths of at least 3000 m.

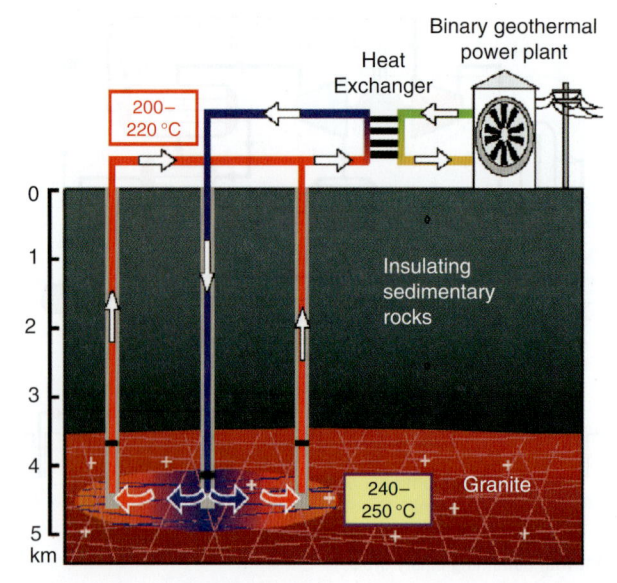

Figure 46 EGS conceptual schematic; values shown are illustrative only [6].

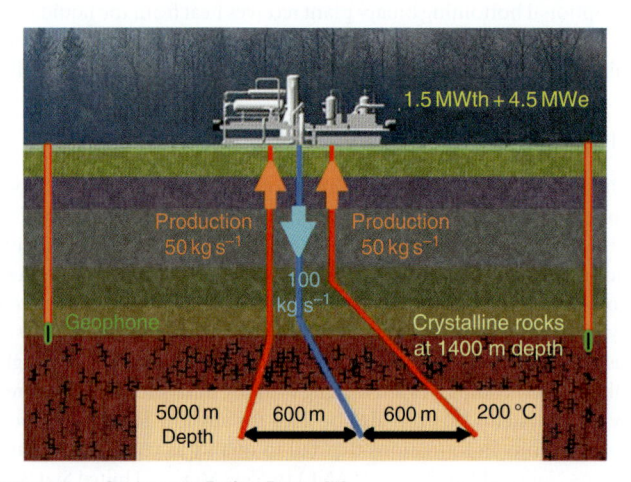

Figure 47 General cross section of the wells at Soultz-sous-Forêts, France [5].

Figure 48 EGS power plant at Soultz-sous-Forêts, France [5].

There is considerable development of EGS underway in Australia where the potential in the southeastern area is estimated to be in the hundreds of megawatts.

7.07.6 Plant Performance Assessment

Various means are used to assess the performance of geothermal plants. Some are grounded in basic thermodynamic concepts, whereas others reflect practical measures of efficiency.

7.07.6.1 Utilization Efficiency

The Second Law of thermodynamics is at the heart of the utilization efficiency, η_U. The net power output of the plant is compared with the maximum theoretical power output. Although the calculation is simple, it involves the concept of 'exergy', which may not be familiar to all. The basic working equations are given here along with some references for further reading.

$$\text{Utilization efficiency:} \quad \eta_U = \frac{\dot{W}_{\text{NET}}}{\dot{E}} \quad [38]$$

where the numerator is the gross power minus all applicable parasitic power loads such as condensate and brine pumps, cooling-water circulation pumps, cooling-tower fan motors, and noncondensable gas compressors. The denominator is the rate of exergy associated with the flow of geofluid from the reservoir, and is calculated using the properties of the geofluid in the reservoir. Although it is possible to use the wellhead properties to compute the exergy, it is not as accurate an assessment of the entire system performance because the geofluid performs some useful work in self-flowing from the depth of the well to the surface, and that is missed when using the wellhead properties.

$$\text{Rate of exergy:} \quad \dot{E} = \dot{m}\,[h_R - h_0 - T_0\,(s_R - s_0)] \quad [39]$$

where $\dot{m}$ is the mass flow rate of geofluid; h_R and s_R are the enthalpy and entropy of the geofluid, respectively, under reservoir conditions; h_0 and s_0 are the enthalpy and entropy of the geofluid, respectively, under ambient (dead-state) conditions; and T_0 is the absolute temperature (Kelvins) of the surroundings. The latter may be taken as the design wet-bulb temperature for plants with water-cooling towers or as the design air temperature for plants with air-cooled condensers.

7.07.6.2 Thermal Efficiency

The thermal efficiency, η_{TH}, is very commonly used in the power industry for conventional power plants. It is based on the First Law of thermodynamics. The net power output of the plant is compared with the rate of heat supplied to the plant, that is,

$$\text{Thermal efficiency:} \quad \eta_{\text{TH}} = \frac{\dot{W}_{\text{NET}}}{\dot{Q}_{\text{IN}}} \quad [40]$$

It is this efficiency that is limited by the famous Carnot efficiency; namely, the maximum thermal efficiency of any cycle operating between two temperature limits is

$$\text{Carnot efficiency:} \quad \eta_{C,\text{Max}} = 1 - \frac{T_L}{T_H} \quad [41]$$

where both temperatures are absolute (Kelvins).

A word of warning is appropriate in the use of thermal efficiency: It can only be applied to closed cycles in which the working fluid is continuously reused in the plant. Thus, it is applicable to binary cycles but not to dry- or flash-steam plants. The latter plants feature a sequence of processes in which the geofluid is produced, processed in various ways using equipment on the surface, and finally disposed of back to the reservoir. Nature yields the geofluid for use and accepts it when the plant is done with it; the processes that occur in the reservoir are beyond human control.

7.07.6.3 Specific Geofluid Consumption

Sometimes plant performance is measured in the amount of geofluid needed to generate a certain amount of net power. This can be applied in terms of steam, brine, or two-phase fluid as received at the wellhead. Although this measure is valid for a given resource and is useful in comparing the efficacy of different proposed designs for a given resource, it lacks thermodynamic applicability to other plants at other resources because it fails to account for the exergy of the geofluid under reservoir conditions. Nevertheless, it is widely reported in case studies.

$$\text{Specific steam consumption (SSC):} \quad \text{SSC} = \frac{\dot{m}_S}{\dot{W}_{\text{NET}}} \quad [42]$$

Table 3 Range of efficiencies for various geothermal plant types

Plant type	Utilization efficiency (%)	Thermal efficiency (%)
Dry-steam	45–55	Not applicable
Single-flash	25–35	Not applicable
Double-flash	35–45	Not applicable
Basic subcritical binary	15–45	5–15
Supercritical binary	16–50	5–15
Binary with recuperator	18–55	14–18
Binary with mixture WF	20–55	15–20

where the numerator is the mass flow rate of steam. This is most useful for dry- and flash-steam plants, and shows how efficient the turbine is in converting the potential of the steam into electrical power.

$$\text{Specific brine consumption (SBC):} \quad \text{SBC} = \frac{\dot{m}_B}{\dot{W}_{\text{NET}}} \qquad [43]$$

where the numerator is the mass flow rate of brine. Clearly, this is most useful for binary-type plants, and shows how efficient the plant is in converting the potential of the brine into electrical power.

$$\text{Specific geofluid consumption (SGC)}: \quad \text{SGC} = \frac{\dot{m}_{\text{GF}}}{\dot{W}_{\text{NET}}} \qquad [44]$$

where the numerator is the mass flow rate of the geofluid. This may be used in cases where the plant receives a two-phase mixture, regardless of the type of plant used.

7.07.6.4 Typical Efficiencies for Geothermal Plants

Table 3 gives typical ranges of the efficiency values for various types of geothermal power plants. The values for all types of binary plants are strongly dependent on the temperature of the geofluid supplied to the plant; generally, the higher the temperature, the higher the efficiency. For a given geofluid temperature, binary cycles with supercritical-pressure working fluids generally have higher efficiencies than ones with subcritical pressures.

References

[1] DiPippo R (2008) *Geothermal Power Plants: Principles, Applications, Case Studies and Environmental Impact*, 2nd edn. Oxford, England: Butterworth-Heinemann; Elsevier (2009, 2nd printing).
[2] Kraml M, Kessels K, Kalberkamp U, *et al.* (2006) The GEOTHERM programme of BGR, Hannover, Germany: Focus on support of the East African Region. *The 1st African Geothermal Conference*. Addis Ababa, Ethiopia. http://www.bgr.de/geotherm/ArGeoC1/pdf/50%20%20Kraml,%20M.%20GEOTHERM%20programme.pdf (accessed 10 June 2010).
[3] Incropera FP and DeWitt DP (1996) *Fundamentals of Heat and Mass Transfer*, 4th edn. New York: John Wiley & Sons.
[4] Wikipedia, the Free Encyclopedia (2010) *Enhanced Geothermal System*. http://en.wikipedia.org/wiki/Hot_dry_rock#European_Union (accessed 12 July 2010).
[5] Genter A (2008) *The EGS Pilot Plant of Soultz-sous-Forêts (Alsace, France): Case Study*. Strasbourg, France: RESTMAC Workshop. http://www.egec.org/target/strasbourg08/EGEC%20WS%20strasbourg%2007%20180608.pdf; Also: http://www.soultz.net/version-en.htm (accessed 20 June 2010).
[6] *Power from the Earth – Zero Emission, Base-Load Power*. Milton, QLD: Geodynamics Ltd. http://www.geodynamics.com.au/IRM/Company/ShowPage.aspx?CPID=2128&EID=99048338 (accessed 2 July 2010).

Further Reading

Geothermal Resources Council Transactions (published annually from 1977 to the present). Davis, CA: Geothermal Resources Council.
Proceedings of World Geothermal Congress (held every 5 years). The IGA Secretariat, c/o Bochum University of Applied Sciences, Bochum, Germany: International Geothermal Association.
Dickson MH and Fanelli M (eds.) (2005) *Geothermal Energy – Utilization and Technology*. New York: John Wiley & Sons, Inc.
DiPippo R (1980) *Geothermal Energy as a Source of Electricity: A Worldwide Survey of the Design and Operation of Geothermal Power Plants*. Washington, DC: US Department of Energy, US Government Printing Office.
DiPippo R (1982) Geothermal power technology. In: Meyers RA (editor-in-chief) *Handbook of Energy Technology and Economics*, ch. 18, pp. 787–825. New York: John Wiley & Sons, Inc.
DiPippo R (1990) *Geothermal Power Cycle Selection Guidelines*. Geothermal Information Series, Part 2. Palo Alto, CA: Electric Power Research Institute.
DiPippo R (1998) Geothermal power systems. In: Elliott TC, Chen K, and Swanekamp RC (eds.) *Standard Handbook of Powerplant Engineering*, 2nd edn., sec. 8.2, 8.27–8.60. New York: McGraw-Hill, Inc.

Duffield WA and Sass JH (2003) *Geothermal Energy: Clean Power from the Earth's Heat*. Menlo Park, CA: US Geological Survey, Circular 1249.
Ghassemi A (editor-in-chief) *Geothermics – International Journal of Geothermal Research and Its Applications*. (published quarterly). New York: Elsevier.
Huenges E (ed.) (2010) *Geothermal Energy Systems – Exploration, Development, and Utilization*. Weinheim, Germany: WILEY-VCH Verlag GmbH & Co. KGaA.
Kagel A, Bates D, and Gawell K (2005) *A Guide to Geothermal Energy and the Environment*. Washington, DC: Geothermal Energy Association.
Kestin J (editor-in-chief), DiPippo R, Khalifa HE, and Ryley DJ (eds) (1980) *Sourcebook on the Production of Electricity from Geothermal Energy*. Washington, DC: US Department of Energy, US Government Printing Office.
Tester JW, Anderson BJ, Batchelor AS, *et al.* (2006) *The Future of Geothermal Energy – Impact of Enhanced Geothermal Systems (EGS) on the United States in the 21st Century*. Cambridge, MA: Massachusetts Institute of Technology. http://geothermal.inel.gov.

7.08 Corrosion, Scaling and Material Selection in Geothermal Power Production

SN Karlsdóttir, Innovation Center Iceland, Iceland

© 2012 Elsevier Ltd. All rights reserved.

7.08.1	**Introduction**	240
7.08.2	**Corrosion Films and Processes**	241
7.08.3	**Forms of Corrosion in Geothermal Environments**	241
7.08.3.1	Uniform Corrosion	241
7.08.3.2	Pitting Corrosion	241
7.08.3.3	Crevice Corrosion	242
7.08.3.4	Intergranular Corrosion	242
7.08.3.5	Galvanic Corrosion	242
7.08.3.6	Stress Corrosion Cracking	243
7.08.3.7	Hydrogen Embrittlement	243
7.08.3.8	Hydrogen-Induced Cracking	243
7.08.3.9	Sulfide Stress Cracking	244
7.08.3.10	Corrosion Fatigue	244
7.08.3.11	Erosion Corrosion	245
7.08.3.12	Exfoliation	245
7.08.4	**Variables and Corrosive Species That Affect Corrosion Rates**	245
7.08.4.1	pH Level	245
7.08.4.2	Temperature	245
7.08.4.3	Suspended Solids and Solid Deposition	245
7.08.4.4	Fluid Velocity	246
7.08.4.5	Hydrogen Sulfide	246
7.08.4.6	Hydrogen Ion	246
7.08.4.7	Chloride Ions	246
7.08.4.8	Carbon Dioxide	246
7.08.4.9	Oxygen	246
7.08.4.10	Ammonia	246
7.08.4.11	Sulfate	247
7.08.4.12	Other Factors	247
7.08.5	**Material Selection and Performance in Geothermal Environments**	247
7.08.5.1	Ferrous Alloys	247
7.08.5.1.1	Carbon and low-alloy steel	247
7.08.5.1.2	Stainless steels	247
7.08.5.2	Nonferrous Metals and Alloys	248
7.08.5.2.1	Nickel alloys	248
7.08.5.2.2	Titanium and its alloys	249
7.08.5.2.3	Copper alloys	249
7.08.5.2.4	Aluminum alloys	249
7.08.5.3	Nonmetallic Materials	249
7.08.5.3.1	Polymers	249
7.08.5.3.2	Cements	249
7.08.6	**Scaling in Geothermal Environments**	249
7.08.6.1	Production Wells	251
7.08.6.2	Wellheads	252
7.08.6.3	Pipelines	252
7.08.6.4	Separators	252
7.08.6.5	Turbines	253
7.08.6.6	Reinjection Wells	253
7.08.7	**Corrosion and Scaling Control**	253
7.08.7.1	Corrosion Control	253
7.08.7.2	Scaling Control	255
7.08.8	**Conclusions**	255
References		256

Glossary

Corrosion Process of deterioration of material into its constituent atoms due to chemical reactions with its surroundings.
Corrosion film A film made of corrosion products that form on the surface of corroded metal as a by-product of a corrosion reaction.
Geothermal fluid Geothermal liquid, steam and gas, together or separately. The state that the fluid is in, i.e., liquid or vapor, depends on the pressure and the temperature.

Geothermal power plants Power plants that use steam from high temperature geothermal wells to produce electricity. They usually also produce hot water.
Scale Chemical substances that form on surfaces of components, e.g., pipes, when precipitated from a liquid.
Scaling This occurs when minerals dissolved in geothermal fluid precipitate from the liquid and deposit onto the surface of the geothermal wells and equipment.
Stainless steel This is classified as steel that contains a minimum of 10.5% chromium by mass which makes it corrosion resistant in air.

7.08.1 Introduction

Materials used in high-temperature geothermal wells and equipment in direct contact with geothermal fluid can be subjected to corrosion; this results in high costs associated with the materials, labor, and production efficiency of wells. Corrosion is described as the natural process of deterioration of metals and alloys in corrosive environments. The corrosion aggressiveness of geothermal fluids depends on the chemical composition and physical characteristics of the fluid, for example, acidity (pH level), and on the exploitation parameters such as temperature, pressure, and flow rate. The principal corrosive agents in geothermal fluids are the dissolved gases hydrogen sulfide (H_2S) and carbon dioxide (CO_2), and chloride ions (Cl^-). Other corrosive components that can be present in geothermal fluids are dissolved ammonium (NH_3), methane (CH_4), and sulfate ions (SO_4^{2-}) [1, 2]. Dissolved hydrogen (H_2) and nitrogen (N_2) gases can also be present. In uncontaminated, high-temperature geothermal fluids, there is no free oxygen. If oxygen gets into wet geothermal steam systems, corrosion is accelerated. In some systems, hydrogen chloride (HCl) is present; if condensation and reboiling occurs, localized enrichment of hydrochloric acid can cause severe corrosion of materials in the systems [3].

There can be significant variation in the physical characteristics and the chemical composition of geothermal fluids (geofluids) in geothermal systems. Thus materials used in geothermal energy production can be subjected to a wide variety of corrosive environments related to the geological conditions under which the geofluids are produced. There can be different conditions in wells within the same geothermal system, which can result in corrosion problems in one well but not in other wells within the same geothermal system. It is therefore not always easy to predict whether corrosion will occur before geothermal well drilling is commenced, even though the surrounding geothermal system is well known. Corrosion of materials inside geothermal power plants is dependent on the design of the power plant and the point of production because these factors influence key parameters such as temperature, velocity of the fluid, and even the composition of the geofluid [3–5]. **Table 1** shows the composition and physical characteristics of geofluid from different high-temperature geothermal fields. This is an example of how the chemical composition and characteristics of geothermal fluids can vary between locations and wells.

Because the composition of geothermal fluids can vary greatly between locations and within a single geothermal system, the fluid can be corrosive at one point but passive and show a trend toward scaling at another, due to a change in its physical and chemical parameters. Scaling occurs when minerals dissolved in geothermal fluid precipitate from the liquid and deposit onto the surface of the geothermal wells and equipment (due to a change in pressure, temperature, or pH value, which disturbs the equilibrium of the system). Thus, geothermal systems can undergo corrosion, scaling, or both simultaneously. When scaling

Table 1 Properties of geothermal fluids and concentration of key corrosive species in the fluid at various high-temperature geothermal fields [5–7]

				Concentration of key species in the fluid (ppm)					
Location	Temperature (°C) (location)	Fluid description[a]	pH	Cl⁻	Total CO_2	Total H_2S	Total NH_3	SO_4^{2-}	CH_4
Salton Sea, California, USA	250 (borehole)	Unflashed wellhead fluid	5.2	115 000	1000	10–30	300	20	
Baca (Valles Caldera), New Mexico, USA	171 (wellhead)	Flashed fluid	6.8	3 770	128	6		59	
Bjarnarflag, North Iceland, Iceland	171 (wellhead)	Flashed fluid	7.9	283	529	1333	1.7		7.6
Reykjanes, Southwest Iceland, Iceland	295 (borehole)	Unflashed wellhead fluid	4.7	19 319	1779	53	2.0	12.2	0.2

[a] Measurements were made at different points of production, before or after flashing; thus, the source fluids cannot be directly compared because often during flashing Cl concentration increases while the concentration of CO_2 and H_2S decreases and increase e in pH will occur.

occurs in geothermal wells and systems, it can create major problems for geothermal operations. Deposition by scaling on the surface of geothermal wells and equipment can result in plugging at these locations, inhibiting production and incurring expensive cleaning costs. High-temperature geothermal resources that have higher water ratios often have an increased level of silica that causes difficult scaling problems. Scaling problems do not usually occur in dry steam fields, but can still entail serious corrosion problems. Unfortunately, at some fields, both scaling and corrosion problems are encountered at the same time [8–10].

It should be noted that corrosion or scaling in geothermal systems is not the limiting factor in the production of geothermal power. However, when it does occur, it can be costly and delay production. These issues can be avoided by correct material selection, good engineering design, and proper corrosion and scaling control methods.

In this chapter, forms of corrosion and scaling that can occur in geothermal systems are presented and discussed. Material selection for geothermal systems is discussed in relation to corrosion, and different materials and their performance in geothermal environments are compared. The mechanism of scaling and the problems associated with it are also a topic in this chapter. Finally, solutions to corrosion and scaling problems are presented and discussed.

7.08.2 Corrosion Films and Processes

The corrosion of a piece of metal may be summarized as the transformation from a metal to a metal ion, or as the loss of one or more electrons from the metallic atom. All corrosion reactions produce by-products, called corrosion products. These are, for example, insoluble hydroxides, carbonates, oxides, sulfides, silicates, and borates that form films on the surface of the corroded metal. Some of the films are porous and loose, allowing diffusion to and from the metal surface. These types of films do not protect the metal surface and allow further corrosion. On the other hand, corrosion films can be nonporous, tight, and adherent. These are substantially more protective toward further corrosion, mainly because they limit access of corrosives to the metal surface. In some environments, the corrosion products are very soluble and no corrosion film forms on the surface of the corroding metal. This is called active corrosion. Some alloys are unreactive, meaning that they form corrosion films made up of mixed oxides that are so nonreactive that they protect the base metal after a short period of active corrosion. This type of corrosion process is called passive corrosion and the films are called passive films [11]. This type of film can occur on metal alloys such as titanium and stainless steels. These alloys can, however, experience active corrosion if the environment or conditions are severe enough, for example, in very corrosive fluids with low pH values.

7.08.3 Forms of Corrosion in Geothermal Environments

There are several forms of corrosion that can occur in metals in geothermal environments. Some of these forms rarely occur, whereas others are more common. The following sections describe these forms.

7.08.3.1 Uniform Corrosion

In general, uniform corrosion is the most common type of corrosion. It can be defined as the attack of the entire metal surface exposed to the corrosive environment resulting in uniform loss of metal from the exposed surface. The metal becomes thinner and eventually fails. Uniform corrosion generally increases when acidity increases (decrease in pH). It is often promoted by oxygen, carbon dioxide, chloride, hydrogen sulfide, or ammonia. In geothermal systems, it is generally promoted by carbon dioxide, hydrogen sulfide, and in some cases chloride [4]. Rapid failure of equipment in geothermal environments due to uniform corrosion is not common. Uniform corrosion is commonly quantified by measuring the corrosion rate (mm yr^{-1}) of the metal by using corrosion tests where specimens are immersed in the corrosive environment, such as geothermal liquid, and the weight change is measured (weight loss) [11].

7.08.3.2 Pitting Corrosion

Pitting is a form of localized corrosion where a small portion of the metallic structure is corroded at a rate much faster than the bulk material. It is a localized form of attack where pits develop on the metal surface. The pits are holes that can be small or large in diameter, but in most cases they are relatively small. They can be isolated or close together so that they look like a rough surface [11]. Pits can deepen due to the breakage of a passive film that forms on some metals [5]. Pitting is one of the most destructive forms of corrosion, causing equipment to fail because of perforation, with only a small percent weight loss of the entire structure. It can be difficult to detect pits because of their small size and they are often covered with corrosion products. It can be hard to measure corrosion pits quantitatively and compare the extent of pitting due to variation in their size and number for identical condition. It can also be difficult to predict pitting in laboratory tests because sometimes it takes a long time for them to occur on the field (it can take several months or even years). Pits most often grow in the direction of gravity, that is, they form and grow downward from horizontal surfaces. Velocity can affect the extent of pitting, wherein they are more severe in stagnant conditions than in high-velocity flow. The most common cause for pitting failures is chloride and chlorine-containing ions [11]. Pitting is especially fierce because its intense and localized form often results in failures that occur with extreme suddenness. In geothermal environments, pitting corrosion has resulted in sudden unexpected failures in pipes and tubes [12].

7.08.3.3 Crevice Corrosion

Another form of localized corrosion is crevice corrosion. It occurs within crevices of equipment and other shielded areas on metal surfaces exposed to corrosive environment. In geothermal environments, crevice corrosion can, for example, occur in metals due to deposits, mill scale, and mechanical crevices. It is geometrically dependent unlike most other forms of corrosion [5]. Crevice corrosion is usually associated with small volumes of stagnant solution caused by gasket surfaces, holes, lap joints, surface deposits, and, as the name implies, crevices under bolt and rivet heads. Deposits that can produce this form of corrosion are, for example, corrosion products, dirt, sand, and other solids. The deposits can act as shields and form a stagnant condition beneath them. Permeable corrosion products can also have this effect. The stagnant condition promotes depletion of oxygen within the crevice due to restricted convection. This results in excess production of positive charges in the solution when the metal continues to dissolve (initially the dissolution and the reduction of oxygen are even). Both hydrogen and chloride ions accelerate the dissolution rate of most metals; these can both be present in the crevice as a result of migration and hydrolysis. The increase in the dissolution increases the migration of the species, which results in accelerated corrosion [11]. **Figure 1** shows crevice corrosion in a stainless-steel tube from an oil cooler where geothermal steam condensate was used as cooling water [13].

7.08.3.4 Intergranular Corrosion

Intergranular corrosion can be defined as localized corrosion at and adjacent to grain boundaries, with relatively little corrosion at the grains. As a consequence, the metal alloy disintegrates and/or it loses its strength. This form of corrosion can be caused by impurities at the grain boundaries and depletion or enrichment of one of the alloying elements in the grain boundary area – such as the formation of chromium carbide at the grain boundary regions of stainless steel resulting in chromium-depleted zones (often called sensitization) – thereby leading to intergranular corrosion [11]. This can usually be avoided by using stainless steel with low carbon content. In geothermal environments, intergranular corrosion can occur in austenitic and ferritic stainless steel [5].

7.08.3.5 Galvanic Corrosion

When two dissimilar metals are immersed in a corrosive or conductive solution, usually a potential difference exists between them. This potential difference produces electron flow between them when they are placed in contact or if they are electrically connected in some other way. In this condition, the metal which is less noble will experience accelerated corrosion; this is called galvanic corrosion. Metals can be ordered in series by increased nobility; this is called the galvanic series and can help in material selection to avoid corrosion. Galvanic corrosion can occur in geothermal environments, for example, in a geothermal iron pipe section in contact with a bronze valve [12]. Environmental factors such as temperature and chemistry can change the order of metals in the galvanic series. The relative area of the two alloys is also an important factor in galvanic corrosion. The severity of the galvanic corrosion is greater when the area of the more active alloy is small compared to the area of the noble metal. Some procedures can be used to prevent galvanic corrosion, for example, selection of combinations of metals as close together as possible in the galvanic series and insulation of dissimilar metals [11].

Figure 1 Crevice corrosion in a stainless-steel tube from an oil cooler where geothermal steam condensate was used as cooling water [13].

Figure 2 Stress corrosion cracking of an AISI 304 stainless-steel float from a geothermal hot water storage tank [13].

7.08.3.6 Stress Corrosion Cracking

Stress corrosion cracking (SCC) is a catastrophic type of failure caused by the simultaneous presence of tensile stress and a corrosive environment. During SCC, the metal is essentially unattacked over most of its surface area, but fine cracks progress through parts of it. This kind of cracking has serious consequences because it can occur at stresses within the range of typical design stress. The fine cracks often form a net of cracks that are spread out, appearing like tree branches. Stress corrosion cracks have the appearance of brittle mechanical fractures and the cracking generally proceeds perpendicular to the applied stress. Important variables that affect the susceptibility of metals to SCC are metal structure and composition, stress, and temperature. If the metal is in a fluid, the pH value and the composition of the fluid are also very important. The chloride and oxygen content in the fluid increases the susceptibility of the metal to SCC. SCC is known to be accelerated by increasing temperature. A 'lower critical temperature' exists for a given concentration of oxygen and chloride and pH level below which SCC does not occur. There is no critical stress above zero stress below which SCC does not occur. SCC can occur in cases where there is no applied stress, for example, when residual stresses exist from cold working and welding in the metal [5, 11]. **Figure 2** displays the SCC of an AISI 304 stainless-steel float from a geothermal hot water storage tank, representing another example of SCC in a geothermal environment [13]. Damages due to SCC have also been observed in rotors, blades, and other components of steam turbines [14–16] as well as in heat exchanger tubes in geothermal power plants. SCC has also occurred and caused problems in geothermal equipment where leaks or condensation on the outside of stainless-steel equipment has promoted SCC.

7.08.3.7 Hydrogen Embrittlement

Hydrogen embrittlement (HE) refers to mechanical damage of a metal due to the penetration of hydrogen into the metal causing loss in ductility and tensile strength. HE can occur due to corrosion of steel by H_2S when hydrogen atoms are generated. During corrosion of steel in geothermal steam, H_2S reacts with the surface and forms a corrosion film (FeS, MnS) and free hydrogen ions (H^+). The free hydrogen ion would normally not diffuse into the metal, but the sulfide (S^{2-}) ion acts as a poison and promotes the uptake of the hydrogen, which gets trapped in the metal structure and results in embrittlement of the metal [11, 17].

7.08.3.8 Hydrogen-Induced Cracking

One form of HE is hydrogen-induced cracking (HIC). HIC occurs when hydrogen ions (H^+) diffuse into weak interfaces (e.g., laminations, inclusions, and voids) in the metal and recombine there to form molecular hydrogen, which is many times larger in volume than H^+, causing the formation of cracks (or blisters) in the metal [17–19]. HIC does not require any external stress to occur. The cracks or blisters caused by the accumulation of the molecular hydrogen generally run parallel to the surface of the material. Under the influence of tensile stress (residual or applied), the cracks can link up and propagate in a step-like manner until catastrophic failure occurs when the effective thickness of the metal is reduced; this is called stress-oriented hydrogen-induced cracking (SOHIC) [17]. The susceptibility of metals to HIC is primarily dependent on the microstructure, impurity content of the material, metallurgical processing, and heat treatments [17, 20]. HIC and SOHIC usually occur in lower strength steels used in plate and pipe products with a yield strength below 700 MPa [17]. HIC was blamed for the cracking of a brine accumulator and steam purifier in a geothermal power plant in New Zealand [21]. **Figure 3** shows HIC causing leakage in a geothermal steam pipe in Iceland [13].

Figure 3 Hydrogen-induced cracking in a weld in a geothermal steam pipe [13].

7.08.3.9 Sulfide Stress Cracking

Sulfide stress cracking (SSC) is a special type of HE and occurs in metals due to the combined effect of tensile stresses and corrosion by H_2S [22, 23]. SSC is a solid-state embrittlement reaction resulting from the interaction between the metal lattice and the atomic hydrogen generated from the corrosion of the metal by H_2S [17]. SSC is a catastrophic failure like SCC that results in a brittle fracture. It can occur at stresses falling within the range of typical design stress [5]. Due to the presence of H_2S in geothermal fluids, there is a danger of SSC in geothermal equipment [24]. Unlike SCC, the severity of SSC decreases as temperature and pH level increase, and as H_2S concentration, yield strength, and stress decrease. Oxygen is known to have little or no effect on the SSC mechanism [5]. The occurrence of SSC depends on the strength of the steel, stress concentration, levels of the stress, chemical composition of the steel, microstructure of the steel, and hydrogen concentration in the steel [25]. High-strength steels are more susceptible to SSC than low-strength steels. Because of this, it is a common industry standard to limit the hardness of these types of steels to 250 HV (Vickers hardness) [26, 27]. This is not an absolute value and SSC can still occur for steels that fulfill this requirement. SSC can, for example, occur in low-strength steels when they are subjected to high residual stresses derived from fabrication techniques [21], or to high stresses or high stress intensities [28]. The low-carbon steel casing material, H40, with a hardness of approximately 120 HV and a relatively low tensile strength (400 MPa), cracked due to SSC in a geothermal environment when subjected to stresses above the yield strength and at high stress intensities [28]. SSC also occurred in the carbon steel casing material API 5CT N-80, and in a high-strength carbon steel wire (tensile strength > 1200 MPa) in a geothermal well with high partial pressure of H_2S and high thermally induced tensile stress. The material selection for this environment was not ideal, the N-80 steel grade does not have any hardness limitation, which increases the possibility of SSC, and the high strength of the wire material makes it more susceptible to SSC [29]. Another example of SSC in geothermal equipment is the cracking of a brine accumulator and a steam purifier in a geothermal power plant in New Zealand because of high residual stresses in the welds attributed to the use of submerged arc welding [21]. The microstructure of steel also has a considerable effect on SSC; for example, fine-grained steels are less susceptible to SSC than coarse-grained steel. Martensitic and ferritic steels are susceptible to SSC, while austenitic steels are less susceptible [5]. In susceptible microstructures, residual stresses can be sufficient to cause cracking.

7.08.3.10 Corrosion Fatigue

Corrosion fatigue can be classified as a premature fracture when cyclic stresses are imposed on a material in a corrosive environment [5]. Corrosion fatigue is most dominant in mediums where corrosion pitting occurs. The pits act as stress raisers and initiate fatigue cracks, which lead to corrosion fatigue failure. Corrosion fatigue can occur in pipes carrying steam or hot liquids at varying temperatures because of cyclic stresses from vibration caused by varying pressure and periodic expansion and contraction of the pipe caused by thermal cycling [30]. Corrosion fatigue can also occur in turbine parts used in geothermal power plants due to the cyclic loading and corrosive environment. This includes parts such as rotors and turbine blades [15]. Corrosion fatigue testing of different types of steel in geothermal steam in high-temperature geothermal fields in Iceland showed that the fatigue lifetime of the steel was lower in the geothermal steam than in air as well as dependent on the microstructure of the steel. The martensitic steels had shorter lifetime in the geothermal steam than the austenitic steels [31].

7.08.3.11 Erosion Corrosion

Erosion corrosion is an accelerated form of corrosion of a metal caused by relative movement between corrosive media and metal surfaces. The corrosive medium can be one of the following: fluids, for example, water or solutions containing suspension; organics; or gases or steam such as geothermal liquid. The metal surface becomes damaged by mechanical or hydraulic wear or abrasion caused by the flow of the medium. In erosion corrosion, the metal surface is not covered by corrosion products, but characterized in appearance by grooves, waves, gullies, rounded holes, or valleys, and it usually exhibits directional pattern. In many cases, failures due to erosion corrosion occur in a relatively short time and they are sometimes unexpected because previous evaluation corrosion tests were run under static conditions, or because the erosion effects were not considered. Most metals and their alloys are susceptible to erosion corrosion damage. Metals that depend on passivity by forming a protective surface film are also susceptible to erosion corrosion as, if the surface film is damaged, the bulk metal or alloy is attacked at a rapid rate. Increased velocity usually results in increased erosion corrosion [11]. Erosion corrosion can occur in equipment used in a geothermal environment that is exposed to moving fluid including piping systems, particularly elbows and tees, pumps, valves, impellers, blowers, heat exchanger tubing, condensers, nozzles, and turbine blades. Erosion corrosion can also be caused by impingement; this can occur in the steam turbine blades in geothermal turbines particularly in the exhaust or wet-steam ends of the turbine [15]. Moreover, another form of erosion corrosion is cavitation damage; it is caused by the formation and collapse of vapor bubbles in a liquid near a metal surface [11]. It occurs in equipment where high-velocity liquid flow and pressure changes are encountered; these conditions can occur, for example, in geothermal wells and equipment. Cavitation can occur in geothermal wells when the water starts to boil when the pressure decreases because of vapor bubbles that form (containing dissolved gases) and collapse at the metal surface at high speed resulting in cavitation damages, that is, holes. In a high-temperature geothermal well (~300 °C) in Iceland containing H_2S, CO_2, and HCl, the steel casing – grade K-55 – underwent extensive cavitation and HE that caused fracture of the steel liner.

7.08.3.12 Exfoliation

Exfoliation is a form of corrosion where discrete layers of corrosion products (sometimes with metal attached that has separated from the lattice) flake off or break loose from the surface, reducing the thickness of the material. The corrosion products are, for example, iron sulfide that forms as a corrosion film on steel pipes carrying steam containing H_2S. These films can flake off and damage other components downstream such as turbines operating directly on flashed steam by causing erosion and possibly erosion corrosion [5].

7.08.4 Variables and Corrosive Species That Affect Corrosion Rates

Variables and corrosive species that affect corrosion in geothermal environments are described here in connection with the corrosion forms previously described.

7.08.4.1 pH Level

In general, corrosion rates increase with decreasing pH, that is, with increased acidity of the fluid. Decreasing pH means increasing amount of hydrogen ions. For example, for carbon steel, the corrosion rates generally increase in environments with pH levels below 7. As mentioned previously, the pH level influences the passivity of many metal alloys. That is, the formation of the passive film for these metals depends on the pH level; if it is too low, the film cannot form and the alloy is vulnerable to corrosion. This can occur in local areas on the metal surface and lead to serious forms of corrosion such as crevice corrosion, SCC, and pitting [5].

7.08.4.2 Temperature

Increased temperature generally increases corrosion rates. This can be explained as being due to the common effect that increased temperature has on reaction kinetics. But the effects of temperature are complicated; for example, at increased temperature, the corrosion rates can also decrease due to the decrease in solubility of gases. For example, in systems with oxygen, increased temperature can lead to acceleration of corrosion rates first but then a decrease due to the lowering of the solubility of oxygen and decrease in oxygen concentration [30]. As mentioned earlier, increased temperature has an opposite effect on SCC and SSC: higher temperature increases the likelihood of SCC while the chances of SSC are reduced. SSC susceptibility reaches a maximum at around room temperature but then decreases with increasing temperature over the range 25–200 °C [17].

7.08.4.3 Suspended Solids and Solid Deposition

Solid deposition on equipment surfaces from the precipitation of liquid phase species (or ions) from the geothermal liquid can influence corrosion and cause erosion [5]; in geothermal energy production, this is called scaling and can influence the performance of the geothermal system. Scaling and its effects in exploitation of geothermal energy are discussed in more detail later in this chapter.

7.08.4.4 Fluid Velocity

Fluid velocity has different effects on different corrosion forms as mentioned previously. For example, low velocity can lead to stagnant areas, which can result in crevice corrosion, while high velocity can result in erosion corrosion. Thus for every geothermal design, the velocity of the fluid has to be included in the design criteria.

7.08.4.5 Hydrogen Sulfide

H_2S is along with CO_2 the main reason for corrosion of steel and iron alloys in geothermal fluids. It is the main source of hydrogen for HE and SSC of metals in geothermal environments [2]. H_2S reacts with carbon steel to form corrosion films. If they break down, it can cause an accelerated corrosion attack. H_2S attacks certain copper/nickel alloys; therefore these alloys are practically unusable in geothermal environments that generally contain H_2S.

7.08.4.6 Hydrogen Ion

The effect of the concentration of hydrogen ions is partially described in the section discussing the effect of pH because the pH level reflects the concentration of hydrogen ions. The general corrosion rate of carbon steel increases rapidly with increasing hydrogen ions, that is, with decreasing pH, as mentioned previously. Hydrogen ions are also the key factors in HE and SSC as well as in HIC, which is closely related to HE.

7.08.4.7 Chloride Ions

Increasing concentration of chloride ions (Cl^-) increases uniform corrosion. Chloride ions can also cause local breakdown of metals that form passive films, which results in a decrease in corrosion resistance of metal and causes localized corrosion. This is usually a more serious effect than the uniform corrosion. The local breakage of the film can lead to pitting and crevice corrosion, and it increases the risk of SCC. The largest risk of SCC occurs when the steam condenses with chloride ions on the steel surface so that the chloride concentration builds up and increases the susceptibility of SCC dramatically. The source of the chloride ions in geothermal steam can be either salt brine (NaCl) in the steam in geothermal areas close to the sea or volatile chloride transported as HCl [3, 32]. HCl in geothermal steam has been reported in geothermal steam fields in different parts of the world: Larderello, Italy; Krafla, Iceland; St. Lucia, Windward Islands; Tatum, Taiwan; and The Geysers, USA [33, 34]. The presence of HCl in superheated geothermal steams has caused severe corrosion problems, which have led to major operating difficulties [3, 32, 34, 35]. The corrosion mechanism due to the presence of HCl is believed to be connected to the partitioning of the HCl into the liquid present and the subsequent dissociation into Cl^- and H^+ ions. Corrosion of carbon steel steam pipelines is negligible due to the presence of chlorides above the dew point, but fast pitting occurs where condensation takes place due to the acid solutions formed, potentially leading to rapid localized failure of geothermal pipes and equipment [32, 34]. In the geothermal area of Larderello in Italy, chloride in the steam (1–10 ppm) was blamed for the etching of turbine components and severe corrosion of a carbon steel liner was attributed to chloride vapor (tens to hundreds of ppm) in contact with condensate [32]. In Krafla – a geothermal area in Iceland – the presence of hydrogen chloride in a well-producing dry superheated steam resulted in condensation and reboiling, which caused localized enrichment of hydrochloric acid and consequently severe corrosion of a wellhead, pipelines, and turbine materials [3].

7.08.4.8 Carbon Dioxide

The pH level of geothermal fluids is largely controlled by CO_2. Increased CO_2 concentration results in decreased pH level and increased acidity. CO_2 is very soluble in water, 100 times more soluble than oxygen [30]. CO_2 can accelerate uniform corrosion of carbon steels in the acidic region. Along with dissolved H_2S its presence is the main reason for corrosion of steel and iron alloys in geothermal fluids [2].

7.08.4.9 Oxygen

Oxygen accelerates corrosion caused by other dissolved gases, such as CO_2 and H_2S [30]. Therefore, even the addition of part-per-billion quantities of oxygen to high-temperature geothermal systems can greatly increase the chance of severe localized corrosion of normally resistant metals. In uncontaminated high-temperature geothermal fluid, there is generally no free oxygen but if a small amount of oxygen enters the systems, materials that are normally corrosion resistant in this environment can experience SCC and other forms of corrosion [4]. In general, the corrosion of steel is sensitive to trace amounts of oxygen [5]. Higher pressure and temperature and lower pH increase the corrosivity of oxygen [30].

7.08.4.10 Ammonia

Ammonia (NH_3) can accelerate uniform corrosion of steel. It can also cause SCC of some copper alloys. However, it is usually found in a very low concentration, if at all, in geothermal steam and thus is not considered a general hazard to the materials used in geothermal applications [5].

7.08.4.11 Sulfate

In most geothermal fluids, sulfate (SO_4) has little effect on corrosion. In some streams containing low amounts of chloride, the sulfate can be an aggressive anion but despite that it rarely causes the same severe localized attack as chloride [5].

7.08.4.12 Other Factors

In liquid-dominated geothermal resources, there are two factors that should be mentioned that can cause difficult corrosion problems. First, carryover of entrained liquid provides chloride ions that often cause localized corrosion attacks and the impingement of high-velocity droplets can induce localized attacks. Thus efficient steam separation is very important; it will, however, not always prevent attacks. The corrosion will often depend on the chloride content and the corrosivity of the liquid stream for a given steam separation efficiency. Second, areas in geothermal systems where local condensation can occur are exposed to corrosion attack by low-pH condensate containing CO_2, H_2S, and chlorides. Areas that are subjected to this in geothermal systems are, for example, the low-pressure turbine section and stagnant or poorly insulated parts of steam transfer sections and liquid traps [5].

7.08.5 Material Selection and Performance in Geothermal Environments

In this section, the performance of different materials in geothermal environments is discussed and rated. The discussion is focused on how these materials perform in relation to different corrosion forms in geothermal steam and fluid. Material selection in geothermal energy exploitation is also discussed, for example, which materials can be and are used for geothermal well casings, pipes, and various components used in geothermal power plants and systems.

7.08.5.1 Ferrous Alloys

7.08.5.1.1 Carbon and low-alloy steel

Carbon and low-alloy steel (i.e., containing no more than 4% alloying elements) are attractive materials for construction purposes in geothermal power plants due to their availability, low cost, and fabrication ability. Their reliability depends, however, on their applications in the power plants. Carbon steel can be used for thick-walled applications in contact with most geothermal fluids [5]. It is commonly used for the wellhead and pipelines for the transportation of two-phase geofluid (mixtures of liquid and vapor, i.e., gas and steam), from the wellhead to the flash separator units, as well as for the transportation of separated liquid and geothermal steam. Carbon steel has also been used for separators and flash units [3]. Low-alloyed carbon steels such as 1% and 2.5% CrMoNiV are commonly used in turbine components such as turbine rotors [36, 37]. The most common forms of corrosion that affect carbon and low-alloy steel in geothermal systems are localized and uniform corrosion. Usage of carbon and low-alloy steel is limited in thin-wall application due to the susceptibility of these materials to localized attacks such as crevice and pitting corrosion. Chloride ions are the main factors in initiating localized attack and H_2S can increase the severity of localized corrosion. Geothermal corrosion field tests indicate that the rate of uniform corrosion for these materials is generally 0.03–0.3 mm yr^{-1} when the chloride concentration is lower than 2% and the pH level is higher than 6. When the pH level is below 6 and the amount of chlorides above 2%, a rapid increase in corrosion rates is observed [5]. In some cases, scales that form on the surface of the steel by precipitation from geothermal fluids are believed to protect the steel surface from corrosion so long as the scale is adherent and reaches sufficient thickness to ensure its mechanical integrity [3]. On the other hand, if this scale is porous and thus prone to cracking – which is true in many cases – corrosive attacks can occur at these small exposed areas.

High-strength low-alloy carbon steel can fail and brittle fractures can occur due to SSC in geothermal environments containing aqueous H_2S. Low-strength low-alloy steels are generally not sensitive to SSC but they can incur SSC when combined with residual stress or high stress intensities and H_2S in geothermal environments. Low-strength low-alloy steel can be subject to HE in geothermal environments when difficult conditions exist due to HCl and H_2S gases and low pH levels, or when coarse-grained structure and residual stress exist within the material [21]. Severe corrosion can occur on the outside surface of carbon and low-alloy steel wellheads just below the soil or cellar floor during a standby due to condensation of the steam when the casing is allowed to cool. To avoid this, it is best to try to keep the wells hot, either by production or bleeding to a small silencer [8].

In general, carbon and low-alloyed steel are preferred for many components in geothermal systems due to economical advantage over other materials, even though their resistance against corrosion is limited, especially at low pH levels, high chloride concentration, and high flow rates. Nevertheless, they serve well in many applications and thus geothermal systems are composed in large parts of them.

7.08.5.1.2 Stainless steels

Stainless steel is classified as steel that contains a minimum of 10.5% chromium (Cr) by mass, which makes it corrosion resistant in air. Stainless steels often have other alloying elements to give them better properties, for example, nickel (Ni) and molybdenum (Mo) are often added to increase the corrosion resistance. Stainless steels are often classified into types corresponding to their iron alloy phases: ferritic (ferrite phase), austenitic (austenite), and martensitic (martensite) steels.

In geothermal fluids, stainless steel exhibits a much lower corrosion rate due to uniform corrosion than carbon and low-alloy steel. Stainless steels can, however, be subject to other forms of corrosion – often labeled as more serious forms of corrosion – such

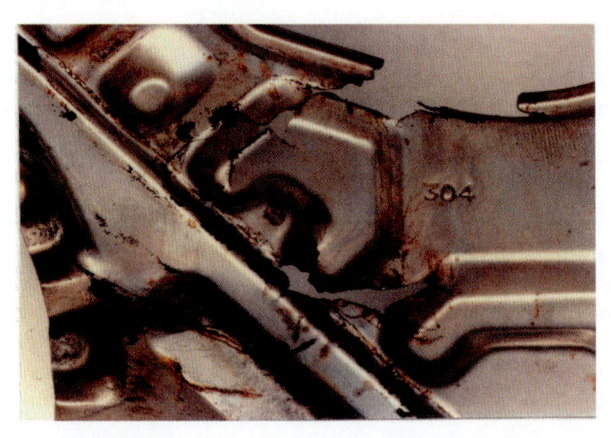

Figure 4 Stress corrosion cracking in an AISI 304 stainless-steel plate from a plate heat exchanger in a geothermal power plant [13].

as crevice corrosion, intergranular corrosion, pitting, SSC, SCC, and corrosion fatigue. Stainless steel along with carbon and low-alloy steel is the main construction material in geothermal systems [38, 39]. Generally, stainless steels are used in geothermal systems in much smaller quantities than carbon and low-alloy steel because of cost.

Austenitic stainless steels form a passive film (an oxide layer) which shows good corrosion resistance to geothermal condensate [40]. The austenitic stainless steels AISI 304 and 316 have been used for components in geothermal power plants, for example, in condensate collection systems, heat exchangers, and parts of cooling towers. AISI 304 contains 19% Cr and 9.5% Ni, whereas AISI 316 contains 17% Cr, 12% Ni, and 2.5% Mo. The selection between 304 and 316 is usually based upon the combination of chloride content and the temperature of the geothermal fluid, where the 316 is more corrosion-resistant against localized corrosion than 304. However, if the geothermal fluid is heavily chlorinated, heat exchangers made of 316 stainless steel can fail due to corrosion because chloride ions easily break down the oxide layer, which leads to localized corrosion such as pitting and SCC.

Stainless steel is also used in turbine components in geothermal power plants. This includes, for example, 13% Cr martensitic stainless steel (AISI 403) used for turbine blades and nozzles [36]. Corrosion fatigue is a potential problem in geothermal turbines and stainless steel is more resistant to corrosion fatigue than carbon and low-alloy steel. Other examples of stainless steels used in geothermal systems are the ferritic steel, AISI 430 (16–18% Cr), and the martensitic steel, AISI 431 (15–17% Cr, 1.25–2.5% Ni), which are used for valve and pump components. If the geothermal fluid contains high amounts of chloride ions or sulfur, the AISI 430 is more suitable because of its higher resistance against pitting and SCC [4]. In general, the corrosion resistance of AISI 431 and 430 is lower than that of AISI 316, but similar to or slightly lower than that of AISI 304. The superaustenitic alloy 254 SMO (19.5–20.5% Cr, 17.5–18.5% Ni, 6.0–6.5% Mo) has shown good performance in corrosion tests in geothermal environments in Italy and Iceland [41, 42]. It is currently not commonly used in geothermal equipment due to high costs, but it has been used when AISI 316 has not been adequate due to corrosion, for example, for pipes in a heat exchanger used in a geothermal plant.

Because stainless steel is often used in complex equipment, localized corrosion such as crevice and pitting corrosion can be a serious problem. Chlorides increase the susceptibility of stainless steels to these localized corrosion problems [5]. The pitting and crevice corrosion resistance of stainless steels is highly dependent on their Mo and Cr content; increased amounts of Mo and Cr increase the resistance to these localized corrosion forms [11]. Nickel has a great effect on the susceptibility of stainless steel to SCC, especially in chloride solutions. Immunity from SCC is usually not obtained unless the Ni content is less than 1% or greater than 42–45% [43, 44]. It is most pronounced at 8–12 wt.%, but decreases at lower and higher levels. Austenitic stainless steels with a Ni content of 42 wt.% and above are considered immune to cracking [44]. By adding Mo and silicon (Si), the resistance to SCC can be improved [5]. Ferritic steels are generally more resistant against SCC in hot chloride solutions than austenitic stainless steel, which is more susceptible. Ferritic steels are, on the other hand, susceptible to SSC like martensitic steels, whereas austenitic steel tends to be more immune [5]. Both ferritic and austenitic stainless steels can be subject to intergranular corrosion. **Figure 4** shows a picture of SCC in an AISI 304 stainless steel plate from a plate heat exchanger in a geothermal power plant. The stainless steel plate was replaced with a titanium plate [13].

7.08.5.2 Nonferrous Metals and Alloys

7.08.5.2.1 Nickel alloys

High nickel containing alloys are commonly used to battle severe corrosion problems. Ni-Cr-Mo-based nickel alloys have shown very good performance in high-temperature geothermal fluid [5, 38–40, 45]. These include nickel alloys such as Inconel 625 and Hastelloy C-276, which are especially resistant to corrosion and can tolerate high flow rates and occasional aeration [5, 38, 39]. Hastelloy C-276 along with titanium had much higher corrosion resistance than carbon and low-alloy steel, stainless steels, and other Ni-base alloys when tested in a flowing two-phase fluid in the Onikobe geothermal field in Japan. The tests in Onikobe were done in geothermal fluid with velocities in the range of 70–100 m s^{-1}, pH of 2–4.5, and temperatures of 102–137 °C [39]. Nickel-base alloys containing more than 8% Mo (Hastelloy C-276 and Alloy 625) and titanium also gave the best performance in a high-temperature fumarole in Japan when tested along with carbon and low-alloy steel, stainless steels (austenitic, duplex, and martensitic), and other Ni-base alloys containing less than 8% Mo [40]. Some nickel alloys have been reported to be susceptible to SSC and HE when H_2S is present [4]. Additionally, some nickel alloys are susceptible to localized corrosion in oxidizing chloride environment at high temperatures [46]. The high cost of nickel alloys is one of the main factors that limit their usage in geothermal applications.

7.08.5.2.2 Titanium and its alloys

Titanium and its alloys have high corrosion resistance and have shown good results when tested for geothermal application [5, 38–40, 46, 47], especially in geothermal brine environments [46, 47]. Their corrosion resistance comes from the formation of a passive and protective titanium oxide film that forms on the surface. Titanium and its alloys are susceptible to crevice corrosion but very resistant to general corrosion, SCC, and erosion corrosion, such as cavitation damage and impingement. Titanium alloys are more resistant against local corrosion than pure titanium; these are alloys such as Ti-0.15Pd, Ti-0.3Mo-0.8Ni, and Ti-6Al-4V-0.1Ru (grade 29). In harsh geothermal conditions where stainless steel cannot be used and high reliability and near zero corrosion allowances are required, titanium and its alloys have been considered as a viable option. This includes environments where the chloride levels exceed 5000 ppm, for example, in hypersaline geothermal brines, and at temperatures greater than 100 °C. Also, when oxygen intrusion is possible, titanium alloys are a better choice in geothermal systems because hot oxidizing chloride conditions are known to cause severe localized attack on stainless steel and nickel-base alloys [46]. Titanium is used in plate heat exchangers where the temperature and chloride concentration requirements are in excess of the capabilities of 316 stainless steel. The titanium alloy, grade 29, is used in geothermal well casings in the Salton Sea, USA, in wells containing highly corrosive brine and at temperatures as high as 315 °C [46]. Titanium has also been used in geothermal turbine components where the steam contains chloride ions from seawater such as in the Reykjanes area in Iceland. It is safe to say that the use of titanium and its alloys in geothermal environments is restricted due to the cost of the material. Perhaps advances in production technology will reduce the cost of titanium in the future.

7.08.5.2.3 Copper alloys

The performance of copper alloys in geothermal fluids is poor due to the presence of H_2S in geothermal fluid. Thus, the use of copper alloys in geothermal application where it is in direct contact with geothermal fluid is not recommended [5].

7.08.5.2.4 Aluminum alloys

Like copper alloys, aluminum alloys have not shown good corrosion resistance in tests that have been done in direct contact with geothermal fluids. The most severe corrosion forms are pitting and galvanic corrosion [5]. It is not advisable to use aluminum in direct contact with geothermal fluid.

7.08.5.3 Nonmetallic Materials

Metallic materials are the primarily used material in geothermal application, but some nonmetallic materials have also been found to be useful for geothermal energy utilization. The following sections briefly discuss two classes of nonmetallic materials that have been used in geothermal applications.

7.08.5.3.1 Polymers

Polymers are used as heat insulators for steel pipelines in geothermal district heating and sometimes as hot water transport lines. Pipes carrying hot water from the power plant for district heating are usually three layered: an inner carrier pipe, a polyurethane (PUR) layer in the middle as isolation material, and an outer layer (a jacket) water insulating for protection against corrosion, made of, for example, polyethylene (PE) or polyvinyl chloride (PVC). The carrier pipe is usually made of steel if the temperature is above ∼90 °C (200 °F), but below 90 °C fiberglass reinforced plastic (FRP) and PVC pipes have been used [48–50].

7.08.5.3.2 Cements

Cement blends are used between steel casings (pipes) inside geothermal wells to seal them from the surrounding rock formation in order to prevent outside corrosion of the steel and to support the system. The cement blends are generally made out of Portland cement, silica, and sand.

7.08.6 Scaling in Geothermal Environments

Geothermal fluids in reservoirs have remained for very long periods of time and reached equilibrium with the minerals in the reservoir rock. Scaling occurs when these minerals dissolved in the geothermal fluid precipitate from the liquid and deposit on the surface of the geothermal wells and equipment due to change in pressure, temperature, or pH value (which disturbs the equilibrium). When scaling occurs in geothermal wells and systems, it can pose major problems for geothermal operations.

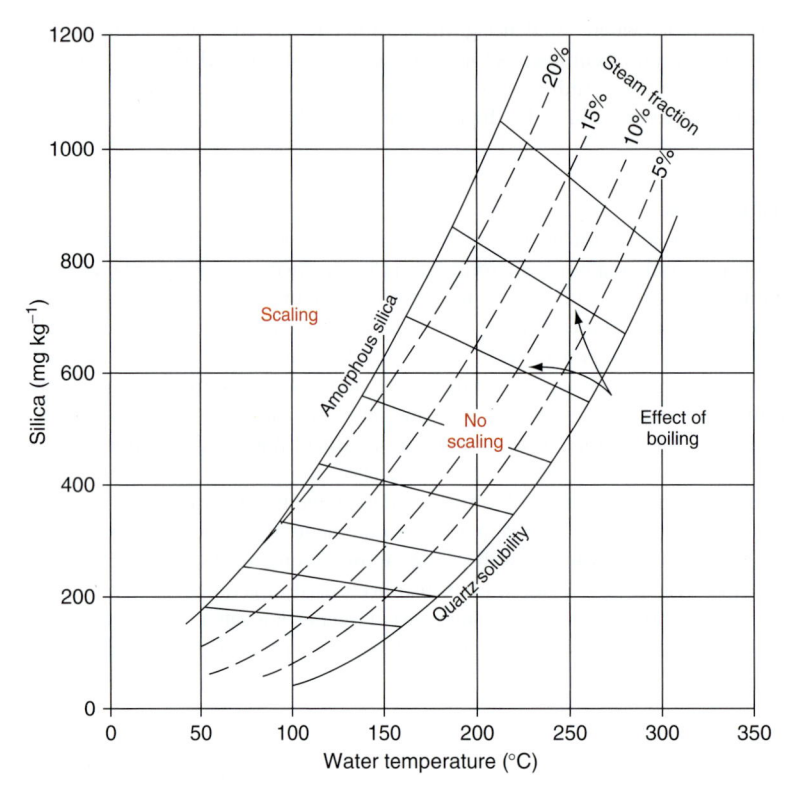

Figure 5 Solubility of silica in water, showing that scaling occurs above the amorphous silica solubility curve [8].

Deposition by scaling on the surface of geothermal wells and equipment can cause plugging at these locations, which can reduce the production and make a costly cleanup effort necessary [8–10, 41, 51, 52].

Types of scales that form in geothermal systems can vary between geothermal areas and between different wells within the same geothermal system. The main classes of geothermal scales are (1) silica and silicates, (2) carbonates, and (3) sulfide compounds [8, 9, 41]. Silica scales are one of the most difficult scales to battle in geothermal systems as they can form amorphous silica scale that is not associated with other cations. Silica is found in almost all geothermal brines, but in varying amounts. In high-temperature geothermal resources, metal silicate and metal sulfide scales such as iron silicates and zinc sulfides are often present [8, 9]. Silica (SiO_2) and calcium carbonate (calcite ($CaCO_3$)) are the two most common geothermal scales and will be described and discussed in more detail.

As mentioned above, silica scales are found to some extent in all geothermal systems. Silica is soluble in hot water and its concentration is directly proportional to the temperature of the geothermal fluid. If the temperature of a geothermal fluid saturated with silica at the reservoir is cooled below a certain temperature, it will become supersaturate and lead to excess concentration of silica, which will eventually precipitate [8, 9, 51]. To illustrate this more clearly, a graph showing the solubility of silica in water is shown in **Figure 5** [8]. In the geothermal reservoir, silica concentration is generally in equilibrium with quartz, which is the crystalline form of silica. When the geothermal water starts to boil and cool down, the silica concentration in the water increases. When this occurs, the liquid will be supersaturated with quartz though no quartz will precipitate because of the slow formation of quartz crystals; the silica scales form when the amorphous silica solubility curve is passed as shown in **Figure 5**. Amorphous silica then precipitates due to supersaturation of the liquid and amorphous silica scales form. Silica scaling can thus be avoided in geothermal applications if the conditions are held within the 'no scaling' area in the graph in **Figure 5**. For example, if a reservoir's water at 250 °C is to be converted into steam, then according to **Figure 5** it has to be separated above 150 °C to avoid scaling. The solubility of amorphous silica is dependent on the amount of steam that is produced, that is, fraction of the steam. In practice, usually only 25% of the water can be converted into steam without the risk of silica scaling [8], as demonstrated in **Figure 5**.

Calcium carbonate (calcite) scales generally form as a result of degassing of CO_2 (which is dissolved in the geothermal liquid). When the CO_2 degasses, there is an increase in the pH of the liquid, leading to the formation of calcite scales. It is common in wells with reservoirs at temperatures in the range of 140–240 °C [8] and is known to frequently cause operational problems in geothermal brine handling systems [9]. Calcite scales are mainly found where the geothermal water starts to boil in the well because at that point the CO_2 degasses and the pH changes. Unlike silica and sulfides, calcite is less soluble at higher temperatures; therefore, the most severe calcite scales occur in lower temperature geothermal wells with fluids below at temperatures between 220 and 240 °C [9]. Calcite scaling is usually not a problem in high-temperature wells, that is, at temperatures higher than 260 °C, because then there is less dissolved calcite to begin with [8].

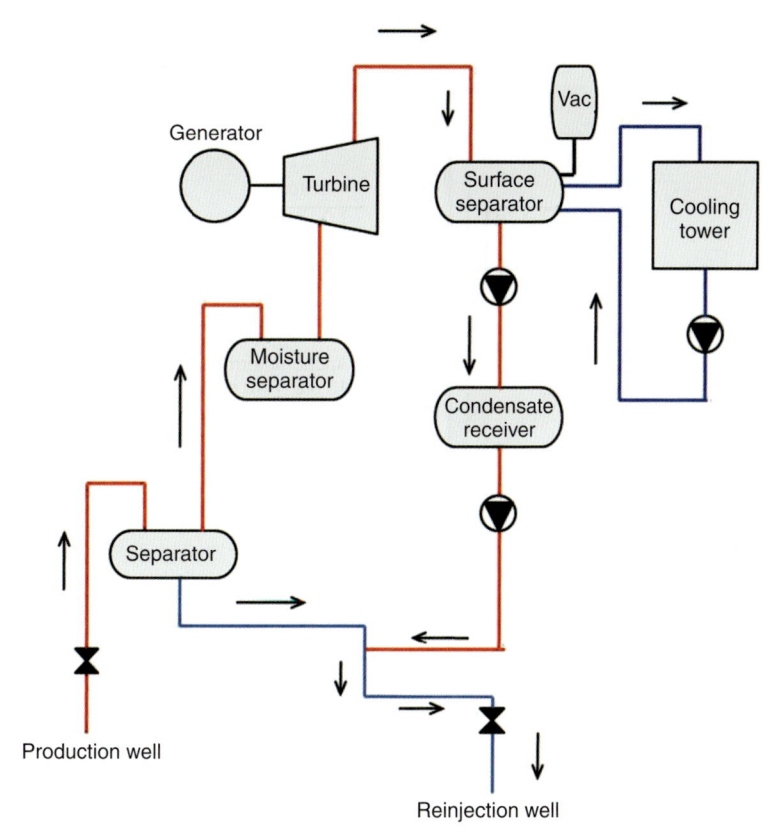

Figure 6 Fluid path of a geothermal power plant with a two-phase flow and a surface condenser, from the geothermal production well to the reinjection well.

Sulfide scales can, on the other hand, form at high temperatures, but they are also found in wells with low/medium-temperature resources. The sulfide scales form when the reservoir temperature decreases due to the supersaturation of the sulfide minerals in the fluid. Sulfide scales combine with other metal cations such as iron and zinc and form scale compounds that are difficult to handle and very hard. They are known to have caused plugging of brine flow from production wells with a two-phase flow [9].

These different types of scales form in geothermal wells in response to changes in the conditions and produced fluid as it moves through the reservoir and up the well. These changes can be in the form of drops in pressure, as well as varying temperature and pH. Scaling is not only a problem inside geothermal wells, but also in other parts of the fluid network such as in aboveground equipment and inside the geothermal power plants [8, 41]. In the following section, where and why these problems occur will be examined in geothermal systems. **Figure 6** shows an example of a fluid path of a geothermal power plant with a two-phase flow and a surface condenser, where it is traced from the geothermal production well to the reinjection well.

7.08.6.1 Production Wells

Scaling in production wells, or downhole scaling as often called, can vary with depth due to the change in the fluid and operating conditions. Scaling in geothermal wells can cause problems such as well and liner (the liner is a slotted pipe in the bottom part of the geothermal well where the water is collected through the slots from the reservoir) clogging, which can restrict the flow or even stop it altogether. **Figure 7** shows an example of the design of a high-temperature geothermal well.

The upper part of a geothermal well is generally constructed with three layers of steel casings at differing depth. The production casing (innermost casing) is the only casing in contact with the geothermal fluid. The liner is hung on the bottom of the production casing. The slots of the liner can become clogged with scales, so the amount of fluid that is collected through the slots decreases, resulting in decreased production. Clogging of the well can also occur in the well casings. The fluid loses gas (degasses) in the liner or the casings, and a bit higher in the well it starts to boil because of changes in pressure. When this occurs, the chemical activity is high because the noncondensable gases (e.g., CO_2, H_2S) are lost from the water, which causes the pH level to increase. This affects the chemical balance and causes scaling. At this point in the well, calcite, silicate, and sulfide scales can form. The calcite will continue to precipitate until the water has cooled sufficiently for it to become undersaturated, that is, when the water is traveling up the well and getting closer to the surface. When the steam has formed, it begins to dominate the volume while the density of the two-phase flow decreases and continues to do so as the fluid rises to the surface [8]. Different scaling profiles in various wells were reported by

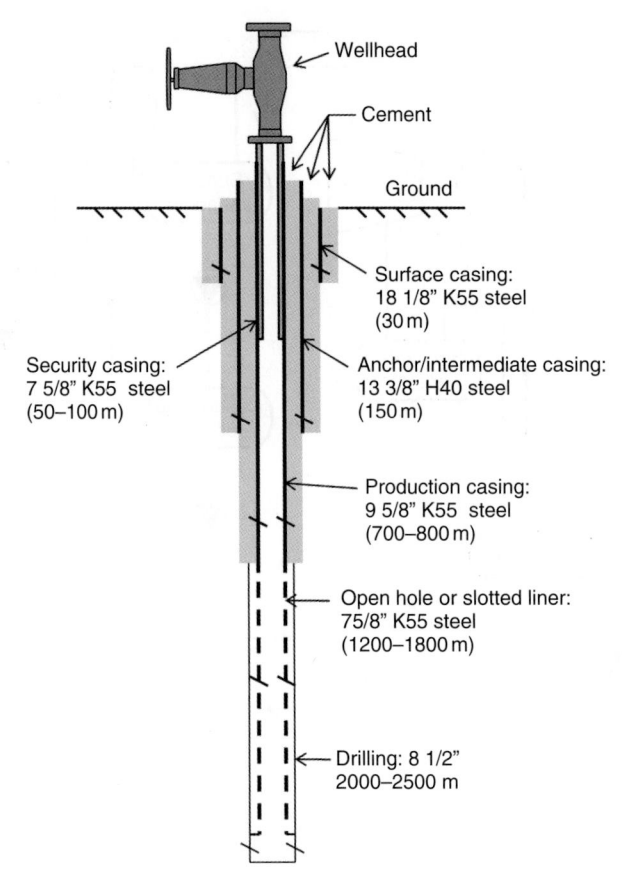

Figure 7 An example of the design of a high-temperature geothermal well.

Ocampo-Díaz et al. [9] in the Cerro Prieto geothermal field in Mexico. Ocampo-Díaz et al. describe scaling problems in the Cerro Prieto geothermal field with over 31 years of commercial operations and explain how different condition in wells can produce different scaling profiles and problems.

7.08.6.2 Wellheads

The main scaling problems in wellheads are in the wellhead valves. A specially designed master valve is usually used to prevent scale buildup so it can be shut tightly. The special design blocks scale buildup in the valve by having a split gate that wedges against the valve seats in both the open and closed position. The master valve is the most crucial valve because it is the only one that can completely shut off the flow. To avoid silica scaling in the wellhead, the well can be operated in the 'no scaling' region in **Figure 5**, as mentioned earlier. This can be achieved by maintaining the wellhead pressure at 10–25 bar while the downstream pressure is in the range of 6–12 bar [8].

7.08.6.3 Pipelines

Geothermal steam and water are transported through pipelines in geothermal systems to different equipment in the flow path as shown in **Figure 6**. Scaling can occur in these pipelines. For example, in pipelines with two-phase flows in Iceland where the water flows at a speed of 70–90 km h^{-1}, at the bottom of the pipe scales sometimes form that cover one-third of the circumference of the pipe [8]. Scales that form inside pipelines usually form a rough surface and peaks of deposits that lie against the flow inside the pipes. This can affect the flow inside the pipe because the pressure drop becomes higher than for smooth pipes, reducing the flow capacity by up to half compared to the design for a clean pipe [8].

7.08.6.4 Separators

For a two-phase flow, the steam and the water flow from the wellheads of the wells through pipes to a central station to separators which are shared with several wells. There the steam is separated from the water to minimize scaling in the equipment handling the steam. This is done by 'flashing' the steam/water flow in the separators, that is, dropping the pressure to a selected pressure so that part of the water is converted to steam. The pressure utilized for 'flashing' the water is usually determined by what the minimum

Figure 8 Inlet diaphragm from a 1 MW turbine from a geothermal power plant almost clogged with silica [13].

temperature for operation can be without getting silica scaling. Separation at too low a pressure can provoke scaling to occur. The water droplets are then collected at the bottom of the separator with the help of gravity and the steam at the top. The separators often need to be inspected and cleaned once a year due to scaling; the scaling mainly occurs in the control valves [8].

7.08.6.5 Turbines

In turbines used in geothermal power plants, the main danger of scaling is on the backside of the first-stage stationary blades in the turbine, which are called nozzles. This is because when the steam starts to do work (driving the blades), it partially condenses (10–15%) when it passes through the turbine [8]. If scaling occurs, it starts to accumulate and builds up with time and restricts the flow of the steam. This causes the pressure to increase (the steam chest pressure), which eventually lowers the output of the generator and the power production. Single-flash turbine and dual-flash turbines are two common types of turbines used in geothermal power plants. The dual-flash turbine, which has a higher pressure and a lower pressure stage, can generate slightly more power than the single-flash turbine; at any rate, there is a potential danger of scaling in the lower pressure stage of the dual-flash turbine. This is because the lower pressure stage of dual-flash turbines is frequently operated in the silica scaling region [8]. **Figure 8** shows a part of a turbine from a geothermal power plant clogged with silica.

7.08.6.6 Reinjection Wells

Nowadays, all wastewater, condensate, or brine from geothermal power plants is generally required to be reinjected into the ground. The wastewater is usually reinjected into wells called reinjection wells. It is generally preferable to place them in hydraulic contact with the reservoir being produced in order to help with maintaining the pressure of the system. The reinjection well should, however, not be located too close to the production well so that it will not cause cooling in the system. Scaling in reinjection wells is a common problem and causes reinjection wells to last for a shorter time. One of the main reasons for this is that the temperature of the wastewater is within the silica scaling region, resulting in silica scale buildup in the well [8].

7.08.7 Corrosion and Scaling Control

As mentioned earlier, the composition of geothermal fluids can vary greatly. The same thermal water can be aggressive and corrosive at one time, but more passive and show a trend toward scaling at another time due to changes in its physical and chemical parameters. Geothermal systems can thus experience corrosion or scaling, and sometimes even both at the same time. High costs and losses in geothermal power production can follow corrosion and scaling problems. In this section, ways to prevent and control corrosion and scaling problems are presented and discussed.

7.08.7.1 Corrosion Control

Corrosion of metals in geothermal fluid is directly associated with the chemical composition, physical characteristics of the fluid, for example, acidity (pH value), and the exploitation parameters of the system, for example, temperature, pressure, and flow rate. Corrosion can be controlled and prevented by correct material selection and good engineering design of equipment in geothermal wells and power plants. When corrosion problems occur after the construction of geothermal wells and equipment, the issues can sometimes be solved by selection of more corrosion-resistant materials such as high-alloy metals (e.g., stainless steels and Ni-base alloys) [9]. This solution is, however, often prohibitively expensive. Other methods to control corrosion are steam scrubbing and corrosion inhibitors. In steam scrubbing, condensate is mixed with the geothermal steam to increase the pH level. This is achieved by adding, for example, geothermal fluid condensate, sodium carbonate solutions, or bases such as sodium hydroxide (caustic soda). Corrosion inhibitors can be used to inhibit corrosion by adding them to the water or process streams in order to lower the corrosion rates to acceptable levels. Corrosion inhibitors generally work in such a way that they incorporate themselves into the corrosion product films to increase the films' capacity to prevent corrosion [12]. Nevertheless, the usage of inhibitors can be prohibitively costly [34]. Their effectiveness is also dependent on factors such as the fluid composition, acidity, and water quantity as well as flow regime and the amount and kind of inhibitors used in each situation. Different types of corrosion inhibitors are available such as phosphates, amines, chromate and nitrite salts, and silicate compounds [12, 21]. The following text describes different situations where some of these corrosion control methods have been applied to reduce and eliminate corrosion problems.

Corrosion problems can occur in disposal systems where the pH level of the geothermal fluid is low (below 4.5), for example, in condensate collection systems and reinjection pipelines. Usually, the condensate collection system is constructed out of stainless steel that is adequately corrosion resistant for these conditions, whereas in reinjection wells and pipelines, it is generally made out of carbon and low-alloy steel, and condensate corrosion can occur. This is because in acidic geothermal fluid with a pH level below 4.5, carbon and low-alloy steel are readily corroded [8, 38]. If corrosion-resistant alloys are not used due to cost or difficulties in implementing them, the corrosion can be controlled by adjusting the pH level by adding sodium carbonate (soda ash), Na_2CO_3, which elevates the pH, or by mixing it with geothermal fluid (waste brine). This kind of pH level controlling has also been used for very acidic production wells where caustic soda (NaOH) is injected through capillary tubing deep into the well in order to elevate the pH level and reduce corrosion [8, 53]. Injection downhole can have some drawbacks. Difficulties can be experienced when the capillary tubing (coiled tubing (CT)) is being inserted at certain desired depths, limiting the long-term reliability of the CT, which can break or get lost in the well due to the harsh environment. Rupture of the CT can occur due to its limited wall thicknesses. Stainless-steel CTs (e.g., 316 or duplex) are not considered viable in systems with high acid chloride content because they are subject to SCC. Carbon steel CT is then used instead [33].

Steam scrubbing was also used in acid chloride corrosion control at the Geysers geothermal fields in California in the United States. In 1986, corrosion damage was observed at the Geysers fields due to volatile chloride from hydrogen chloride (HCl) gas causing acid chloride corrosion of geothermal well casings, production piping, and power plant equipment. A corrosion mitigation system was thus developed where a steam scrubbing system was built that involved both geothermal water and caustic injection (NaOH) at each production wellhead, with subsequent liquid removal via vertical separators and a final two-stage steam washing/separator combination at the power plant inlet. The injection points for the Geysers wells depended on the type of wells, that is, whether they produced dry steam, saturated steam, or mainly condensate. The corrosion mitigation system was reported to have been successful in preventing corrosion damage to well casings, production piping, and power plant equipment [34]. A similar steam scrubbing system involving injection of NaOH solution was developed at the geothermal fields in the Larderello area in Italy. There corrosion problems had also arose due to volatile chloride from HCl [32]. Similarly, steam scrubbing systems involving injection of geothermal separated water were developed at the geothermal fields in the Wairakei area in New Zealand and in the Krafla area in Iceland to control corrosion. At the Wairakei geothermal field, the corrosion problems were first observed in the 1970s due to erosion corrosion of carbon steel pipelines. The problem was blamed on the reduction in separated water carryover from steam/water separators present in the steam line which led to acid dissolution of a protective magnetite (Fe_3O_4) film. This allegedly dislodged the film during operations, resulting in an increased erosion corrosion rate up to 0.5 mm yr^{-1}. By injecting separated geothermal water containing dissolved silica, the corrosion was controlled by the stabilization of the magnetite film as well as allowing the formation of a new protecting film on the corroded areas [54]. In the Krafla area, the corrosion occurred in a well with dry superheated steam in the wellhead equipment and the geothermal fluid collection pipelines. The corrosion was attributed to localized enrichment of hydrochloric acid due to condensation and reboiling due to the presence of HCl. The steam was thus scrubbed with liquid-dominated geothermal fluid from two other wells in the high-temperature geothermal field, which resulted in very low corrosion rates on the metal exposed to the scrubbed steam [3]. As in Wairakei, it was reported that a protective film formed on the steel components after the scrubbing played an important role as a protection against corrosion provided that the mechanical integrity of the film was ensured. The film was reported to be iron sulfide (FeS), which often forms on steel components when exposed to two-phase geothermal fluid, separated geothermal fluid, or dry saturated steam and its condensate.

Wells drilled deep (3500–4000 m) in the Larderello area in Italy in recent years are reported to have very aggressive steam due to the presence of high contents of acid chloride. This results in the steam condensate being characterized by very acidic fluid (low pH level) and high levels of total dissolved solids (TDSs), particularly at the dew point condition [33]. To avoid corrosion in these wells, corrosion-resistant materials were used near (down to 100 m in depth) and up to the wellhead; also, wellhead and its components were coated to allow steam scrubbing at the wellhead instead of downhole. The corrosion-resistant material used was 13% chromium stainless steel. This type of steel is known to perform well when there is a high content of chloride, but not as well when there is also a substantial amount of H_2S gas [33]. Overall, a combination of steam scrubbing, correct material selection, and engineering design provides the best solution against corrosion.

In some of the high-temperature wells in the Cerro Prieto geothermal field in Mexico, internal and external corrosion of steel casings occurred due to the corrosiveness of the geothermal brine as well as due to the formation of reservoir steam zones with high amounts of H_2S gas. The casing materials that underwent severe corrosion were carbon steel casings called J-55, K-55, and N-80, which are generally considered a good choice for most geothermal well casings. The solution chosen for this difficult environment was to select a more corrosion-resistant grade for the casing and to increase the thickness of the casing [9]. This action effectively eliminated the corrosion problems in these wells.

7.08.7.2 Scaling Control

The methods that are used to control and prevent scaling in geothermal wells and equipment depend on which minerals and chemical species are present in the geothermal fluid. With information on the concentration of the chemical species and on the chemical activity, the solubility product of selected minerals can be calculated to find out whether the fluid is supersaturated with respect to these minerals and whether scales are expected to form. These kinds of calculations all assume equilibrium to be reached. For many minerals, this happens quite rapidly (e.g., calcite, sulfides); however, for some minerals (e.g., silica, metal silicates), it takes a longer time to equilibrate [8, 9]. Sometimes, these slow rates can be taken advantage of by having the fluid travel very rapidly through the equipment. Therefore, by knowing the precipitation rate (scaling rate) of these minerals and how quickly equilibrium is reached, the risk of scaling can be diminished. The precipitation rate of silica and metal silicates is strongly influenced by the temperature, pH value, and the salinity of the fluid. Low temperature, pH, and salinity slow down the scaling rate of the silica; this can be taken advantage of in the process design in an effort to prevent scaling problems [8, 9, 41, 51]. If geothermal fluid saturated with silica at the reservoir temperature is cooled below a certain temperature, it will supersaturate and lead to an excess concentration of silica, which will eventually precipitate as shown in **Figure 5** [8]. Consequently, geothermal waters are usually disposed of at temperatures above amorphous silica saturation temperatures (commonly above 150 °C). Scaling risks can be greatly mitigated in geothermal brines by reducing the temperature rapidly on a second flash separator, for example, by using a vacuum [8]. Then, the second flash steam can be used, and the waste brine exits the processing equipment without clogging it. Precipitation of silica is also dependent on the pressure of the system; for example, in geothermal wells that have poor inflow or are fully opened for maximum flow, restriction to flow will cause a great loss in pressure and a consequent temperature drop that can fall within the 'scaling region' (**Figure 5**). In cases like these, the valve on the wellhead should be partly closed or the flow should be restricted by other means to reduce the flow and keep the pressure loss within acceptable limits. When downhole scales have built up and are clogging the well, they are sometimes removed by drilling rigs. They are then drilled out with a common drill bit to a depth just below the start of boiling [8].

The salinity of the geothermal liquid also affects the precipitation rate of silica, as mentioned previously. For example, it is possible to take advantage of the slow scaling rate of silica in dilute geothermal water and operate heat exchangers and binary units within the scaling region. This is not possible for brines because the saline solution (brines) will precipitate the silica faster due to a higher reaction rate than in dilute solutions. Silica scaling can also be controlled by changing the pH level of the fluid [55, 56], for example, by adding acid or caustic solution to influence the precipitation rate. This must be done with much caution because it may increase the corrosion rate of pipelines and other equipment. Another method to control scaling is to use certain chemicals called scale inhibitors. Because of the large volume of fluid that requires treatment, only scale inhibitors that can be used in very small concentrations can be considered (because of costs). The scale inhibitors function in such a way that they affect the surface chemistry rather than a particular chemical reaction. Scale inhibitors have been used for reducing the risk of scaling for both calcite and silica [8, 57].

Some of the methods described above have been used to mitigate damage to reinjection wells due to scaling. This includes 'hot injection' of the wastewater, that is, when the water temperature is maintained above the scaling limit for amorphous silica, as well as mixing the condensate (where the surface condensers are used) with brine before reinjection (ideally to dilute it below the silica saturation limit). In some geothermal fields that are nonsaline, water supersaturated with silica is being reinjected. In an effort to prevent clogging of the reinjection wells due to scaling, the silica is allowed to polymerize in retention tanks or open ponds [57, 58]. This will usually work for few years, but with time the wells may clog due to scaling. Then they might require expensive solutions to solve the scaling problem, such as drilling out the scale as previously described, acidizing by adding hydrochloric or hydrofluoric acid into the aquifer to dissolve the silica in the veins, or making a new well parallel to the old one [8].

Methods that are used to clean scaling products in equipment after they form include high-pressure water blasting and equipment washing. High-pressure water blasting is, for example, used to clean level control valves on separators [8]. Turbine washing is a commonly applied method to clean scaling products in turbines. This is done by injecting a steady stream of condensate into the inlet steam line, just in front of the turbine, in sufficient quantity for the steam to be below the saturation line at the exit of the nozzles. Thus, the steam condensate can be delivered to the steam chest of the units to dissolve the scaling deposits within the turbine. This can be done while the turbine is in normal operation [8, 59, 60].

There is no one universal method to prevent scaling but there are different methods previously described that have proved successful in individual geothermal areas and wells. The scaling conditions are constantly changing as the geothermal fluid is traveling from the reservoir to the wells via the pipelines and then to the power plant equipment and back again to the reservoir, making prediction of scaling a fairly uncertain and difficult endeavor. By using different tools such as chemical modeling calculations, knowledge from practical experiences, results from pilot studies, along with the scaling prevention and cleaning methods previously described, it is nevertheless usually possible to find a solution that will solve the most severe scaling problems. For most geothermal power plants, there will still be minor scaling problems that are then dealt with as maintenance issues and can be solved as such with the solutions described above.

7.08.8 Conclusions

Scaling and corrosion in geothermal systems cause problems during geothermal power production, resulting in high costs associated with labor, materials, and production efficiency. Corrosion of materials in geothermal systems is due to the corrosiveness of the geothermal fluid in the system. Corrosion also depends on exploitation parameters such as temperature, pressure, and flow rate. The main corrosive agents in geothermal fluid are dissolved gases such as H_2S and CO_2 and dissolved solids such as chloride ions. HCl gas also exists in some systems and it can cause severe corrosion if condensation and reboiling occur. There are several forms of corrosion that can occur for metals in geothermal environments and these include uniform corrosion, pitting corrosion, SCC, crevice corrosion, HE, HIC, and SSC.

The corrosion resistance of materials used in a geothermal environment was discussed and rated. In general, carbon and low-alloyed steel are preferred for many components in geothermal systems. This is because of the economical advantage in using them over other materials and in spite of the fact that their resistance against corrosion is limited (especially at low pH levels). In geothermal fluids, stainless steel exhibits a much lower corrosion rate due to uniform corrosion than carbon and low-alloy steel. Stainless steel along with carbon and low-alloy steel is the main construction material in geothermal systems. Stainless steels are, however, used in much smaller quantities than carbon and low-alloy steel due to their cost. Even though stainless steels have a strong resistance to uniform corrosion, they can experience other forms of corrosion such as crevice corrosion, intergranular corrosion, pitting, SSC, SCC, and corrosion fatigue. Nickel-base alloys containing more than 8% Mo (Hastelloy C-276 and Alloy 625) and titanium have shown very good performance against corrosion in geothermal environments compared with carbon and low-alloy steel, stainless steels (austenitic, duplex, and martensitic), and other Ni-base alloys containing less than 8% Mo. The high cost of high-alloyed nickel-base alloys and titanium limits their usage in geothermal applications.

Geothermal fluid can be corrosive at one point, but passive and show a trend toward scaling at another point due to a change in its physical and chemical parameters. Scaling occurs when minerals dissolved in the geothermal fluid precipitate from the liquid and deposit on the surface of the geothermal wells and equipment due to changes in pressure, temperature, or pH value which disturb the equilibrium of the system. The two most common types of scales are silica and calcium carbonate. These scales form in response to changes in the produced fluid, such as composition and pH level, as well as due to conditions such as changes in pressure and temperature as it moves from the reservoir and through the power plant to the injection well. Scaling is thus not only a problem inside geothermal wells and wellheads due to clogging, but also in other parts of the fluid network such as in equipment aboveground and inside geothermal power plants, for example, in pipelines, separators, and turbines.

Corrosion and scaling can be prevented or controlled with different methods. The best way to prevent corrosion is by correct material selection and good engineering design of equipment in geothermal wells and power plants. Other methods to control corrosion are steam scrubbing and corrosion inhibitors. Silica scaling can be avoided in geothermal application if the conditions are held within the so-called 'no scaling' area. Thus, geothermal waters are usually disposed of at temperatures above amorphous silica saturation temperatures (commonly above 150 °C). Low temperature, pH, and salinity slow down the scaling rate of the silica, which can be taken advantage of in the design process in an effort to prevent scaling problems. This includes having the fluid travel very rapidly through the equipment to avoid precipitation and rapidly reducing the temperature of geothermal brine on a second flash separator, for example, by using a vacuum. Other methods to control scaling include using scale inhibitors or changing the pH level of the fluid by adding acid or caustic solution to influence the precipitation rate. Methods that are used to clean scaling products in equipment after they form include high-pressure water blasting and equipment washing.

Corrosion or scaling in geothermal systems is generally not considered as a limiting factor in the production of geothermal power. Corrosion and scaling problems can be avoided by correct material selection and good engineering design. If they do occur, there are several methods that have proved successful in preventing or controlling these problems so that the production of geothermal power can be achieved in the most cost-effective and efficient way.

References

[1] Bridges CE and Hobbs GWM (1987) *Corrosion Control in the Geothermal Drilling Industry, Material Performance*, pp. 34–41. Houston, TX: NACE (National Association of Corrosion Engineers).
[2] Banás J, Lelek-Borkowska U, Mazurkiewicz B, and Solarski W (2007) Effect of CO_2 and H_2S on the composition and stability of passive film on iron alloys in geothermal water. *Electrochimica Acta* 52: 5704–5714.
[3] Eliasson ET and Einarsson A (1982) Corrosion in Icelandic high temperature geothermal systems. *Materials Performance* 10(21): 35–39.
[4] Kaya T and Hoshan P (2005) Corrosion and materials selection for geothermal systems. *Proceedings of the World Geothermal Congress*, pp. 1–5. International Geothermal Association (IGA), Antalya, Turkey, 24–26 April.
[5] Conover M, Ellis P, and Curzon A (1980) Material selection guidelines for geothermal power systems – an overview. In: Casper LA and Pinchback TR (eds.) *Geothermal Scaling and Corrosion*, ASTM STP 717, pp. 24–40. Philadelphia, PA: American Society for Testing and Materials.
[6] Olafsson M (2008) Report by ISOR, Icelandic Geosurvey Research, no. ISOR-08087, project no. 520003. Reykjavik, Iceland, September.
[7] Fridriksson T and Giroud N (2008) Report by ISOR, Icelandic Geosurvey Research, no. ISOR-2008/021, project no. 530107. Reykjavik, Iceland, June.
[8] Thorhallsson S (2005) Common problems faced in geothermal generation and how to deal with them. Paper presented at the *Workshop for Decision Makers on Geothermal Projects and Management*, pp. 1–12. Organized by UNU-GTP and KengGen in Naivasha, Kenya, 14–18 November, pp. 1–12.
[9] Ocampo-Díaz JDD, Valdez-Salaz B, Shorr M, *et al.* (2005) Review of corrosion and scaling problems in Cerro Prieto geothermal field over 31 years of commercial operations. *Proceedings of the World Geothermal Congress*, pp. 1–5. International Geothermal Association (IGA), Antalya, Turkey, 24–26 April.
[10] Pátzay G, Kármán FH, and Póta G (2003) Preliminary investigations of scaling and corrosion in high enthalpy geothermal wells in Hungary. *Geothermics* 32: 627–638.
[11] Fontana G and Green ND (1978) *Corrosion Engineering*, 2nd edn. New York: McGraw-Hill.
[12] Koutsoukos PG and Andritos N (2002) Corrosion in geothermal plants. Paper presented at the *International Summer School on Direct Application of Geothermal Energy*, pp. 190–201. Organized by IGA and UNESCO.
[13] Einarsson A (2010) Personal communications. Pictures provided by Einarsson A.
[14] Melekhov RK and Lytvyntseva OM (1994) Corrosion cracking of rotor steels of steam turbines. *Materials Science* 30(5): 531–541.

[15] Sakuma A, Matsuura T, Suzuki T, et al. (2006) Upgrading and life extension technologies for geothermal steam turbines. *Japan Society of Mechanical Engineers International Journal, B* 49: 2.
[16] Roberts BW and Greenfield P (1970) Stress corrosion of steam turbine disk and rotor steels. *Corrosion* 35(9): 402–409.
[17] Kane RD and Cayard MS (1998) Roles of H$_2$S in the behavior of engineering alloys: A review of literature and experience. *Corrosion* 274: 1–28.
[18] Kim WK, Koh SU, Yang BY, and Kim KY (2008) Effect of the environmental and metallurgical factors on hydrogen induced cracking of HSLA steels. *Corrosion Science* 50: 3336–3342.
[19] Kittel J, Smanio V, Fregonese M, et al. (2010) Hydrogen induced cracking (HIC) testing of low alloy steel in sour environment: Impact of time of exposure on the extent of damage. *Corrosion Science* 52: 1386–1392.
[20] Sojka J, Jerome M, Sozanska M, et al. (2008) Role of microstructure and testing conditions in sulfide stress cracking of X52 and X60 API steels. *Materials and Engineering A* 480: 237–243.
[21] Licthi KA, Firth DM, and Karstensen AD (2005) Hydrogen induced cracking of low strength steels in geothermal fields. *Proceedings of the World Geothermal Congress*, pp. 1–11. International Geothermal Association (IGA), Antalya, Turkey, 24–26 April.
[22] Berkowitz BJ and Heubaum FH (1984) The role of hydrogen in sulfide stress cracking of low-alloy steels. *Corrosion* 40(5): 240–245.
[23] Ramirez E, González-Rodriguez JG, Torres-Islas A, et al. (2008) Effect of microstructure on the sulfide stress cracking susceptibility of a high strength pipeline steel. *Corrosion Science* 50: 3534–3541.
[24] Troiano AR and Hegeman RF (1979) Hydrogen sulfide stress corrosion cracking for geothermal power. *Materials Performance* 18(1): 31–39.
[25] Lopez HF, Bharadwaj R, Albarran JL, and Martinez L (1999) The role of heat treating on the sour gas resistance of an X-80 steel for oil and gas transport. *Metal and Materials Transactions A* 30A: 2419–2428.
[26] NACE Standard MR0175 (2003) *Sulfide Stress Cracking Resistant Metallic Materials for Oil Field Equipment.* Houston, TX: NACE International.
[27] NACE MR0175/ISO 15156-2:2003(E) (2003) *Petroleum and Natural Gas Industries – Materials for Use in H$_2$S Containing Environments in Oil and Gas Production*, Parts 1–3. Houston, TX: NACE International/ISO.
[28] Marshall T and Tombs A (1969) Delayed fracture of geothermal bore casing steels. *Australian Corrosion Engineering* 13(9): 1–8.
[29] Kane DR Evaluation of geothermal production for sulfide stress cracking and stress corrosion cracking. www.corrosionsource.com (last accessed 25 May 2009).
[30] Chawla SL and Gupta RK (1993) *Materials Selection for Corrosion Control*, 1st edn. Materials Park, OH: ASM International.
[31] Þorbjornsson I (1995) Corrosion fatigue testing of eight different steels in an Icelandic geothermal environment. *Materials & Design* 16(2): 97–102.
[32] Viviani E, Paglianti A, Sabatelli F, and Tarquini B (1995) Abatement of hydrogen chloride in geothermal power plants. *Proceedings of the World Geothermal Congress, Section 11 – Corrosion and Scaling*, pp. 2421–2426. International Geothermal Association (IGA), Firenze, Italy, 18–31 May.
[33] Lazzarotto A and Sabatelli F (2005) Technological developments in deep drilling in Larderello area. *Proceedings of the World Geothermal Congress*, pp. 1–6. International Geothermal Association (IGA), Antalya, Turkey, 24–26 April.
[34] Hirtz P, Buck C, and Kunzmann R (1991) Current techniques in acid chloride corrosion control and monitoring at the Geysers. *Proceedings of the Sixteenth Workshop on Geothermal Reservoir Engineering*, pp. 83–95. Stanford University, Stanford, CA, 23–25 January.
[35] Allegrini G and Benvenuti G (1970) Corrosion characteristics and geothermal power plant protection. *Geothermics (Special Issue 2)* 2(Pt. I): 865–881.
[36] Kato H, Furuya K, and Yamashita M (2000) Exposure tests of turbine materials in geothermal steam from a deep production well. *Proceedings of the World Geothermal Congress*, pp. 3193–3198. International Geothermal Association (IGA), Kyushu–Tohoku, Japan, 28 May–10 June.
[37] Takaku H, Niu L-B, Kawanishi K, et al. (2004) Corrosion behavior of steam turbine materials for geothermal power plants. *Proceedings of the 14th International Conference on the Properties of Water and Steam, Kyoto, Japan, August 29–September 3*, pp. 718–723.
[38] Sanada N, Kurata Y, Nanjo H, et al. (2000) IEA deep geothermal resources subtask C: Materials, progress with database for materials performance in deep and acidic geothermal wells. *Proceedings of the World Geothermal Congress*, pp. 2411–2416. International Geothermal Association (IGA), Kyushu–Tohoku, Japan, 28 May–10 June.
[39] Sanada N, Kurata Y, Nanjo H, and Ikeuchi J (1995) Material damage in high velocity acidic fluids. *Geothermal Resources Council Transactions* 19: 359–363.
[40] Kurata Y, Sanada N, Nanjo H, et al. (1995) Material damage in a volcanic environment. *Proceedings of the World Geothermal Congress* 4: 2409–2414.
[41] Corsi R (1986) Scaling and corrosion in geothermal equipment: Problems and preventive measures. *Geothermics* 15(5/6): 839–856.
[42] Einarsson A (1980) Report for Landsvirkjun. Results from corrosion testing in high temperature geothermal well K-12 in the Krafla area in Iceland.
[43] Latanision RM and Staehle RW (1967) Stress corrosion cracking of iron–nickel–chromium alloys. *Proceedings of the Conference on Fundamental Aspects of Stress Corrosion Cracking*, p. 214. Ohio State University, Columbus, OH, September.
[44] Lichti KA, Johnson CA, Mallhone PGH, and Wilson PT (1995) Corrosion of iron–nickel base and titanium alloys in aerated geothermal fluids. *Proceedings of the World Geothermal Congress*, pp. 2375–2380. International Geothermal Association (IGA), Antalya, Turkey, 24–26 April.
[45] Kurata Y, Sanada N, Nanjo H, and Ikeuchi J (1992) Material damages in geothermal power plants. *Proceedings of the 14th New Zealand Geothermal Workshop*, Auckland University, New Zealand, November, pp. 159–164.
[46] Thomas R (2003) Titanium in the geothermal industry. *Geothermics* 32: 679–687.
[47] Pye DS, Holligan D, Cron CJ, and Love WW (1989) The use of Beta-C titanium for downhole production casing in geothermal wells. *Geothermics* 18(1/2): 259–267.
[48] Rafferty KD (1998) Piping. Section: Equipment/materials. *Geo-Heat Center Quarterly Bulletin* 19(1): 14–19.
[49] Rafferty KD (1990) Piping materials for geothermal district heating systems, section: Equipment/materials. *Geo-Heat Center Quarterly Bulletin* 12(2): 12–19.
[50] Oktay Z and Aslan A (2007) Geothermal district heating in Turkey: The Gonen case study. *Geothermics* 36: 167–182.
[51] Henley RW (1983) pH and silica scaling control in geothermal field development. *Geothermics* 12(4): 307–321.
[52] Gunnarsson I and Arnorsson S (2005) Impact of silica scaling on efficiency of heat extraction from high-temperature geothermal fluids. *Geothermics* 34: 320–329.
[53] Alescio S, Ricciardulli R, Vallini A, and Caponi N (1999) Coiled tubing injection string for geothermal wells. Society of Petroleum Engineers, Inc. Paper SPE 54510. Presented at the *1999 SPE/ICoTA Tubing Roundtable*, pp. 1–12. Houston, TX, 25–26 May.
[54] Lichti KA and Bacon LG (1998) Corrosion in Wairakei steam pipelines. *Proceedings of the 20th New Zealand Geothermal Workshop*, Auckland University, New Zealand, November, pp. 51–58.
[55] Gill JS (1993) Inhibition of silica–silicate deposition in industrial waters. *Colloids and Surfaces A* 74: 101–106.
[56] Gudmundsson SR and Einarsson E (1989) Controlled silica precipitation in geothermal brine at the Reykjanes geo-chemical plant. *Geothermics* 18: 105–112.
[57] Gunnarsson I and Arnorsson S (2005) Treatment of geothermal waste water to prevent silica scaling. *Proceedings of the World Geothermal Congress*, pp. 1–5. International Geothermal Association (IGA), Antalya, Turkey, 24–26 April.
[58] Yanagase T, Suginohara Y, and Yanagase K (1970) The properties of scales and methods to prevent them. *Geothermics* 2: 1619–1623.
[59] Thain IA and Carey B (2009) Fifty years of geothermal power generation at Wairakei. *Geothermics* 38: 48–63.
[60] Shimoda M, Suzuki K, Tsujita M, et al. (2005) Scaling protection technology for Hachijyo-Jima geothermal power plant. *Proceedings of the World Geothermal Congress*, pp. 1–5. International Geothermal Association (IGA), Antalya, Turkey, 24–26 April.

7.09 Geothermal Cost and Investment Factors

H Kristjánsdóttir, University of Iceland, Reykjavík, Iceland
Á Margeirsson, Magma Energy Iceland, Reykjanesbaer, Iceland

© 2012 Elsevier Ltd. All rights reserved.

7.09.1	Introduction	259
7.09.2	Theoretical Overview	260
7.09.3	Geothermal Industry: Microeconomic Analysis	260
7.09.4	Geothermal Industry: Macroeconomic Analysis	263
7.09.4.1	Model Setup	263
7.09.4.2	Data	263
7.09.4.3	Regression Results	265
7.09.5	Summary and Conclusions	265
References		270

Glossary

CAPEX Capital expenditure.
Environmental factors The environmental factor applied in this research is the following: CO_2 emissions by metric tons per capita.
Foreign direct investment Foreign direct investment occurs when a firm invests abroad to acquire a lasting management interest in a foreign company, acquiring 10% ownership of voting stock or more. By undertaking foreign direct investment, firms become multinationals.
Geothermal energy Energy extracted from ground heat.
Infrastructural factors In this study, we use proportion of roads paved to present infrastructure or infrastructural status.
Macroeconomic factors The macroeconomic factors applied in this research are the following – installed geothermal power capacity (MW), electric power consumption (kWh per capita), energy use (kg of oil equivalent per capita), gross domestic product (GDP) (current USD), capita, representing GNI per capita PPP (current international $), inflation GDP deflator (annual %), population variable POP, workers' remittances, and compensation of employees as received in (current USD).
Multinational firms Firms operating in many countries.
OLS Ordinary least squares procedure is used for estimating linear regression model parameters.
OPEX Operating expense.
Power plants Operational plants producing electric power by extracting heat from the ground.
Productivity Production process presenting output from one unit of input.

7.09.1 Introduction

At the United Nation's Climate Change Conference in December 2009, there were talks of the importance of helping countries to develop clean energy [1]. The wealth and growth of countries is often related to their natural resources in combination with human resources [2]. Energy resources have significant impact on economic development, with renewable energy becoming increasingly important in the overall energy supply in the world. Geothermal energy is a clean and sustainable source of electricity. Few countries are rich in geothermal resources, so this type of energy represents a small proportion of overall electricity supply in the world. International investment in geothermal activities has therefore been minimal compared to international investment in other energy resources [3].

One of the main objectives of this research is to analyze what drives international investment in geothermal electricity projects. An important factor affecting geothermal investment is that generally the risk is higher than in the traditional energy sector, which attracts fewer investors, although return tends to be higher. Furthermore, the average investor does not have an appetite for exploration risk. Loans for projects of this kind, especially in the exploration phase, are often very hard or impossible to get, and they therefore tend to be financed by owners' equity. Because of this, it is sometimes more feasible for domestic firms to look for foreign investors. By acquiring foreign direct investment, the firm is able to increase its owners' equity and thereby project potentials. Also, a factor affecting the risk to return ratio is the high fixed cost sometimes associated with power intensive industries, which has proven to be important to foreign investors [4]. This may be explained by the simple fact that geothermal energy development requires higher investment costs than, for example, fuel-based energy development cost, and much less operational costs as fuel is not needed for the operation.

For decades, economists have sought to explain what drives investors to seek opportunities in other countries [5]. What factors affect investors in their decision to undertake an investment in a foreign country? Foreign direct investment takes place when a firm invests in projects in another country by buying a controlling stock ownership of 10% or more [6]. Economic researchers have developed two main theories about the major types of foreign direct investments. The first is the theory of vertical FDI, where investors select projects that provide access to abundant factors such as natural resources [7]. The second is the theory of horizontal FDI, when investors choose projects in order to overcome trade costs between countries and thereby gain access to foreign markets [8]. In the 1980s, the New Trade Theory was introduced, combining the horizontal and vertical incentives for FDI [9]. These theories apply here in determining the reasons why national and multinational firms might invest in geothermal projects.

This chapter incorporates both microanalysis and macroanalysis concerning the geothermal industry. We start by providing analysis of the geothermal industry from a microeconomic perspective, using actual firm-level data for comparison. We compare various firms based on information from their business operations available from annual reports and additional information from individual companies, with the goal of determining whether there is a difference between firms in the geothermal industry that are based in one country only or those that operate in more than one country as multinational corporations. We then conclude by investigating to what extent the geothermal industry in various countries is subject to the macroeconomic environment there [10]. This is done to shed light on how significant the economic environment is for these geothermal firms.

7.09.2 Theoretical Overview

Markusen *et al.* [11] introduced the Knowledge-Capital (KK) model of multinational activities. They analyzed incentives for why firms invest across countries and become multinationals by undertaking foreign direct investment. In their research, Markusen *et al.* [11] applied variables representing cost of labor endowments and raw materials, source and host country market size, and the distance between them. Numerical simulation of the KK model is provided by Markusen *et al.* [11] and Markusen [12]. Foreign direct investment is said to be vertical when production is located in foreign countries in order to get access to abundant factors [7]; however, horizontal if foreign investment location is chosen to gain access to larger market and overcome trade costs [8].

The conventional international economic literature was enriched by the addition of the New Trade Theory in the 1980s. The New Trade theory models incorporated imperfect competition, increasing returns to scale, and product differentiation both in partial and general equilibrium models of trade [13]. Krugman [14] provided a valuable contribution to the literature, and later the Economic Geography developed, with important contribution by Krugman [15] where he explained region and country industry agglomeration.

In recent years there has been increasing economic literature on the activities of multinational firms. Nationals firms become multinational firms when they expand their operations to another country, often by undertaking foreign direct investment. The literature has until recently, been mainly incorporated into general equilibrium models of two types, vertical and horizontal. A model on vertical FDI was introduced by Helpman [7], accounting for the cases when multinationals place their activities vertically across countries, based on the production stage, as to take advantage of relative factor endowment differences. Moreover, a model on horizontal FDI was introduced by Markusen [8], accounting for multinational firms that place analogous operations in various countries. The horizontal model of Markusen [8], however, applies to the situation of countries being similar in size and relative endowments, together with trade costs being moderate to high.

Economic research indicates that the flow of foreign direct investment between parts of the world is not mainly between the developed countries, rather than flowing mainly from the developed countries to the developing countries as earlier literature suggested [9].

Further research on incentives for firms in international operations across countries is put forward in an econometric specification of the KK model by Carr *et al.* [13]. By presenting the KK model of the multinational enterprise, they seek to explain how foreign direct investment is determined by relative endowments of countries and their economic size. The paper applies industrial organization approach to international trade, and allows for interaction of country characteristics with industrial organizational approach. Carr *et al.* [13] seek to incorporate both issues presented in the horizontal and vertical models, applying factors like the skilled labor, calculated as the sum of administrative workers and professional, technical, and kindred workers, divided by sum of all occupational categories as registered by the International Labor Organization. Furthermore, other specifications of the KK model have been developed by Bloningen *et al.* [16] and Davies [4].

7.09.3 Geothermal Industry: Microeconomic Analysis

Cost comparison between geothermal projects in different countries and companies is highly sensitive to various factors. In this research, investment cost (CAPEX) figures are found to range from around USD 2 million per installed MW to USD 8 million MW^{-1}. Most of the analyzed projects have an investment cost in the order of USD 2.5–5 million per installed MW.

The main factors determining the investment costs are the following:

1. Resource conditions
   a. Temperature of reservoir
   b. Depth of reservoir
   c. Drilling conditions
   d. Permeability/fluid yield
   e. Quality of the geothermal brine.

Through exploration, the resource conditions lead to design parameters of a power plant. The two main types of geothermal power plants are based on the two following categories of turbines:
- Flash steam turbines (in high enthalpy fields)
- Binary cycle turbines (in low enthalpy fields).

Flash turbines are typically built in units of 20–50 MW and make use of the flashed geothermal brine. Binary cycle turbines are typically smaller, 2–15 MW units, and make use of a secondary working fluid in a closed cycle. This requires a set of heat exchangers that are not required for a flash turbine. Accordingly, the equipment cost is higher for binary cycle units.

There is not a clear line between the two categories and some development projects require an analysis of which alternative is the most suitable one. Generally, the binary solutions are applied where fluid temperatures are below 200 °C and flash turbines where the fluid temperatures are 200 °C or higher. An alternative to the binary solution is a low-pressure flash turbine. The cost structure for such a project is more in line with that of a binary unit, rather than of a high-pressure flash unit. The difference clearly relates to the energy content or enthalpy of the geothermal brine.

2. Geographical conditions
    a. Location of reservoir
        i. Topography, access
        ii. Distance to market
    b. Availability of technical services, workforce, material, equipment, and contractors
    c. Investment environment, taxes, government support, and so on.
3. Global conditions
    a. Development of commodities price, for example, oil and steel
    b. Availability of manufacturers and lead time.

Referring to the investment costs mentioned earlier, a typical split of a USD 4 million MW^{-1} geothermal project is:
- Exploration: USD 0.5 million MW^{-1}
- Reservoir development: USD 1.0 million MW^{-1}
- Construction: USD 2.5 million MW^{-1}
- Total investment cost: USD 4.0 million MW^{-1}.

In addition to this, the cost of developing geothermal projects has been increasing due to more stringent environmental requirements. Factors that have been developing for the last one or two decades and are continuing to develop further, are, for example, requirements for reinjection, extraction of gases, and visibility of structures. Generally, the increased requirements lead to higher investment costs. It has to be kept in mind that this is with time somewhat leading to technical advancements that contribute to reduce the cost increase.

The decision making for developing geothermal projects mainly consists of a technical evaluation and a market evaluation combined with an economical analysis; a feasibility study. By far the most important factors in the market evaluation are the need for power in the market as well as the power price. An additional important factor is subsidies for clean energy or state support, for example, in the form of exploration grants or tax incentives.

Figure 1 and **Table 1** exhibit well the global trends in sustainable energy investment in recent years. What is noteworthy is the tiny share of overall investment in geothermal activities.

In our research we compare the following companies: Mighty River Power in New Zealand, Reykjavik Energy and HS Orka in Iceland, PNOC-EDC in the Philippines, and ORMAT Technologies in the United States. The research is based on the annual reports of these companies along with further information submitted by some of these companies. Some of the companies are national and some multinational.

Table 2 shows a comparison between the following companies: Mighty River Power [17], Reykjavik Energy [18], HS Orka [19], PNOC-EDC [20] and ORMAT Technologies [21].

The countries presented in **Table 2** are New Zealand, Iceland, Philippines, and United States. Companies in these countries are chosen for comparison, since they are believed to shed light on differences in the operating environments and the countries, and therefore the feasibility of investing in geothermal activities, as well as reflecting on variation in productivity between countries.

Table 2 provides comparison between several companies. For company comparison, we use operational size measured by MW operated and owned, and we also apply expense measures by using capital expenditure, CAPEX (from property, plant, and equipment items in BS 2008), and operating expense, OPEX (in IS 2008). Those indicators are chosen, since they are believed to best represent daily operations and potential investment incentives. Furthermore, we use OPEX per MW and CAPEX per MW to provide comparison between cost ratios of the companies.

The only multinational firm in **Table 2** is ORMAT; the other firms operate nationally. For example, the activities of Reykjavik Energy abroad are in the stage of prefeasibility, and therefore not classified as investment in projects abroad. Projects start out in the prefeasibility stage, then develop to feasibility stage, construction stage, and operational stage.

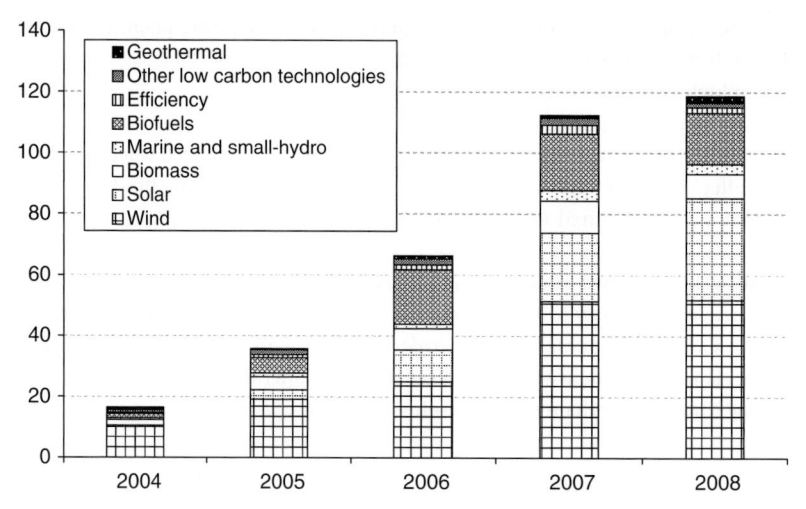

Figure 1 Global trends in sustainable energy investment, USD billions. From United Nations Environment Programme (2009) Global trends in sustainable investment 2009. Analysis of trends and issues in the financing of renewable energy and energy efficiency: 18–19. http://sefi.unep.org/fileadmin/media/sefi/docs/publications/Global_Trends_2009__July_09__ISBN.pdf.

Table 1 Global trends in sustainable energy investment, values, USD billions

	2004	2005	2006	2007	2008
Wind	10.0	19.1	25.0	51.3	51.8
Solar	0.6	3.2	10.3	22.5	33.5
Biomass	1.8	4.1	7.0	10.6	7.9
Marine and small hydro	0.6	1.3	1.5	3.4	3.2
Biofuels	1.3	5.1	18.0	18.6	16.9
Efficiency	0.5	0.9	1.6	2.8	1.8
Other low carbon technologies	0.8	1.6	1.9	2.4	1.5
Geothermal	0.9	0.4	1.0	0.9	2.2

Reproduced from United Nations Environment Programme (2009) Global trends in sustainable investment 2009. Analysis of trends and issues in the financing of renewable energy and energy efficiency: 18–19. http://sefi.unep.org/fileadmin/media/sefi/docs/publications/Global_Trends_2009__July_09__ISBN.pdf.

Table 2 Geothermal company operations: Several cost factors

	Section 1.01 PNOC-EDC	Section 1.02 Reykjavik energy	Section 1.03 HS Orka	Section 1.04 Mighty river power	Section 1.05 ORMAT Technologies
	Philippines	Iceland	Iceland	New Zealand	USA
CAPEX		USD 914 351 500	USD 186 579 407	USD 302 400 000	USD 414 606 000
Total MW owned		345 MW	175 MW	132 MW	101 MW
OPEX	USD 203 560 638	USD 157 010 903[a]	USD 18 526 341	USD 22 166 760	USD 41 418 000
Total MW operated	1200 MW	345 MW[b]	175 MW	247 MW	454.5 MW
OPEX per MW	USD 169 633		USD 105 865	USD 89 744	USD 91 129

[a]Includes 'energy purchase' in OPEX and all DH (district heating) operating expenses.
[b]Whereof 333 MW are geothermal power, the remainder being hydropower.
Reproduced from Orka HS (2008) Annual Report 2008, Mighty River (2008) Annual Report, ORMAT Technologies Inc. and Subsidiaries (2008) Consolidated Balance Sheets (2008), PNOC-EDC (2008) Annual Report, and Reykjavik Energy (2008) Annual Report.

As explained before, there are basically two types of geothermal power plants, low enthalpy (binary) and high enthalpy. The low enthalpy plants are generally more expensive than the high enthalpy ones.

Further information that the two Icelandic companies Reykjavik Energy and HS Orka have submitted for several projects indicate an investment cost of flash steam plants to be ranging from USD 1.7–2.5 million MW^{-1} installed. It is noteworthy that the lowest

CAPEX figures are for geothermal plants where the production of power is combined with thermal production; hot water for direct use, such as district heating. Such plants make more use of the thermo dynamical properties or the energy content of the geothermal brine, hence lower investment costs. While comparing with other countries and companies, the figures for the combined heat and power plants are excluded.

Overall when the firms are compared, we find that the Icelandic and New Zealand firms Reykjavik Energy, HS Orka, and Mighty River Power have the lowest CAPEX cost of USD 2.2–2.6 million MW^{-1}, whereas the American firm ORMAT has a CAPEX of just over USD 4 million MW^{-1}. The main reason for this is the different technology applied (flash vs. binary) and the resource characteristics. We also find that the biggest developer in 2008 is Reykjavik Energy with the highest total CAPEX.

Furthermore, when the OPEX is analyzed, we find PNOC-EDC in the Philippines to have the highest OPEX of USD 203 560 638 and operating the most MW. However, when companies are compared based on OPEX per MW, we find PNOC-EDC to have the highest OPEX per MW, close to 170 000 USD, whereas the information from the other companies gives an OPEX ranging from around 90–105 000 USD MW^{-1}.

Overall, comparison indicates that we get mixed evidence on whether national or multinational firms are more productive. We can therefore not conclude that either form of ownership is more productive.

7.09.4 Geothermal Industry: Macroeconomic Analysis

7.09.4.1 Model Setup

When undertaking a geothermal project, several key factors need to be in place. Among the most important are access to the geothermal resource, knowledge of how to harness it, capital, market, and the price of energy. First of all, the geothermal resource needs to be available. All research related to ground exploration is 100% risk capital. Knowledge in the field is in fact readily available and mobile in the main geothermal countries in the world, but the problem is that developing countries have difficulties paying for the knowledge and are therefore dependent on financial support. Capital is always available to some degree, but for projects of this kind, one needs to find capital that is relatively risk-seeking, especially for research and exploration. More risk adverse capital is then needed for the construction itself. Since the energy can be only transferred relatively short distances, the market is generally local and needs to be connected to the resource, but the cost increases and efficiency decreases if distance between market and resource is too high. The last issue to be considered is the energy price. Energy price has a high impact on whether geothermal projects are able to develop within a particular country. Sometimes these projects receive financial aid or support, such as the direct subsidies for the purchase of green energy in Germany or tax incentives and exploration support in the United States.

Not all of these issues can be easily measured directly, so we use several proxies to account for them in our macroeconomic modeling. Our country sample is selected from countries abundant with geothermal resources. Local 'market size' of these countries is presented using the variable 'population' as a proxy. Due to difficulties in receiving direct measure of 'knowledge' in the field, we apply both GNI per capita PPP to indicate purchasing power and workers' remittances and compensation of employees. As to a proxy the 'capital' involved in geothermal projects in these countries, we use installed MW. Finally, 'energy price' is indirectly proxied by electric power consumption and energy use kilogram of oil equivalent per capita to indicate energy use.

The economic model applied in this research is put forward to seek an explanation for the megawatt power output by eqn [1]:

$$\text{MW}_{ij,t} = \beta_0 + \beta_1 \text{CO}_{2i,j,t} + \beta_2 \text{El\_Con}_{ij,t} + \beta_3 \text{En\_Use}_{ij,t} + \beta_4 \text{GDP}_{ij,t} + \varepsilon_{ij,t} \quad [1]$$

In this model, we use geothermal-installed power capacity by country, measured in installed MW, as the dependent variable in this research. The independent variables are the following: CO$_2$ emissions (metric tons per capita), electric power consumption (kWh per capita), energy use (kg of oil equivalent per capita), GDP (current USD), GNI per capita PPP (current international $), inflation GDP deflator (annual %), population total, workers' remittances and compensation of employees as received in (current USD), and roads paved (% of total roads).

7.09.4.2 Data

International information on foreign direct investment in the geothermal industry in different countries tends to be hard to find. In conventional business activities, affiliate sales abroad are often used to proxy FDI [9]. However, we use geothermal generating capacity in various countries as to proxy for investment in geothermal activities. More specifically, we use data on geothermal installed power capacity (MW), since it is believed to well present the geothermal capacity in these countries. The world's greatest future potential in geothermal is probably in Indonesia, which has considerable operations today. Chile also has a great potential, but there are no operations in Chile yet.

Table 3 presents geothermal-installed power capacity, and number of units by country. **Table 3** presents the years 1990, 1995, 2000, and 2005, to give an indication of the increased capacity development. We apply this database since it runs over many

Table 3 Geothermal-installed power capacity and number of units by country

Article II.	1990	1995	2000	2005	2005	2005
Article III.	MW	MW	MW	MW	MW	Units
Article IV.	Installed	Installed	Installed	Installed	Running	Number
USA	2775	2817	2228	2564	1935	209
Philippines	891	1227	1909	1930	1838	57
Italy	545	632	785	791	699	32
Mexico	700	753	755	953	953	36
Indonesia	145	310	590	797	738	15
Japan	215	414	547	535	530	19
New Zealand	283	286	437	435	403	33
Iceland	45	50	170	202	202	19
Costa Rica	0	55	143	163	163	5
El Salvador	95	105	161	151	119	5
Nicaragua	35	70	70	70	38	3
Kenya	45	45	45	129	129	9
Guatemala	0	33	33	33	29	8
China	19	29	29	28	19	13
Russia (Kamchatka)	11	11	23	79	79	11
Turkey	21	20	20	20	18	1
Portugal (The Azores)	3	5	16	16	13	5
Ethiopia	0	0	9	7.3	7.3	2
France (Guadeloupe)	4	4	4	15	15	2
Australia	0	0	0	0.2	0.1	1
Thailand	0	0	0	0.3	0.3	1
Argentina	1	1	0	0.2	0.1	1
Austria	0	0	0	1.2	1.1	2
Germany	0	0	0	0.2	0.2	1

Reproduced from ABS Energy Research (2009).

Table 4 Summary statistics for the basic sampleReproduced from author's calculations.

Section 4.01 Variable	Section 4.02 Observations	Section 4.03 Mean	Section 4.04 Standard deviation	Section 4.05 Minimum	Section 4.06 Maximum
MW	96	308.260 4	605.996 2	0	2 817
CO_2	96	5.520 833	5.217 338	0	20
El_Con	96	4 442.281	5 281.382	22	27 987
En_Use	96	2 696.01	2 571.276	286	12 179
GDP	96	9.25×10^{11}	2.01×10^{12}	1.01×10^9	1.24×10^{13}
Capita	96	12 366.46	10 757.46	390	42 090
Inflation	96	84.229 17	551.148 9	−2	5 018
POP	96	1.11×10^8	2.44×10^8	254 800	1.30×10^9
Worker	92	2.68×10^9	3.80×10^9	5 000 000	2.31×10^{10}
Roads	69	51.188 41	31.952 76	10	100

Reproduced from author's calculations.

countries over time, although knowing that capacity has been increasing substantially since 2005. For example, in the United States the installed capacity was up to 2830.65 MW by the end of year 2006 (ABS Energy Research, 2009).

We obtained data on installed MW from the ABS Energy Research (2009), for the dependent variable MW. However, for the independent variables we choose to apply World Bank [22] data, since it is an excellent source for developing countries like Ethiopia and Nicaragua (Ethiopia and Nicaragua are classified as developing countries by the International Monetary Fund [23]), see Table 4.

The database runs over 24 countries, and 4 years, providing us with a dataset of 96 observations. The years included in this research are 1990, 1995, 2000, and 2005. We obtain data on these independent variables from the ABS Energy Research (2009).

In this research, we find data on the following countries: United States, Philippines, Italy, Mexico, Indonesia, Japan, New Zealand, Iceland, Costa Rica, El Salvador, Nicaragua, Kenya, Guatemala, China, Russia (Kamchatka), Turkey, Portugal (The Azores), Ethiopia, France (Guadeloupe), Australia, Thailand, Argentina, Austria, and Germany.

7.09.4.3 Regression Results

Table 5 presents the basic empirical specification, estimated with the OLS estimation procedure. All regression obtained in this macroeconomic research are obtained using STATA version 9.

The first variable CO_2, representing CO_2 emissions by metric tons per capita, is estimated to have a positive, however, insignificant effect on country geothermal-installed power capacity (MW). A similar story holds for the second and third variables in the model specification El_Con and En_Use, indicating that geothermal power capacity (MW) is positively, however, insignificantly effected by both electric power consumption (kWh per capita) and energy use (kg of oil equivalent per capita). The variable measuring impact of gross domestic product (GDP) (current USD) is estimated to have slightly positive, however, highly significant effects on geothermal capacity. The coefficient sign for the variable capita, representing GNI per capita PPP (current international $) is estimated to have negative, however, insignificant effects on geothermal capacity. Inflation, that is, the inflation GDP deflator (annual %), is estimated to have positive, however, insignificant effects on geothermal power capacity. The population variable POP accounts for country total population, and is found to have negative, however, insignificant effects on geothermal capacity. A worker variable is also included, measuring workers' remittances and compensation of employees as received in (current USD). The regression results indicate that the worker variable has slightly positive significant effects on geothermal capacity. Finally, the roads variable, accounting for roads paved (% of total roads), has negative, however, insignificant effects on geothermal capacity.

The model regression results in Table 6 present a restricted version of the model, the variable electric power consumption is omitted from this specification. In Table 6, CO_2 is estimated to have positive significant effects on geothermal capacity, however, per capita GNI to have negative significant effects on geothermal capacity. The remaining regression results for other explanatory variables are similar for Tables 5 and 6, continuing to have the same sign, and being of similar significance and size.

Table 7 exhibits further restriction on the basic model specification, this time omitting both electric consumption and inflation from the model. The overall regression results obtained from omitting energy use in addition to the two previously omitted variables is analogous to the results obtained in Table 6, with all previously significant variables continuing to be significant and become more highly significant compared to Table 6.

The final regression results are presented in Table 8. This time the regression results are shown for the case when the specification is restricted by omitting energy use, in addition to omitting both electric consumption and inflation from the model. Overall regression results are analogous to the ones obtained in Table 7, with the expectance of the roads variable, accounting for roads paved (% of total roads), which is now estimated to significantly negatively affect geothermal capacity. Also noteworthy is that the CO_2 variable is estimated to have more highly significant effects on geothermal capacity.

Taken together, the overall regression results can be interpreted such that geothermal installed power capacity (MW) is subject to several macroeconomic, environmental, and infrastructural factors. Most importantly, we find geothermal capacity to be positively and highly significantly subject to economic size, measured by gross domestic product of the hosting country. Also, remittances and compensation of workers is found to have significant positive effect on geothermal capacity. Furthermore, CO_2 emissions have positive effects on geothermal capacity according to our estimation. Finally, the wealth of nations measured by GNI per capita is estimated to have negative effects on geothermal activities, and also the infrastructure variable roads is found to have negative effects on geothermal capacity.

7.09.5 Summary and Conclusions

The geothermal industry has great potential for future world energy supply. The business knowledge in the field is increasing fast and the number of firms in the industry is growing, with locations all over the world. Now is an exciting time to investigate the potential in this climate-friendly vision of the future. In our analysis, we develop a model using regression analysis to find how investors may decide on geothermal projects abroad, dependent on various factors. We seek to explain how these diverse factors affect the amount of investment in several countries.

The microeconomic company comparison considers potential differences between national and multinational firms, and shows that we get mixed evidence on whether national or multinational firms are more productive. We can therefore not conclude that either form of ownership is more productive.

In our macroeconomic research, we find that geothermal-installed power capacity (MW) is subject to several macroeconomic, environmental, and infrastructural factors. Most importantly, gross domestic product, remittance and compensation of workers, and CO_2 emissions are found to have positive effects on geothermal capacity. Wealth as gross national income per capita and infrastructure robustness are found to negatively affect activity in industries attempting to harness geothermal energy.

Table 5 Basic model specification regression results

Source	SS	Degrees of freedom	MS		
				Number of observations = 65	
				$F(9, 55) = 11.63$	
Model	15 357 522	9	1 706 391.33	Probability > F = 0.000 0	
Residual	8 068 576.06	55	146 701.383	$R^2 = 0.6556$	
				Adjusted $R^2 = 0.5992$	
Total	23 426 098.1	64	366 032.782	Root MSE = 383.02	

MW	Coefficient	Standard error	T	P>t	95% Confidence interval
CO_2	34.688 58	27.105 79	1.28	0.206	−19.632 63 to 89.009 79
El_Con	0.010 286 2	0.085 601 8	0.12	0.905	−0.161 263 7 to 0.181 836 1
En_Use	0.023 759 9	0.189 640 3	0.13	0.901	−0.356 287 6 to 0.403 807 5
GDP	$2.20 \times 10^{-10}**$	3.99×10^{-11}	5.52	0.000	1.41×10^{-10} to 3.00×10^{-10}
Capita	−0.025 339 6	0.015 571 9	−1.63	0.109	−0.056 546 4 to 0.005 867 1
Inflation	0.884 155 7	4.130 78	0.21	0.831	−7.394 113 to 9.162 424
POP	-1.90×10^{-7}	2.57×10^{-7}	−0.74	0.462	-7.04×10^{-7} to 3.24×10^{-7}
Worker	$3.19 \times 10^{-8}**$	1.56×10^{-8}	2.04	0.046	5.84×10^{-10} to 6.32×10^{-8}
Roads	−1.666 666	2.600 467	−0.64	0.524	−6.878 119 to 3.544 786
Constant	164.022 8	128.606 9	1.28	0.208	−93.711 19 to 421.756 8

Robust *t*-statistics are in parentheses below the coefficients. ***, **, and * denote significance levels of 1%, 5%, and 10%, respectively.

Table 6 Sample restriction applied to electric consumption

Source	SS	Degrees of freedom	MS	Number of observations = 65
				$F(8, 56) = 13.32$
Model	15 355 403.8	8	1 919 425.47	Probability > $F = 0.0000$
Residual	8 070 694.3	56	144 119.541	$R^2 = 0.6555$
				Adjusted $R^2 = 0.6063$
Total	23 426 098.1	64	366 032.782	Root MSE = 379.63

MW	Coefficient	Standard error	T	P>t	95% Confidence interval
CO_2	32.406 65**	19.170 51	1.69	0.097	−5.996 491 to 70.809 79
En_Use	0.045 976 1	0.041 834 3	1.10	0.276	−0.037 828 2 to 0.129 780 4
GDP	2.19×10^{-10}***	3.66×10^{-11}	5.98	0.000	1.45×10^{-10} to 2.92×10^{-10}
Capita	−0.024 339 2**	0.013 043	−1.87	0.067	−0.050 467 6 to 0.001 789 1
Inflation	0.840 077 6	4.078 094	0.21	0.838	−7.329 327 to 9.009 482
POP	-1.82×10^{-7}	2.45×10^{-7}	−0.74	0.462	-6.73×10^{-7} to 3.09×10^{-7}
Worker	3.12×10^{-8}**	1.44×10^{-8}	2.17	0.034	2.44×10^{-9} to 6.00×10^{-8}
Roads	−1.757 63	2.465 856	−0.71	0.479	−6.697 334 to 3.182 074
Constant	158.189 2	118.039 4	1.34	0.186	−78.272 07 to 394.650 5

Robust t-statistics are in parentheses below the coefficients. ***, **, and * denote significance levels of 1%, 5%, and 10%, respectively.

Table 7 Sample restriction applied to electric consumption and inflation

Source	SS	Degrees of freedom	MS	Number of observations = 65
				$F(7, 57) = 15.47$
Model	15 349 288	7	2 192 755.44	Probability > F = 0.000 0
Residual	8 076 810.01	57	141 698.421	R^2 = 0.655 2
				Adjusted R^2 = 0.612 9
Total	23 426 098.1	64	366 032.782	Root MSE = 376.43

MW	Coefficient	Standard error	T	P > t	95% Confidence interval
CO_2	32.693 69*	18.958 52	1.72	0.090	−5.270 088 to 70.657 46
En_Use	0.045 670 3	0.041 455 3	1.10	0.275	−0.037 342 6 to 0.128 683 2
GDP	2.18×10^{-10}***	3.63×10^{-11}	6.02	0.000	1.46×10^{-10} to 2.91×10^{-10}
Capita	−0.024 594 7*	0.012 874 4	−1.91	0.061	−0.050 375 3 to 0.001 185 9
POP	$−1.82 \times 10^{-7}$	2.43×10^{-7}	−0.75	0.456	$−6.69 \times 10^{-7}$ to 3.04×10^{-7}
Worker	3.14×10^{-8}**	1.42×10^{-8}	2.22	0.031	3.03×10^{-9} to 5.99×10^{-8}
Roads	−1.832 347	2.418 461	−0.76	0.452	−6.675 231 to 3.010 537
Constant	171.737 8*	97.191 06	1.77	0.083	−22.883 9 to 366.359 6

Robust *t*-statistics are in parentheses below the coefficients. ***, **, and * denote significance levels of 1%, 5%, and 10%, respectively.

Table 8 Sample restriction applied to electric consumption, inflation, and energy use

Source	SS	Degrees of freedom	MS	Number of observations = 65
				$F(6, 58) = 17.79$
Model	15 177 310.6	6	2 529 551.76	Probability > F = 0.0000
Residual	8 248 787.48	58	142 220.474	R^2 = 0.6479
				Adjusted R^2 = 0.6115
Total	23 426 098.1	64	366 032.782	Root MSE = 377.12

MW	Coefficient	Standard error	T	$P > t$	95% Confidence interval
CO_2	42.327 18**	16.852 4	2.51	0.015	8.593 445 to 76.060 91
GDP	2.01×10^{-10}***	3.25×10^{-11}	6.17	0.000	1.35×10^{-10} to 2.66×10^{-10}
Capita	−0.013 710 8*	0.008 270 4	−1.66	0.103	−0.030 265 9 to 0.002 844 3
POP	-8.27×10^{-8}	2.26×10^{-7}	−0.37	0.716	-5.35×10^{-7} to 3.70×10^{-7}
Worker	2.84×10^{-8}**	1.39×10^{-8}	2.04	0.046	4.84×10^{-10} to 5.63×10^{-8}
Roads	−3.360 583*	1.984 718	−1.69	0.096	−7.333 427 to 0.612 260 4
Constant	203.097 7**	93.100 08	2.18	0.033	16.737 67 to 389.457 8

Robust *t*-statistics are in parentheses below the coefficients. ***, **, and * denote significance levels of 1%, 5%, and 10%, respectively.

References

[1] COP15 (2009) http://en.cop15.dk/news/view+news?newsid=3086
[2] Gylfason T and Zoega G (2001) *Natural Resources and Economic Growth: The Role of Investment.* CEPR Discussion Paper No. 2743.
[3] United Nations Environment Programme (2009) Global trends in sustainable investment 2009. Analysis of trends and issues in the financing of renewable energy and energy efficiency: 18–19. http://sefi.unep.org/fileadmin/media/sefi/docs/publications/Global_Trends_2009__July_09__ISBN.pdf
[4] Davies Ronald B (2003) *Hunting High and Low for Vertical FDI.* Working Paper. Eugene, OR: University of Oregon.
[5] Kristjánsdóttir H (2010) Foreign direct investment: The knowledge-capital model and a small country case. *Scottish Journal of Political Economy* 7(5): 591–614.
[6] Lane P and Milesi-Ferretti GM (2003) *International Financial Integration.* CEPR Working Paper DP3769.
[7] Helpman E (1984) A simple theory of international trade with multinational corporations. *Journal of Political Economy* 92(31): 451–471.
[8] Markusen JR (1984) Multinationals, multi-plant economies, and the gains from trade. *Journal of International Economics* 16(3–4): 205–226.
[9] Markusen JR (2002) *Multinational Firms and the Theory of International Trade.* Cambridge, MA: MIT Press.
[10] ABS Energy Research (2007) The geothermal energy report. *Direct Use and Power Generation*, 4th edn, pp. 28–29.
[11] Markusen JR, Eby-Konan D, Venables AJ, and Zhang KH (1996) *A Unified Treatment of Horizontal Direct Investment, Vertical Direct Investment, and the Pattern of Trade in Goods and Services.* Working Paper No. 5696. Cambridge, MA: National Bureau of Economic Research.
[12] Markusen JR (1997) Trade Versus Investment Liberalization. NBER Working Paper 6231. Cambridge, MA: National Bureau of Economic Research.
[13] Carr DL, Markusen JR, and Maskus KE (2001) Estimating the knowledge-capital model of the multinational enterprise. *American Economic Review* 91(3): 693–708.
[14] Krugman PR (1979) Increasing returns, monopolistic competition, and international trade. *Journal of International Economics* 9: 469–479.
[15] Krugman PR (1991) Increasing returns and economic geography. *Journal of Political Economy* 99: 183–199.
[16] Blonigen BA, Davies RB, and Head K (2003) Estimating the knowledge-capital model of the multinational enterprise: Comment. *American Economic Review* 93(3): 980–994.
[17] Mighty River (2008) Annual Report.
[18] Reykjavik Energy (2008) Annual Report.
[19] Orka HS (2008) Annual Report 2008.
[20] PNOC-EDC (2008) Annual Report.
[21] ORMAT Technologies Inc. and Subsidiaries (2008) Consolidated Balance Sheets (2008).
[22] World Bank (2009) IMD Online.
[23] International Monetary Fund (2009) World Economic Outlook Report, October.

7.10 Sustainable Energy Development: The Role of Geothermal Power

B Davidsdottir, University of Iceland, Reykjavík, Iceland

© 2012 Elsevier Ltd. All rights reserved.

7.10.1	Introduction	272
7.10.2	Sustainable Development: The Tale of Three Conferences	273
7.10.3	Sustainable Development and Energy	274
7.10.3.1	Economic Dimension	274
7.10.3.2	Social Dimension	275
7.10.3.3	Environmental Dimension	276
7.10.3.4	Summary	276
7.10.4	Sustainable Energy Development	276
7.10.4.1	History	276
7.10.4.2	Definitions, Goals, and Indicators	277
7.10.4.3	Energy Indicators for Sustainable Development	278
7.10.5	Contribution of Geothermal Power to SED	279
7.10.5.1	The Use of Geothermal Power – Setting the Stage	279
7.10.5.1.1	Geothermal heat pumps	279
7.10.5.1.2	Direct use	279
7.10.5.1.3	Power generation – indirect use	279
7.10.5.2	Assessing the Potential Role of Geothermal Power to SED	280
7.10.5.2.1	The economic dimension	280
7.10.5.2.2	The social dimension	282
7.10.5.2.3	The environmental dimension	283
7.10.5.2.4	Summary	285
7.10.6	Geothermal Development in Iceland – Toward SED?	286
7.10.6.1	History	286
7.10.6.2	Current Situation	286
7.10.6.3	Toward SED?	286
7.10.6.3.1	Economic dimension	286
7.10.6.3.2	Social dimension	287
7.10.6.3.3	Environmental dimension	287
7.10.6.4	Summary	287
7.10.7	The MDGs and Geothermal Energy	287
7.10.7.1	Goal 1: Eradicate Extreme Hunger and Poverty	288
7.10.7.2	Goal 2: Achieve Universal Primary Education	288
7.10.7.3	Goal 3: Promote Gender Equality and Empower Women	288
7.10.7.4	Goal 4: Reduce Child Mortality Rate	288
7.10.7.5	Goal 5: Improve Maternal Health	289
7.10.7.6	Goal 6: Combat HIV/AIDs, Malaria, and Other Diseases	289
7.10.7.7	Goal 7: Ensure Environmental Sustainability	289
7.10.7.8	Goal 8: Develop a Global Partnership for Development	290
7.10.7.9	Summary	290
7.10.8	Climate Change, CDM, and Geothermal Energy	290
7.10.8.1	The Potential of Geothermal Power to Mitigate GHG Emissions	290
7.10.8.2	CDM and Geothermal Energy	291
7.10.9	Toward SED Using Geothermal Power	292
7.10.10	Conclusion	292
References		293

Glossary

Energy security Energy security refers to a resilient energy system both in terms of supply and infrastructure. A secure energy system is capable of withstanding threats such as attacks, supply disruptions, and environmental threats, through a combination of active, direct security measures – such as surveillance and guards – and passive or more indirect measurements – such as through redundancy, duplication of critical equipment, diversity in fuel, other sources of energy, and reliance on less vulnerable infrastructure [51].

Millennium development goals (MDGs) The MDGs are eight international development goals with a focus on human development that all United Nations member states and numerous international organizations have agreed to achieve by the year 2015 [52].
Renewable energy Renewable energy is energy derived from an energy resource that is replaced by a natural process at a rate that is potentially equal to or faster than the rate at which that resource is being extracted.
Sustainability index An index that is based on the sustainability concept and indicates, e.g., if a change in a system is towards sustainability or not.
Sustainable development Sustainable development is development that meets the needs of the present without compromising the ability of future generations to meet their own needs [53].

Sustainable energy development Sustainable energy development is the provision of adequate energy services at affordable cost in a secure and environmentally benign manner, in conformity with social and economic development needs [54].
Sustainable production of geothermal power For each geothermal system, and for each mode of production there exists a certain level of maximum energy production, E0, below which it will be possible to maintain constant energy production from the system for a very long time (100 to 300 years). If the production rate is greater than E0, it cannot be maintained for this length of time. Geothermal energy production below or equal to E0 is termed sustainable production while production greater than E0 is termed excessive production [55].

7.10.1 Introduction

As scarcity of fossil fuels increases and the threat of climate change becomes more evident, the push amplifies each year to develop alternative energy sources that can replace fossil fuels. Furthermore, over 2 billion people do not have access to high-quality fuels, and providing these households with affordable and reliable access to energy services remains a major challenge [1].

According to forecasts of future energy demand set forth by the World Energy Council, primary energy consumption is expected to increase 50 to 275% by 2050 [56]. Similarly the IEA in their reference scenario, expects that total global primary energy needs will grow 45% between 2006 and 2030 [57].

Fulfilling the growing energy needs, enabling access to the billions of individuals without access to high-quality fuels, and reducing emissions of greenhouse gases (GHGs) requires a radical departure away from the fossil fuel-focused business-as-usual scenarios. What needs to replace past emphasis is a new energy paradigm that will encourage transforming our current energy systems towards relying on sustainable low-carbon energy sources. This new paradigm differs from the conventional energy development paradigm in at least eight important aspects [26]:

1. increased consideration of social, economic, and environmental impacts of energy use;
2. planetary boundaries with respect to the assimilative capacity of the Earth and the atmosphere must be respected;
3. increased emphasis on developing a wider portfolio of alternative energy resources and on cleaner energy technologies;
4. finding ways to internalize negative externalities;
5. understanding the links between the environment and the economy;
6. recognizing the need to address environmental issues at all scales (local to global);
7. emphasizing expanding energy services, widening access, and increasing efficiency; and
8. recognizing our common future and the welfare of future generations.

Derived from these aspects, the core of this new paradigm is a vision for improving the provisioning and use of energy so that it contributes to sustainable development [26]. For this to happen and embedded in the eight aspects is that negative health and environmental impacts of energy use must be reduced, access and affordability of energy must be increased, and energy security and the efficiency of energy use and generation must increase, all in the context of alternative energy sources and in the name of sustainable energy development (SED).

The potentially sustainable low-carbon, alternative energy resources being considered range from renewable resources such as biomass, wind, wave and tidal power, hydropower, and geothermal power to non-renewable energy sources such as nuclear power [2]. Clearly though, no single alternative source of energy will replace fossil fuels worldwide as countries enjoy different alternative energy sources and have different energy need profiles.

A renewable resource is defined as a resource in which the rate of replenishment is equal to or higher than the rate of extraction and, thus, is able to sustain production for a long time. Geothermal power is a widely available, low-carbon energy source and certainly contains features of a renewable energy source, however, within limits [2]. The limits are defined by the recharge rate to the geothermal reservoir, which should be approximately equal to the extraction rate, securing longevity or sustained yield of the resource at relatively low production levels [2, 3].

Sustainable production or yield of geothermal energy from an individual geothermal system is defined as

> For each geothermal system, and for each mode of production there exists a certain level of maximum energy production, E0 below which it will be possible to maintain constant energy production from the system for a very long time (100 to 300 years). If the production rate is greater than E0, it cannot be maintained for this length of time. Geothermal energy production below or equal to E0 is termed sustainable production while production greater than E0 is termed excessive production. [4]

The sustained yield of energy resources is generally agreed to be a necessary but not a sufficient requirement for sustainable development within a society [5]. SED requires a sustainable supply of energy resources that in the long run are readily available and accessible at an affordable cost without having a negative social or environmental impact [5, 6]. Therefore, the contribution of any alternative energy resource to sustainable development must be viewed in a much broader context.

This chapter examines the concept of sustainable development and SED in the context of geothermal utilization, with a particular focus on how the use of geothermal power can contribute to the development of sustainable energy systems and thus aid the transition toward global sustainability.

The first section of this chapter briefly examines the development of the sustainable development paradigm and then introduces energy into this context. The next section depicts the concept of SED, with a focus on goals and indicators that capture movement and contribution of changes in energy systems toward SED, followed by a section that introduces the development of geothermal power into this context. This section illustrates the potential contribution of geothermal power to SED, followed by a section on the contributions of geothermal power to achieving the Millennium Development Goals (MDGs) and in combating climate change. The chapter closes with an overall assessment.

7.10.2 Sustainable Development: The Tale of Three Conferences

Throughout millennia, humans have been concerned about the relationship between the environment and human and economic development. Before the early 1960s, the discussion of this relationship revolved around local resource scarcity. Early writers such as Thomas Malthus, in his paper *An Essay on the Principle of Population* published in 1798, eloquently captured this sentiment by illustrating the relationship between population growth and increases in food supply. Malthus illustrated that since the human population can grow exponentially but food production only linearly through a gradual increase in cultivated land, food supply will always set limits to the ultimate size and well-being of the human population. Malthus did not account for resource degradation in his assessments, but David Ricardo added this factor into his elaboration of how to define and assess resource rent. Environmental degradation did not factor into their arguments, but evolved later, as evidence mounted on the potential negative environmental and health implications of industrial development. This, beginning in the early 1960s, evolved into a global discourse on the simultaneous challenge of securing economic development, while still subject to social and environmental objectives.

The beginning of the contemporary movement toward a holistic analysis of economic and human development and the environment is most commonly traced back to the year 1964, to the publication of the book *Silent Spring* written by Rachel Carson. In her book, initially aimed at the general North American public, Carson brought together research on toxicology, ecology, and epidemiology to suggest that the use of agricultural pesticides was leading to build-up of chemicals in the environment, which could be linked to damage to the environment and to human health. In essence, Carson's book vividly illustrated that nature's capacity to absorb or dilute pollution was limited, a view forcefully supported by a recent publication by Rockstrom *et al.* [58], who define planetary boundaries in the context of human pressures on the planet Earth. Other publications followed, such as Paul Ehrlich's *Population Bomb* [59].

In 1968, the United Nations General Assembly (UNGA) authorized the 1972 UN Conference on the Human Environment in Stockholm. It was at that conference that the concept sustainable development received for the first time international attention as it was argued as a potential solution to the economic development versus the environmental dilemma. Furthermore, the principal components of the sustainable development doctrine were established with a focus on (1) the interdependence of human beings and the natural environment; (2) the links between economic and social development and environmental protection; and (3) the need in this context for a global vision and common principles.

The next milestone in the evolution of the sustainable development ideology was the creation of the World Commission on Environment and Development in 1983. Chaired by the former Norwegian Prime Minister Gro Harlem Brundtland, the commission worked for 3 years, weaving together a report on social, economic, cultural, and environmental issues in the context of sustainable development. In 1987, their report 'Our common future' was published. It was in this publication that the concept sustainable development was defined as

> Sustainable development is development that meets the needs of the present without compromising the ability of future generations to meet their own needs. [7]

Immediately upon publication of Our common future, the second major conference on the environment and development was authorized to be held in Rio in 1992. The Rio conference or the Earth Summit as it often is called was the first major international manifestation of the acceptance and importance of sustainable development. The focus at the conference was on economic growth in the context of sustainable development, which was a necessary departure away from what was coined as environmentally destructive economic growth. The issues addressed included, for example, systematic scrutiny of patterns of production with a particular emphasis on (1) the production of toxic components, such as lead in gasoline, or poisonous waste; (2) alternative sources of energy to replace the use of fossil fuels that are linked to global climate change; (3) new reliance on public transportation systems to reduce vehicle emissions, congestion in cities, and the health problems caused by polluted air and smog; and (4) the growing scarcity of water. The conference agreed to the Rio Declaration on Environment and Development, which includes 27 principles, intended to guide future sustainable development around the world. In addition Agenda 21, which is a comprehensive blueprint of action to be taken globally, nationally, and locally, was accepted at the conference. Agenda 21 categorized the primary themes and goals of sustainable development into three key dimensions (economic, social, and environmental), theorizing that the challenge for future development is to balance – within current political institutions – economic development with social and environmental objectives [8, 9].

In 2000, the Millennium Summit was held, where the United Nations Millennium Declaration was adopted, from which the eight Millennium Development Goals (MDG) were later derived (http://www.un.org/millenniumgoals/). The aim of defining the MDGs was to encourage development by improving social and economic conditions in the world's poorest countries, finally shifting the focus toward poverty, human rights, and protection of the vulnerable. The eight MDGs are as follows:

Goal 1: Eradicate extreme hunger and poverty
Goal 2: Achieve universal primary education
Goal 3: Promote gender equality and empower women
Goal 4: Reduce child mortality
Goal 5: Improve maternal health
Goal 6: Combat HIV/AIDS, malaria, and other diseases
Goal 7: Ensure environmental sustainability
Goal 8: Develop a global partnership for development

Energy was and is not an explicit part of the MDGs, but the provision of modern energy services during their development was recognized as a critical foundation for sustainable development [10].

The final milestone of significant importance in the development of the sustainable development concept and ideology was the World Summit on Sustainable Development held in Johannesburg in 2002. The premise of the Johannesburg conference was to assess progress of implementation towards the aims of the Rio summit – in particular Agenda 21. The conference agreed to the Johannesburg Plan of Implementation, which affirmed the UN commitment to 'full implementation' of Agenda 21 and achievement of the MDGs and the international agreements agreed to in Rio in 1992.

The combined effect of the three conferences was to bring the sustainable development concept and ideology as a necessary and implicit part of any economic development strategy worldwide. They also solidified the notion of sustainable development as having three dimensions. The Stockholm conference highlighted the environmental dimension, the Rio conference focused on the economic dimension, and the Johannesburg conference reinforced the importance of the social dimension [11, 12]. The next section explores the relationship between energy and sustainable development using the lens of the three dimensions of sustainable development.

7.10.3 Sustainable Development and Energy

When assessing the relationship between sustainable development and energy, it is useful to examine its importance in the context of the three established dimensions of sustainable development: the economic, the environmental, and the social dimensions.

7.10.3.1 Economic Dimension

Energy use is an important driver of economic and social development as it provides basic services such as heat, illumination, refrigeration, communication, and power for agricultural processes, industry, and transportation [11, 13, 14, 60, 61]. From early on as human societies developed from being hunter-gatherer societies toward agricultural and then industrial societies, energy has always been at the center of economic and social development. Initially, the original prime mover was the human muscle, and the shift toward using draught animals as agricultural communities developed has been coined the first great energy transition [15]. The second energy transition occurred several millennia later, where prime movers shifted somewhat toward waterwheels and windmills, which enabled more powerful and efficient energy conversions. The third energy transition codified as the Industrial Revolution was characterized by two traits: the substitution of animate prime movers by engines and biomass energy replaced by fossil fuels. Electrification began in 1882, when the world's first electricity-generating stations were commissioned in London and New York. Since the third transition, all developed economies have been consuming increasing shares of fossil fuels, both directly and indirectly e.g. through electricity production and consumption. All these major transitions have meant major changes in economic development, and thus it is possible to codify history as the story of control over energy sources for the benefit of society [15].

Modern economies are energy dependent, and energy consumption per capita has been seen as an indicator of economic progress. Energy use has, for example, been linked empirically to economic growth and economic prosperity [9, 62]. Stern [62] illustrates that for the US economy, energy 'Granger causes' GDP, illustrating that the use of energy is necessary for continued economic growth and that energy is a limiting factor to economic production. Energy prices are also seen to have a significant impact on economic performance indicators. For example, empirical evidence links rising oil prices to economic losses, and energy prices are key determinants of inflation and unemployment [12]. Consequently, if sustainable development requires continued economic growth, employment, and low inflation, ensuring energy security and proper planning of the development of our energy systems are essential components of planning for sustainable development.

7.10.3.2 Social Dimension

The relationship between high-quality energy use and human welfare has been established as core indicators of human welfare such as income per capita, life expectancy, and literacy rates exhibit a significant logistic relationship to high-quality energy use [11, 13, 16, 17, 63].

At high levels of energy use per capita, the returns to increasing energy use per capita diminish as indicators for human welfare approach their maximum limit (**Figure 1**).

At low levels of high-quality energy use per capita, literacy is low, life expectancy for both males and females is low, and infant mortality is high, with a drastic improvement in these indicators at marginally higher levels of per-capita energy use. The reasoning behind these observed relationships is that energy services are a crucial input to the challenge of providing adequate food, shelter, clothing, water, sanitation, medical care, schooling, and access to information. Less affluent households rely on a different set of energy carriers than those that are better off. The poor use more of low-quality fuels, such as wood, dung, and other biomass fuels that, when used in poorly ventilated houses result in high levels of indoor air pollution. As a result, the use of such lower quality fuels has adverse impacts on the health of household members, in particular women, children, and the elderly. In addition, more time is spent on gathering low-quality fuels, reducing, for example, the time spent in school and on other more productive activities. In households that rely on collected biomass for fuels, up to 6 h is spent every day on collecting wood and dung. In areas that rely on purchased charcoal or paraffin or coal, a significant fraction of the household disposable income is spent on energy.

As a result, because of its linkages to social issues, the development of sustainable energy systems can contribute to increased human welfare as access to high-quality energy is necessary for increasing living standards and improving welfare [18]. As an acknowledgement of this relationship, the Johannesburg declaration coins access to high-quality energy as a basic human right [12].

Energy has also a direct link to gender issues as clearly illustrated in the World Energy Assessment [9]. The link between energy and women is affected by four factors: the nature of the resource base, the characteristics of the household and community that directly affect disposable household income, the features of energy policy, and the position of women in families and communities ([9], p. 47).

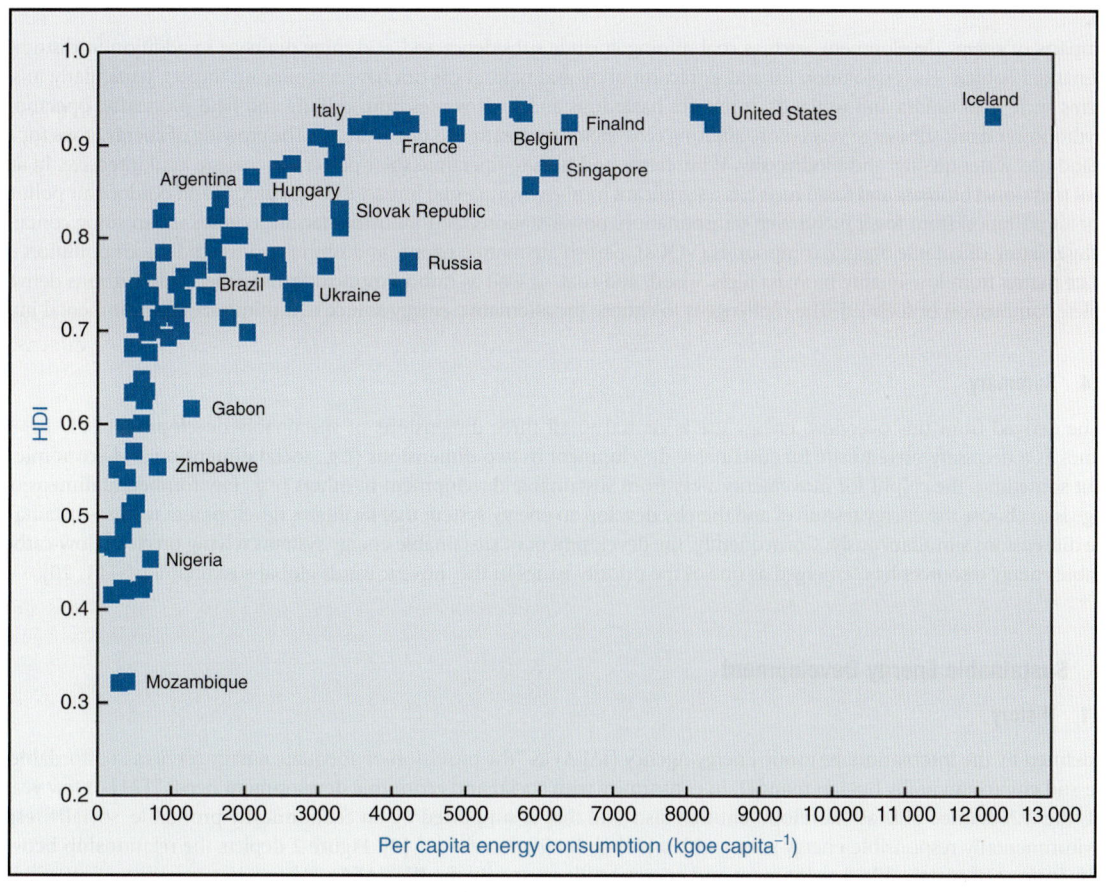

Figure 1 Energy use per capita and the human development index (HDI). Source: UNDP, UNDESA, WEC (2004) World Energy Assessment Overview: 2004 update. United Nations Development Policy, New York [26].

As biomass resources are being degraded, more time and effort is required to meet the minimum household needs. In many countries, women and children fulfill this role. In addition, the health impacts of the incomplete burning of low-quality biomass fuels expose women and children to high levels of particulate matter, carbon monoxide, and hundreds of other pollutants [9].

Household and community characteristics in addition to energy policy affect energy choices, where, for example, high-quality energy resources are not equally available to all, with agricultural, domestic, rural, and women users receiving the least attention of policy-makers [9].

Given this, the social dimension of sustainable development thus demands that the incidence of energy deprivation be determined and tackled.

7.10.3.3 Environmental Dimension

The relationship between energy production and use and environmental degradation is evident at global, regional, and local scales [9].

At the global level, we witness fossil fuel-derived emissions of GHGs contributing to climate change and its corollary impact on ecosystems worldwide [64]. Climate change will lead to higher average global temperatures, dramatic fluctuations in rainfall, increased frequency of severe weather events, and sea-level rise, leading to loss of life and property [64]. Climate change will also significantly affect patterns of agricultural production as precipitation patterns will change, affect the acidity of the oceans, change the spread of diseases such as malaria, and severely affect biodiversity. The energy sector is by far the largest contributor to emissions of GHGs and therefore is the largest contributor to the climate change problem [64].

The most commonly cited regional environmental impact of energy use is acid rain. Acid rain is derived from emissions of sulfur dioxide and nitrous oxides, mostly from fossil fuel-driven power plants but also, to a smaller extent, from geothermal power plants as they emit hydrogen sulfides. Because acid rain can be transported over long distances in the atmosphere, the problem is transboundary and regional in scope. The implications of acid rain include

- acidification of lakes, streams, and groundwater and resulting damage to fish and aquatic life;
- toxicity to plants due to acidic conditions and release of heavy metals;
- impact on plants and forests due to, for example, reduced frost hardiness;
- deterioration of materials – for example, buildings and fabrics; and
- health impacts.

Local impacts of energy development, such as coal mining, include subsidence and acid mine drainage in addition to disturbing vast areas of natural habitat. The exploration for and extraction of oil and natural gas can have a significant impact, particularly in sensitive ecosystems such as in tundra and wetlands; it releases hazardous and toxic wastes from drilling and field processing operations [12]. Large hydropower dams submerge vegetation, affecting ecosystems upstream and downstream. The growing of energy crops for biofuels affects land use, water quality, and biodiversity. Wind farms and high-temperature solar power systems are land intensive. In addition, the use of traditional biomass and fossil fuels has a significant local environmental impact through indoor and outdoor air pollution [1]. Outdoor air pollution from fossil fuel-driven transportation, power stations, and industrial facilities causes urban smog containing an unhealthy mixture of volatile organic compounds (VOCs), particulate matter, ozone, and nitrous oxides. Indoor air pollution includes particulate matter from low-quality biomass fuels, wood, and coal, as well as carbon monoxide and other hydrocarbons derived from incomplete combustion of fuels [9]. The challenge is to choose the alternative energy source that minimizes environmental impact.

7.10.3.4 Summary

As can be derived from this overview, energy use is central to all three dimensions of sustainable development [11, 12, 14, 19], sometimes as a necessary prerequisite for sustainable development in two dimensions (e.g., social dimension and economic dimension) but sometimes the culprit for movements away from sustainable development in others (e.g., environmental dimension). The challenge is to choose the energy resources and thereby develop an energy system that facilitates development toward sustainability in all three dimensions simultaneously. Consequently, the development of sustainable energy systems relying on clean, low-carbon, and sustainable energy resources has "emerged as one of the priority issues in the move towards global sustainability" [11, 20].

7.10.4 Sustainable Energy Development

7.10.4.1 History

SED is defined by the International Atomic Energy Agency (IAEA) as "the provision of adequate energy services at affordable cost in a secure and environmentally benign manner, in conformity with social and economic development needs" [21]. A few years later, in 2001, the IEA defined SED as "development that lasts and that is supported by an economically profitable, socially responsive and environmentally responsible energy sector with a global, long-term vision" [8]. **Figure 2** depicts the relationship between the three dimensions of sustainable development and energy as illustrated by the IEA/IAEA [21].

Initially, energy did not factor heavily into the sustainable development discussion. However, it gradually became a central issue at the three defining events, which anchor the evolution of the sustainable development paradigm as mentioned earlier: the three

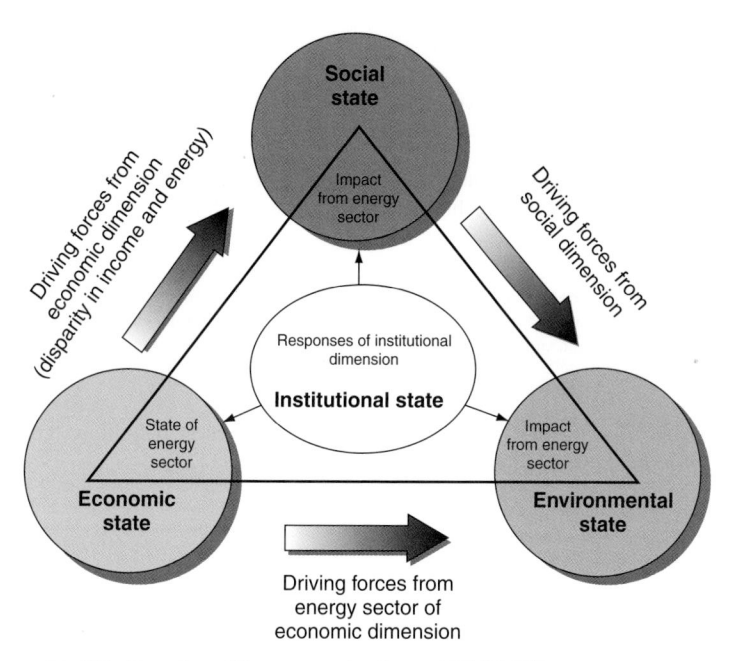

Figure 2 Interrelationship among sustainability dimensions of the energy sector. Source: IAEA/IEA [21].

global conferences on environment and development in Stockholm (1972), Rio de Janeiro (1992), and Johannesburg (2002). Each of these three conferences had a unique and vital role in elucidating the fundamental bonds between energy use and the three dimensions of sustainable development [11].

At the Stockholm conference, energy was referred to as a source of environmental stress, directly linking energy to the environmental dimension of sustainable development. The Stockholm action plan directly refers to the environmental effects of energy use and production and the environmental implications of different energy systems [12].

At the Rio conference in 1992, energy was not directly on the agenda; the Rio Declaration on Environment and Development did not contain any specifics on energy, and energy did not have its own chapter in Agenda 21, which sometimes has been coined as the first blueprint toward sustainability. However, energy issues were a central theme in Chapter 9 in Agenda 21 'Protection of the Atmosphere' as energy use is a major source of atmospheric pollution [1]. Also, other sections of Agenda 21 illustrate the need to balance economic growth, energy use, and its environmental impacts. Indeed, prescriptions in various chapters of Agenda 21 provide guidance toward decreased energy consumption (Chapters 4 and 7), increased energy efficiency (Chapters 4 and 7), and accelerated development of cleaner sources of energy (Chapter 9) and in all cases bringing energy to the center of the economic growth versus environmental degradation dilemma. The Commission for Sustainable Development (CSD) was established at the Rio conference, but it was not until 1997 that energy was finally placed on the agenda of the CSD [1]. Yet it was not until the ninth session of the Commission of Sustainable Development (CSD9) that energy was for the first time addressed in an integrated way in the UN system [1]. This was important as the conclusions of the ninth session set the basis for the World Summit on Sustainable Development held in Johannesburg in 2002.

The conclusions and recommendations from CSD9 on energy were organized both by subsectoral issues as well as cross-cutting issues. Subsectoral issues addressed included access to energy, energy efficiency, renewable energy and rural energy, and cross-cutting issues included research and development, capacity building, and technology transfers [1]. Derived from the work of CSD9, a clear and direct reference to energy as a central issue of sustainable development was made at the third milestone conference, held in Johannesburg in 2002, and repeated references were made to energy and the three dimensions of sustainable development. Unlike the Rio Declaration on Environment and Development, the Johannesburg plan of implementation clearly treated energy as a specific issue rather than a facet of other issues. Most importantly, though, was the strong emphasis on the social attributes of energy use, and access to high-quality energy was for the first time explicitly stated as a basic human right [11, 12]. This brought forth the social dimension, in addition to the already defined environmental and economic dimensions.

The cumulative effect of these three conferences solidified the notion of SED as central to all three dimensions of sustainable development by identifying the relationship between energy and the environment (defined at Stockholm), the economy (defined at Rio) and society (defined at Johannesburg) [11, 12]. Energy use and energy development over time became a specific issue rather than a subset of other concerns, cross-cutting the three dimensions of sustainable development.

7.10.4.2 Definitions, Goals, and Indicators

SED had been defined earlier by the IAEA/IEA [21] as

> the provision of adequate energy services at affordable cost in a secure and environmentally benign manner, in conformity with social and economic development needs

The IEA and the OECD [8] defined it a few years later as

> development that lasts and that is supported by an economically profitable, socially responsive and environmentally responsible energy sector with a global, long-term vision.

Yet, given the development of the links between energy and sustainable development, it logically follows that Article 8 from the Johannesburg declaration offered the most comprehensive definition of SED as development that should involve (Article 8, Johannesburg declaration)

> …improving access to reliable, affordable, economically viable, socially acceptable and environmentally sound energy services and resources, taking into account national specificities and circumstances through various means such as enhanced rural electrification and decentralized energy systems, increased use of renewable energy, cleaner liquid and gaseous fuels and enhanced energy efficiency…recognizing the specific factors for providing access to the poor.

Combining information derived from the literature (e.g., [22, 23, 26]) with these definitions, energy sources and systems that contribute to sustainable development should have the following characteristics [23]:

1. Renewable or perpetual
2. Efficiently produced and used
3. Economically and financially viable
4. Secure and diverse
5. Equitable (readily accessible, available, and affordable)
6. Has positive social impacts
7. Minimizes environmental impacts

Combining these features of the Johannesburg definition with the IAEA definition, four central goals/themes of SED emerge [11]:

1. *Improving energy efficiency*: An increase in the technical and economic efficiency of energy use and production constitutes a move toward SED as it effectively enhances energy supply. However, care must be taken that an increase in energy efficiency does not lead to an increase in total energy use, and thereby falling into the Jevons Paradox trap [65].
2. *Improving energy security*: Energy security includes the security of both supply and infrastructure and refers to the "availability of energy at all times in various forms, in sufficient quantities, and at affordable prices" [9] and thus is present in all dimensions of SED. It is possible to improve energy security through various means such as by decentralizing power generation and increasing redundancy, enhancing supply, shifting to renewable domestic energy resources and ensuring their sustainable use, and diversifying energy supply.
3. *Reduce environmental impact*: Reducing the life-cycle environmental impact of energy use and production via the use of clean technologies and fuels to ensure that solid and gaseous waste generation and disposal does not exceed the Earth's assimilative capacity.
4. *Expand access, availability, and affordability*: Expanding and ensuring reliable access to affordable and high-quality energy services constitutes a move toward SED.

Goals one and two fall under the economic dimension of sustainable development, the third goal falls under the environmental dimension, and the fourth goal captures the social dimension. Based on these goals, indicators have been developed that measure progress toward SED and thus the contributing effect individual energy system developments have on the transition toward sustainable energy systems (see, e.g., Reference 11).

7.10.4.3 Energy Indicators for Sustainable Development

In 1999, the IAEA, in collaboration with the UN Committee on Sustainable Energy and the UN Work Programme on Indicators of Sustainable Development in cooperation with other agencies initiated a project to develop energy system indicators with a twofold objective: (1) to complement the overall UN Work Programme on Indicators of Sustainable Development and (2) to foster energy and statistical capacity building needed to induce energy sustainability (see p. 876 in Reference 18). This project, entitled 'Indicators for Sustainable Energy Development', has emerged as the most comprehensive effort toward identifying SED relevant indicators. The original set of indicators, now termed Energy Indicators for Sustainable Development (EISD), was truncated from 41 to 30 indicators in 2005 and put into the context of CSD terminology of themes and subthemes within each sustainable development dimension [18]. The EISD indicator set has been tested in several countries such as Thailand, Russia, Lithuania, and Brazil (see a special issue in the journal *Natural Resources Forum* 2005). The chosen themes and subthemes align closely with the goals stated earlier, and therefore we will assess the contributing role of geothermal energy to sustainable development through the lens of the EISD indicator project.

7.10.5 Contribution of Geothermal Power to SED

7.10.5.1 The Use of Geothermal Power – Setting the Stage

Geothermal resources have been identified in approximately 90 countries, and there is quantified information of use in 72 countries, with 24 countries relying on geothermal power for electricity generation [24].

From very early on, humans have used the geothermal energy that flows from underground reservoirs to the Earth's surface. The use ranged from bathing and washing of clothes since the dawn of civilization to using the hot water to treat various diseases as well as to heat the city of Pompeii. Native Americans and the Maoris of New Zealand used the heat for cooking and there is evidence of use from China since 2000 years ago [25].

Geothermal energy was for the first time in the twentieth century harnessed on a large scale for space heating, electricity generation, and industry. Electric power was first generated from Larderello, Italy, in 1904 and commercial-scale electricity generation began in Larderello in 1913. The first large-scale municipal geothermal district heating service began in Iceland in 1930 [25].

Today, geothermal energy primarily is utilized in three technology categories:

- heating and cooling buildings via geothermal heat pumps that utilize shallow sources;
- heating structures with direct-use applications; and
- generating electricity through indirect use.

Stefansson [66] provided an estimate of the technical potential of geothermal resources suitable for indirect use of electricity generation to be 240 GWe. He also provided an estimate of the use of lower temperature resources for direct use to be 140 EJ yr^{-1} [3, 24].

In comparison, the total worldwide capacity for geothermal utilization for electricity generation in 2007 was approximately 10 GWe and for direct use it was 330 PJ yr^{-1} [3]. Approximately one-third of the direct use is through ground source heat pumps. Fridleifsson *et al.* [24], as cited in [3], illustrate that by 2050 electricity generation potential may reach 70 GWe, amounting to a sevenfold increase.

7.10.5.1.1 Geothermal heat pumps

There is great potential for the use of geothermal heat pumps as they take advantage of the fact that the uppermost 3 m of the Earth's crust maintains temperatures ranging from 10 to 15.5 °C (50 to 60 °F). Consequently, most areas of the world are suitable for the installation of geothermal heat pumps, and in 2009 Sweden had the largest installed heat pump capacity [24].

A geothermal heat pump system can have different features but, for example, consists of pipes buried in the shallow (ca. 3 m) upper layers of the ground, with a connection to a ventilation system of an adjacent building, relying on the ground as a heat exchanger. A liquid is passed through the pipes, and as the ground is naturally warmer than the atmosphere in the winter, it absorbs the warmth and delivers it to the building. In the summer, the circulation can be reversed, cooling the building by bringing warmth from the building to the ground. This in essence enables the use of the heat of the Earth for heating and cooling [25].

7.10.5.1.2 Direct use

Direct-use applications utilize groundwater that in most cases has been heated to less than 100 °C (212 °F). Direct use of geothermal energy includes use in urban areas such as for melting of snow, in industrial processes, in agricultural and aquaculture production by heating greenhouses, soils, and aquaculture ponds. Direct use also includes use in swimming pools and spas and as such is very important to tourism, as well as in residential and regional (district) heating.

In various countries, the direct use of geothermal power significantly contributes to the total energy use. In Iceland, for example, approximately 90% of residential and commercial buildings are heated with geothermal water. Larger countries such as China have geothermal water in almost all provinces and is expanding direct utilization at a rate of about 10% per year [25].

7.10.5.1.3 Power generation – indirect use

Indirect use of geothermal power conventionally involves the production of electricity. In 2007, 24 countries produced electricity using geothermal power [24].

During electric power generation from geothermal power, wells are drilled into geothermal reservoirs where temperatures may exceed 360 °C (680 °F), leading the steam or the water to a geothermal power plant.

Three types of geothermal power plants are operating today [24]:

- *Dry steam plants* are used when geothermal steam is directly used to turn turbines. In this case, steam is brought to the surface under its own pressure where the steam is utilized to turn the turbines of an electrical generator.
- *Flash steam plants* rely on high-pressure hot water, pulling it into lower pressure tanks, creating flashed steam that is used to drive turbines.
- *Binary cycle plants* pass (in a separate piping) moderately hot geothermal water by a secondary fluid, such as ammonia, with a much lower boiling point than water. This causes the secondary fluid to create steam, which then drives the turbines onward.

Five countries, Costa Rica, El Salvador, Iceland, Kenya, and the Philippines, obtain 15–22% of their national electricity production from geothermal power [24]. The United States produced 3000 MW from geothermal power plants in 2000, supplying electricity to about 4 million people [25].

7.10.5.2 Assessing the Potential Role of Geothermal Power to SED

EISD can be used to organize and assess the potential contribution of energy system development to SED.

In the EISD indicator set, the 30 indicators are classified by the three dimensions of sustainable development: the economic, the environmental, and the social. Then each dimension is broken further into the themes and subthemes within each dimension as defined by the CSD. Finally, indicators are defined for each subtheme and metric assigned to each indicator. Below, the use of geothermal power will be discussed in the context of each dimension and subtheme of sustainable development.

7.10.5.2.1 *The economic dimension*

The goal of SED within the economic dimension is to maximize the efficiency of the energy system and to ensure energy security. The economic dimension, therefore, includes two broad themes: use and production patterns and energy security.

The theme 'use and production patterns' contains subthemes including overall use, overall productivity, supply efficiency, end use, and prices.

The theme energy security contains subthemes including imports, strategic fuel stocks, sustained production, and diversification.

Each theme and subtheme is described and put into the context of geothermal energy below.

Table 1 illustrates the set of energy system indicators within the economic dimension.

7.10.5.2.1(i) *Use and production patterns*

7.10.5.2.1(i)(a) Efficiency of use and production Energy consumption per capita and energy use per GDP capture the general relationship of energy consumption to population and economic growth. At low levels of economic development, this ratio is relatively low but increases at decreasing rates at higher levels of development. However, at higher levels at the income scale, achieving some decoupling between primary or secondary energy use and either per GDP or per capita will move countries toward SED. One method of doing so is to increase supply and end-use energy efficiency [26].

Increased use of geothermal power can contribute to this goal by increased 'direct use' of geothermal heat or in combined applications of electricity generation and direct use of waste heat. 'Direct use' is far more efficient than electricity generation from geothermal power and places less demanding temperature requirements on the heat resource. As a result, geothermal heating is economic at many more sites than geothermal electricity generation. 'Heat' for direct use may come from cogeneration via a geothermal electrical plant or from smaller wells or heat exchangers such as geothermal heat pumps. In areas where natural hot springs are available, the warm water can be directly pumped into the district heating system, to industrial or other economic applications. However, in areas where the ground is dry, but still warm, it is possible to use heat exchangers to capture the heat. In 'cold' areas, this is also possible with the use of geothermal heat pumps, using the natural heat gradient of the Earth. Therefore, it is possible in nearly all areas to capture heat more cost-effectively and cleanly than by conventional furnaces [67]. As described earlier, low-temperature geothermal resources are typically used in direct-use applications; nevertheless, some low-temperature resources can generate electricity using binary cycle electricity-generating technology [68].

While direct uses of geothermal energy are very efficient, the efficiency of indirect use, for example, for electricity generation, varies depending on the temperature of the geothermal resource and the type of plant technology used. Overall, the thermal efficiency of geothermal electric plants is relatively low, ranging from 9% to 23%. Exhaust heat is wasted, unless cogeneration occurs and the hot water is used directly and locally, for example, in greenhouses, industrial applications, aquaculture, or district heating [24]. As a result, it is vital, if geothermal power is used indirectly for electricity generation to enhance SED, to ensure that the waste fluids are utilized at cascading levels of lower heat or reinjected [23].

7.10.5.2.1(i)(b) Prices Heat production from renewable energy is generally competitive with conventional energy sources in terms of prices. The current cost of direct heat from biomass is 1–6 US¢ kWh^{-1} and solar heating 2–25 US¢ kWh^{-1}. In comparison, the current

Table 1 Energy indicators for sustainable development within the CSD conceptual framework: the economic dimension

Theme – use and production patterns	Metric	Theme – energy security	Metric
Overall use	Energy use per capita	Imports	Net energy import dependency
Overall productivity	Energy use per GDP	Strategic fuel stocks	Stocks of critical fuels per corresponding fuel consumption
Supply efficiency	Efficiency of energy conversion and distribution	Sustained production	Reserves to production ratio
End use	End-use intensities		Resources to production ratio
Prices	End-use prices by fuel and by sector	Diversification	Fuel shares in energy and electricity
			Renewable energy share in energy and electricity

Source: Vera I and Langlois L (2007) Energy indicators for sustainable development. *Energy* 32: 875–882.

cost of heat from geothermal energy is 0.5–5 US¢ kWh^{-1}. Furthermore, future environmental costs of heat derived from geothermal power are expected to be the lowest of all alternative energy resources [26]. In addition, turnkey costs for the direct use of geothermal energy are significantly lower than for other alternative renewable energy sources, as well as conventional coal-driven power plants.

With respect to electricity generation, the current cost of electricity generation from geothermal power is 2–10 US¢ kWh^{-1}, the lowest of all alternative energy sources. The cost of electricity generation from biomass is 5–15 US¢ kWh^{-1}, wind power 5–13 US¢ kWh^{-1}, and solar thermal electricity 12–18 US¢ kWh^{-1}. Also, the expected environmental cost of electricity derived from geothermal power is expected to be the lowest of all alternative energy resources [26]. The turnkey investment cost, however, is higher for geothermal power or 800–3000 US$ kW^{-1} compared with 1100–1700 US$ kW^{-1} for wind energy and 800 US$ kW^{-1} for conventional coal-driven power plants. Other alternative resources are, however, more expensive [26].

Since geothermal power is not an intermittent energy source, not reliant on weather conditions, and generally available domestically, electricity and heat derived from geothermal resources are unlikely to be subject to the extreme price fluctuations that conventional and many alternative energy sources are subject to [86].

7.10.5.2.1(ii) Energy security

Since sustainable development should be 'development that lasts', it must minimize risks in the energy system by ensuring long-term, secure supplies of energy. Therefore, energy security is seen as an integral part of sustainable development. Energy security involves, for example, aiming for energy independence for a nation and thereby reducing import dependency, that is, reducing geopolitical security risks as well as diversifying the nation's energy portfolio, increased decentralization, and sustained supply [26].

7.10.5.2.1(ii)(a) **Diversification and reduced import dependency** As geothermal energy is theoretically a renewable energy resource, and is in most cases used domestically, expanded investment in geothermal energy contributes to reduction in import dependency and enhances the fractional share of renewable energy of total primary energy use.

Energy supply diversification by increased use of domestic renewable energy sources is one way of minimizing supply risk, where risk minimization necessitates that a given energy choice is evaluated in the context of the entire energy system and not as an individual choice. An energy portfolio with favorable risk qualities should be composed of elements with, at least, partially offsetting risks [11]. This can be reached by, for example, expanding the use of renewable energy sources such as geothermal energy, which with proper utilization strategies and the use of the same reservoir can be sustained over very long time periods; and unlike fossil fuels, its supply and price are not susceptible to external geopolitical issues (International Energy Agency, Contribution of Renewables to Energy Security, 2007). An illustration of this is that the cost of geothermal energy does not fluctuate like the price of gas and oil, which further contributes to a nation's energy security. Furthermore, geothermal power also has desirable risk attributes in the context of other renewable energy resources such as hydropower as it is not easily affected by, for example, drought or other climate-related events. Therefore, for example, in electricity generation, the use of geothermal power can enhance energy security in an electric generation system largely dominated by fossil fuels as its supply risks are very different from fossil fuel supply risks as well as the supply risks of other renewable energy sources [23].

SED calls for increased decentralization, locally available resources, and thus self-sufficiency, which can potentially create local investment and employment opportunities. Geothermal energy fulfills all these attributes as most countries have an opportunity to use geothermal energy in some form, and it can be utilized in remote areas for small, decentralized energy generation.

7.10.5.2.1(ii)(b) **Sustained production and strategic fuel stocks** Sustained production levels are depicted by nondeclining resource to production ratios as well as nondeclining reserve to production ratios, which implies assumed renewability of the resources. Strategic fuel stocks must be maintained to enable energy consumption for at least 90 days. The inherent storage ability of geothermal power and if used sustainably immediately contributes to the existence of sufficient strategic fuel stocks.

7.10.5.2.1(ii)(c) **Renewability and sustainable utilization** Renewability is seen as a necessary but not sufficient characteristic of sustainable energy, as the resource must remain available for future generations, and reserve or resource production ratios should be nondeclining [23].

Experience shows that it is possible to harness geothermal power over an extended period of time. A previously unexploited geothermal system can reach equilibrium after it begins to be used, and this new equilibrium can be maintained for a long time. Research illustrates that pressure decline during production in geothermal systems can cause the recharge to the system to increase approximately in balance with extraction rates [3]. Two commonly cited examples are the Laugardalur area and Matsukawa geothermal system in Japan [3]. Important contributing factors to renewability and sustainable utilization are utilization time, recovery time, and utilization modes and management strategies [23].

Utilization time While the lifespan for geothermal power plants ranges from 30–50 years, a recent definition for sustainable utilization has been given as utilization that can be maintained for 100–300 years, for any mode of production [23, 27].

It is possible to maintain constant but low production levels to ensure sustainable utilization. Yet, this may not be economically viable. As a result, other production options that enhance the economic returns from utilization as well as prolong the time frame for utilization may be used. This includes production strategies such as (1) stepwise production up to the sustainable use limit; (2) periods of intense or excessive production followed by long breaks in production; or (3) greatly reduced production following a short period of intense production [3]. These types of 'cyclical production' can be just as economically viable as intensive unsustainable production, which will derive economic benefits for only a short time [23, 28].

Recovery time Sustainable utilization of geothermal systems can also be based on the time it takes to recover the resource after use. The timescale that is considered acceptable to 'technological or societal systems is 30–300 years' [23, 28]. For example, if a geothermal resource is used for indirect use such as electricity production, the recovery time cannot exceed 300 years. In addition to this criteria, it is necessary to secure that if a system is used in an excessive manner and requires a recovery break or a rest, other systems must be ready for use in the same volcanic area. As a result, when planning for sustainable utilization of geothermal resources, several geothermal systems must be taken into account simultaneously, as well as interactions between them [23, 27].

Utilization modes and management strategies For each mode of utilization, sustainable utilization has its own management requirements. As illustrated earlier, two main management strategies that enable sustainable yield include (1) constant production and (2) stepwise increase in production until sustainable yield has been reached [3, 23].

Sustainable yield in low-enthalpy systems is possible, even without reinjection. An example of this is the Laugarnes geothermal field in Iceland, where increased production caused a pressure drop in the system and the naturally enhanced recharge led eventually to sustainable production level [23, 29].

Unlike low-enthalpy resources, high-enthalpy resources are in many cases used for electricity generation and, thus, are frequently subjected to excessive use. Such excessive use may lead to a large drop in pressure, eventually rendering the resource not economically viable. In such cases, reinjection of spent fluids may mitigate the drop in pressure. Such reinjection schemes may, however, result in rapid cooling of the reservoir as well as lead to seismic events [23].

7.10.5.2.2 The social dimension

The social dimension (**Table 2**) contains two themes, equity and health. The goal is to ensure reliable and affordable access to quality energy sources for all members of any given population, regardless of income or gender to facilitate increased employment and productivity and foster societal stability and equity [11, 32, 70]. SED regards access to high-quality energy as a basic human right because it provides people with the services required to meet basic human needs and maintain a sensible quality of life [13]. Nearly 2 billion people do not have access to high-quality energy sources and instead primarily rely on poor quality energy sources such as biomass, which can seriously threaten human health when burned in poorly ventilated areas [9, 33, 34]. It is not sufficient, however, to only provide access to high-quality energy because it also must be affordable, such that the population also has the means to purchase it.

7.10.5.2.2(i) Equity

Sustainable development is generally accepted to raise the living standards of the world's poor. For energy to be equitable, it must be affordable, accessible, and available to all income groups [11, 23, 70].

7.10.5.2.2(i)(a) Availability
High-temperature geothermal energy resources currently suitable for electrical generation are only found in certain areas worldwide, near tectonic plate boundaries where the temperature is high enough, which means they are only available to populations living in these areas. However, low-temperature resources are available in many areas of the world and geothermal heat pumps can be used anywhere. In the year 2000, it was possible to use geothermal resources for direct and/or indirect applications in over 90 countries and 72 countries had quantified records of geothermal utilization [24].

Given the amount of geothermal power currently utilized and the available technical potential there clearly is room for accelerated use of geothermal energy [48]. Furthermore, since geothermal energy is not heavily weather or climate dependent, it is possible to produce energy from geothermal sources with more consistency than with other variable renewable sources such as wind or solar energy [35].

Table 2 Energy indicators for sustainable development within the CSD conceptual framework: the social dimension

Theme equity	Metric	Theme health	Metric
Accessibility	Share of households or population without electricity or commercial energy or heavily dependent on noncommercial energy	Safety	Accident fatalities per energy produced by fuel mix
Affordability	Share of household income spent on fuel and electricity		
Disparities	Household energy use for each income group and corresponding fuel mix		

Source: Vera I and Langlois L (2007) Energy indicators for sustainable development. *Energy* 32: 875–882.

7.10.5.2.2(i)(b) Accessibility Access to high-quality energy services is key to economic and social development. The IAEA measures accessibility as share of households (or population) without electricity or commercial energy, or heavily dependent on noncommercial energy, and affordability as share of household income spent on fuel and electricity [70].

As geothermal resources are often located in rural areas previously not connected to an electrical supply, their use could enable unconnected areas to gain access to high-quality energy. Furthermore, small geothermal plants could be used to improve the living standards of rural populations living in remote areas where supplying power is uneconomical due to transmission losses and long transmission line costs [23, 46]. Rural populations in developing countries typically have low per-capita energy demands, so many small generating units rather than fewer larger ones could serve such markets, making the use of geothermal power a viable choice. For example, in developing countries such as Kenya, Latin America, the Caribbean, and the Philippines, estimates show that with demands of 100 W per household for lighting, a 1 MW plant can serve about 10 000 households [23, 71]. The ability of geothermal power to be harnessed in small, decentralized units coupled with its consistency and relative independence from climatic and sociopolitical events make its use likely to significantly be able to raise the living standards in remote rural areas as well as in urban centers and thereby contribute to SED worldwide.

7.10.5.2.2(i)(c) Affordability Although it is necessary to widen access to high-quality energy for all, it is not sufficient to ensure demand as the targeted population must be able to afford the energy. Affordability illustrates whether populations of all income groups can afford the available energy. According to the Advisory Group on Energy and Climate Change [72], electricity is considered affordable if the cost to end users is not more than 10–20% of disposable income. Fluctuating energy prices derived from fossil fuels, in particular in winter, often create significant burden on low-income households. However, as geothermal energy is usually a domestic energy source, it is not subject to such fluctuations.

Levelized cost analyses for geothermal power generation illustrate that it is fully competitive with electricity generation using fossil fuels [73]. The use of geothermal power to heat or cool houses is also fully competitive with fossil fuels and is the most affordable when it comes to alternative energy sources [26]. The combined effect of these characteristics is that geothermal energy can be fully cost-competitive and, in addition, is less subject to energy price fluctuations, making it a desirable choice when possible.

7.10.5.2.2(i)(d) Disparities Disparities may exist as a function of uneven income distribution, insufficient energy transport in the region, and major geographical differences and is manifested as differences in access or affordability between regions or between income groups within a region [70].

As stated before, since geothermal resources are often easily used in small decentralized units and located in areas previously unconnected to a grid, the development of geothermal power may have significant impacts on reducing disparities.

7.10.5.2.2(i)(e) Health The use and production of energy often has serious implications for human health such as due to accidents or air pollution. The goal is to reduce these negative impacts. As air pollution is dealt with in the environmental dimension, only indicators for accidents are included in the health subtheme, including accidents that occur in all phases of energy use and production, from extraction to use.

The use of geothermal resources, in particular in electric power generation, involves working with resources under high heat and pressure. This creates cause for concern. However, lack of data prevents analysis of the relative danger associated with working with geothermal power versus other energy resources.

7.10.5.2.3 The environmental dimension

The environmental dimension contains four themes – atmosphere, water, land, and waste – and six subthemes – climate change, air quality, water quality, soil quality, forest, and solid waste generation and management. The goal within the environmental dimension is to reduce the environmental impact of energy production and use by focusing on these key themes and subthemes.

Table 3 illustrates the themes, subthemes, and appropriate indicators [18].

Environmental impacts associated with geothermal projects fall into all these categories in addition to visual pollution, noise pollution, induced seismicity, and impacts on rare species. However, in comparison with other energy sources, the relative impact in many cases is smaller. The environmental implications are discussed below.

7.10.5.2.3(i) Atmosphere

7.10.5.2.3(i)(a) Climate change and air quality Carbon dioxide, hydrogen sulfides, and ammonia may be emitted from geothermal plants, depending on site characteristics. These gases may have an impact on the environmental conditions of an area as well as on human health and manmade structures. Technologies to separate and isolate and control concentrations to acceptable levels can be used. The reinjection of spent brines can also limit emissions [36].

Geothermal energy is generally regarded as a low-carbon and climate-friendly energy source, as for example, GHG emissions per kWh derived from geothermal power are on average lower than many other types of energy. CO_2 emissions range from 13 to 380 g kWh^{-1}, with a weighted average of 122 g kWh^{-1} [37, 49]. This figure is significantly lower than CO_2 emissions of fossil fuel power plants (natural gas, coal, and oil), which range from approximately 450 g kWh^{-1} (natural gas) to 1040 g kWh^{-1} (coal) [37]. They are, however, higher than emissions from other alternative energy sources such as wind or

Table 3 Energy indicators for sustainable development within the CSD conceptual framework: the environmental dimension

Themes	Subthemes	Indicator
Atmosphere	Climate change	GHG emissions from energy production and use per capita and per unit of GDP
	Air quality	Ambient concentration of pollutants
		Air pollutant emissions from energy systems
Water	Water quality	Contaminant discharges in liquid effluents from energy systems
Land	Soil quality	Soil area where acidification exceeds critical load
	Forest	Rate of deforestation attributed to energy use
Waste	Solid waste generation and management	Ratio of solid waste generation to units of energy produced
		Ratio of solid radioactive waste to units of energy produced
		Ratio of solid radioactive waste awaiting disposal to total generated solid radioactive waste

Source: Vera I and Langlois L (2007) Energy indicators for sustainable development. *Energy* 32: 875–882 [18].

hydropower. Currently, experiments are ongoing that enable scrubbing the CO_2 out of the emissions stream and either sequestrating it through chemical sequestration or utilizing it as a feedstock to create methanol to be used as a transportation fuel [74]. Carbon emissions from low-temperature geothermal fields used in direct use applications, are usually only a fraction of the emissions from the high-temperature fields used for electricity generation.

However, significant emission of hydrogen sulfide can occur, in the range of 0.5–6.8 g kWh^{-1} [23, 37]. Although H_2S does not directly cause acid rain, it may be oxidized to sulfur dioxide (SO_2), which reacts with oxygen and water to form sulfuric acid, a component of acid rain. Locally H_2S is usually considered to be an odor nuisance and is also toxic to humans at concentrations above a certain level. As a result allowable exposure is limited to levels of 5 ppm in the UK and 20 ppm in the US [39].

Absorption and stripping techniques are available for the removal of H_2S gas and there are no emissions at all if a binary plant is used [23, 36].

Finally, other pollutants such as traces of ammonia, hydrogen, nitrogen, methane, radon, and the volatile species of boron, arsenic, and mercury may be present in emissions from geothermal power plants, although in most cases in very low concentrations [23, 37]. Boron is of specific concern due to its impact in low concentrations on vegetation. Emissions of mercury are comparable to those of coal-fired power plants [76].

7.10.5.2.3(ii) Land

Energy-related activities affect land in various ways, resulting, for example, in land and soil degradation as well as acidification and sometimes contribute to deforestation, all of which have implications for biodiversity [70]. Waste accumulation, such as the accumulation of radioactive waste, has implications for soil and water quality. Land is also very important for tourism, and the use of geothermal energy has significant visual implications.

7.10.5.2.3(ii)(a) **Impact on soils and forests** The most important impact of energy production and use on soil resources is acidification. As sulfur dioxide is formed as a result of, for example, burning of coal in coal-fired power plants, it is emitted into the atmosphere and transformed to sulfuric acid, which later falls as acid rain.

The use of geothermal power results in emissions of hydrogen sulfides that can be oxidized to sulfuric acid, also resulting in acid rain. It is possible that acidification may exceed critical loads in specific areas, thereby affecting both soils and vegetation such as forests. However, the fate of H_2S in the atmosphere is a matter of debate, and this impact warrants further investigation [40].

Geothermal brines can also affect soils; boron, in particular, is dangerous, which is shown to be harmful to most plants [40].

7.10.5.2.3(ii)(b) **Visual impact** Geothermal energy development occupies relatively little land compared with other types of power plants such as those that rely on fossil fuels or nuclear energy [35]. Yet the overall visual implications can be relatively significant because the areas that are suitable for geothermal development are often highly valued for their spectacular geodiversity, and thus have high touristic importance [40].

The development of geothermal power will result in some surface disturbances due to drilling, excavation, construction, and the creation of new roads, and long pipelines may need to be built for space-heating purposes [23, 40]. Plumes of steam will also be visible, affecting the aesthetics of the area. The extraction of geothermal fluid can also lead to a pressure drop in the geothermal reservoir, resulting in a reduction or change in the activity of geysers [36, 40].

7.10.5.2.3(ii)(c) Subsidence The excavation of fossil resources such as coal may lead to subsidence, which is the lowering of land-surface elevation. Ground subsidence can affect the stability of pipelines, drains, and well casings. It can also cause the formation of ponds and cracks in the ground and, if the site is close to a populated area, can lead to instability of buildings [35].

The removal of geothermal fluid from underground reservoirs may lead to subsidence on the surface due to drop in pressure, the presence of compressible rock formations, or the presence of high-permeability paths. While this is rare in vapor-dominated fields, it can happen in liquid-dominated fields if reinjection is not practiced to maintain reservoir pressures [23, 35–37, 40].

7.10.5.2.3(iii) Water

7.10.5.2.3(iii)(a) Water quality The extraction and use of geothermal water may affect water quality and water availability through release of spent geothermal fluids, drilling fluids, and due to thermal pollution [23, 36, 37, 40]. Spent geothermal fluids can be brines, with significant salt concentration that can directly damage the environment [40]. Brines can have high concentrations of metals such as iron, manganese, lead, zinc, and boron. Other contaminants can include aluminum, lithium, cadmium, arsenic, mercury, and others. As heavy metals are toxic to humans and bio-accumulate in organisms, the presence of high metal concentrations in brines if released into the environment represent a potentially significant environmental and health hazard [36, 40]. Surface and ground waters can be affected due to release of drilling fluids, release of spent geothermal fluids, and spray [23, 36].

7.10.5.2.3(iii)(b) Thermal pollution Thermal pollution of air and water usually accompany the use of geothermal fields. Excess heat emitted in the form of steam may affect cloud formation and change weather locally. Discharge of hot water to rivers, streams, lakes, and ponds can damage aquatic ecosystems [36, 40].

Water pollution and thermal pollution can be mitigated through effluent treatment, the careful storage of wastewater in ponds, and reinjection into deep wells which is considered the most effective for combating water pollution [36, 40].

7.10.5.2.3(iv) Other factors

- **Induced seismicity** Seismic instability may occur in active areas in association with geothermal energy utilization, in particular in relation to fluid reinjection [23, 41]. However, this effect can be minimized by keeping reinjection pressures to a minimum [23].

- **Noise** Unwanted noise that is noise pollution can be a nuisance or a health concern, depending on strength. The World Health Organization has published guidelines for community noise, which illustrate that noise levels should not exceed 55 dB for outdoor residential areas and 70 dB for industrial areas [23, 42].

Noise pollution due to the utilization of geothermal power can occur during drilling periods as well as from plant operations. The noise however rarely exceeds 90 dB. Yet, noise pollution is a nuisance to residents living close to the geothermal development and can also affect tourism in the area. In Kenya, anecdotal accounts state that drilling noises have been reported to scare away wild animals and pipelines pylons have reportedly affected migration of certain species [23]. If drilling or operations takes place near a populated area, noise abatement measures should be considered. Silencers may be used to mitigate plant noises during operation, for example a noise muffler can keep the noise below 65 dB as regulated by the US Geological survey [23, 40].

7.10.5.2.4 Summary

Based on the assessment of the role geothermal energy plays in SED, it is clear that the development of geothermal energy is likely to have significant positive economic and social implications.

The use of geothermal energy may enhance national or regional energy security beyond business-as-usual fossil fuel-driven scenarios through reduced import dependence, increased energy source diversification, and small-scale operations; contribute positively to resource availability at home; and enhance the fractional share of renewable energy in total primary energy supply. As geothermal energy is more affordable in terms of both variable and turnkey cost, when compared to other energy sources, its development will contribute positively to economic production and economic prosperity. Direct-use applications of geothermal energy such as for district heating is highly efficient, but indirect use for electricity generation is significantly less efficient. In such cases, cogeneration or closed-loop utilization with reinjection is recommended.

Geothermal energy will contribute significantly to social development, as it is affordable, is widely available, and is accessible in remote rural areas that are without energy services. It may also contribute positively to public health due to reduced air pollution.

With respect to the environmental dimension, the utilization of geothermal power may have significant environmental implications. Emissions of GHGs as well as nitrous oxides are significantly reduced when compared with the use of fossil fuels, but emissions of other air pollutants such as H_2S are increased. Absorption and stripping techniques are available for the removal of H_2S gas, and there are no emissions at all if a binary plant is used. Traces of ammonia, hydrogen, nitrogen, methane, radon, and the volatile species of boron, arsenic, and mercury may be present as emissions, although generally in very low concentrations.

Direct land-use impact can also be significant, as many geothermal energy resources are located in regions that are considered to be of great natural beauty, such as in national parks and in aesthetically or historically valuable areas. The geothermal station may have an impact on the aesthetic quality of the landscape, as may pipes and plumes of steam. This may affect tourism in the area being developed and reduce the aesthetic and recreational value.

The extraction and use of geothermal energy resources can affect water quality and water availability through drilling fluids, release of spent geothermal fluids, and spray. Released spent liquids may contaminate shallow groundwater reservoirs, and extraction may lower the water table in certain areas. In addition, thermal pollution of both air and water does accompany the use of geothermal fields. Excess heat emitted in the form of steam may affect cloud formation and change the local weather conditions. Discharge of hot water to rivers, streams, lakes, and ponds can damage aquatic ecosystems. Both water and thermal pollution can be mitigated through effluent treatment or reinjection into deep wells.

Overall, it can be concluded that geothermal power has the potential to contribute significantly to SED in all dimensions of sustainability, with the caveat that environmental impact must be ameliorated. The next section examines one practical case study in this context.

7.10.6 Geothermal Development in Iceland – Toward SED?

7.10.6.1 History

The Icelandic energy system underwent three transitions since the early 1900s [47]. Until the mid-twentieth century, peat and dried sheep dung were the most widely used fuels in Iceland – used for cooking and heating. Horses provided transport, and natural hot springs were used for bathing and washing. It was not until the mid-twentieth century that the age of mechanization took off with the first automobile arriving in 1904 and steam trawlers and motor-powered boats arriving around the same time. Electricity was first produced in 1899 using a kerosene-fuelled power station [77]. The use of geothermal brine to heat houses was first tried in 1908 and successfully executed in 1911. The first hydropower turbine began operating in 1904, but widespread electrification of the country did not occur until after the 1940s.

Yet, similar to other countries, Iceland needed high-quality energy to develop, and as a result, fossil fuels were imported that mostly consisted of coal and petroleum products. The first transition of the Icelandic energy system led to a departure away from the use of peat to coal as a source of heat and to power fishing boats [43]. At the end of World War II, geothermal and hydropower provided only about 16% of the country's energy requirements, the remainder fulfilled mostly by coal.

The second transition consisted of a shift from coal to oil and renewable energy. It occurred in a relatively short period of time between 1945 and 1965 and was driven by an increase in car ownership in Iceland, mechanization of the fishing fleet, further electrification, environmental pressures, and the occasional scarcity of coal [43, 47, 78].

The third transition began in 1965 and lasted until the 1980s. It involved a shift from fossil fuels as a main source of electricity generation and heat to using renewable heat and power for the same purpose. This transition was driven by an increase in prices of imported fossil fuels, government incentives to shift the energy infrastructure toward the use of domestic renewable energy, and demand for electricity from heavy industry [47, 79].

7.10.6.2 Current Situation

Currently, 82% of the total primary energy use is derived from potentially renewable energy sources, with 63% derived from geothermal sources. Approximately 19% is derived from hydropower and 18% from fossil fuels. The total installed capacity of electric power plants in Iceland was 2547 GW and the total electric power generation in 2008 was 16.5 TWh [80]. Close to 100% of all electricity in Iceland is derived from renewable domestic energy, with 75% derived from hydropower and 24% derived from geothermal power.

Geothermal energy is mostly used for heating houses or 45% but 90% of all houses in Iceland are heated with geothermal power. Geothermal energy is also used for electricity generation (39%). Smaller amounts, or 4% each, are used to heat swimming pools, for snow melting, and for fish farming, and 2% each is used in industry and fish farming.

Fossil fuels account for 18% of the total and are mostly used in the transportation and fishing sectors.

Iceland's unexploited geo- and hydropower energy resources, however, are by no means unlimited. There is considerable uncertainty in the estimation of to what extent the existing energy resources can be harnessed with regard to what is technically possible, cost-efficient, and environmentally desirable. The estimated figure most commonly proposed for annual hydropower maximum potential is 30 TWh and a maximum of 20 TWh derived from geothermal resources [77]. This gives a maximum of 50 TWh a^{-1}, with the lower bound on this figure being 30 TWh. Assuming these estimates are accurate and relying on the maximum estimate, 34% of usable power, 41% of available hydropower, and 20% of available geo-power have already been tapped into.

7.10.6.3 Toward SED?

The question whether Iceland with its transition toward renewable fuels such as geothermal power has led to a more sustainable energy system and thereby contributed to sustainable development in the country remains. The first step toward answering that question is to realize that the development of geothermal power replaced the use of imported fossil fuels for house heating and further expanded the percentage share of renewable energy in electricity generation.

7.10.6.3.1 Economic dimension

The development towards increased use of renewable energy in Iceland led to an increase in the fractional share of renewable energy in total primary energy supply and reduced import dependence [47]. It also reduced total energy use per capita from business-as-usual fossil fuel-driven scenarios due to the high efficiency of using geothermal resources for house heating. Even if final energy use per GDP and per capita has increased in Iceland in recent years, the increased use of geothermal power has not been the culprit for this trend, but an expansion in aluminum production in the country.

According to a report from the Icelandic Energy Authority [81], the economic benefits of switching to geothermal power included the following:

- reduction in the cost of house heating as geothermal power was replacing imported fuel oil, at the amount of ISK 67 billion in 2009, which is approximately 12% of government spending that year;
- increased innovation and new employment opportunities in industry, greenhouses, tourism, and in the energy industry itself; and
- positive impacts on regional development.

The speed at which geothermal resources are planned to be developed in Iceland, however, creates some cause for concern as extraction rates not necessarily are expected to provide sustained yields. If extraction is beyond what is considered sustainable, production versus reserve and resource ratios will be negatively affected. This, however, has not been the case in the past.

Overall, it can be concluded that increased development of geothermal resources in Iceland has provided significant and tangible economic benefits.

7.10.6.3.2 Social dimension
Affordable high-quality energy sources can be accessed everywhere in Iceland; however, this was not always the case. The use of low-cost and abundant geothermal power for house heating has made energy for house heating affordable throughout nearly the entire country. Its abundant use in horticulture has secured a steady supply of locally grown high-quality vegetables; the availability of hot water in homes, for example, in Reykjavík, has improved the cleanliness with significant positive health impacts and reduced the time spent for washing and cleaning, tasks traditionally performed by women. The availability of swimming pools has also contributed significantly to improved public health as well as significant decline in air pollution in the country [44]. More research, however, is needed on quantifying the direct health implications of the use of geothermal power; yet it is clear that the use of geothermal power has significantly contributed in a positive way for all the sustainability subthemes within the social dimensions of sustainable development.

7.10.6.3.3 Environmental dimension
The environmental advantages that the shift to cleaner energy sources led to were less air pollution in the capital area (Reykjavík) and smaller emissions of GHGs. According to Kristmannsdottir and Halldorsdottir [44], total emissions of GHGs would be 45% higher if geothermal power was replaced with fuel oil for heating. However, the use of geothermal power has increased the incidence of thermal pollution as well as emissions of hydrogen sulfides, which as stated earlier is dangerous to human health and may result in acidification. An increase in emissions of heavy metals or waterborne pollution has not been confirmed.

As a result, the conclusion on the impact of geothermal development on the environmental dimension is somewhat of a mixed bag. If, however, Icelanders would apply stricter rules on scrubbing hydrogen sulfides from the emissions stream and apply reinjection of spent geothermal fluids, the movement in the environmental indicators for sustainability would mostly be positive. Visual and noise pollution, however, will continue.

7.10.6.4 Summary

Transforming the Icelandic energy system toward increased reliance on geothermal power has, without question, moved the Icelandic energy system toward sustainability as the economic, social, and some environmental benefits outweigh the environmental costs by a large margin and thus significantly contributed to sustainable development in the country. However continued development should proceed with caution.

7.10.7 The MDGs and Geothermal Energy

The social dimension of sustainable development was forcefully pushed to the frontlines of the sustainable development discussion when The Millennium Declaration and the MDGs were adopted in the year 2000 by the UN member states. The MDGs include eight measurable time-bound targets to reduce extreme hunger and poverty, illiteracy, gender inequality, disease, and environmental degradation by 2015 [10, 45, 52].

Although energy is not mentioned explicitly in the eight goals, the provision of modern energy services is recognized as a critical foundation for moving toward sustainable development, in particular in the social dimension [10, 45, 82, 83]. Evidence clearly illustrates that access to modern energy services is essential to social and economic development and widening access to energy services is critical in achieving the eight MDGs. Energy services include lighting, heating for cooking and thereby enabling meeting nutritional human needs, warmth, power for transport and communications, water pumping, and grinding, to name a few [10].

Development of geothermal energy, due to its relative cleanliness, small ecological footprint, reliability, and potential availability in rural areas without access to high-quality energy as well as ability to use in decentralized small units, will bring heat and electricity closer to the people who do not currently have access to high-quality energy services and thereby can have a positive impact on the MDGs [45]. The contributing impact of geothermal power on the MDGs is discussed below.

7.10.7.1 Goal 1: Eradicate Extreme Hunger and Poverty

Since high-quality energy and modern energy services facilitate economic growth through increased productivity and employment generation through, for example, improved agricultural development, they can be an effective means to reduce hunger and poverty [10].

Food insecurity and poverty in developing countries are often caused by climatic events leading to crop failure, land degradation, inadequate pasture, and water availability leading to higher livestock mortality, migration and conflicts, poor market access and poor infrastructure, high food prices, and retrogressive cultural practices in addition to lack of education [45].

The use of geothermal energy, where possible, in areas that suffer from food insecurity and poverty can drastically enhance social welfare through, for example, provision of electricity for water pumping for irrigation and food preservation as well as cooking, lighting, use of greenhouses for commercial production as well as for hunger relief. Farmers may also have the possibility to grow multiple harvests, and postharvest losses will be reduced through better preservation and the possibility of chilling and/or freezing [45].

At both local and national scales anywhere in the world, lack of reliable and affordable electricity supply is an impediment to income-generating industrial, commercial, and service activities. As geothermal energy is best harnessed locally, in small decentralized units, it can provide a local source for heat and electricity, at an affordable price by locally owned businesses and thereby create local employment opportunities. Also microenterprises such as high-value aloe production or honey/wax production as well as tourism require access to energy and will contribute to a shift from economic dependency on livestock only and lead to income diversification.

Hence, the use of geothermal power can significantly contribute to the attainment of MDG goal 1 [45, 46].

7.10.7.2 Goal 2: Achieve Universal Primary Education

The MDG goal 2 target for education is to ensure that, by 2015, children everywhere, boys and girls alike, would be able to complete a full course of primary schooling.

Access to high-quality energy helps in creating a child-friendly atmosphere [10]. Particularly for school-age girls, improved access to modern energy services can free time for going to school and for after-school study. Energy scarcity creates time pressure on children to collect fuel, to fetch water, and to participate in agricultural work and contributes to low school enrollment [10].

For example, in Kenya, the high level of school dropout is due to traditional and cultural practices and is higher among the pure pastoralists than the agropastoralists. The illiteracy rate is estimated in East Pokot in Kenya to range between 85 and 95% [45]. Since East Pokot is at the end of the power line in the area, most of the schools in the area do not have access to electricity, and the children neither have enough time to study in the evening nor light to do so at night [45].

The use of local alternative energy sources such as geothermal power for electricity production and accompanying infrastructure will improve access to educational services, improve communication, and reduce the household dependence on child labor and thereby contribute to attainment to MDG2 [10, 45].

7.10.7.3 Goal 3: Promote Gender Equality and Empower Women

The third MDG target is to eliminate gender disparity in primary and secondary schools by 2005 and at all levels by 2015. Education plays a critical role in creating equal opportunities between men and women [45].

Access to energy services affects men and women differently, and the specific energy services used by men and women differ based on the economic and social division of labor in the workplace and at home [10].

Women in many cultures in developing countries perform various duties such as construction of houses, domestic work, milking, herding cows, fetching firewood and water, cooking, and farming in irrigated areas. Travels in search of firewood, pasture, and water create additional work for women and usually girls in addition to walking long distances, in often dangerous areas. These household chores interfere with schooling of girls due to the fact that they have to assist in seeking for pastures, water, and firewood and perform other household chores. The source of this gender disparity is culture and traditions, which define gender roles and responsibilities [45].

Access to high-quality energy services such as those derived from geothermal power will reduce the time spent looking for firewood and fetching water, enabling more time for education and information sharing. This may influence gender roles and perception. Additionally, opportunities to create wealth from resulting energy services will open up possibilities for new gender-differentiated roles, which will in turn empower women and enlighten the men [45].

7.10.7.4 Goal 4: Reduce Child Mortality Rate

Goal 4 is to reduce by two-thirds, between 1990 and 2015, the mortality rate of children under 5.

A close link exists between health issues and energy use and between the quality of health services and the availability of quality energy services. Electricity is essential for many medical instruments, illumination, medical record keeping, communication facilities for reporting medically significant events, and medical training, and high heat is needed for sterilization of equipment.

Increasing evidence exists that the burning of solid biomass fuels for cooking in indoor environments, especially using traditional stoves in inadequately ventilated spaces, can lead to an increased incidence of respiratory diseases. WHO now estimates that the impact of indoor air pollution on morbidity and premature death of women and children is the number one public health issue in many developing countries, particularly for the poorest segments of the population. Once again, women and small children are likely to share a disproportionate burden [10]. According to WHO [84], indoor air pollution contributes to respiratory infections that account for up to 20% of the 11 million child deaths each year [10, 84].

In addition to poor ventilation and use of low-quality fuels for cooking, lack of adequate nutrition, low immunization coverage, poverty, poor sanitation, and inadequate health facilities are the main issues that need to be tackled when combating child mortality and malnutrition levels in many developing countries. Clearly, provision of nutritious cooked food, space heating, and boiled water contribute to better health, all of which can be attained by the use of geothermal power.

Access to high-quality fuels such as electricity will help in achieving the goal of reducing child mortality rate, and a relatively affordable and clean alternative energy source such as geothermal power will significantly contribute in this regard.

7.10.7.5 Goal 5: Improve Maternal Health

The MDG goal 5 is to reduce by three-quarters, between 1990 and 2015, the maternal mortality ratio and achieve by 2015 universal access to reproductive health.

Health-care infrastructure even in the smallest clinics and health centers relies on refrigeration for vaccines and sterilization in addition to electricity [10]. Lights for patient care after dark, for operating rooms, and for public safety surrounding hospitals increase the health systems' ability to serve poor populations.

Improved lighting and hygiene help reduce women's mortality rate at childbirth. Modern fuels and/or electricity is essential for these functions. Improved access to electricity from geothermal development as well as access to hot water for sterilization will have an impact on improved reproductive health facilities and equipments, which will have a significant contribution in reducing maternal mortality [10, 45].

Furthermore, reducing the level of exposure to indoor air pollution that results from the use of poor quality fuels, alleviating the heavy workload on women, and the difficult manual labor they need to perform such as carrying fuelwood or water will contribute positively to women's general health and well-being [45].

7.10.7.6 Goal 6: Combat HIV/AIDs, Malaria, and Other Diseases

MDG goal 6 focuses on beginning to reverse the spread of HIV/AIDS, to achieve by 2010 universal access treatment of HIV/AIDS for all those who need it, and to halt and begin to reverse the incidence of malaria and other diseases.

Poor nutrition affects the immune system and increases vulnerability to HIV/AIDS, malaria, diarrhea, skin infections, and pneumonia. These diseases when contracted lead to lower productivity and immediately increase the cost of medical care for the household. This results in less time being available and weakened ability to fight malnutrition and poverty, resulting in a negative impact on household food and income security [45].

Unlike hydropower, which through its stagnant reservoirs creates a breeding ground for mosquitoes, utilization of geothermal energy does not increase the incidence of malaria, skin diseases, and other waterborne diseases. Also, with access to electricity, doctors will have electricity they need to treat patients 24 h a day and enable the use of equipment that is needed, for example, for sterilization, refrigeration, and operating rooms [45].

7.10.7.7 Goal 7: Ensure Environmental Sustainability

The MDG goal 7 targets integration of principles of sustainable development with a focus on (1) reducing biodiversity loss by 2010, (2) reducing by half the proportion of people without sustainable access to safe drinking water by 2015, and (3) reducing by half the proportion of people without sustainable access to basic sanitation services by 2015.

Geothermal power has a relatively low ecological footprint and is not very land intensive and in many cases is not located in ecological hot spots. Therefore, its development in many cases has a relatively lower potential impact on biodiversity than other energy sources.

The distance to water sources is dictated by climatic conditions such as availability of rain, geography and geology, and proximity to permanent sources of water. The distance is also determined by availability of boreholes to groundwater, their functioning condition, and water quality. The use of geothermal power can aid in the pumping of water, but the use of high- and low-temperature geothermal energy may affect water availability negatively. Water is required for geothermal development, especially for drilling. Drilling one geothermal well takes approximately 60 days and consumes 100 000 m^3 of water [85]. The pumping of geothermal energy may also lower water tables, and if wastewater is released into the environment, it may affect groundwater resources [45].

As a result, it is important that if geothermal energy is to be used, then the resources are to be used sustainably and reinjection or some form of cogeneration should be mandatory [45]. Other issues such as reducing GHG emissions, alleviating soil erosion, and reducing pressures on expansion of agricultural land as agriculture becomes more productive are positively affected by increased use of geothermal power, when compared with traditional or fossil fuel energy sources.

7.10.7.8 Goal 8: Develop a Global Partnership for Development

The MDG goal 8 mainly focuses on the relationship between developed and developing countries in the attainment of the MDG's [45]. The relevant targets are (1) development of open, rule-based, predictable, nondiscriminatory trading and financial system; (2) dealing comprehensively with debt problems of developing countries through national and international measures to make it sustainable in the long term; (3) working in cooperation with pharmaceutical companies to provide access to affordable, essential drugs in developing countries; and (4) cooperation with private sector to make available the benefits of new technologies, especially information and communication.

The development of geothermal power can aid in this regard by reducing disparities in the access to high-quality energy and thus access to markets and financial systems, aid in income generation and thereby aid in the alleviation of debt problems, and ease the access to essential drugs by creating the conditions necessary for their use. In addition, developed countries can invest in geothermal development in developing countries through the clean development mechanisms (CDMs) of the Kyoto Protocol, thereby contributing to MGD goal 8.

7.10.7.9 Summary

The overview of the relationship between energy services and the MDGs, with a particular focus on the importance of geothermal power, clearly illustrates that access to high-quality energy services will accelerate progress toward the set MDGs. For this to happen, three different service types are needed: (1) energy for cooking; (2) electricity for lights, domestic and commercial appliances, and the provision of social services; and (3) mechanical power to operate agricultural and food-processing equipment, carry out supplementary irrigation, and support new local enterprises and other productive uses [10].

Geothermal power can fulfill all these roles as explained above. It has the advantage of being a relatively clean source of hot water and, if necessary precautions are taken, also a relative clean source of electricity. It is generally available domestically, often in remote areas, and can be used at a small scale, and is available in stable quantities, enabling enhanced access in areas that currently do not have access to high-quality energy.

7.10.8 Climate Change, CDM, and Geothermal Energy

7.10.8.1 The Potential of Geothermal Power to Mitigate GHG Emissions

Currently, climate change is one of the most threatening environmental problems globally. Given its expected impacts on nature and society, it is likely that climate change will affect the world's ability to move toward sustainable development. It is internationally accepted that the continuation of increasing use of fossil fuels and its corollary increases in GHG emissions must be halted.

Geothermal energy can play a significant part in reducing GHG emissions, as emissions per kilowatt hour of electricity derived from high-temperature fields are significantly lower than derived from fossil fuel sources (see **Figure 3**). The emission range, however, is large. According to data derived from 85 geothermal plants in 11 countries, emissions of GHG measured in grams per kilowatt hour range from 4 to 740 g, with a weighted average of 122 g kWh^{-1} [24]. Data from the United States illustrate a similar range, with a weighted average of 91 g kWh^{-1} [86].

In addition, as space and water heating as well as space cooling are significant parts of the energy budget worldwide, where in industrialized countries energy use in buildings accounts for approximately 35–40% of the total primary energy consumption, increased direct use of geothermal power or the use of heat pumps can significantly reduce GHG emissions literally everywhere (given that geothermal power is replacing fossil fuel applications). The largest potential is, however, in China, as low-temperature resources are found nationwide [24]. Furthermore, as technology has been developed, enabling power plants to utilize temperatures around 100 °C, that is, low-temperature resources, the potential has further increased [24]. GHG emissions from low-temperature fields are normally only a small fraction of emissions from high-temperature systems, with emissions, for example, from the district heating system in Reykjavík only about 0.5 mg CO_2 kWh^{-1} [24]. Geothermal heat pumps can also contribute to GHG mitigation, the extent of which depends on the efficiency of the heat pump and the fuel sources used for electricity generation. Results from Europe illustrate that if electricity is produced from either oil or natural gas, the reduction in GHG emissions by using heat pumps amounts to 45% or 33%, respectively [24].

High-temperature geothermal power for electricity generation is, however, less abundant and mainly limited to regions on active plate boundaries or with active volcanoes. The regions most promising with respect to reduced GHG emissions are located in Central America and in the East African Rift Valley, with 39 countries potentially able to produce 100% of their electricity needs from geothermal resources [24]. According to Fridleifsson et al. [24], overall it is possible to produce up to 8.3% of the total world electricity demand with geothermal resources.

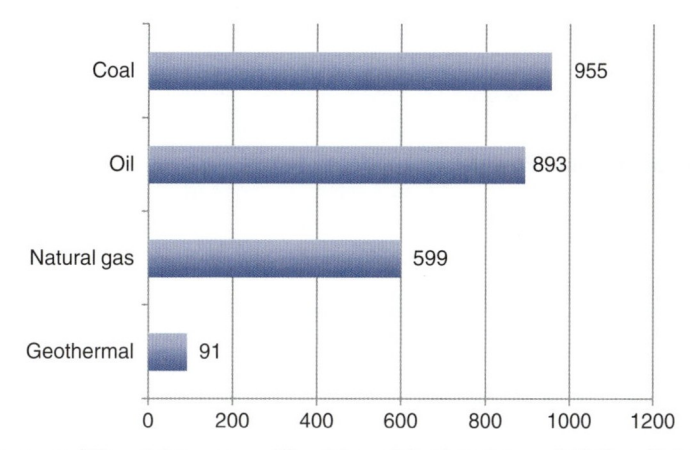

Figure 3 Emissions of greenhouse gases (CO$_2$ equiv.) in grams per kilowatt hour of electricity. Sources: Fridleifsson IB, Bertani R, Lund JW, *et al.* (2008) The possible role and contribution of geothermal energy to the mitigation of climate change. *IPCC Special Report.* Geneva, Switzerland; Bloomfield KK, Moore JN, and Neilson RN (2003) Geothermal energy reduces greenhouse gases. *Geothermal Resources Council Bulletin* 32: 77–79.

Coal: 955
Oil: 893
Natural gas: 599
Geothermal: 91

Fridleifsson *et al.* [24] evaluated the potential of geothermal energy to reduce GHG emissions. If assuming a gradual increase in the use of geothermal power for electricity generation with accelerated investment, geothermal energy may supply 140 GWe by 2050. Assuming that this investment will replace coal-fired energy applications Fridleifsson *et al.* [24] illustrate that the investment will mitigate slightly less than 1 billion tons of CO$_2$ emissions in 2050. Ogola *et al* [86] illustrate an even wider potential or a range between 1 billion tons to 5 billion tons in 2050. Furthermore, the potential of geothermal heat pumps to mitigate GHG emissions has been estimated to be 1.2 billion tons by 2050 [24]. Together, this amounts up to 12% of total GHG emissions in business-as-usual scenarios by 2050.

7.10.8.2 CDM and Geothermal Energy

The international response to climate change began with the adoption of the United Nations Framework for Climate Change (UNFCCC) in 1992 and the Kyoto Protocol in 1997. The objective of the convention was to stabilize GHG emissions and reduce emissions on average by 5.2% below 1990 levels during the 2008–12 budget period. Three flexibility mechanisms were incorporated into the protocol: emissions trading (ET), joint implementation (JI), and the CDM. The CDM is the only mechanism open to participation by parties from both industrialized and developing countries. The objectives of the CDM are (1) to help Annex I Parties to meet their emissions targets and (2) to assist non-Annex I Parties to achieve sustainable development and avoid future emissions. The aim of the CDM is to speed up technology transfer from developed to developing countries, to trigger investment in less developed countries, to push countries to a low carbon trajectory, as well as facilitate sustainable development in the receiving nation.

Provided that geothermal development, as has been illustrated in earlier sections of this chapter, can contribute to sustainable development and given that the potential for the use of geothermal power is large in the developing world such as in China, followed by countries in Central America and in the East African Rift Valley, geothermal energy projects certainly should be considered as potential CDM projects. If implemented, it will displace fossil fuel-driven energy applications. The effectiveness of geothermal energy on GHG mitigation already has been illustrated through the CDM of the Kyoto protocol.

Currently, however, only a few geothermal-certified CDM projects exist in comparison with other renewable energy projects. This could be attributed to investment risks associated with geothermal development as well as the lead time in such developments in comparison with wind, solar, landfill, energy efficiency, and biomass projects, which dominate the energy portfolio under CDM statistics [86]. In October 2011 only 11 registered CDM projects were based on geothermal development, out of a total of 1762 projects based on investment in renewable energy [86].

With the expected capacity expansion plan for geothermal energy development all over the world, many of the geothermal projects could be considered as CDM projects as CDM projects must contribute not only to reduced GHG emissions but also to sustainable development. Under CDM, the measure for sustainable development is defined by the designated national authority (DNA), which is usually in the form of a checklist including key areas of social, environmental, economic, and technological well-being. Unfortunately, sustainable development criteria as required in the project design document are not monitored like the GHG emissions to verify that they are real and measurable. When the designated operating entities verify the project's GHG reductions, the contribution to sustainable development is not included in the assessment and it is not a requirement at the international level or at the national level that sustainable development benefits are actually realized. In the absence of an international sustainability standard, sustainable development is usually not visible in non-Annex 1 countries that have implemented CDM projects [86, 87]. Standards for sustainability assessment are, however, available, such as the Gold standard (www.cdmgoldstandard.org).

In sum, geothermal development projects should more often be considered as CDM projects as they have been shown to contribute to SED and thus to sustainable development nation- and worldwide, in addition to GHG mitigation.

7.10.9 Toward SED Using Geothermal Power

Based on the assessment of the role geothermal energy plays in SED, it is clear that the development of geothermal energy is likely to have significant positive economic and social implications, yet possibly significant negative environmental implications as well if not properly dealt with.

The use of geothermal energy will enhance national or regional energy security through reduced import dependence, increased energy source diversification, and small-scale operations; contribute positively to resource availability at home; and enhance the fractional share of renewable energy in the total primary energy supply. However, as the geothermal resource must be used sustainably, care must be taken not to 'mine' the resource by excessive extraction rates as such extraction behavior may render the resource unusable for decades.

As geothermal energy is in many cases more affordable in terms of both variable and turnkey cost, when compared with other alternative energy sources, its development will contribute positively to economic production and economic prosperity. Direct-use applications of geothermal energy such as for district heating are highly efficient, but indirect use for electricity generation is significantly less efficient. In such cases, cogeneration or closed-loop utilization with reinjection is recommended. Overall, it must be certain that the development of the resource provides sustainable yield and provides net national economic benefits.

Geothermal energy will contribute significantly to social development, as it is affordable, is widely available, and is accessible in remote rural areas that are without energy services. As a result, it is likely to contribute significantly to poverty and hunger alleviation. It will also contribute positively to public health due to reduced air pollution as well as to education and gender equality. Consequently, it is likely to contribute significantly to the realization of the MDGs. Overall, however, it must be certain that the development of the resource provides net national social benefits.

With respect to the environmental dimension, the utilization of geothermal power may have significant environmental implications. Emissions of GHGs as well as nitrous oxides are significantly reduced when compared with emissions derived from fossil fuels, but emissions of other air pollutants such as hydrogen sulfides may increase. Traces of ammonia, hydrogen, nitrogen, methane, radon, and the volatile species of boron, arsenic, and mercury may be present as emissions, although generally in very low concentrations. Direct land-use impact can also be significant, possibly reducing the aesthetic and recreational value of the affected area. The extraction and use of geothermal water can also affect the water quality and water availability. The released spent liquids may also contaminate shallow groundwater reservoirs, and extraction may lower the water table in certain areas. In addition, thermal pollution may be significant. Both water and thermal pollution can be mitigated through effluent treatment or reinjection into deep wells.

In order to ensure that the development of geothermal power fulfills the sustainability criteria, the following 11 sustainability goals have been developed [23, 50], and it is recommended that the development of geothermal power follows these principles. The sustainability goals are as follows [23, 50] (Box 1):

7.10.10 Conclusion

The use of geothermal resources can contribute to SED and as a result the use of geothermal power as well as other alternative energy resources is intimately related to the realization of global movement toward sustainability.

It is clear that geothermal resources can significantly contribute to the movement toward economic and social goals of SED, if harnessed sustainably. Geothermal power is relatively abundant, affordable and a stable energy source, and can be utilized in small-scale units in remote areas. If used in direct-use applications such as for district heating, the efficiency of use is relatively high. However, in indirect-use applications, the efficiency is significantly lower, and therefore cogeneration or reinjection is recommended.

Nevertheless, the environmental impact of geothermal development can be significant. GHG emissions are significantly lower, if geothermal energy is replacing fossil fuels. Yet, emission of other air pollutants such as H_2S increases, and the potential for water pollution is significant. Furthermore, since areas suitable for geothermal development have high recreational value, due to their natural beauty and significant geodiversity, development of such areas must provide net national or regional benefits.

The high-quality energy services that will accelerate progress toward the eight MDG goals must deliver at least one of the three service types: (1) energy for cooking; (2) electricity for lights, domestic and commercial appliances, and the provision of social services; and (3) mechanical power to operate agricultural and food-processing equipment, carry out supplementary irrigation, and support new local enterprises and other productive uses [10]. Geothermal power has the potential to fulfill all these roles.

Geothermal energy can play a significant part in reducing GHG emissions. As space and water heating are significant parts of the energy budget worldwide, increased direct use of geothermal power or the use of heat pumps can significantly reduce GHG emissions in all countries, provided that the geothermal resource is replacing fossil fuels. In addition, since the development of

> **Box 1 Sustainability goals**
>
> *Resource Management/Renewability*
>
> 1. For each geothermal system and each mode of production, there exists a certain level of energy production below which it will be possible to maintain constant energy production from the system for at least 100–300 years. Production of energy at this level is termed sustainable production, whereas production above this level is termed excessive production.
>   If possible, sustainable production should be the goal during geothermal utilization. Reinjection of spent geothermal fluids is recommended where possible, to support long-term utilization of the resource.
> 2. Water usage for the power plant is compatible with other water usage needs in the hydrological catchment area of the geothermal resource.
>
> *Efficiency*
>
> 3. The geothermal resource is managed in such a way as to obtain the maximum use of all heat and energy produced and to minimize the waste of energy by adequate forward planning and design of plants, the use of efficient technologies, reinjection where appropriate, and cascaded energy uses.
>
> *Research and Innovation*
>
> 4. New technologies for the exploitation of previously untapped geothermal, or other, energy resources, should be actively researched by, e.g., universities, energy companies or the government, in addition to any research that contributes to increased knowledge of geothermal resources, increases the efficiency of utilization, reduces environmental impact and increases sustainable use.
>
> *Environmental Impacts*
>
> 5. The geothermal resource is managed so as to minimize local and global environmental impacts through thorough resource and environmental impact assessment before development, appropriate reinjection management, usage of mitigation technologies, and environmental management strategies during all phases of development.
>
> *Social Aspects*
>
> 6. The use of the geothermal resource generates net positive social impacts.
>
> *Energy Equity and Security*
>
> 7. The energy supplied by the geothermal resource is readily and equally available, accessible, and affordable.
> 8. The energy supplied from a geothermal resource is secure, reliable and contributes to energy security for a nation or region.
>
> *Economic and Financial Viability*
>
> 9. The geothermal energy development is cost-effective, financially viable, and maximizes resource rents. The project should carry positive net national economic benefits.
> 10. The enterprise managing the geothermal resource practices corporate social responsibility.
>
> *Knowledge Sharing*
>
> 11. Knowledge and experience gained during the development of geothermal utilization projects should be accessible and transparent to the public and other interested groups.

geothermal resources significantly contributes to sustainable development and at the same time reduces GHG emissions, geothermal development projects could be considered as CDM projects when applicable.

In conclusion, if geothermal development is to securely contribute to SED, and thus to sustainable development worldwide, the 11 principles of sustainable geothermal utilization must be adhered to.

References

[1] Spalding-Fecher R, Winkler H, and Mwakasonda S (2005) Energy and the World Summit on Sustainable Development: What next? *Energy Policy* 33: 99–112.
[2] Rybach L (2003) Geothermal energy: Sustainability and the environment. *Geothermics* 32: 463–470.
[3] Axelsson G (2010) Sustainable geothermal utilization – Case histories: Definitions, research issues and modelling. *Geothermics* 39: 283–291.

[4] Axelsson G, Guðmundsson A, Steingrímsson B, *et al.* (2001) Sustainable production of geothermal energy: Suggested definition. *IGA-News*, Quarterly No. 43, January–March 2001, pp. 1–2.
[5] Dincer I (2000) Renewable energy and sustainable development: A crucial review. *Renewable and Sustainable Energy Reviews* 4: 157–175.
[6] Dincer I and Rosen MA (1999) Energy, environment and sustainable development. *Applied Energy* 64: 427–440.
[7] World Commission on Environment and Development (WCED) (1987) *Our Common Future: Report of the World Commission on Environment and Development.* New York: Oxford University Press.
[8] IEA OECD (2001) *Towards a Sustainable Energy Future.* Paris, France: OECD.
[9] UNDP, UNDESA, and WEC (2000) *World Energy Assessment: Energy and the Challenge of Sustainability.* Goldemberg J (Chairman, editorial board). New York: United Nations Development Programme, Bureau for Development Policy.
[10] Modi V, McDade S, Lallement D, and Saghir J (2005) *Energy Services for the Millennium Development Goals.* New York: Energy Sector Management Assistance Programme, UNDP; UN Millennium Project; and World Bank.
[11] Davidsdottir B, Basoli D, Fredericks S, and Enterline C (2007) Measuring sustainable energy development: The development of a three dimensional index, Chapter 16 in Gowdy J and Erickson J (eds.) *Frontiers in Environmental Valuation and Policy.* Cheltenham, UK: Edward Elgar.
[12] Najam A and Cleveland C (2003) Energy and sustainable development at global environmental summits: An evolving agenda. *International Journal of Environment and Sustainability* 5(2): 117–138.
[13] Johansson TB and Goldemberg J (2002) *Energy for Sustainable Development: A Policy Agenda.* New York: UN Development Programme.
[14] Munasinghe M (1995) Sustainable energy development (SED): Issues and policy. *Environmental Department Papers.* The World Bank.
[15] Smil V (2004) World history and energy. *Encyclopaedia of Energy* 6: 549–561.
[16] Goldemberg J (1996) *Energy, Environment and Development.* London, UK: Earthscan.
[17] Reddy AKN (2002) Energy technologies and policies for rural development. In: Johansson TB and Goldemberg J (eds.) *Energy for Sustainable Development: A Policy Agenda.* New York: UN Development Program, pp. 115–137.
[18] Vera I and Langlois L (2007) Energy indicators for sustainable development. *Energy* 32: 875–882.
[19] Munasinghe M (2002) Sustainable development and climate change: Applying the sustainomics transdisciplinary meta-framework. *International Journal of Global Environmental Issues* 1(1): 13–54.
[20] Malkina-Pykh IG, Pykh IA, and Pykh YA (2002) *Sustainable Energy: Resources Technology and Planning.* Southampton, UK: WIT Press.
[21] IAEA/IEA (2001) Indicators for sustainable energy development. *Presented at the 9th Session of the United Nations Commission on Sustainable Development.* 16–17 April 2001, New York.
[22] Prindle B and Eldridge M (2007) The twin pillars of sustainable energy: Synergies between energy efficiency and renewable energy technology and policy. *Research Paper.* Washington, DC: American Council for an Energy-Efficient Economy. ACEEE Report No E074.
[23] Shortall R (2010) A Sustainability Assessment Protocol for Geothermal Utilization, Environment and Natural Resources. MSc Thesis, School of Engineering and Natural Sciences, University of Iceland.
[24] Fridleifsson IB, Bertani R, Lund JW, *et al.* (2008) The possible role and contribution of geothermal energy to the mitigation of climate change. *IPCC Special Report.* Geneva, Switzerland.
[25] Fridleifsson IB (2001) Geothermal energy for the benefit of the people. *Renewable and Sustainable Energy Reviews* 5: 299–312.
[26] World Energy Council (WEC) (2004) *World Energy Assessment Overview: 2004 Update, 2004.* UNDP; WEC; UN ECOSOC.
[27] Axelsson G, Stefansson V and Bjornsson G (2004) Sustainable utilization of geothermal resources for 100–300 years. *Proceedings of the Twenty-Ninth Workshop on Geothermal Reservoir Engineering.* Stanford University, Stanford, CA, 26–28 January.
[28] Bromley CJ, Mongillo M, and Rybach L (2006) Sustainable utilisation strategies and promotion of beneficial environmental effects – Having your cake and eating it too. *New Zealand Geothermal Workshop.* Auckland, New Zealand, November.
[29] Rybach L and Mongillo M (2006) Geothermal sustainability – A review with identified research needs. *GRC Transactions* 30: 1083–1090.
[30] Bromley C, Rybach L, Mongillo MA, and Matsunaga I (2006) Geothermal resources – Utilisation strategies to promote beneficial environmental effects and to optimize sustainability. *Renewable Energy Conference* 2006. Chiba, Japan.
[31] Axelsson G, Stefansson V, and Bjornsson G (2005) Sustainable management of geothermal resources for 100–300. *Proceedings of the World Geothermal Congress 2005.* Antalya, Turkey, 24–29 April.
[32] World Bank (2003) *World Development Report 2003: Sustainable Development in a Dynamic World.* Washington, DC: World Bank.
[33] IEA (2002) Energy and poverty. In: *World Energy Outlook 2002,* ch. 13. Paris, France: IEA, pp. 365–393.
[34] Johannsson TB and Goldemberg J (2002) The role of energy in sustainable development: Basic facts and issues. In: Johannsson TB and Goldemberg J (eds.) *Energy for Sustainable Development: A Policy Agenda.* New York: UNDP, pp. 25–41.
[35] Shibaki M and Beck F (2003) Geothermal energy for electric power. *Renewable Energy Policy Project Brief.* Washington, DC, December.
[36] Heath MJ (2002) Environmental aspects of geothermal energy resources utilization. In: Chandrasekharam D and Bundschuh J (eds.) *Geothermal Energy (Resources) for Developing Countries.* Rotterdam, The Netherlands: A. A. Balkema, pp. 269–280.
[37] Phillips J (2010) Evaluating the level and nature of sustainable development for a geothermal power plant. *Renewable and Sustainable Development for a Geothermal Power Plant* 14: 2414–2425.
[38] Kagel A and Gawell K (2005) Promoting geothermal energy: Air emissions comparison and externality analysis. *The Electricity Journal* 18: 90–99.
[39] International Volcanic Health Hazard Network (2009) Gas and Aerosol Guidelines. http://www.dur.ac.uk/claire.horwell/ivhhn/guidelines/gas/h2s.html (accessed 10 November 2009).
[40] Kristmannsdottir H and Armannsson H (2003) Environmental aspects of geothermal energy utilization. *Geothermics* 32: 451–461.
[41] DiPippo R (1991) Geothermal energy: Electricity generation and environmental impact. *Energy Policy* 19(8): 798–807.
[42] WHO (2001) *Factsheet No. 258: Occupational and Community Noise.* Geneva, Switzerland: WHO
[43] Kjartansson HS (2002) *Ísland á 20. öld.* Reykjavík, Iceland: Sögufélag.
[44] Kristmannsdottir H and Halldorsdottir S (2008) Health impacts from using geothermal power. *Working Paper,* University of Akureyri, Iceland.
[45] Ogola P, Davidsdottir B, and Fridleifsson IB (2011a) Lighting villages at the end of the line with geothermal energy in Eastern Baringo Lowlands, Kenya: Steps towards reaching the Millennium Development Goals. *Sustainable and Renewable Energy Reviews* 15(8): 4067–4079.
[46] Ogola P, Davidsdottir B, and Fridleifsson IB (2011b) Potential contribution of geothermal energy to climate change adaptation in Eastern Baringo lowlands, Kenya. *Sustainable and Renewable Energy Reviews* (in Press).
[47] Davidsdottir B (2007) Sustainable energy development: The case of Iceland. *Proceedings of the ACEEE Summer Study.* New York, USA.
[48] Fridleifsson IB (2005) Geothermal energy amongst the world's energy sources. *Proceedings of the World Geothermal Congress.* Antalya, Turkey, 24–29 April.
[49] International Geothermal Association (IGA) (2002) Geothermal power generating plant CO_2 emission survey. *IGA News* No 49, pp. 1–3.
[50] Ketilsson J, Björnsson A, Sveinbjörnsdóttir ÁE, *et al.* (2010) *Sjálfbær vinnsla og nýting jarðhita – Álitsgerð faghóps.* Orkustofnun, OS-2010/04, 109 pp.
[51] Brown M, Rewey C, and Gagliano T (2003) *Energy Security.* Washington, DC: National Conference of State Legislatures.
[52] United Nations (2000) *UN Development Goals.* New York: United Nations.
[53] WCED (1987) *Our Common Future: Report of the World Commission on Environment and Development.* New York: Oxford University Press.
[54] IAEA/IEA (2001) Indicators for sustainable energy development. *Presented at the 9th Session of the United Nations Commission on Sustainable Development.* April.

[55] Axelsson G, Guðmundsson Á, Steingrímsson B, *et al.* (2001) Sustainable production of geothermal energy: Suggested definition. *IGA-News, Quarterly No. 43*, January–March, pp. 1–2.
[56] Fridleifsson IB (2010) Capacity building in renewable energy technologies in developing countries. *Submitted to the World Energy Congress.* Montreal, QC, Canada, 12–16 September.
[57] International Energy Agency (IEA) (2009) *World Energy Outlook 2008.* Paris, France: International Energy Agency.
[58] Rockström J, Steffen W, Noone K, *et al.* (2009) A safe operating space for humanity. *Nature* 461: 472–475.
[59] Ehrlich P (1968) *The Population Bomb.* New York: Ballantine Books.
[60] Smil V (1994) *Energy in World History.* Boulder, CO: Westview Press.
[61] Smil V (2003) *Energy at the Crossroads: Global Perspectives and Uncertainties.* Cambridge, MA: MIT Press.
[62] Stern DA (2000) A multivariate cointegration analysis of the role of energy in the US macroeconomy. *Energy Economics* 22(2): 267–283.
[63] Joyeux R and Ripple RD (2007) Household energy consumption versus income and relative standard of living: A panel approach. *Energy Policy* 35: 50–60.
[64] Intergovernmental Panel on Climate Change (IPCC) (2007) *Contribution of Working Groups I, II and III to the Fourth Assessment Report of the Intergovernmental Panel on Climate Change.* Geneva, Switzerland: IPCC.
[65] Polimeni JM, Mayumi K, Giampietro M, and Alcott B (2008) *The Jevons Paradox and the Myth of Resource Efficiency Improvements.* London: Earthscan.
[66] Stefansson V (1998) Estimate of the world geothermal potential. *Proceedings of the 20th Anniversary Workshop of the UNU Geothermal Training Programme*, pp. 111–121. Reykjavik, Iceland, October.
[67] Lund JW (2006) Geothermal energy focus: Tapping the Earth's natural heat. *Refocus* 7: 48–51.
[68] http://www1.eere.energy.gov/geothermal/powerplants.html.
[69] Kristmannsdottir H and Armannsson H (2003) Environmental aspects of geothermal energy utilization. *Geothermics* 32: 452–461.
[70] International Atomic Energy Agency (IAEA) (2005) *Energy Indicators for Sustainable Development.* Austria: IAEA.
[71] Cabraal AM, Davies C, and Schaeffer L (1996) *Best Practices for Photovoltaic Household Electrification Programs. Lessons from Experiences in Selected Countries.* World Bank Technical Paper 324, Asia Technical Department Series. Washington, DC: World Bank.
[72] The Secretary Generals Advisory Group on Energy and Climate Change (AGECC) (2010) Energy for a sustainable future. *Summary Report and Recommendations.* New York.
[73] Renewable Energy Transmission Initiative (RETI) (2008) *Phase IA Final Report.* State of California.
[74] Davidsdottir B, *et al.* (2009) *Options to Mitigate Greenhouse Gas Emissions in Iceland.* Reykjavik, Iceland: Ministry of the Environment.
[75] REPP-CREST (2003) *Geothermal Energy* (online). http://www.repp.org/geothermal/index.html.
[76] Barbier E (2002) Geothermal energy technology and current status: An overview. *Renewable and Sustainable Energy Reviews* 6: 3–65.
[77] The Icelandic Energy Authority (2006) *Energy in Iceland – Historical Perspective, Present Status, Future Outlook.* Reykjavik, Iceland: Orkustofnun (Iceland Energy Authority).
[78] Ragnarsson A (2006) Energy use in Iceland. *A Paper Presented at the Energy Conference.* Reykjavik, Iceland, 12–13 October. Reykjavik, Iceland: Samorka.
[79] Sumarliði R and Isleifsson SR (1996) *Í straumsamband. Rafmangnsveita Reykjavíkur 75 ára 1921–1996* (in Icelandic). Iceland: Rafmagnsveita Reykjavikur.
[80] The Icelandic Energy Authoiry (2009) *Energy Statistics in Iceland.* Reykjavik, Iceland: The Icelandic Energy Authority.
[81] Ingimar G, Haraldsson I, Thorisdottir Th, and Ketilsson J (2010) Economic comparison of using geothermal heat versus fuel from 1970 to 2009. The Icelandic Energy Authority OS 2010:04 (in Icelandic).
[82] Department for International Development (DFID) (2002) *Energy for the Poor – Underpinning the Millennium Development Goals.* UK Department for International Development.
[83] Fridleifsson IB (2007) Geothermal energy and the millennium development goals of the United Nations. *Proceedings of the European Geothermal Congress.* Unterhaching, Germany, 30 May–1 June.
[84] World Health Organization (WHO) (2002) *The World Health Report 2002.* Geneva, Switzerland: WHO.
[85] Ogola PFA (2004) Appraisal Drilling of Geothermal Wells in Olkaria Domes (IV). Baseline Studies and Socio-economic Impacts. *UNU GTP Reports.* Reykjavik, Iceland.
[86] Ogola FPA, Davidsdottir B, and Fridleifsson IB (2011) Opportunities for Adaptation–Mitigation Synergies in Geothermal Energy Utilization – Initial conceptual frameworks, Mitigation and Adaptation Strategies for Global Change (in press, available online 2011).
[87] Brunt C and Knechtel A (2005) Delivering Sustainable Development Benefits through the Clean Development Mechanism. Canada: The Pembina Institute.